# *TURBULENT FLOWS AND HEAT TRANSFER*

I. Thermodynamics and Physics of Matter. Editor: F. D. Rossini
II. Combustion Processes. Editors: B. Lewis, R. N. Pease, H. S. Taylor
III. Fundamentals of Gas Dynamics. Editor: H. W. Emmons
IV. Theory of Laminar Flows. Editor: F. K. Moore
V. Turbulent Flows and Heat Transfer. Editor: C. C. Lin
VI. General Theory of High Speed Aerodynamics. Editor: W. R. Sears
VII. Aerodynamic Components of Aircraft at High Speeds. Editors: A. F Donovan, H. R. Lawrence
VIII. High Speed Problems of Aircraft and Experimental Methods. Editors: A. F. Donovan, H. R. Lawrence, F. Goddard, R. R. Gilruth
IX. Physical Measurements in Gas Dynamics and Combustion. Editors: R. W. Ladenburg, B. Lewis, R. N. Pease, H. S. Taylor
X. Aerodynamics of Turbines and Compressors. Editor: W. R. Hawthorne
XI. Design and Performance of Gas Turbine Power Plants. Editors: W. R. Hawthorne, W. T. Olson
XII. Jet Propulsion Engines. Editor: O. E. Lancaster

VOLUME V

HIGH SPEED AERODYNAMICS

AND JET PROPULSION

# *TURBULENT FLOWS AND HEAT TRANSFER*

EDITOR: C. C. LIN

LONDON

OXFORD UNIVERSITY PRESS

1959

*London:* Oxford University Press

L. C. CARD 58-5028





Printed in the United States of America by
The Maple Press Company, Inc., York, Penna.

# *FOREWORD*

On behalf of the Editorial Board, I would like to make an acknowledgement to those branches of our military establishment whose interest and whose financial support were instrumental in the initiation of this publication program. It is noteworthy that this assistance has included all three branches of our Services. The Department of the Air Force through the Air Research and Development Command, the Department of the Army through the Office of the Chief of Ordnance, and the Department of the Navy through the Bureau of Aeronautics, Bureau of Ships, Bureau of Ordnance, and the Office of Naval Research made significant contributions. In particular, the Power Branch of the Office of Naval Research has carried the burden of responsibilities of the contractual administration and processing of all manuscripts from a security standpoint. The administration, operation, and editorial functions of the program have been centered at Princeton University. In addition, the University has contributed financially to the support of the undertaking. It is appropriate that special appreciation be expressed to Princeton University for its important over-all role in this effort.

The Editorial Board is confident that the present series which this support has made possible will have far-reaching beneficial effects on the further development of the aeronautical sciences.

Theodore von Kármán

# *PREFACE*

Rapid advances made during the past decade on problems associated with high speed flight have brought into ever sharper focus the need for a comprehensive and competent treatment of the fundamental aspects of the aerodynamic and propulsion problems of high speed flight, together with a survey of those aspects of the underlying basic sciences cognate to such problems. The need for a treatment of this type has been long felt in research institutions, universities, and private industry and its potential reflected importance in the advanced training of nascent aeronautical scientists has also been an important motivation in this undertaking.

The entire program is the cumulative work of over one hundred scientists and engineers, representing many different branches of engineering and fields of science both in this country and abroad.

The work consists of twelve volumes treating in sequence elements of the properties of gases, liquids, and solids; combustion processes and chemical kinetics; fundamentals of gas dynamics; viscous phenomena; turbulence; heat transfer; theoretical methods in high speed aerodynamics; applications to wings, bodies and complete aircraft; nonsteady aerodynamics; principles of physical measurements; experimental methods in high speed aerodynamics and combustion; aerodynamic problems of turbo machines; the combination of aerodynamic and combustion principles in combustor design; and finally, problems of complete power plants. The intent has been to emphasize the fundamental aspects of jet propulsion and high speed aerodynamics, to develop the theoretical tools for attack on these problems, and to seek to highlight the directions in which research may be potentially most fruitful.

Preliminary discussions, which ultimately led to the foundation of the present program, were held in 1947 and 1948 and, in large measure, by virtue of the enthusiasm, inspiration, and encouragement of Dr. Theodore von Kármán and later the invaluable assistance of Dr. Hugh L. Dryden and Dean Hugh Taylor as members of the Editorial Board, these discussions ultimately saw their fruition in the formal establishment of the Aeronautics Publication Program at Princeton University in the fall of 1949.

The contributing authors and, in particular, the volume editors, have sacrificed generously of their spare time under present-day emergency conditions where continuing demands on their energies have been great. The program is also indebted to the work of Dr. Martin Summerfield who guided the planning work as General Editor from 1949–1952. The cooperation and assistance of the personnel of Princeton University Press and of the staff of this office has been noteworthy. In particular, Mr. H. S.

Bailey, Jr., the Director of the Press, and Mr. R. S. Snedeker, who has supervised the project at the Press, have been of great help. The figures were prepared by Mr. Zane Anderson. Special mention is also due Mrs. E. W. Wetterau of this office who has handled the bulk of the detailed editorial work for the program.

Coleman duP. Donaldson
General Editor

# PREFACE TO VOLUME V

This volume deals with the interrelated problems of turbulent flow and heat transfer. It begins with an article on transition from laminar to turbulent flow. This is followed by a discussion of the problem of shear flow from the experimental and semi-empirical points of view and of the statistical theory of turbulence from a deductive point of view. Future developments in our knowledge should result in the merging of these two approaches into a comprehensive and unified treatment.

The three modes of heat transfer—conduction, convection, and radiation—are presented in the remaining part of this volume. These articles are especially oriented toward high speed flows with high temperature differences. Free convection due to gravitational forces is considered in this portion of the volume only in connection with boiling heat transfer. In the sections on the physical basis of radiation and on the method of engineering calculations in radiant heat exchange, it is an interesting reflection on the current status of our knowledge in this important field that these two phases of the problem are presented from somewhat different points of view.

As originally planned, this volume was to be the second part of a larger volume comprising the present Volumes IV and V, under the joint editorship of Lester Lees and myself. The desirability of separating the material into two volumes soon became clear, on account of both the size of the articles and the nature of the material involved. Professor Lees had the major share of the editorial work at the early stages. Unfortunately, he was unable to continue with his editorship after he moved from Princeton University to the California Institute of Technology, with the consequent increase of pressure from his duties. I believe I may speak for Professor Lees as well as for myself as I express appreciation for the fine cooperation of all the authors, the General Editor, and the Princeton University Press.

C. C. Lin
Volume Editor

# *CONTENTS*

A. Transition from Laminar to Turbulent Flow 3

Hugh L. Dryden, National Aeronautics and Space Administration, Washington, D.C.

1. Introduction 3
2. Transition on a Flat Plate in a Stream of Constant Velocity 3
3. Effect of Pressure Gradient on Transition on a Flat Plate 6
4. Effect of Curvature of Surface on Transition of a Two-Dimensional Boundary Layer 8
5. Effect of Surface Roughness and Waviness on Transition of a Two-Dimensional Boundary Layer 8
6. Application of Dimensional Analysis to Transition of a Two-Dimensional Boundary Layer 19
7. Transition of Shear Layers in the Free Fluid 21
8. Transition of Shear Layers with Reattachment Following Laminar Separation 24
9. Breakdown of Laminar Flow vs. Transition 27
10. Tentative Conceptual Picture of Transition 28
11. Theory of the Influence of Turbulence on Transition 30
12. Schlichting's Procedure for Computing Transition on an Airfoil 32
13. Adequacy of Transition Theories Based on Local Parameters 37
14. Transition to Turbulent Flow in a Pipe of Circular Cross Section 39
15. Transition in Pipes of Noncircular Cross Section 40
16. Transition on an Elliptic Cylinder 41
17. Transition on Airfoils 41
18. Transition on Airplane Configurations and on Airplanes in Flight 45
19. Transition on Bodies of Revolution 46
20. Transition in Flow between Rotating Cylinders 49
21. Transition in Flow near Rotating Disks 52
22. Transition in Flow at Boundary of a Jet 52
23. Transition at Subsonic Speed as Affected by Heat Transfer 53
24. General Remarks on Transition at Supersonic Speed 54
25. Effect of Mach Number on Transition for Bodies without Heat Transfer at Supersonic Speeds 55
26. Effect of Heat Transfer on Transition at Supersonic Speeds 63
27. Present Status and Future Direction 67
28. Cited References 70

B. Turbulent Flow 75

Galen B. Schubauer, Fluid Mechanics Section, National Bureau of Standards, Washington, D. C.
C. M. Tchen, Aerodynamics Section, National Bureau of Standards, Washington, D. C.

*Chapter 1. Introduction*

1. Subject Treatment 75
2. Nature of Turbulent Flow 76
3. Diffusiveness of Turbulence 79

*Chapter 2. General Hydrodynamical Equations for the Turbulent Motion of a Compressible Fluid*

4. Equations of Continuity and Momentum 80
5. Equation of Kinetic Energy 83
6. Equation of Energy and Enthalpy 85

*Chapter 3. Turbulent Boundary Layer of a Compressible Fluid*

7. Introduction 87
8. Fundamental Equations of Motion of a Compressible Boundary Layer 89
9. Relationships between Velocity, Pressure, and Temperature Distributions 90
10. Phenomena of Transport of Properties in a Turbulent Fluid 97
11. Reynolds Analogy between Heat Transfer and Skin Friction 104
12. Basis of Skin Friction Theories 107
13. Empirical Laws of Skin Friction 113
14. Comparison between Experiments and Theories 116

*Chapter 4. General Treatment of Incompressible Mean Flow along Walls*

15. Power Laws 119
16. Wall Law and Velocity-Defect Law 122
17. Logarithmic Formulas 124
18. Smooth Wall Incompressible Skin Friction Laws 127
19. Effect of Pressure Gradient 129
20. Equilibrium Boundary Layers According to Clauser 135
21. Law of the Wake According to Coles 139
22. Mixing Length and Eddy Viscosity in Boundary Layer Flows 143
23. Effect of Roughness 147
24. Integral Methods for Calculating Boundary Layer Development 153
25. Three-Dimensional Effects 156

*Chapter 5. Free Turbulent Flows*

26. Types and General Features 158

27. Laws of Mean Spreading and Decay 159
28. General Form and Structure 163
29. Transport Processes in Free Turbulent Flow 168
30. Velocity Distribution Formulas for Jets and Wakes 172
31. Effect of Density Differences and Compressibility on Jets with Surrounding Air Stationary 176
32. Effect of Axial Motion of Surrounding Air on Jets 179

*Chapter 6. Turbulent Structure of Shear Flows*

33. The Nature of the Subject 184
34. References on Structure of Shear Turbulence 185
35. Cited References 190

C. Statistical Theories of Turbulence 196

C. C. Lin, Department of Mathematics, Massachusetts Institute of Technology, Cambridge, Massachusetts

*Chapter 1. Basic Concepts*

1. Introduction 196
2. The Mean Flow and the Reynolds Stresses 197
3. Frequency Distributions and Statistical Averages 198
4. Homogeneous Fields of Turbulence 200
5. Conventional Approach to the Statistical Theory of Turbulence 201

*Chapter 2. Mathematical Formulation of the Theory of Homogeneous Turbulence*

6. Kinematics of Homogeneous Isotropic Turbulence. Correlation Theory 202
7. Dynamics of Isotropic Turbulence 208
8. The Spectral Theory of Isotropic Turbulence 210
9. Spectral Analysis in One Dimension 214
10. Spectral Analysis in Three Dimensions 216
11. General Theory of Homogeneous Anisotropic Turbulence 218

*Chapter 3. Physical Aspects of the Theory of Homogeneous Turbulence*

12. Large Scale Structure of Turbulence 219
13. Small Scale Structure of Turbulence. Kolmogoroff's Theory 221
14. Considerations of Similarity 225
15. The Process of Decay 230
16. The Quasi-Gaussian Approximation 236
17. Hypotheses on Energy Transfer 238

*Chapter 4. Turbulent Diffusion and Transfer*

18. Diffusion by Continuous Movements 240
19. Analysis Involving More Than One Particle 243

20. Temperature Fluctuations in Homogeneous Turbulence 244
21. Statistical Theory of Shear Flow 245

*Chapter 5. Other Aspects of the Problem of Turbulence*

22. Turbulent Motion in a Compressible Fluid 247
23. Magneto-Hydrodynamic Turbulence 248
24. Some Aerodynamic Problems 249
25. Cited References 251

D. Conduction of Heat 254

M. Yachter, Special Projects Department, The M. W. Kellogg Company, Jersey City, New Jersey
E. Mayer, Arde Associates, Newark, New Jersey. Now with Rocketdyne, division of North American Aviation, Inc.

*Chapter 1. Introduction*

1. General Remarks 254
2. Mathematical Formulation 255
3. Thermal Property Data and Range of Heat Transfer Coefficients 260

*Chapter 2. One-Dimensional Heat Conduction in a Homogeneous Medium*

4. Slab of Thickness *d* 260
5. The Semi-Infinite Solid 262
6. Applications 263

*Chapter 3. Transient Radial Heat Conduction in a Homogeneous Hollow Cylinder*

7. Classical Results for Newtonian Heat Transfer 266
8. Applications. Thermal Stresses 268
9. Remarks on Thermal Shock 270

*Chapter 4. Transient Heat Conduction in a Unidimensional Composite Slab*

10. General Results for Newtonian Heat Transfer 272
11. The "Thin" Shield 276
12. "Thick" Thermal Shields 277
13. Design Criterion for Minimum Weight 278
14. Remarks on the Composite Hollow Cylinder 280

*Chapter 5. Some Special Problems*

15. Variable Thermal Properties 280
16. Surface Melting and Erosion 284
17. Axial Heat Conduction in Nozzle Walls 285
18. Cited References 287

E. Convective Heat Transfer and Friction in Flow of Liquids 288

R. G. Deissler, Lewis Flight Propulsion Laboratory, National Aeronautics and Space Administration, Cleveland, Ohio
R. H. Sabersky, Division of Engineering, California Institute of Technology, Pasadena, California

*Chapter 1. Turbulent Heat Transfer and Friction in Smooth Passages*

1. Introduction 288
2. Basic Equations 288
3. Expressions for Eddy Diffusivity 290
4. Analysis for Constant Fluid Properties 292
5. Analysis for Variable Fluid Properties 303
6. Concluding Remarks 313

*Chapter 2. Survey of Problems in Boiling Heat Transfer*

7. Introduction 313
8. General Results 314
9. Nucleate Boiling 319
10. Film Boiling 333
11. Closing Remarks 334
12. Cited References and Bibliography 335

F. Convective Heat Transfer in Gases 339

E. R. van Driest, North American Aviation, Incorporated, Downey, California

1. Introduction 339
2. The Mechanism of Convective Heat Transfer 339

*Chapter 1. Survey of Theoretical Results Applicable to Aerodynamic Heat Transfer. Status of Experimental Knowledge*

LAMINAR FLOW

3. Flat Plate Solution 341
4. Heat Transfer 348
5. Numerical Results for Zero Pressure and Temperature Gradients along the Flow 350
6. Cone Solution 362
7. Stagnation Point Solution 365
8. Effect of Variable Free Stream Pressure and Variable Wall Temperature 368
9. Status of Experimental Knowledge 368

TURBULENT FLOW

10. Flat Plate Solution 370
11. Heat Transfer 372
12. Cone Solution 388
13. Stagnation Point Solution 388
14. Effects of Variable Free Stream Pressure, Wall Temperature, etc. 391
15. Rough Walls 391
16. Status of Experimental Knowledge 391

TRANSITION

17. Stability of the Laminar Boundary Layer and Relation to Transition 396
18. Effect of Supply Tunnel Turbulence 399
19. Effect of Surface Roughness 403

*Chapter 2. Application of Theory to Engineering Problems at High Speeds*

20. Aerodynamic Heating of High Speed Vehicles 405
21. Heat Transfer in Rocket Motors 415
22. Dissociation Effects 419
23. Cited References 425

G. Cooling by Protective Fluid Films 428

S. W. Yuan, Department of Aeronautical Engineering, The University of Texas, Austin, Texas

1. Introduction 428
2. Flow through Porous Metal 430
3. Physical Nature of Transpiration-Cooling Process 434
4. Heat Transfer in Transpiration-Cooled Boundary Layer 437
5. Heat Transfer in Transpiration-Cooled Pipe Flow 460
6. Comparison with Experimental Results on Transpiration Cooling 475
7. Film Cooling and Its Comparison with Transpiration Cooling 481
8. Cited References and Bibliography 485

H. Physical Basis of Thermal Radiation 489

S. S. Penner, Division of Engineering, California Institute of Technology, Pasadena, California

1. Introduction 489
2. Black Body Radiation Laws 489
3. Nonblack Radiators 491
4. Basic Laws for Distributed Radiators 492
5. Theoretical Calculation of Gas Emissivities 494
6. Cited References 500

I. Engineering Calculations of Radiant Heat Exchange 502

Hoyt C. Hottel, Department of Chemical Engineering, Massachusetts Institute of Technology, Cambridge, Massachusetts

1. Radiating Characteristics of Surfaces 502
2. The View Factor. Direct Interchange between Surfaces 507
3. Radiation from Flames and Gases 511
4. Radiant Exchange in an Enclosure of Source-Sink and No-Flux Surfaces Surrounding a Gray Gas 523
5. Enclosure of Gray Source-Sink Surfaces Containing a Real (Nongray) Gas 531
6. Application of Principles 535
7. Cited References 539

*TURBULENT FLOWS AND HEAT TRANSFER*

# SECTION A

# *TRANSITION FROM LAMINAR TO TURBULENT FLOW*

H. L. DRYDEN

**A,1. Introduction.** The motions of real fluids exhibit phenomena of a bewildering degree of diversity. The pressure distribution and the resultant force and moment on a body moving through a fluid are but grosser manifestations of complex motions of the fluid in the surrounding space. The body is surrounded by a flow field in which the velocity and pressure vary. There is no single theory adequate to describe this flow field in its entirety. Progress can be made only by recognizing characteristic phenomena in limited regions of complex flow fields that can be reproduced and studied in a simpler experimental environment.

Transition is one of these characteristic phenomena of wide occurrence. Everyone has observed it in the rising column of smoke from a cigarette lying on an ash tray in a quiet room, and at the same time has observed the types of flow which we designate as laminar and turbulent. For some distance above the cigarette the smoke rises in smooth filaments characteristic of laminar flow, only to break up into the confused swirling turbulent motion at a height which is dependent on the quietness of the surrounding air. If the drafts or convective air currents are strong, transition occurs close to the cigarette. If the air is very quiet, the filament may persist to a considerable height. This breakdown of the laminar flow is transition.

Considerable progress has been made in the study of transition at low subsonic speeds where the motion may be regarded as that of an incompressible fluid of uniform temperature. While transition has also been observed in localized regions of flow at transonic and supersonic speed, the information available is less extensive. The effects of heat transfer at subsonic speed are discussed in Art. 23. Art. 24, 25, and 26 deal with transition at supersonic speed. Art. 2 to 23, inclusive, deal with low speed subsonic flow.

**A,2. Transition on a Flat Plate in a Stream of Constant Velocity.** Transition is observed to occur in the boundary layer, that region of the flow field near the surface of the body where the steepest velocity gradients are concentrated through the action of viscous forces. Hence the simplest situation for the study of transition is the simplest boundary layer that can be investigated both theoretically and experimentally. This is the flow along a smooth thin flat plate, parallel to the flow in a stream of uniform velocity and hence without longitudinal pressure gradient, for which the theoretical laminar flow solution was given by Blasius

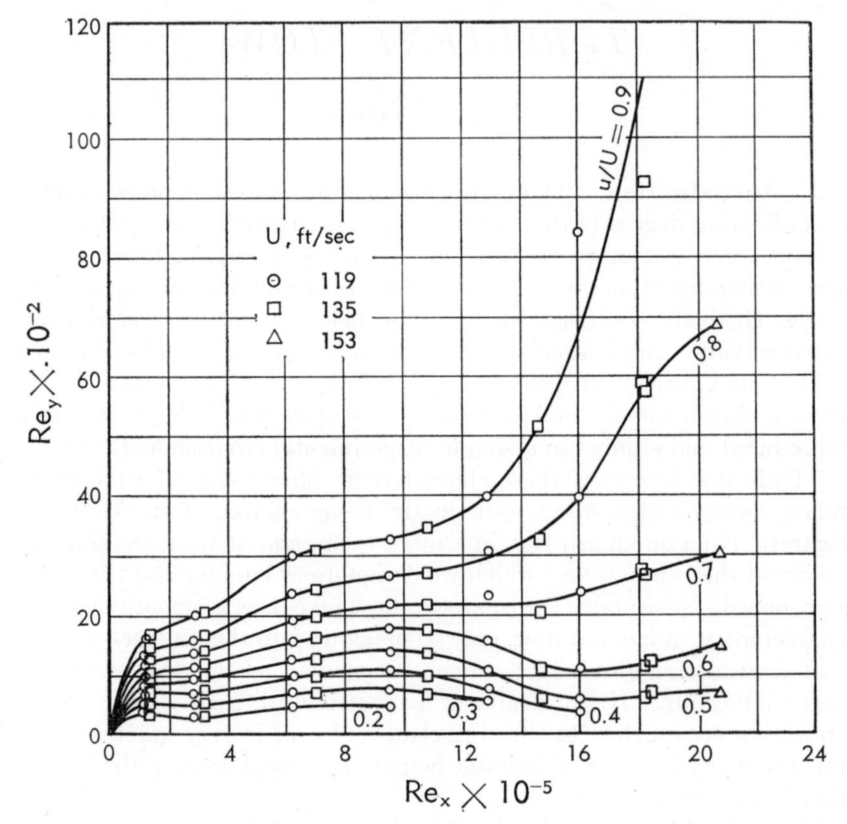


Fig. A,2a. Velocity distribution in the boundary layer of a plate. Contours of equal local mean speed as function of $x$ and $y$ Reynolds number. Turbulence of free stream, 0.5 per cent.

in 1908. Many measurements have been made on the velocity distribution near such a plate and transition is easily recognized by a typical departure from the Blasius distribution of the type illustrated in Fig. A,2a. Here for measurements in air [*1*] contour lines of equal values of $u/U$ are plotted on abscissas and ordinates of $Re_x$ and $Re_x$, $u$ being the local velocity at the point where distances from the leading edge and the surface of the plate are $x$ and $y$, $U$ the free stream speed, and $Re_x$ and $Re_y$ the Reynolds number formed from $x$ and $y$, respectively. Transition accelerates the fluid close to the plate.

For the particular measurements illustrated in Fig. A,2a transition occurred at $Re_t = 1.1 \times 10^6$. However, other measurements have yielded values varying from $9 \times 10^4$ to $2.8 \times 10^6$. The principal variable controlling transition is the turbulence initially present in the air stream (V,B and IX,F). For present purposes we will use as the quantitative measure of the turbulence the quantity

$$\frac{100\sqrt{\frac{1}{3}(u'^2 + v'^2 + w'^2)}}{U}$$

where $u'$, $v'$, and $w'$ are the root-mean-square values of the three components of the turbulent velocity fluctuations. Fig. A,2b shows a plot of

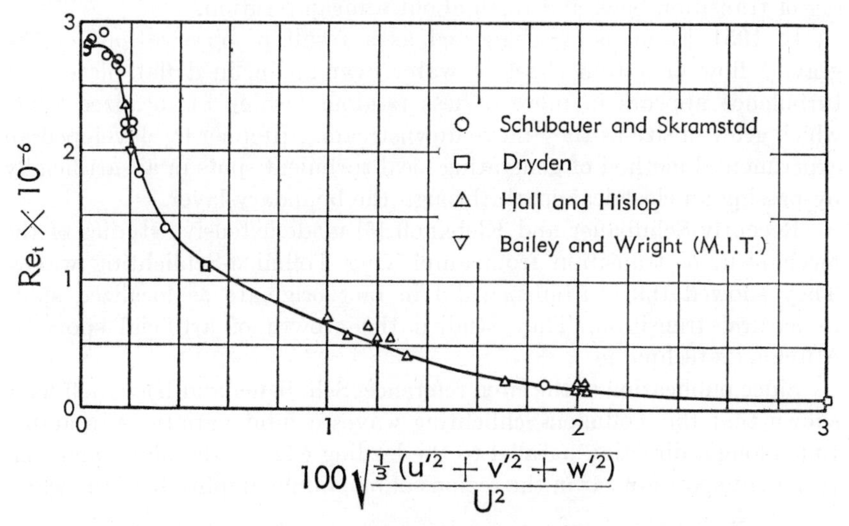


Fig. A,2b. Effect of intensity of free stream turbulence on the transition Reynolds number of a plate.

$Re_t$ against the intensity of turbulence for the available experimental data. While the scale of the turbulence is also known to be of importance, there is insufficient evidence for flat plates to demonstrate its effect. (See Art. 11.) The magnitude of the effect of small fluctuations of velocity amounting to less than one per cent of the average stream velocity is quite surprising.

When the free stream turbulence is less than about 0.1 per cent, Schubauer and Skramstad [*2*] found that transition was preceded by the appearance of the Tollmien-Schlichting oscillations predicted by the theory of instability of laminar boundary layers (IV,F). These oscillations grew in amplitude until transition ensued. The oscillations are not observed at higher turbulence, the random turbulent fluctuations apparently imposing random fluctuations within the boundary layer which mask the Tollmien-Schlichting oscillations.

The exact mechanism by means of which the growing oscillations produce transition is not yet completely understood. It appears, however, that the laminar instability is not a factor except when all sources of disturbance are made very small.

When the transition region is investigated with a hot wire anemometer capable of indicating the instantaneous velocity, it is found that, whereas, from measurements of mean speed, transition appears to be a gradual process, it is in fact quite sudden [*1*]. As the test probe is moved downstream, turbulent "bursts" appear, at first infrequently, then more frequently and of longer duration, until finally the flow is continually and completely turbulent. These observations were interpreted as a wandering of transition back and forth about a mean position.

In 1951 Emmons [*3*] suggested as a result of observations of the gravity flow of a thin sheet of water over an inclined flat plate that turbulence appears in more or less random fashion at localized spots which grow in size as they move downstream. Mitchner [*4*] developed an experimental method of generating local turbulent spots in air artificially by passing an electrical spark through the boundary layer.

Recently Schubauer and Klebanoff [*5*] made extensive studies of the mechanism of transition from amplifying Tollmien-Schlichting waves. They showed that turbulence did in fact originate as localized spots in natural transition. They studied the growth of artificial spots by Mitchner's technique.

Since publication of the cited reference, Schubauer and Klebanoff have shown that the Tollmien-Schlichting waves exhibit variations in amplitude along a direction parallel to the leading edge of the plate, and that turbulent spots appear in the regions of maximum amplitude of the wave.

**A,3. Effect of Pressure Gradient on Transition on a Flat Plate.** The variation of pressure along the outer edge of the boundary layer has a marked effect on the location of transition. Many years ago experiments were made by Wright and Bailey [*6*] on the effect of pressure gradient on transition in a tunnel in which the turbulence was about 0.2 per cent. Relatively small gradients produced large effects, changing $Re_t$ from $2 \times 10^6$ for zero pressure gradient to $0.7 \times 10^6$ and $2.5 \times 10^6$ for small positive and negative gradients. Schubauer and Skramstad [*2*] gave the striking demonstration shown in Fig. A,3 of the stabilizing effect of a pressure which decreases in the downstream direction and the destabilizing effect of a pressure which increases in the downstream direction. In those cases where transition results from the instability of laminar flow at low turbulence levels, transition is hastened by a positive (adverse) pressure gradient and delayed by a negative (favorable) one. The behavior of the Tollmien-Schlichting oscillations in a pressure gradient has been computed [*7*] and the above-mentioned observations are in qualitative agreement with the theory. The computed effect is very large. A suitable nondimensional measure of the pressure gradient is $\lambda = (\delta^2/\nu)(du_e/dx)$ where $du_e/dx$ is the velocity gradient and $\delta$ is the boundary layer thickness defined by the Pohlhausen four-term approximation to the velocity distribution in the boundary layer. For $-3 < \lambda < 3$, stability theory yields a critical Reynolds number $Re_{\delta^*}$ based on displacement thickness

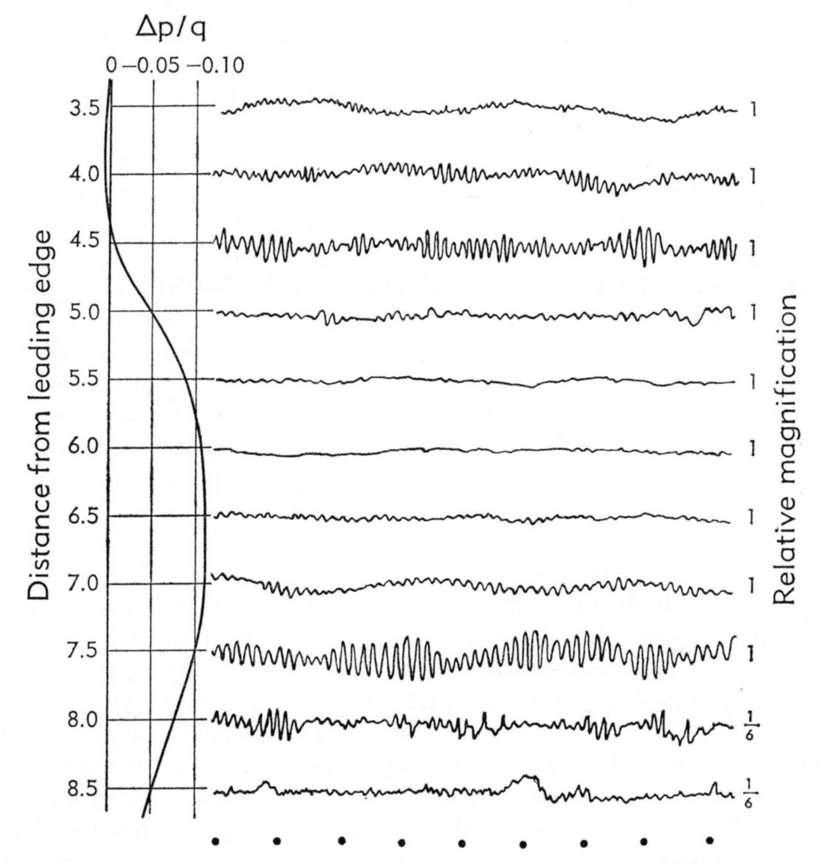


Fig. A,3. Effect of pressure gradient on laminar boundary layer oscillations. Oscillograms of $u'$ at $y$ = 0.021 in., $U$ = 95 ft/sec. Time interval between dots, $\frac{1}{30}$ sec.

(see Art. 6 and IV,C) approximately proportional to $e^{0.6\lambda}$. The actual values are 160, 575, and 4000 for $\lambda$ equal to $-3$, 0, and 3, respectively, corresponding to values of $Re_t$ for zero pressure gradient of 8500, 110,000, and 5,300,000. The critical Reynolds number for transition is, however, considerably greater than that at which amplification of disturbances begins and by an unknown ratio which may vary with $\lambda$.

Liepmann made some measurements of the influence of pressure gradient on transition [*8*] on the convex surface of a plate of 20-foot radius of curvature obtaining changes in transition Reynolds number from $2.2 \times 10^6$ to 0.9 and $3.2 \times 10^6$ for $\lambda = 0, -5.7$, and $+1.9$, respectively.

Feindt [*9*] studied the influence of pressure gradient on smooth and roughened hollow cylinders with axes parallel to the air stream at a stream turbulence of approximately 1.2 per cent, the turbulence level being inferred from sphere measurements. (From the observed value of $Re_t$ for the smooth cylinder at zero pressure gradient, the turbulence level derived from Fig. A,2b is 1.0 per cent.) For pressure gradient parameter $\lambda = 0, -4.4$, and 3.7, the observed transition Reynolds numbers for the smooth cylinder were $0.66 \times 10^6$, $0.36 \times 10^6$, and $0.80 \times 10^6$, respectively. The effects of pressure gradient on roughened cylinders were also large. Thus the influence of pressure gradient has been observed to be large and qualitatively the same over a wide range of roughness and free stream turbulence.

**A,4. Effect of Curvature of Surface on Transition of a Two-Dimensional Boundary Layer.** Liepmann made a systematic study [*10*] of the effect of a uniform radius of curvature of the surface on the transition of a two-dimensional laminar boundary layer. On convex surfaces up to values of displacement thickness $\delta^*$ equal to 0.0026 times the radius of curvature $r$, the same Tollmien-Schlichting instability occurs as for the flat plate and the effect of curvature is negligible. The effect of turbulence is large as in the case of the flat plate.

On a concave surface, the behavior is the same as for a flat plate, provided the ratio $\delta^*/r$ is less than 0.00013. If $\delta^*/r$ exceeds 0.0013, the laminar flow is dynamically unstable because of centrifugal forces producing three-dimensional disturbances as studied theoretically by Görtler [*11*]. Görtler used as a measure of the stability boundary the parameter $Re_\theta \sqrt{\theta/r}$, based on the momentum thickness $\theta$ which is approximately equal to $0.386\delta^*$. Liepmann found the Görtler parameter equal to 9.0 in an air stream of the lowest turbulence available to him (turbulence intensity 0.2 per cent as judged from his flat plate measurements, $u'/u_e = 0.0006$, $v'$ and $w'$ not measured), whereas at a higher turbulence level ($u'/u_e = 0.003$, $v'/u_e$ and $w'/u_e$ not measured) the value was about 6.0. For values of $\delta^*/r$ between 0.00013 and 0.0013 there appears to be a more or less continuous change from the Tollmien-Schlichting instability to the Görtler instability.

**A,5. Effect of Surface Roughness and Waviness on Transition of a Two-Dimensional Boundary Layer.** Surface roughness and waviness are known to influence transition presumably because of the disturbances introduced by their presence. The general nature of the effect of a single roughness element has been studied in detail by Liepmann [*12*], the roughness element being a half cylinder with axis normal to the stream in the boundary layer of a flat plate. In every case tried, the flow separated from the surface of the roughness element but did not in every case lead to immediate transition. The results of many experiments suggest that a single roughness element must be comparable in height with the displacement thickness in order to produce transition. In Liepmann's experiments an element for which $k = 0.76\delta^*$ did not produce immediate transition, whereas elements for which $k > 0.92\delta^*$ did produce immediate transition. Certain experiments of Fage [*13*], when analyzed, show that the minimum height to cause transition on a plate at certain definite locations downstream from the roughness element varies from 0.82 to $1.77\delta^*$ for smooth

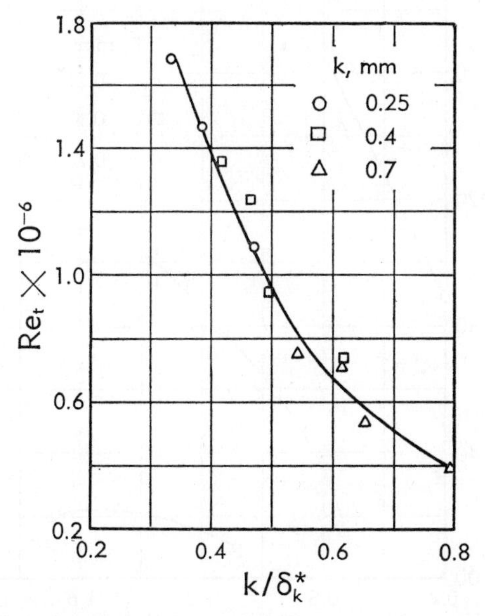


Fig. A,5a. Effect of single cylindrical roughness element on the transition Reynolds number of a plate. Original measurements of Tani, Hama, and Mituisi [*15*].

bulges, 1.44 to $1.62\delta^*$ for a smooth hollow, and 0.43 to $0.67\delta^*$ for a flat ridge. The higher values are required to cause transition to approach the roughness element; the values to cause transition at the element as determined by extrapolation are $1.8\delta^*$, $1.6\delta^*$ and $0.98\delta^*$, respectively. Holstein [*14*] has also found that roughness heights comparable to the displacement thickness are required to move transition appreciably forward.

In Fage's experiments it was found that a roughness element can influence the position of transition far downstream, presumably because it imposes a disturbance akin to turbulent fluctuations which slowly grow until transition occurs. This effect was not observed in Liepmann's experiments since observations were made only to a downstream distance of 6 inches. It is probable that, in the case in which Liepmann observed no transition, transition did in fact occur earlier when the roughness element was present than when it was absent.

Systematic experiments by Tani, Hama, and Mituisi [*15*] have clarified the effect of a two-dimensional roughness element. Their experiments were made on a flat plate with zero pressure gradient in a wind tunnel in which $Re_t$ was about $1.7 \times 10^6$ with cylindrical wires as roughness elements. In the original paper the data were analyzed according to the concept suggested by Schiller [*16*, pp. 189–192] that a roughness element

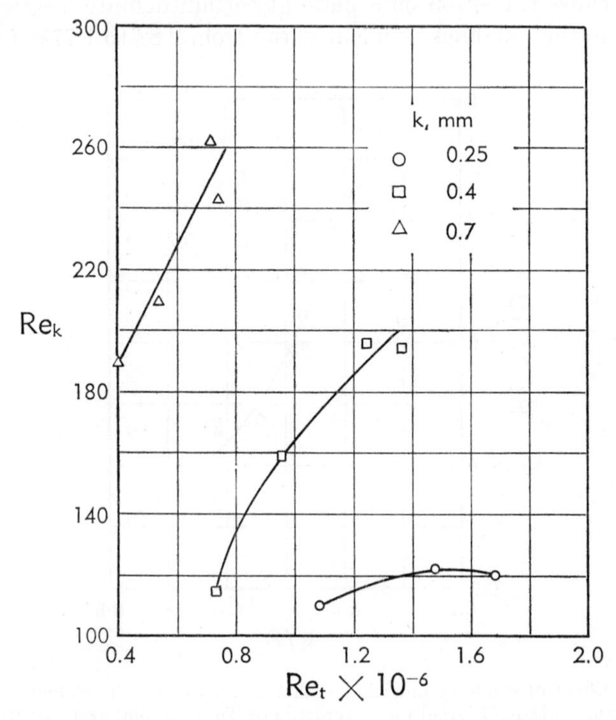


Fig. A,5b. Relation between Reynolds number of roughness element and transition Reynolds number of a plate. Original measurements of Tani, Hama, and Mituisi [*15*].

induces transition when the Reynolds number of the element itself reaches a definite critical value at which vortices appear in its wake. Dryden [*17*] reanalyzed the data and showed much better agreement with the concept that $Re_t$ is a function of $k/\delta_k^*$ where $k$ is the height of the roughness element and $\delta_k^*$ is the displacement thickness of the boundary layer at the location of the roughness element. Fig. A,5a shows $Re_t$ as a function of $k/\delta_k^*$ whereas Fig. A,5b shows the relationship between $Re_t$ and $Re_k$.

Tani and Hama presented additional results in a later paper [*18*]. They are plotted in Fig. A,5c. As the roughness height is increased, the position of transition moves forward from the smooth plate position until it reaches the position of the roughness element. $Re_t$ is a function of $k/\delta_k^*$

so long as transition is forward of the smooth plate position but downstream from and not too close to the roughness element. The dotted upward branches in Fig. A,5c correspond to transition at the roughness element. The location of these branches is determined by the parameter $x_k/k$, where $x_k$ is the position of the roughness element.

The results of Fage [*13*] analyzed in this way are shown in Fig. A,5d; typical results of Stüper [*19*], discussed at some length in [*17*], are shown

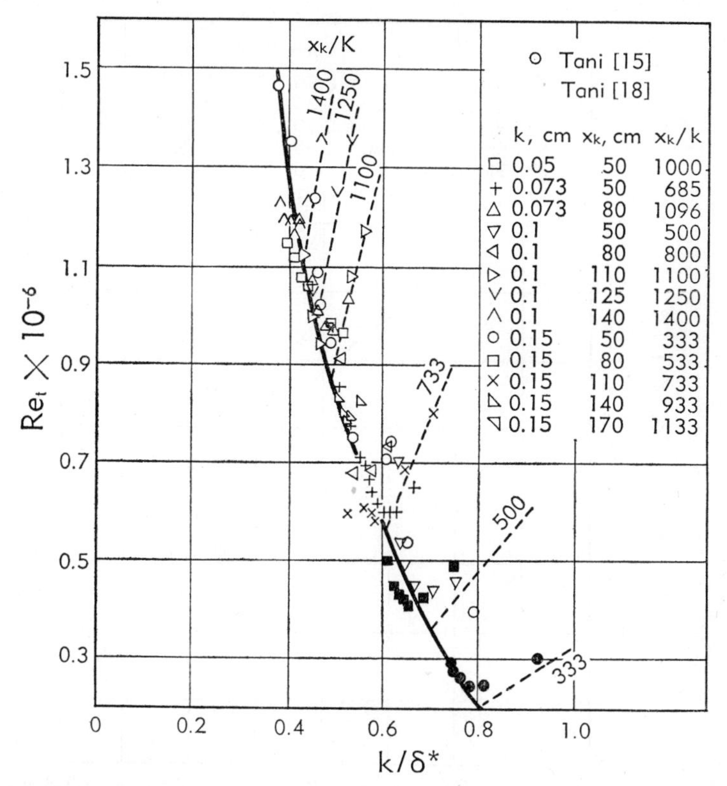


**Fig. A,5c.** Effect of single cylindrical roughness element on the transition Reynolds number of a plate. Measurements of Tani, Hama, and Mituisi [*15*] and Tani and Hama [*18*].

in Fig. A,5e. A few results by Scherbarth as reported by Quick [*20*] are plotted in Fig. A,5f. These refer to flat ridges 20 mm wide and varying in height from 0.1 to 1.0 mm.

Tani and his collaborators repeated Dryden's analysis using the original data found in Japan and applying corrections for the small departures of the pressure from uniformity [*21*]. These revised values, the data of Fig. A,5f, results of more recent measurements by Tani, Iuchi, and Yamamoto [*22*], and results obtained by Feindt [*9*] on a hollow cylinder with axis parallel to the wind are shown in Fig. A,5g. These data cover values of $Re_t$ for the smooth plate from 700,000 to 2.6 million corresponding to free stream turbulence levels (according to Fig. A,2b) ranging from 0.92 per cent to 0.14 per cent. The effects of roughness are present at all turbulence levels. At $k/\delta_k^* = 0$ there is a large variation of $Re_t$ with turbulence level. However, for values of $k/\delta_k^*$ greater than 0.6, the effect of turbulence is small. A roughness element for which $k/\delta_k^*$ is 0.5 has about the same effect on transition as a turbulence level of 0.6 per cent.

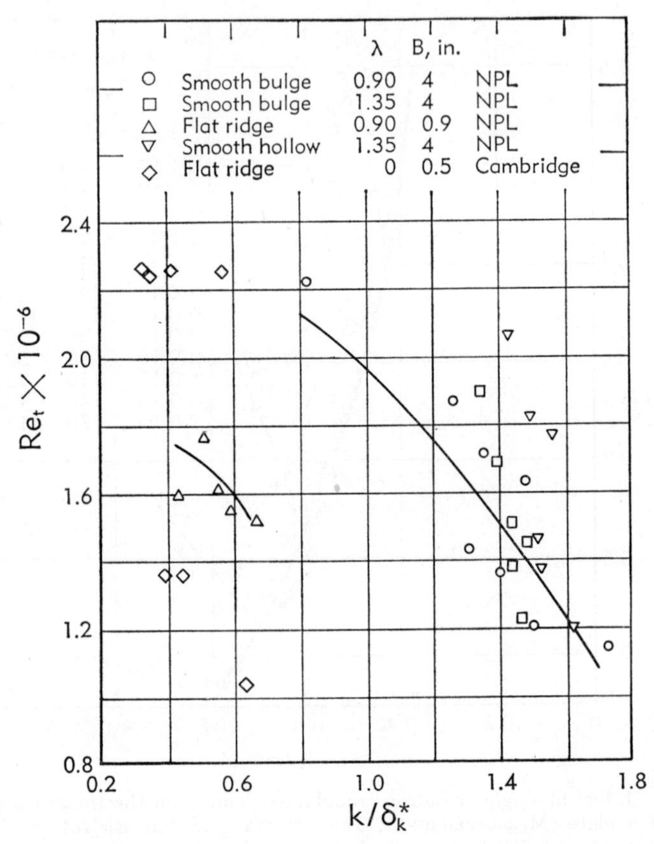


Fig. A,5d. Effect of single roughness elements on the transition Reynolds number of a plate. Measurements of Fage [13]. $\lambda$ = pressure gradient parameter $(\delta^2/\nu)(du_e/dx)$. $B$ = chord of roughness element.

Dryden suggested that the ratio of $Re_t$ for the rough plate to the transition Reynolds number $(Re_t)_0$ for the smooth plate was a universal function of $k/\delta_k^*$ independent of air stream turbulence. The data shown in Fig. A,5g, in particular the measurements by Tani, Iuchi, and Yamamoto [22] and by Feindt [9] disprove this hypothesis. Fig. A,5h is a plot of $Re_t/(Re_t)_0$ vs. $k/\delta_k^*$ for presently available data. At high turbulence levels the ratio falls off more slowly than at low turbulence levels; thus transition

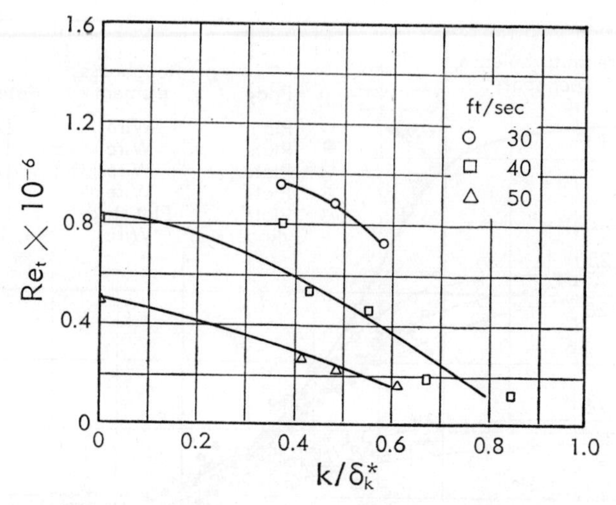


Fig. A,5e. Effect of single cylindrical roughness element on the transition Reynolds number of a plate. Measurements of Stüper [*19*].

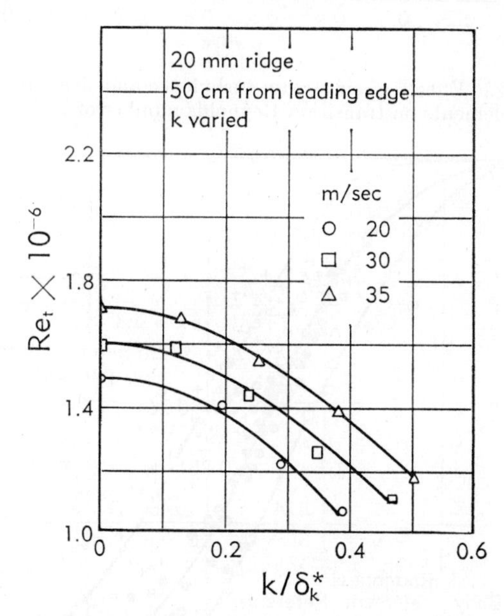


Fig. A,5f. Effect of single flat-ridge roughness element on the transition Reynolds number of a plate. Measurements of Scherbarth [*20*].

is relatively less sensitive to roughness at high turbulence levels. However, the change in $k/\delta_k^*$ for a reduction of the transition Reynolds number to one half its original value is only from 0.47 to 0.66. Curves are drawn for several turbulence levels; they are applicable only to single roughness elements in the form of cylindrical wires and flat ridges for

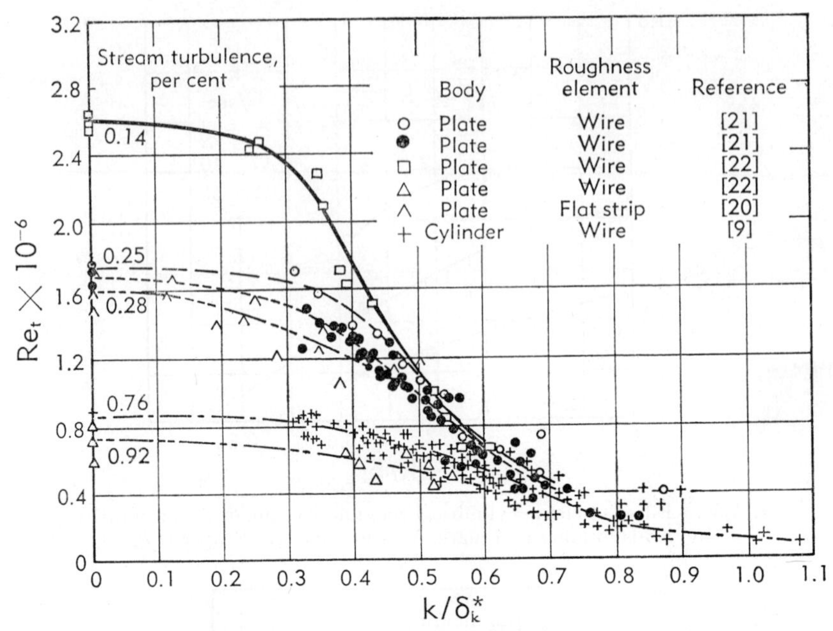


Fig. A,5g. Effects of air stream turbulence and single roughness elements on transition Reynolds number of plate.

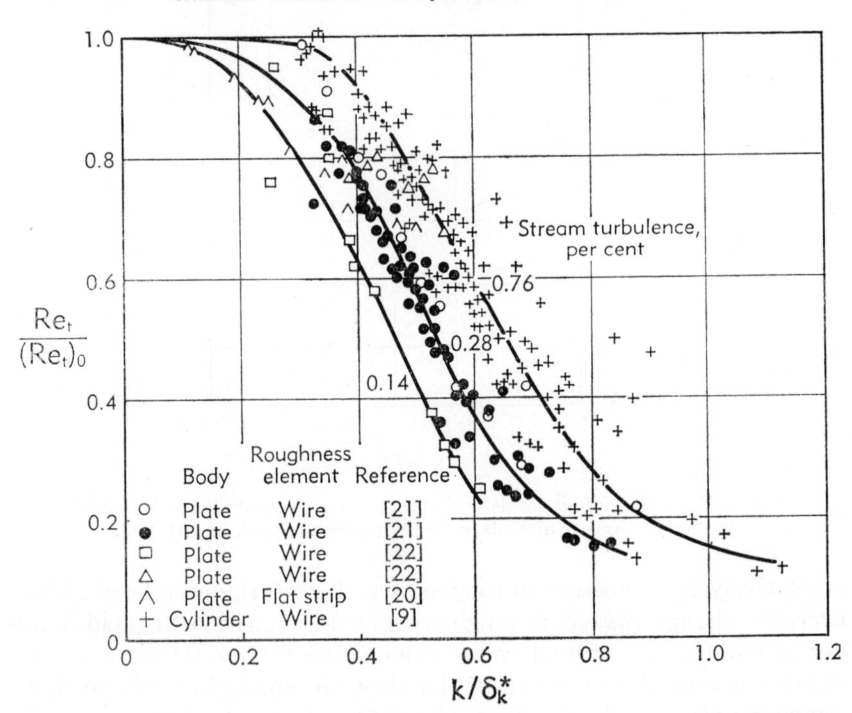


Fig. A,5h. Ratio of transition Reynolds number for plate with single roughness element to that for smooth plate in air streams of different turbulence.

conditions in which transition occurs downstream from the roughness element. Appreciable effects of roughness occur for roughness elements of height equal to 0.2 to 0.4 the displacement thickness of the boundary layer at the roughness element depending on the turbulence level. At a certain value of $k/\delta_k^*$ which depends on many quantities, including the speed, location of the roughness element, and air stream turbulence, the transition position in its forward motion reaches the roughness element and remains there. The curve of Fig. A,5h does not apply after transition reaches the roughness element.

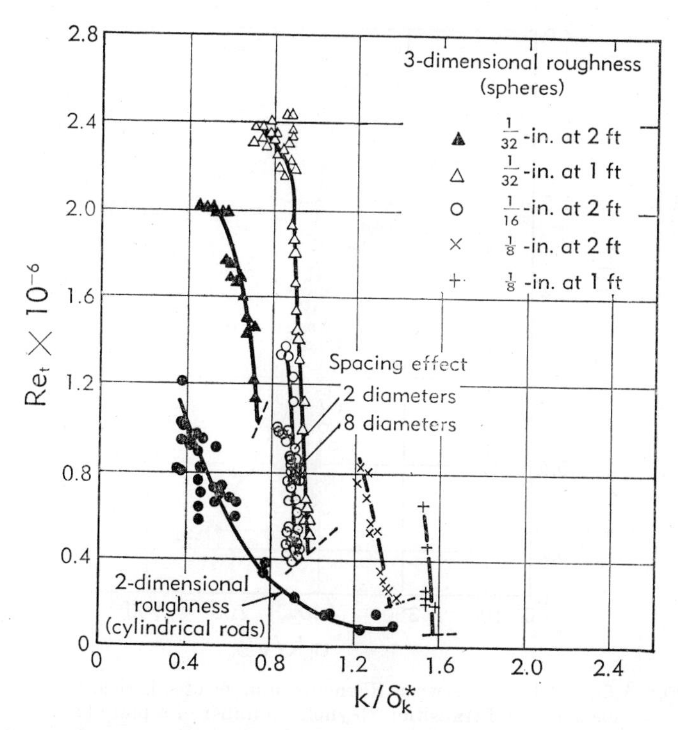


Fig. A,5i. Effect of spherical roughness elements on the transition Reynolds number of a plate. Measurements of Klebanoff, Schubauer, and Tidstrom [*23*].

As contrasted with this behavior of two-dimensional roughness elements, the data on three-dimensional elements correlate best with the assumption of a critical Reynolds number of the roughness element. Experiments have been made by Klebanoff, Schubauer, and Tidstrom [*23*] on single rows of spherical elements of various spacings at various distances from the leading edge of a flat plate. The results are shown in Fig. A,5i and A,5j, showing $Re_t$ vs. $k/\delta_k^*$ and $Re_t$ vs. $u_k k/\nu$ respectively, where $u_k$ is the velocity in the boundary layer at a distance $k$ from the wall. There is considerable scatter, but from the results for the smallest spheres the surface may be considered aerodynamically smooth, i.e. the roughness element has little effect on transition, if $u_k k/\nu$ is less than 300. If the free stream velocity $U$ were used, the corresponding value of $Uk/\nu$ would be about 800. The numerical values obviously depend on the shape of the elements, although systematic data are not available.

There are only a few experiments on distributed roughness on a flat plate, and these are difficult of analysis because of the necessary experimental treatment of the leading edge. Thus Holstein [*14*], using a "plate" consisting of a structure of wood about 11 feet long and 1.4 inches thick with an elliptical nose piece about 7.09 inches long, left the nose piece

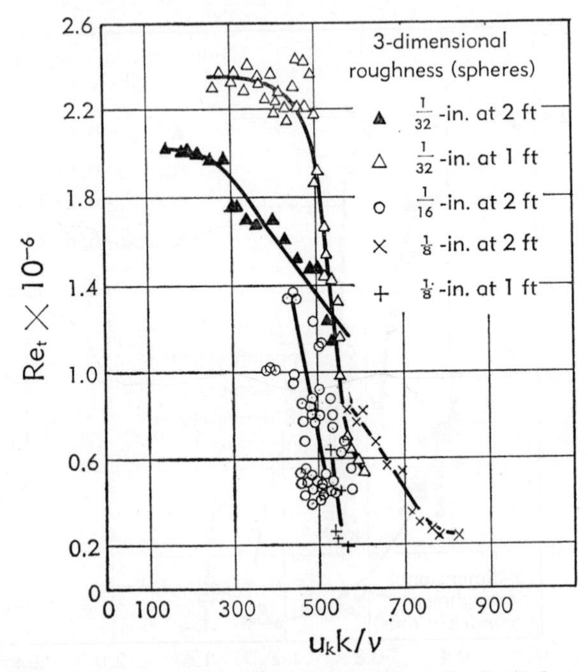


Fig. A,5j. Relation between Reynolds number of spherical roughness elements and transition Reynolds number of a plate [*23*].

smooth and roughened the remainder of the surface by attaching emery paper of various degrees of roughness. The value of $Re_t$ for the smooth plate varied with the speed, perhaps because of variation of the turbulence with speed. Furthermore, the plate was not aerodynamically smooth since fine emery paper often increased the transition Reynolds number. Holstein believed that the paper covered up the surface waviness. The average value of $Re_t$ was about 650,000 corresponding to a turbulence of 1.0 per cent, or more probably to departures from aerodynamic smoothness.

The emery paper had a thickness of about 0.3 mm and the sharp step at the leading edge of the paper was smoothed with plasticine over a length of about 1 cm, according to a letter from Holstein. The roughness height given did not include the paper thickness. It seems probable that the front edge of the paper is the critical roughness rather than the distributed roughness. Fig. A,5k shows $Re_t$ plotted against $k/\delta_0^*$ where $k$ is

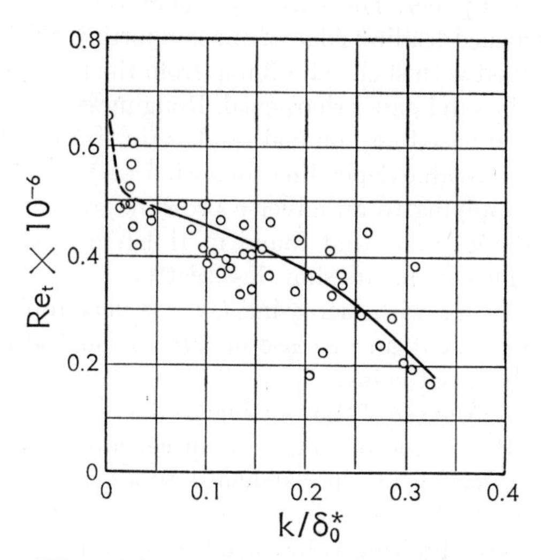


Fig. A,5k. Effect of distributed roughness on the transition Reynolds number of a plate. Measurements of Holstein as reported.

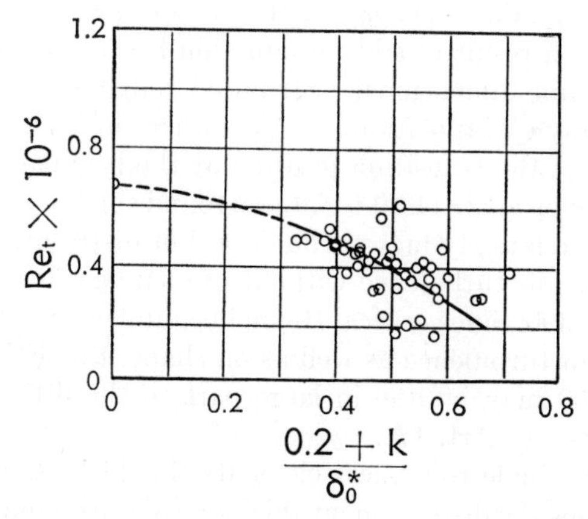


Fig. A,5l. Effect of distributed roughness on the transition Reynolds number of a plate. Measurements of Holstein with suggested correction.

the nominal roughness height and $\delta_0^*$ is the displacement thickness at the beginning of the roughened portion. Fig. A,5l shows a plot of the same results on the assumption that the roughness height is the tabulated value plus 0.2 mm.

If Holstein's results are analyzed in terms of the Reynolds number of the roughness element based on free stream velocity and nominal roughness height, it appears that $Uk/\nu$ must be less than about $100 \pm 50$ if the surface is to be considered aerodynamically smooth.

Feindt [*9*] studied the effect of distributed roughness on a hollow cylinder, using sand paper. The sand paper cylinder was extended 12 mm beyond the sharpened leading edge of the supporting cylinder. The sand paper was smoothed with shellac for 3 mm from the leading edge, and the leading edge of the sand paper sharpened. Roughness for which $Uk/\nu$ was less than 60 to 100 based on nominal sand grain size had little effect on transition, the exact value depending somewhat on the pressure gradient, the lower value applying to an adverse pressure gradient. This value is approximately the same as that found in Holstein's measurements, although Feindt's measurements show less scatter.

The decrease in $Re_t$ with increasing $Uk/\nu$ is very rapid. For the case of zero pressure gradient an increase of $Uk/\nu$ from 100 to 150 reduces $Re_t$ to one half its initial value.

Feindt proposed the use of the Göttingen equivalent sand grain roughness, defined as that value of roughness in certain Göttingen measurements of friction coefficients in roughened tubes which gave the same friction coefficient as his samples. Based on this Göttingen equivalent roughness height, the limiting value of $Uk/\nu$ is from 100 to 170.

The applicability of these limiting values of $Uk/\nu$ to smoother surfaces for which $k$ lies outside the range of the experimental values or to higher Reynolds numbers is somewhat uncertain. Since transition is believed to arise as a result of eddy production by the roughness elements in the case of three-dimensional distributed roughness, it appears more logical to base any extrapolation on $u_k k/\nu$ where $u_k$ is the velocity in the boundary layer at the transition position at the height of the roughness element. A value of $u_k k/\nu$ of 30 to 50 was found for sand grain roughness in air streams of relatively high turbulence. For distributed small spheres in a flow of very low turbulence without pressure gradient, the observed value was about 300. Since critical Reynolds numbers are usually dependent on air stream turbulence as well as on shape, the difference between 30 to 50 and 300 may be due in large part to the different air stream turbulence levels (see Art. 17).

In summary, single roughness elements should be limited to heights less than 0.2 times the displacement thickness of the boundary layer at the element under the prevailing conditions of speed, viscosity, and element location to avoid reduction of transition Reynolds number. Distributed roughness should be limited to heights for which the Reynolds number based on nominal roughness height and the velocity in the boundary layer at the transition position at the height of the element is less than a value of the order of 30 to 300. The former value applies to sand roughness in a stream of turbulence of 1.0 per cent; the latter to small spheres in a stream of turbulence of less than 0.1 per cent. Favorable pressure gradients increase the permissible roughness height considerably.

**A,6. Application of Dimensional Analysis to Transition of a Two-Dimensional Boundary Layer.** So far we have considered the study of transition on a flat plate, first without pressure gradient, then with simple linear variation of the pressure, with uniform curvature, and with simple roughness, each variable considered singly. However, in the cases of technical interest, all of the variables may vary simultaneously along the surface of the body generating the boundary layer. Further attempts have been made to apply the knowledge gained in the simpler cases by means of dimensional analysis.

For a series of geometrically similar two-dimensional bodies the position at which transition occurs depends on the Reynolds number at which the measurement is made and on the intensity and scale of the turbulence of the main stream. Dimensional reasoning gives the result that

$$\frac{x_t}{c} = F\left(\frac{Uc}{\nu}, \frac{u'}{U}, \frac{L}{c}\right)$$

where $x_t$ is the coordinate locating the transition point with relation to a selected system of axes, $c$ is the reference dimension, for example, the chord of an airfoil, $U$ is the free stream velocity, $\nu$ the kinematic viscosity of the fluid, $u'$ the intensity, and $L$ the scale of the turbulence.

Since, as previously noted, transition occurs within the boundary layer, one would like to relate its occurrence more directly to boundary layer parameters rather than to the shape of the body. Boundary layers on different two-dimensional bodies differ only in the variation of pressure to which they are exposed by the flow around the body, and in the curvature and roughness of the surface on which they are formed. Measuring $x$ along the surface from the stagnation point, $x_t$ is dependent on the three functions of $x$ describing the variation of the stream velocity just outside the boundary layer with $x$ (which fixes the pressure variation), the variation of the curvature of the boundary with $x$, and the variation of the roughness with $x$, as well as on the free stream turbulence. Since the number of possible functions is indefinitely large, no simplification results from this approach. It was for the reason of gaining some insight into the problem that we considered in Art. 2 to 5 the simplest types of functional variation, namely constant values of the parameters independent of $x$, or linear variations.

Since transition occurs suddenly, another approach is to relate transition to the local boundary layer parameters, eliminating $x$ as a variable. The local situation is usually described by the boundary layer thickness $\delta$, the velocity $u_e$ at the outer edge and its derivative $du_e/dx$ which is a measure of the pressure gradient, and the kinematic viscosity $\nu$. To these must be added the free stream turbulence, and the radius of curvature $r$ and roughness $k$ of the surface at the selected location. There is no obvious reason for omitting higher derivatives of $u_e$ or the complete distribution of velocity within the boundary layer. If, however, the quantities listed are sufficient, dimensional reasoning yields the result that

$$\left(\frac{u_e \delta}{\nu}\right)_t = F\left(\frac{\delta^2}{\nu}\frac{du_e}{dx}, \frac{\delta}{r}, \frac{k}{\delta}, \frac{L}{\delta}, \frac{u'}{u_e}\right)$$

In line with this approach to the problem, it has become customary to state the location of transition in terms of the local boundary layer

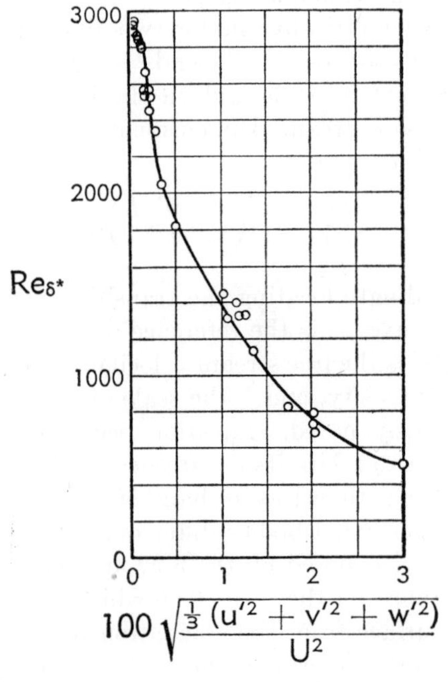


Fig. A,6. Effect of intensity of free stream turbulence on the transition Reynolds number of a plate expressed in terms of displacement thickness of the boundary layer.

Reynolds number rather than in terms of $x_t$ in the hope that values for bodies of different shape would be more nearly comparable. There is considerable diversity of practice in selection of the particular boundary layer thickness to be used. Since the velocity in the boundary layer approaches asymptotically that outside, there is no accurately determinable value of the actual thickness. The displacement thickness $\delta^*$ is frequently used and will be used hereafter. NACA writers have used the value of $y$ for which $u/u_e = 0.707$ as the thickness, because of the ease with which it can be read from experimental curves and because it is approximately proportional to $\delta^*$. Thus for the Blasius exact solution, the NACA value of $\delta$ is equal to $1.34\delta^*$ and for the Pohlhausen 4-term approximations to flows with pressure gradient the NACA value of $\delta$ is 1.28 and $1.32\delta^*$ for values of $\lambda = 12$ and $-12$. The value of $Re_{\delta^*}$ for transition is often converted to an equivalent flat plate value of $Re_t$ by the approximate relation $Re = \frac{1}{3}Re^2_{\delta^*}$. The values of $Re_{\delta^*}$ at transition on a smooth flat plate with zero pressure gradient vary from 515 to 2900 corresponding to the values of $Re_t$ of $9 \times 10^4$ to $2.8 \times 10^8$ previously quoted. A plot of $Re_{\delta^*}$ against intensity of turbulence is shown in Fig. A,6.

**A,7. Transition of Shear Layers in the Free Fluid.** Another of the frequently observed characteristic phenomena in addition to transition is that of separation of the flow from a solid boundary and we shall see that there is an interplay between the two phenomena. Separation of the flow is accompanied by a reversal in the direction of the flow very close to the boundary behind the separation line and by the formation of a wake in which the velocity is much reduced. Separation is a boundary layer phenomenon; it occurs when the pressure increases in the downstream direction, or in our previous terminology, when the boundary layer encounters an adverse pressure gradient of sufficient magnitude. When the pressure rises, the flow in the boundary layer is retarded by the pressure as well as by the surface friction and the fluid near the surface is ultimately brought to rest. When separation occurs, the boundary layer becomes a shear layer in the free fluid, sometimes called a vortex layer. Such shear regions in which the velocity gradient is much larger than elsewhere are found where discontinuities of velocity, or of the physical properties of the fluid are introduced, as for example, in the case of a jet of fluid issuing in a surrounding quiescent fluid.

The flow in such a shear layer may be laminar or turbulent and transition is observed to occur in shear layers as well as in boundary layers. An early rule of thumb was that if the Reynolds number formed from the velocity at the outer edge of a boundary layer and its thickness were less than about 2000, transition would not occur. However, shear layers are much more unstable (IV,F) and transition has been observed at Reynolds numbers less than 100. Thus a laminar boundary layer often exhibits transition immediately following separation.

If the Reynolds number is sufficiently low a laminar boundary layer may separate and continue as a laminar shear layer for a considerable distance. Transition in such a laminar shear layer has been studied in some detail by Schiller and Linke [*24,25*]. The shear layer was found in the flow field around a circular cylinder at Reynolds numbers (based on cylinder diameter) of 2000 to 20,000. Pitot tube traverses of the wake showed the existence of a shear layer proceeding from the separating laminar boundary layer. Its thickness increased relatively slowly and then much more rapidly at a line which approached the line of separation as the Reynolds number was increased. This behavior is typical of transition. Fig. A,7 shows the results obtained at three Reynolds numbers. The boundaries of the shear layer were determined as the point at which the Pitot pressure "begins to decrease" and the point at which the Pitot pressure "reaches a constant minimum value." The critical Reynolds number for transition based on this thickness varied systematically with the Reynolds number of the cylinder, increasing from 510 at a cylinder Reynolds number of 3540 to 900 at a cylinder Reynolds number of 8540. A most important observation was that a disturbance introduced by a wire of small diameter in the boundary layer of the cylinder moved the transition closer to the cylinder. Hence the transition of a laminar shear layer is a function of the initial turbulence as is transition in a boundary layer.

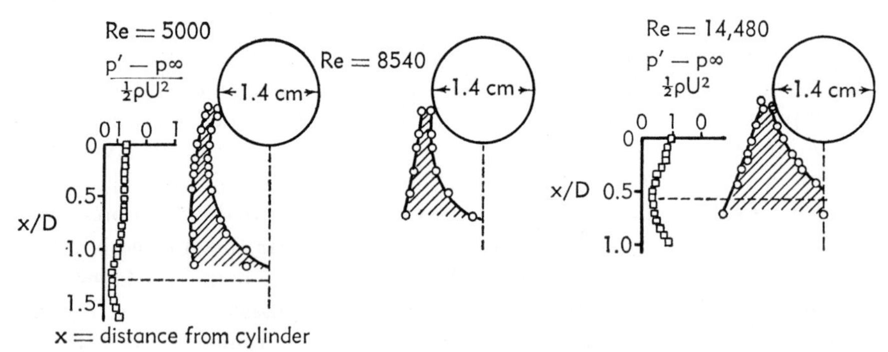


Fig. A,7. Free shear layers behind a circular cylinder exhibiting transition.

The shear layer behind the cylinder is subjected to pressure gradients. However, no accurate static pressure measurements could be made in the wake. The total pressure along the plane of symmetry of the wake falls to a minimum at the point where the shear layers from the two sides meet. The shear layers are not very thin and probably the static pressure is not constant across them. However, the rising value of the critical Reynolds number of the shear layer and the more rapid fall of the total pressure along the plane of symmetry of the wake suggests that transition in a shear layer may be delayed by a favorable pressure gradient as in the case of a boundary layer.

Schiller and Linke do not give their data in sufficient detail to permit an accurate calculation of the displacement thickness which in this case might be defined by the relation

$$(u_e - u_0)\delta^* = \int (u - u_0)dy$$

where $u_0$ is the velocity at the inner boundary. As a rough guess $\delta^*$ is of the order of 0.3 the thickness defined by Schiller and Linke, and hence $Re_{\delta^*}$ is of the order of 150 to 270 at the turbulence of Schiller and Linke's stream which was probably quite high. This compares with an estimated value of the order of 515 for a boundary layer under similar conditions (Fig. A,6).

At cylinder Reynolds numbers from about 20,000 to about 200,000 the laminar boundary layer becomes turbulent immediately on separation. Since the value of $Re_{\delta^*}$ at any fixed point on the cylinder varies as the square root of the cylinder Reynolds number, the critical $Re_{\delta^*}$ for the boundary layer is of the order of $\sqrt{10}$ or 3.2 times that for a shear layer. This is an independent experimental determination of the relative values of $Re_{\delta^*}$ for transition. In similar layers with zero pressure gradient and low turbulence, the distance from stagnation point to transition would be ten times as great for a boundary layer as for a shear layer.

It is well known that a surface of discontinuity in an incompressible frictionless fluid is unstable in the sense that any small disturbance increases exponentially in amplitude with time as originally discussed by Helmholtz and by Rayleigh. Rosenhead [*26*] attempted to follow the motion to a later stage and showed that the disturbance becomes unsymmetrical and tends to concentrate the vorticity at points spaced at equal intervals. Because of the nonlinear character of the equations, the final stages cannot be computed by superposition of the effects of separate wavelengths. Rosenhead believed that the determination of the wavelength which ultimately dominates cannot be determined except by considering the effects of viscosity and diffusion. The rolling-up process was well advanced in the time required for the fluid to travel a distance equal to one third of the wavelength.

The effect of viscosity is not only to convert a discontinuity into a shear layer of finite thickness but also to provide a damping effect. Lessen [*27*] attempted to compute the stability of a shear layer using the Tollmien-Schlichting theory. His computations are not complete but they indicate a critical $Re_{\delta^*}$ for the beginning of amplification of about 15 and a predominant wavelength of approximately 35 times $\delta^*$.

Shear layers produced by separation of the flow from a flat plate normal to the wind have been studied experimentally by Fage and Johansen [*28*]. These were, however, turbulent from their origin at the edge of the plate, the value of $Re_{\delta^*}$ being of the order of 600 or more.

Flachsbart [*29*] shows some smoke flow pictures of the transition of free vortex layers behind a flat plate. Reynolds numbers based on the observed width of the smoke trail at transition vary from 40 to 100, but it is unlikely that the width of the smoke filament has anything to do with the usual measures of shear layer width. The values of $Re_{t-s}$ based on distance from separation point to transition are better defined and from them we infer values of $Re_{\delta^*}$ of the order of 95 to 100. These values are somewhat less than those found by Schiller and Linke for a cylinder, perhaps due to different turbulence of the air streams.

**A,8. Transition of Shear Layers with Reattachment Following Laminar Separation.** It has been noted that the laminar boundary layer of a cylinder appears to undergo transition immediately following separation when the cylinder Reynolds number is greater than 20,000. When the curvature of the body is not large, it is observed that the turbulent shear layer may reattach to the surface, leaving a localized region of separation usually referred to as a separation "bubble." The attached layer continues as a turbulent boundary layer along the surface to the trailing edge or until separation of the turbulent boundary layer

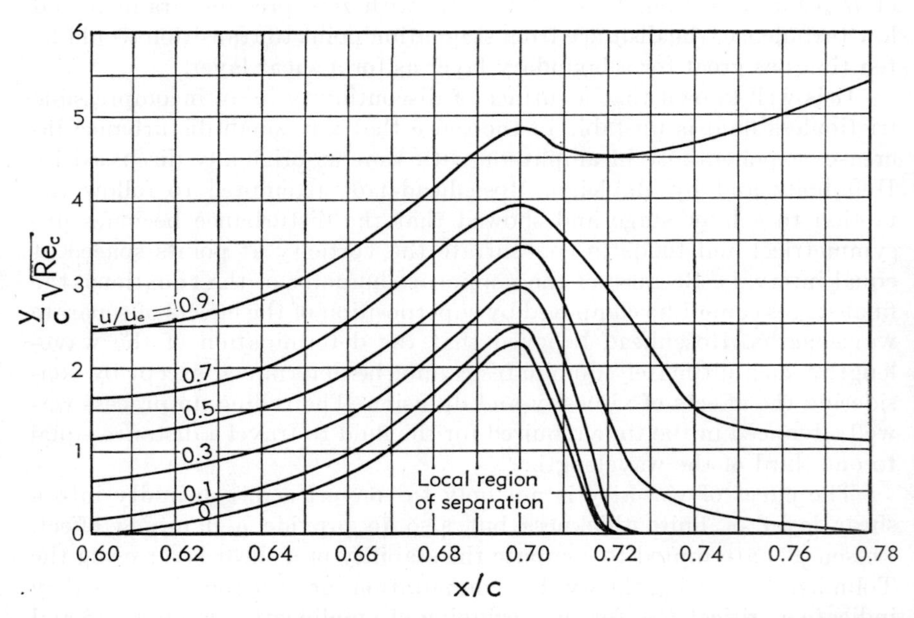


Fig. A,8a. Velocity distribution in the boundary layer of an airfoil exhibiting a separation bubble. Airfoil NACA $66_3$-018, $Re_c = 1.7 \times 10^6$. Contours of equal local mean speed.

occurs. This reattachment is due to the much greater lateral diffusion of momentum in a turbulent as compared to a laminar layer.

Separation bubbles on airfoils were noted by Jones [*30*] some years ago and there have been a number of studies of the detailed structure of separation bubbles. In addition, various attempts have been made to develop semiempirical theories.

Fig. A,8a shows the velocity distribution in the localized region of laminar separation behind the position of minimum pressure on an NACA $66_3$-018 airfoil section at zero angle of attack taken from measurements by Bursnall and Loftin [*31*] in the NACA Langley low turbulence wind tunnel. The corresponding pressure distribution on the airfoil is given in

Fig. A,8b. Further studies on the same airfoil and on a modified NACA 0010 airfoil were made by Gault [*32*].

Similar separation bubbles have been observed in the vicinity of the leading edge of airfoils at relatively high angles of attack [*33*], and on an elliptic cylinder [*34*].

Attempts to correlate the observations into a unified scheme have been unsuccessful, the data for bubbles near the leading edge exhibiting different relationships than the data for bubbles near or behind the mid-chord position.

Jacobs and von Doenhoff [*35*, p. 311] suggested that transition occurred when the Reynolds number $Re_{x-s}$ formed from the local free stream speed and the distance along the shear layer from the separation point attained the critical value of 50,000, according to their fragmentary

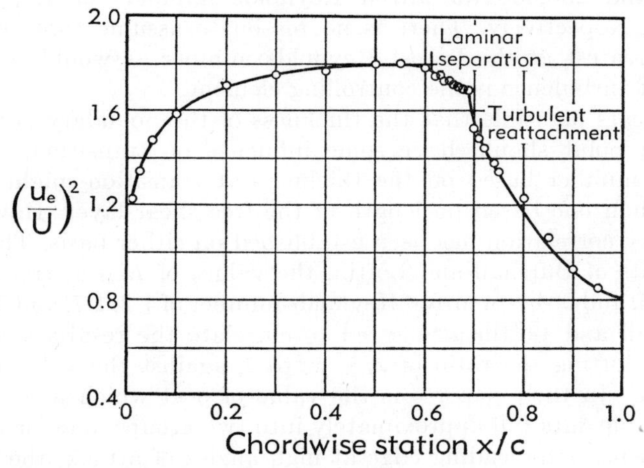


Fig. A,8b. Pressure distribution over airfoil with separation bubble.

measurements. Gault [*32,33*] obtained values for the shear layer in separation bubbles near the leading edge of 13,000 to 103,000 for the NACA $66_3$-018, 0 to 171,000 for the modified NACA 0010, and 20,000 to 60,000 for the NACA 63-009 airfoil. Schiller and Linke's values [*24,25*] of $Re_{t-s}$ for the shear layer from a circular cylinder vary from 4000 to 5000, and $Re_{t-s}$ was reduced to about 2000 by a turbulence-producing wire. Schubauer's value [*34*] for the shear layer in a separation bubble on an elliptic cylinder is about 28,000 in an air stream of turbulence 0.85 per cent. Maekawa and Atsumi [*36*] obtained a value of 25,000 for the shear layer in a separation bubble from the ridge of a model consisting of two flat plates making an angle of nearly 180° at the ridge. These authors infer that this value is independent of air stream turbulence from indirect evidence based on observations of the point of reattachment and a theory which is not too well established. Bursnall and Loftin's data [*31*] give values of $Re_{t-s}$ from 150,000 to 260,000 for the shear layer in a separation bubble at 61 per cent of the chord on an NACA $66_3$-018 airfoil, whereas Gault's values [*32*] for the same airfoil vary from 160,000 to 380,000. Thus the values of $Re_{t-s}$ vary from 0 to 380,000, an even wider range than observed for the boundary layer on a plate without pressure gradient.

One might assume that the large variation is a reflection of the influences of free stream turbulence and pressure gradient on transition of the free shear layer entirely analogous to those demonstrated to exist for boundary layers. However, the available data do not establish this assumption conclusively. The difficulties may be illustrated by Bursnall and Loftin's measurements. Their values of $Re_{t-s}$ vary with the Reynolds number of the airfoil, yet the pressure distribution is substantially independent of the airfoil Reynolds number. The values of $Re_{t-s}$ are 148,000, 197,000, and 256,000 for airfoil Reynolds numbers of 1.2, 1.7, and $2.4 \times 10^6$, respectively. There is no reason to assume that the turbulence is greatest at the lowest Reynolds number as would seem to be required if turbulence is the controlling element.

It appears plausible that the thickness of the boundary layer at the separation point should have some influence on transition, or that a Reynolds number based on the thickness at transition might be more suitable than one based on length of the free shear layer. However, no satisfactory correlation has been established on either basis. Thus in the experiments of Bursnall and Loftin, the values of $Re_{\delta^*}$ at transition are 2070, 2560, and 2940 for airfoil Reynolds number of 1.2, 1.7, and $2.4 \times 10^6$.

Bursnall and Loftin attempted to correlate the results available to them by plotting the ratio of $x_t - x_s$ to $\delta_s$ against the value of $Re_\delta$ at separation. (In their paper $\delta$ is the value of $y$ at which $u/u_e = 0.707$.) The available data fall approximately into two groups, one for regions of separation near the leading edge at high angles of attack, the other for regions of separation near the midchord position at 0° angle of attack. Hence this attempt does not yield an integrated picture.

Gault [*32*] attempted further analysis of his measurements and those of Bursnall and Loftin, but the results are not satisfactory.

Some work on the effect of turbulence was carried out by Gault on the NACA $66_3$-018 airfoil. Increased turbulence moved transition upstream for all conditions and completely eliminated the separation bubble near midchord for all Reynolds numbers from 1.5 to 10 million. Separation bubbles near the leading edge were not eliminated but their size was greatly reduced. The effect of increasing the turbulence from 0.2 to 1.1 per cent at a Reynolds number of 2 million was approximately the same as increasing the Reynolds number from 2 to 4 million at a turbulence level of 0.2 per cent.

Whereas the values of $Re_{\delta^*}$ for a completely free layer are from 100 to 300 as noted in the last article, the values for the separated layers in bubbles vary from 600 to 2000 for the bubbles near the leading edge and are of the order of 2000 to 3000 for those near midchord.

It is obvious that there is room for much additional research, but the turbulence of the air stream and the pressure gradient must be varied and measured if progress is to be made in understanding the phenomena.

**A,9. Breakdown of Laminar Flow vs. Transition.** Transition is often regarded as synonomous with the breakdown of laminar flow but wider experimental experience shows that finer distinctions must be made. Breakdown of laminar flow may be followed by a flow varying periodically with time, exhibiting regular vortex patterns. Such flows can be described without the introduction of the random element characteristic of that type of flow for which the name "turbulent" should be reserved. The more familiar examples of flows of this type for which theoretical treatments are available are (1) the Kármán vortex street behind a circular cylinder; (2) the Taylor three-dimensional vortex cells between two concentric rotating cylinders; (3) the Görtler vortices near a concave surface; and (4) the vortex cell pattern in a thin layer of fluid heated from below. These periodic patterns are well defined and mainly laminar in their motion only at Reynolds numbers not too far above that for flow breakdown. In the case of the cylinder, for example, the beautiful pictures of Kármán vortices can be obtained only at Reynolds numbers based on a cylinder diameter of a few thousand.

Turbulent flow is characterized by the presence of irregular and random velocity fluctuations of relatively high frequency, but the experimental detection and measurement of the velocity fluctuations require equipment not widely available because of its complexity and cost. Turbulent flow is most readily detected by the very high rate of diffusion of momentum, heat, vapor, and material particles as compared with the molecular diffusion present in laminar flow. Some of the very large number of techniques of determining the occurrence of transition based on diffusion phenomena are described in IX,F. A familiar method used by Osborne Reynolds depends on the diffusion of dye particles in water, or of smoke particles in air. In laminar flow, filaments maintain their identity over great distances whereas in turbulent flow the dye or smoke is diffused laterally very rapidly, destroying the filament.

In many flows, as for example that behind a circular cylinder at Reynolds numbers from a few thousand to a few hundred thousand, the flow is of mixed character. The flow in the wake shows a periodic character with definite frequency but the rapid diffusion of smoke in the wake shows that the flow there is turbulent. The laminar boundary layer is shed periodically and alternately from the two sides but immediately becomes turbulent on separation. The vorticity in the layers which roll up into Kármán vortices at lower Reynolds numbers is now rapidly diffused to give a typical error-law distribution of vorticity across the wake a short distance downstream from the cylinder [*37*].

Accordingly, transition should not be defined as breakdown of laminar flow but as the onset of the highly diffuse turbulent motion of random character.

**A,10. Tentative Conceptual Picture of Transition.** The account that has been given of the several typical flow situations in which transition is recognizable and of the influence of many of the controlling variables suggests that we are dealing with an effect which may have many causes. Each variable, initial turbulence, pressure gradient, roughness, in the absence of the influence of the other variables, fixes transition at a definite location for a given Reynolds number of the body. That variable which gives the most forward location of transition is the one which will be the controlling one under the given set of circumstances. Thus any of the variables may be controlling depending on the values of the other variables. If the initial turbulence and roughness are sufficiently small, transition will be preceded by regular Tollmien-Schlichting oscillations of increasing amplitude.

There has been considerable progress in understanding the breakdown of laminar flow as a result of the theoretical and experimental work on the stability of laminar flow as described in IV,F. There is, however, no mathematical theory of the transition process itself. A satisfactory mathematical theory most certainly will have to take into account the nonlinear terms in the equations of motion of a viscous fluid. A great deal of experimental material is available. In most of the experiments essential measurements of the controlling variables were not made; especially lacking are measurements of the intensity and scale of the initial turbulence of the fluid stream which is now known to be one of the most important controlling factors. In other cases the surface roughness and waviness are not known. For the most part the experiments were made in the absence of any guiding theory. For all these reasons it is exceptionally difficult to systematize and analyze the data.

During the course of the past 15 years as the experimental data accumulated, new physical aspects of the phenomena have unfolded and suggestions as to a descriptive physical mechanism have come to mind. It has been suggested that an immediate prerequisite in every case is separation with the resulting formation of a free shear layer within the boundary layer or shear layer under observation, the scale of the newly formed shear layer being an order of magnitude lower than that of the layer under study. This separation is presumed to occur even when the apparent dominating experimental variables are initial turbulence or surface roughness. Like the progression of eddies of successively decreasing size in the modern theory of turbulence bounded at the lower end by eddies so small that viscosity quickly damps their motion, this theory of transition requires a progression of separations with formation of free shear layers of successively smaller scale until the chain is broken by shear layers of such small Reynolds number that turbulence is not generated. This tentative conceptual picture of transition can hardly be said to be firmly demonstrated, but such a picture may serve, at least for a time, as a useful guide in the presentation of existing data and as a guide to future more systematic study of the basic phenomena.

Let us examine the observed experimental fact that transition is greatly affected by exceptionally small disturbances in an otherwise steady flow. Fluctuations with time of amplitude as small as one tenth of one per cent of the mean velocity have measurable effects on the position of transition. Dryden [*1*] calculated the effect of a small sinusoidal

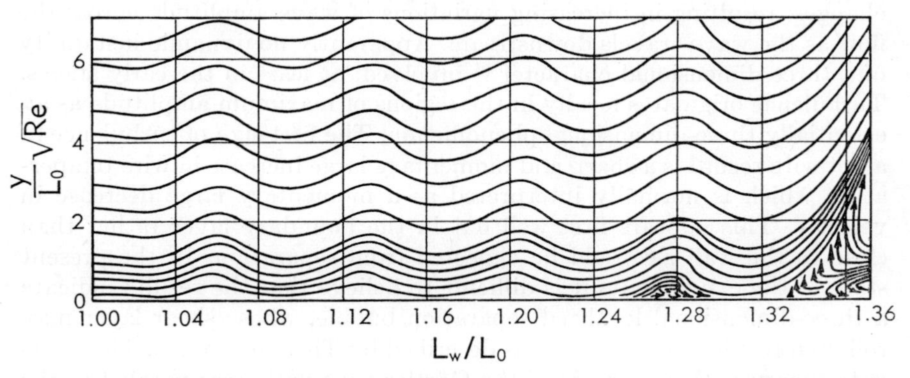


**Fig. A,10. Streamlines for flow in the boundary layer of a plate subjected to periodically oscillating pressure variations beginning at distance $L_0$ from the leading edge. Amplitude of free stream velocity variation—$\frac{1}{2}$ per cent of mean value. Wavelength $L_w$ equal to 0.072 times initial length $L_0$.**

variation of the free stream velocity with distance along the outer edge of a boundary layer using the Kármán-Pohlhausen approximate method of solution of the Prandtl boundary layer equations. Separation of the flow was found to occur after three complete cycles of a sinusoidal variation of amplitude two per cent of the mean velocity. A far more satisfactory computation was made in Germany during the war by Quick and Schröder [*38*] by a step-by-step procedure. A sinusoidal velocity variation of one-half per cent of the mean velocity and of wavelength of the order of the boundary layer thickness produced 15 to 20 per cent variations in displacement thickness with a separation bubble during the third cycle and complete separation at the fourth cycle. The streamlines for this case are shown in Fig. A,10. It is surmised from these considerations that small disturbances from any source will lead to intermittent separation and the formation of free shear layers in the fluid. If the Reynolds numbers of these shear layers are sufficiently high, small scale turbulence will be generated and spread throughout the boundary layer. Even if the shear layer does not itself undergo transition, it will roll up into discrete vortices of a very small scale which diffuse through the boundary layer.

The recent work of Schubauer and Klebanoff [*5*] shows clearly that the concept of two-dimensional separation is not applicable to transition in a boundary layer in an air stream of small turbulence, and raises serious doubts as to the utility of the separation concept in describing the phenomena involved. The periodic Tollmien-Schlichting waves rapidly lose their two-dimensional character, their amplitude varying along a direction normal to the flow. These variations have been shown to be directly coupled with very small variations of mean velocity across the air stream on a line parallel to the leading edge of the plate. The boundary layer parameters, including the amplification ratio, are sensitive to these small changes, resulting in increasing variations of wave amplitude across the flow as the wave travels downstream. Apparently no dynamic instability of a three-dimensional character is involved, at least in the early stages. Turbulence originates locally in the regions of maximum amplitude as an essentially three-dimensional phenomenon. The first sign of turbulence in a hot wire record is a sharp and momentary large increase in wire temperature which is normally interpreted as a momentary large decrease in velocity. This appears first well out in the boundary layer rather than close to the wall as would be expected from separation. In the present state of the experiments it is difficult to believe that the results indicate a three-dimensional localized separation bubble, whose shear layer may roll up into a horseshoe vortex as described by Theodorsen [*39*]. The alternate theory is that vortices of the Görtler type with axes parallel to the flow develop at the wave amplitude maxima.

**A,11. Theory of the Influence of Turbulence on Transition.** Taylor [*40*] assumed that transition due to turbulence resulted from momentary separation of the boundary layer caused by the pressure gradients within the layer resulting from the fluctuating pressure gradients of the turbulence. Separation is determined by the parameter $\lambda = (\delta^2/\nu)(du_e/dx)$ which may also be written as $-(\delta^2/\nu)(1/\rho u_e)(\partial p/\partial x)$ where $\delta p/\partial x$ is the instantaneous pressure gradient. From the theory of isotropic turbulence the root-mean-square pressure gradient is proportional to $(u'^5/L)^{\frac{1}{2}}(\rho/\nu^{\frac{1}{2}})$. Hence, the root-mean-square value of $\lambda$ is $(u_e l/\nu)^{\frac{3}{2}}(\delta^2/l^2)$ $(u'/u_e)^{\frac{5}{2}}(L/l)^{-\frac{1}{2}}$ where $l$ is a reference dimension. Hence if separation occurs at a fixed value of $\lambda$, we have, noting that $\delta/l$ at the transition is some function of the Reynolds number $Re_t = (u_e l/\nu)_t$,

$$Re_t = F\left[\frac{u'}{u_e}\left(\frac{l}{L}\right)^{\frac{1}{5}}\right]$$

According to this theory transition depends only on this combination of the intensity and scale of turbulence and not on the two properties separately.

Fig. A,11a shows the critical Reynolds number of a sphere plotted as a function of the Taylor turbulence parameter [*41*] and Fig. A,11b shows the location of transition on an elliptic cylinder as a function of the same

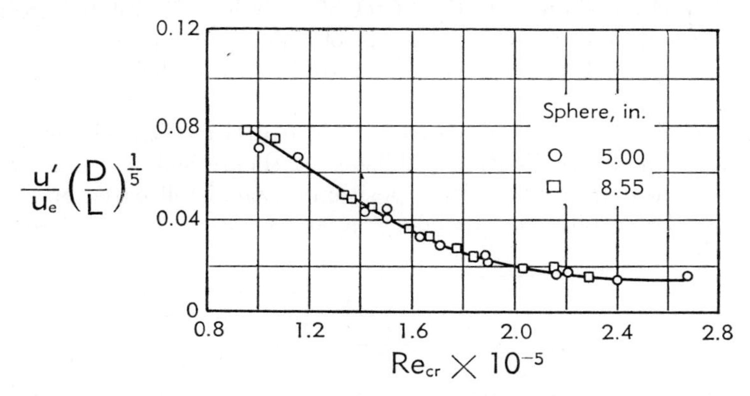


Fig. A,11a. Effect of intensity and scale of free stream turbulence on the critical Reynolds number of spheres. $L$ = scale of turbulence, $D$ = diameter of sphere.

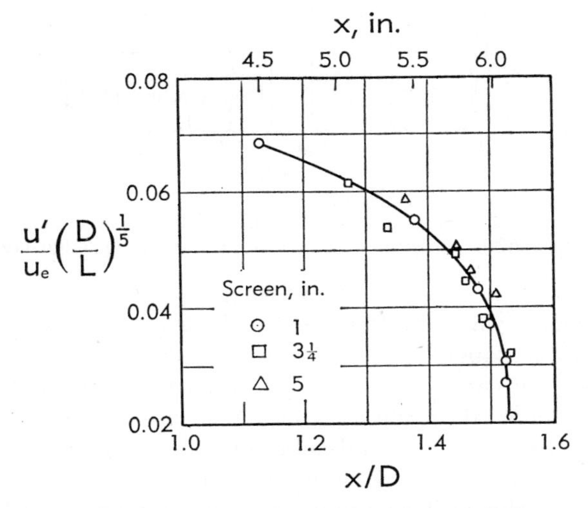


Fig. A,11b. Effect of intensity and scale of free stream turbulence on transition on an elliptic cylinder. $L$ = scale of turbulence, $D$ = length of minor axis of elliptical section.

parameter [*34*]. This theory accounts for the influence of stream turbulence when the turbulence is greater than about two tenths of one per cent.

Experiments on a flat plate with zero pressure gradient were made by Hall and Hislop [*42*] in turbulent air streams behind two square-mesh screens. In this case there was little overlap between the results for the two screens and the scatter of points is about the same whether $Re_t$ is plotted against $u'/u_e$ or the modified Taylor parameter $(u'/u_e)(x/M)^{\frac{1}{5}}$ where $M$ is the mesh of the screen. Nevertheless, the results are not inconsistent with Taylor's theory.

Experiments on airfoils were made by Drougge [*43*] and the results were analyzed to show that the effect of turbulence is related to intermittent separation. Another analysis of this type has been made by Dorodnitsein and Loitsianskii [*44*] and applied to published data.

**A,12. Schlichting's Procedure for Computing Transition on an Airfoil.** In 1940 Schlichting published a theoretical method [*45*] for the computation of the transition position on an airfoil based on computations of the stability of boundary layers in accelerated and retarded

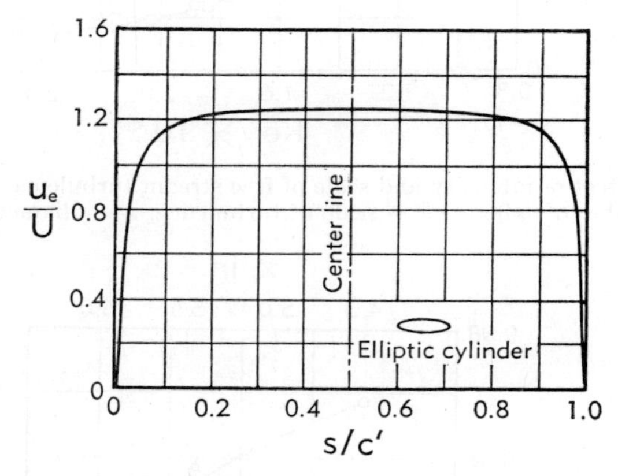


Fig. A,12a. Velocity distribution around elliptic cylinder of fineness ratio 4. $s$ = distance along surface, $c'$ = distance from leading to trailing edge measured along surface.

flows. The method was further refined in 1942 [*46*]. On the basis of the experimental data available to him at the time, Schlichting assumed that transition always occurred ahead of the separation of the laminar boundary layer; in other words he did not consider separation bubbles with transition in the separated layer and subsequent reattachment. Schlichting also observed that for Reynolds numbers up to 3 million, transition never occurred ahead of the position of minimum pressure on the airfoil. Experiments available to Schlichting showed values of $Re_t$ for a flat plate with zero pressure gradient lying within the range 350,000 to 500,000 whereas now values between 90,000 and 2,800,000 have been observed.

As a preliminary to his airfoil computations, Schlichting computed the stability characteristics of a boundary layer subjected to uniform pressure gradients (Art. 3 and IV,F). Schlichting then assumes that transition depends only on the local boundary layer Reynolds number $Re_{\delta^*}$;

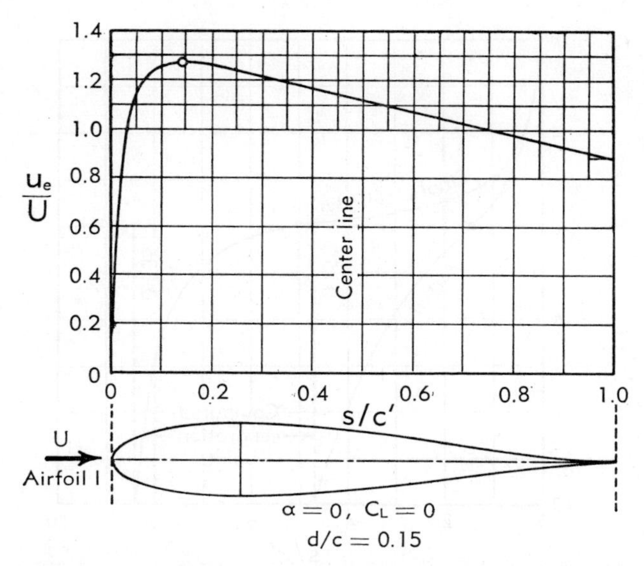


Fig. A,12b. Velocity distribution around Schlichting's Joukowsky I airfoil. $s$ = distance along surface, $c'$ = distance from leading to trailing edge measured along surface.

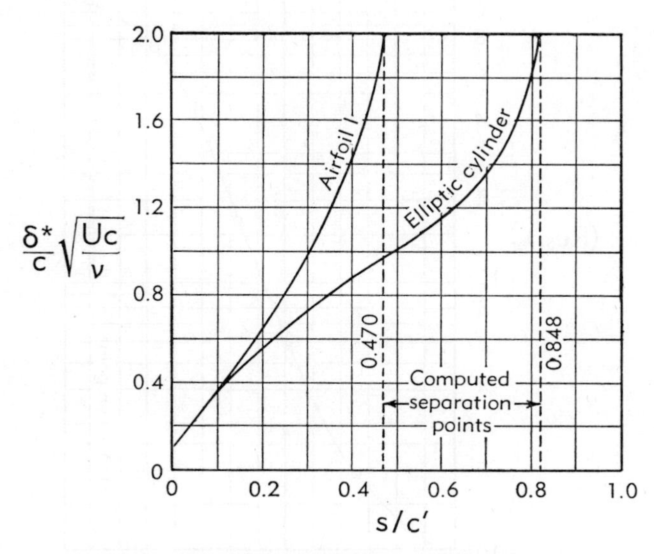


Fig. A,12c. Displacement thickness of boundary layer for elliptic cylinder and Joukowsky I airfoil.

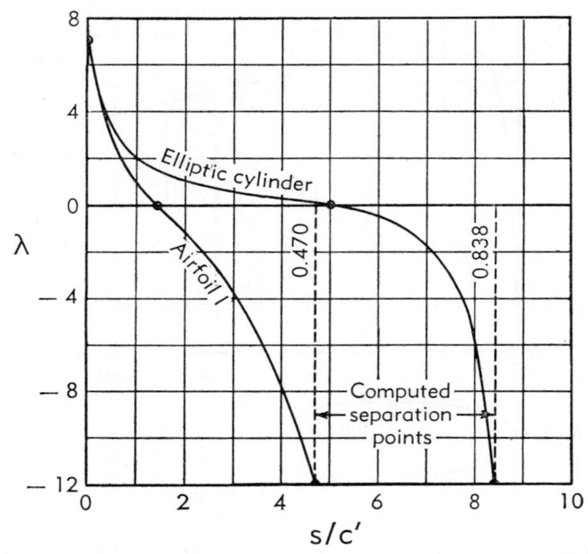


Fig. A,12d. Pohlhausen pressure gradient parameter λ of boundary layer for elliptic cylinder and Joukowsky I airfoil.

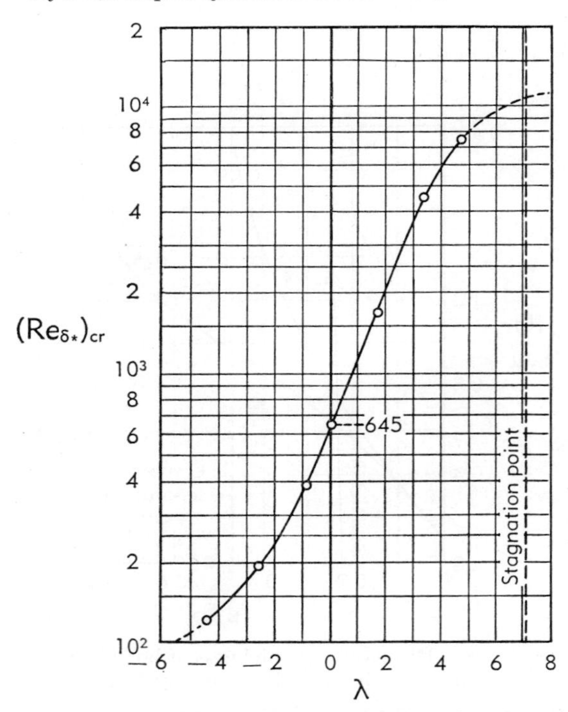


Fig. A,12e. Critical Reynolds number at which boundary layer oscillations are amplified as function of pressure gradient parameter λ.

transition occurs when $Re_{\delta^*}$ reaches the critical value computed for the local velocity distribution which is in turn determined by the local pressure gradient. The location of transition is then computed by the following procedure:

1. Compute the theoretical pressure distribution over the body from potential flow theory. The result is expressed as a plot of $u_e/U$ vs. $s/c'$ where $u_e$ is the velocity at a distance $s$ measured along the surface from the stagnation point, $U$ is the stream velocity at a great distance, and

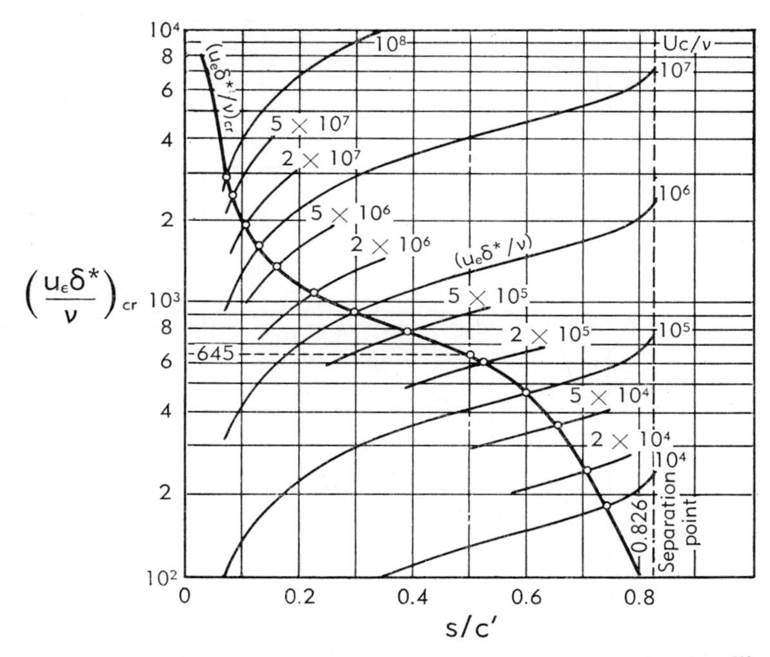


Fig. A,12f. Variation of displacement-thickness Reynolds number for elliptic cylinder as function of cylinder Reynolds number and local position.

   $c'$ is the distance from leading to trailing edge measured along the surface. Fig. A,12a and A,12b show this curve for an elliptic cylinder of fineness ratio 4 and a Joukowski airfoil respectively.
2. Compute by Pohlhausen's method (4-term polynominal approximation to the velocity distribution) the displacement thickness $\delta^*$ of the boundary layer. Compute also the Pohlhausen parameter $\lambda$. There result curves of $(\delta^*/c)\sqrt{Uc/\nu}$ and $\lambda$ vs. $s/c'$ as shown in Fig. A,12c and A,12d.
3. From the stability calculations and the values of $\lambda$, plot the critical Reynolds numbers $(Re_{\delta^*})_{cr}$ corresponding to each $\lambda$ vs. $s/c'$. The relation of $(Re_{\delta^*})_{cr}$ to $\lambda$ as used by Schlichting is shown in Fig. A,12e.
4. From the values of $(\delta^*/c)\sqrt{Uc/\nu} = (U/u_e)(Re_{\delta^*}/Re^{\frac{1}{2}})$, where $Re$ is

the body Reynolds number $Uc/\nu$, plot curves of $Re_{\delta^*}$ vs. $s/c'$ for several values of $Re$ as in Fig. A,12f and A,12g. On the same diagram plot $(Re_{\delta^*})_{cr}$ vs. $s/c'$ as computed in 3.

5. For each value of $Re$ determine the intersection of the $Re_{\delta^*}$ curve with the $(Re_{\delta^*})_{cr}$ curve and read the value of $s/c'$ which is the location of transition for this Reynolds number. Plot the values of $(s/c')_{cr}$ vs. $Re$ to give the transition position as a function of $Re$ as shown in Fig. A,12h and A,12i.

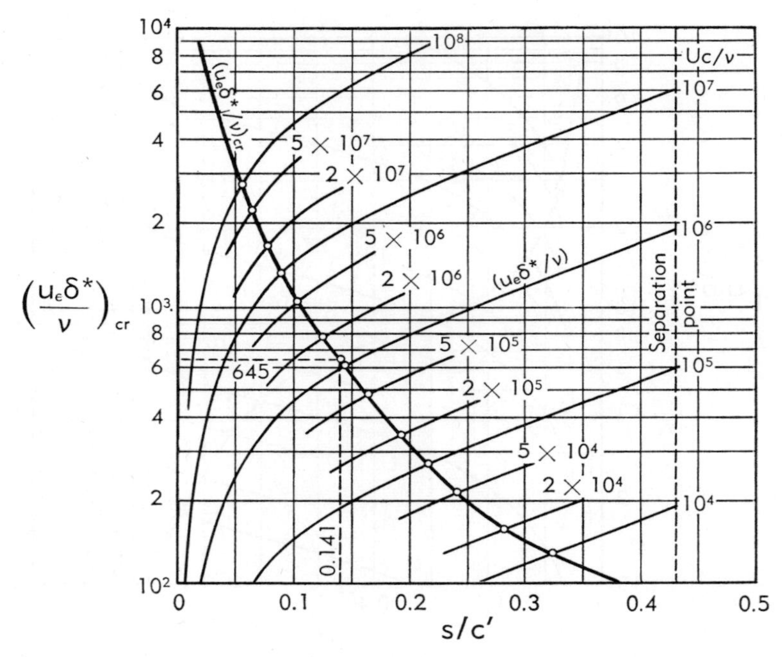


**Fig. A,12g.** Variation of displacement-thickness Reynolds number for Joukowsky I airfoil as function of airfoil Reynolds number and local position.

Schlichting had no reliable data in air streams of low turbulence to compare with his theoretical computations. The method as outlined is capable of considerable improvement, since the approximate methods used both for the stability calculations and the boundary layer thickness calculations are relatively crude. Furthermore it is desirable to use the experimental pressure distribution, if available, rather than that computed on potential flow theory. The most serious criticism, however, is that we know definitely that transition does not occur at the critical Reynolds number for instability of the laminar boundary layer but at a considerably higher Reynolds number, and no method is known for computing the ratio of the two. Hence the method as described cannot be expected to give valid results.

Schlichting's approach suggests the investigation of a procedure in which the critical Reynolds number is taken not from stability calculations but from experimental values determined under simplified conditions. Let us suppose that $(Re_{\delta^*})_{cr}$ could be determined from available experimental data as a function of air stream turbulence, local pressure gradient, and local surface roughness. We could then carry out a modified

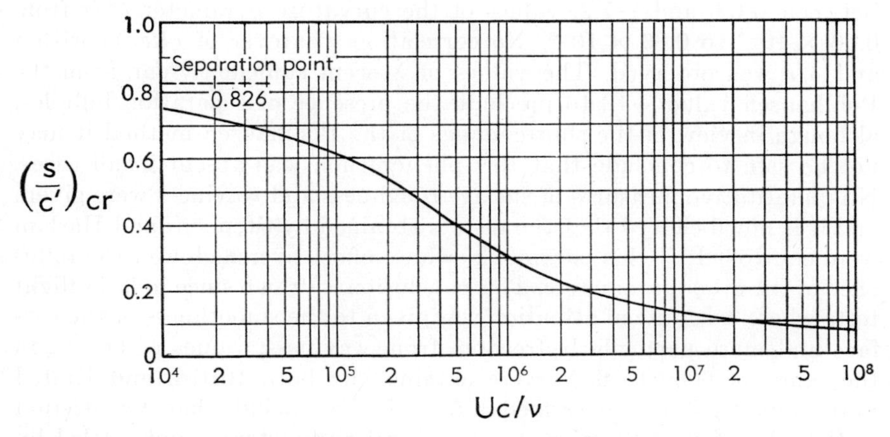


**Fig. A,12h.** Location on elliptic cylinder at which boundary layer oscillations are amplified as function of cylinder Reynolds number.

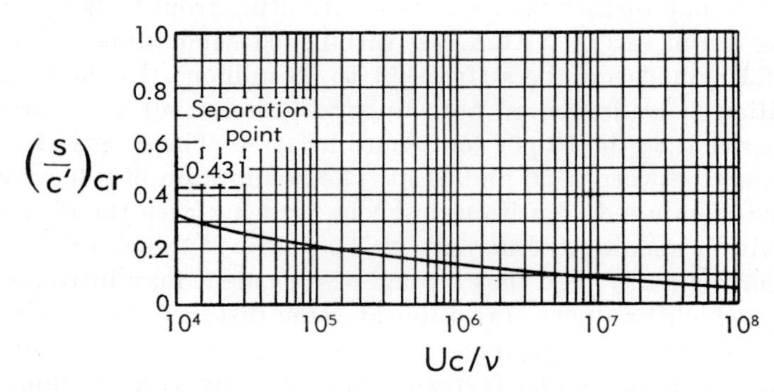


Fig. A,12i. Location on Joukowsky I airfoil at which boundary layer oscillations are amplified as function of airfoil Reynolds number.

Schlichting computation with some hope of better agreement with experimentally observed transition points. Unfortunately, sufficient experimental data are not available, and a complete test of this type of theory must await further research.

**A,13. Adequacy of Transition Theories Based on Local Parameters.** The key assumption in Schlichting's approach is that transition is determined by the local values of mean speed distribution, pressure gradient, curvature, and surface roughness; that the critical Reynolds number is the same as if all of these quantities were constant and independent of the distance $s$ along the surface. Attempts have been made to check the adequacy of this assumption by Stephens and Haslam [*47*] in actual flight tests. In the flight tests values of $(Re_{\delta^*})_{cr}$ were observed ranging from 1460 to 3240, values of $\lambda$ at the point of transition between $+0.3$ and $-7.2$, values of the curvature parameter $\delta^*/r$ from $0.06 \times 10^{-3}$ to $0.86 \times 10^{-3}$. No correlation whatever of $(Re_{\delta^*})_{cr}$ with $\lambda$ and $\delta/r$ was observed. The values of $\lambda$ seem sufficiently far from the Pohlhausen value $-12$ to preclude the presence of separation bubbles, although in view of the shortcomings of the Pohlhausen method it may not be safe to conclude that this phenomenon was absent in all cases. No quantitative measures of surface roughness and waviness were given, and it is now believed that the results obtained by Stephens and Haslam were controlled by this parameter, whose effect overshadowed the influence of the other parameters. This conclusion is drawn since in later flight tests where exceptional attention was given to the smoothness of the surface and more particularly freedom from waviness, values of $(Re_{\delta^*})_{cr}$ in the range of 6000 to 6500 were obtained by both British and United States investigators as described in Art. 17. We conclude that the question of the adequacy of theories based on local parameters is not settled by these measurements.

There is one further bit of evidence resulting from tests on a smooth low drag airfoil in the NACA low turbulence wind tunnel over a wide range of Reynolds numbers (from 14 to 58 million). In these tests [*48*] the position of transition on both upper and lower surfaces varied from the 25 per cent to the 50 per cent chord location. The observed values of $(Re_{\delta^*})_{cr}$ were between 5150 and 6150. The assumption of a fixed value of 6150 gives computed transition positions agreeing with the observed positions with a maximum difference of 7 per cent of the chord.

We have already seen that a roughness element may introduce a disturbance which produces transition at some distance downstream from the element. Hence it is clear that the disturbances originating upstream, which are not indicated by instruments measuring average values, must be considered in addition to the local values of $\delta^*$, $\lambda$, $k$, and $r$. Whether a theory based on local parameters is adequate or not depends on whether all the important local parameters are included. So far as disturbances from upstream roughness elements are concerned, we may consider instead the direct influence of all upstream roughness elements on the critical Reynolds number for transition. If any upstream value of $k/\delta^*$ produces a value of $(Re_{\delta^*})_{cr}$ greater than the value of $Re_{\delta^*}$ at the point under study, its effect is negligible at that point. If, however, the local $Re_{\delta^*}$ equals the $(Re_{\delta^*})_{cr}$ of *any* upstream roughness element, transition will occur at that point due to roughness. By this device it may be possible to retain the framework of the modified Schlichting method. Much careful experimental work needs to be done, however, before the adequacy of this method of predicting transition can be evaluated.

At the Ninth International Congress of Applied Mechanics held in Brussels in September, 1956, A. M. O. Smith, in a paper entitled "Transition, Pressure Gradient, and Stability Theory," advanced the hypothesis that transition occurs when the amplification ratio of the initial disturbances as computed from the Tollmien-Schlichting theory reaches $e^9$ or about 8100, and showed a comparison of experimental data with computed results which indicated reasonably good agreement. It is difficult to understand how the magnitude of the initial disturbance can be omitted; certainly the theory cannot deal with the effects of free stream turbulence on a smooth plate in a flow with zero pressure gradient. However, in many cases the amplification ratio varies so rapidly with increasing distance along the surface because of the effects of pressure gradient that the computed transition position varies slowly with changes in the selected value of the initial disturbance amplitude or amplification ratio.

**A,14. Transition to Turbulent Flow in a Pipe of Circular Cross Section.** The nature of the flow in a pipe depends on the value of the Reynolds number $Re = u_m d/\nu$ where $u_m$ is the mean velocity, $d$ the diameter, and $\nu$ the kinematic viscosity of the fluid. Since the velocity distribution in laminar flow is parabolic, the Reynolds number may be written as $u_{max} r/\nu$ where $u_{max}$ is the velocity at the center and $r$ is the radius. For comparison with transition in boundary layers we note that the Reynolds number $Re_{\delta^*}$ based on the displacement thickness, which in this case is the thickness of an annulus bounded by the pipe wall which would pass all of the fluid at the maximum velocity, is equal to $0.303Re$.

Transition from laminar to turbulent flow depends greatly on the initial disturbances which in turn depend on the shape of the entrance to the pipe and the disturbances in the flow in the tank or reservoir ahead of the pipe entry. The lowest critical Reynolds number for large initial disturbances has been measured by many investigators [*49*, p. 319] with results lying between 1900 and 2320 for $Re$ or 576 and 703 for $Re_{\delta^*}$. At lower values of $Re$, initial disturbances die out far downstream. Reynolds was able to increase $Re$ to 13,000 by reducing the initial disturbances. Other experimenters have had greater success, obtaining values of $Re$ of 20,000 (Barnes and Coker [*50*] and Schiller [*51*]), 32,000 (Taylor [*49*, p. 321]), and 50,000 (Ekman [*52*]). Ekman's value corresponds to $Re_{\delta^*}$ of 15,150. The values vary by a factor of 26, dependent on initial disturbances which were not quantitatively measured. It is probable that the initial turbulence in these experiments varied from several per cent to less than one hundredth of one per cent.

For comparison with transition measurements in boundary layers it should be noted that transition in a pipe actually begins near the entrance to the pipe. If the entrance is bell-mouthed or rounded such that separation does not occur, a thin boundary layer develops on the pipe wall and grows in thickness until it equals the pipe radius. Because of the continuity relation the flow near the axis must accelerate and hence the static pressure falls more rapidly than in the finally developed flow where the drop in pressure is due only to friction. Transition thus occurs in the wall boundary layer which is subjected to a favorable stabilizing pressure gradient and to whatever turbulence is present in the entering flow. For the same turbulence the critical Reynolds number would be expected to be somewhat higher than for the boundary layer on a plate with zero pressure gradient.

With sharp-edged entrances, separation occurs at the entry with the formation under some conditions of regular vortex patterns [*53,54*]. These vortices give very large disturbances and hence low values of the critical Reynolds number.

For very rough pipes the critical Reynolds number appears to be the same as for a smooth pipe with very disturbed entry conditions. However, if the initial turbulence is small, roughness may produce larger disturbances than those already present and reduce the critical Reynolds number. Depending on the shape of the roughness elements, the maximum permissible height to avoid disturbance in a smooth pipe has been estimated to be of the order of $4/Re^{\frac{1}{2}}$ times the radius of the pipe [*49*, p. 311]. The fact that any roughness is permissible is thought to be associated with the fact that roughness elements also possess a critical Reynolds number below which they set up no disturbance. For example for a flat plate roughness element, the critical Reynolds number is about 30. The above relation corresponds to a critical Reynolds number of 32 and the assumption that the critical height is small compared to the radius. See, however, the discussion in Art. 5.

The effect on the critical Reynolds number of curving the axis of cylindrical pipes of circular cross section has been studied by several investigators [*55,56*]. The breakdown of the laminar flow does not in this case lead immediately to turbulent motion but to a regular type of secondary motion under the influence of the centrifugal forces. Turbulence sets in at a critical Reynolds number which depends on $L/d$ where $L$ is the radius of curvature of the axis of the pipe and $d$ is the diameter of the pipe. The values obtained increase as $L/d$ is reduced, from about 2300 at $L/d = 1025$ to 7600 at $L/d = 7.6$.

**A,15. Transition in Pipes of Noncircular Cross Section.** Transition has been studied in pipes of rectangular, square, and annular cross section. Basing the Reynolds number on the hydraulic radius, values of 2100 for the square cross section, 1600 for a rectangular section with ratio of sides of 2.43 to 1, 2800 for rectangular sections with ratio of sides between 104 and 165, and 2400 for an annular section with ratio of radii of 0.818 to 1, were obtained [*49*, p. 319]. The disturbances were relatively large in these measurements, so that the values are comparable with 1900–2320 for a circular cross section.

**A,16. Transition on an Elliptic Cylinder.** Studies of transition on an elliptic cylinder of fineness ratio 2.96 have been made by Schubauer [*34*] over a Reynolds number range of 21,000 to 160,000, the Reynolds number being based on the minor axis of the elliptical section. The turbulence of the stream was relatively high, from 0.85 to 4.0 per cent. At a turbulence level of 0.85 per cent, and Reynolds numbers from 21,000 to 30,000, the boundary layer flow is laminar until separation occurs, and transition occurs in the shear layer so far downstream that the flow around the cylinder is not affected by it. From the observed pressure distributions, transition at higher Reynolds numbers occurs in the free layer and the boundary layer reattaches. The pressure distribution, position of separation, and reattachment change with Reynolds number until a value of about 120,000 is reached. For still higher Reynolds numbers the flow and pressure distribution were independent of Reynolds number up to the maximum value reached of about 160,000. Here transition occurred soon after separation, as described in Art. 8.

The air stream turbulence was increased by the use of turbulence-producing screens and the location of transition was measured as a function of the intensity and scale of the turbulence. The results have already been given in Fig. A,11b for comparison with Taylor's theory.

Unfortunately the gap between a turbulence of 0.85 per cent and the lower end of the curve in Fig. A,11b was not covered, but the curve must turn sharply to the right at a smaller value of the turbulence parameter to reach values of $x/D$ of about 2.7 as experimentally observed at a turbulence of 0.85 per cent. The relatively stationary position of transition at $x/D$ of about 1.53 corresponds approximately to the point of minimum pressure where the pressure gradient changes from favorable to adverse.

**A,17. Transition on Airfoils.** The measurements of transition on airfoils as reported in the literature constitute a record of the development of wind tunnels of lower and lower turbulence and of improved techniques of producing smooth surfaces free from waviness. At first no detailed boundary layer measurements were made and the only data given were drag curves vs. Reynolds number based on the air stream velocity and airfoil chord. The critical Reynolds number of the airfoil was taken as that at which the minimum drag coefficient was reached or at which a perceptible rise occurred. Later the location of transition was determined by the surface-Pitot technique, but boundary layer data were not taken and a small separation bubble might possibly be overlooked. During the same period the laminar flow airfoils were being developed, permitting much more extensive runs of laminar flow because of the extent of the favorable pressure gradient. Both wind tunnel and flight data give estimated equivalent flat plate Reynolds numbers covering a range from about 600,000 to about 14,000,000, the high values being obtained much more recently on laminar flow sections in wind tunnels of turbulence less than 0.1 per cent and in flight on models in which extreme care had been taken to remove surface roughness and waviness. In any particular measurement it is almost impossible to separate the effects of the many variables.

Fig. A,17a illustrates wind tunnel data on the chordwise position of transition on airfoils at approximately zero angle of attack [*43,48,57,58,*

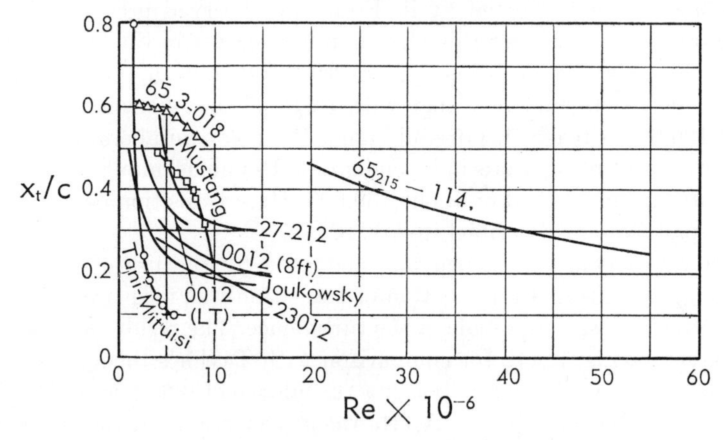


Fig. A,17a. Transition position on airfoils as a function of airfoil Reynolds number.

*59,60,61*]. In every case transition moves forward with increasing Reynolds number but the rate and the value of the Reynolds number at which the most rapid change occurs are dependent on the type of airfoil section, the smoothness and fairness of the surface of the airfoil, and on the turbulence of the wind tunnel in which the measurements are made.

The results for the $65_{215}$-114 airfoil [*48*], showing transition as far back as 25 to 30 per cent of the chord at Reynolds number of 40 to 55 million, were obtained in the low turbulence wind tunnel of the Langley Aeronautical Laboratory in which the turbulence intensity is a few hundredths of 1 per cent. The results for the Tani-Mituisi airfoil at the extreme left of Fig. A,17a were obtained in the FFA wind tunnel at Stockholm [*43*] behind a turbulence grid giving a turbulence level of approximately 1 per cent. Although there is some influence of airfoil shape and surface waviness in this comparison, the principal differences between these two curves are believed to be due to effects of wind tunnel turbulence.

The effect of airfoil shape may be seen by comparing the curves for the 0012 airfoil [*58*] and that for the $65_{215}$-114 low drag airfoil, although data at the same Reynolds number are not available. The results for the 0012 airfoil [*58*] in the NACA 8-ft wind tunnel as compared with the results on the same airfoil in the NACA low turbulence wind tunnel show the effect of an increase in wind tunnel turbulence from a few hundredths to several tenths per cent on a conventional airfoil.

From the totality of information available on airfoils and other bodies, we may reconstruct the qualitative picture of the influence of Reynolds number on the location of transition. At extremely low Reynolds numbers the boundary layer separates from the surface as a laminar layer and the separated shear layer remains laminar far downstream. As the Reynolds number increases, transition occurs in the shear layer nearer and nearer the point of separation. At some Reynolds number the flow reattaches to form a separation bubble which decreases in size as the Reynolds number increases. Over a certain range of Reynolds numbers, transition remains fixed just beyond laminar separation. With further increase in Reynolds number, transition moves forward, more rapidly while in the region of adverse pressure gradient and more slowly as the pressure minimum is passed to reach the region of favorable pressure gradient. At very large Reynolds numbers, transition approaches closer and closer to the forward stagnation point. Most of the available data are for the Reynolds number range in which the transition lies between the laminar separation point and the leading edge.

When the airfoil is placed at a different angle of attack the pressure distribution changes and aerodynamically we have to do with a different body. A low drag airfoil experiences adverse pressure gradients at sufficiently high angles of attack and leaves the low drag region. In general terms transition moves forward on the upper surface and backward on the lower surface as the angle of attack is increased. Typical experimental data are found in the references previously cited.

Fig. A,17b shows the data plotted in Fig. A,17a in a slightly different form, the ordinate now being $(x_t/c)Re$ which is a rough approximation to the equivalent flat plate Reynolds number at transition. Exact data from boundary layer computations are shown for the $65_{215}$-114 airfoil for comparison; in this case the approximate values are too high by from 2 to 14 per cent. For most of the data plotted the equivalent flat plate Reynolds number of transition increases with the airfoil Reynolds number. It is believed that this increase is associated with the increased stability of the boundary layer at the more forward positions of transition corresponding to the higher airfoil Reynolds numbers, where the pressure gradient is increasingly more favorable.

The available wind tunnel data on roughness effects [*13,15,62,63*] are plotted in Fig. A,17c as transition Reynolds numbers based on airfoil

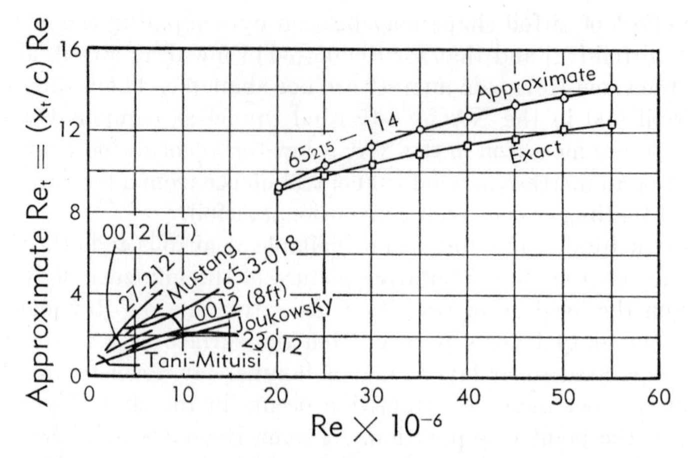


Fig. A,17b. Approximate transition Reynolds number (equivalent flat plate value) for airfoil boundary layers as function of airfoil Reynolds number.

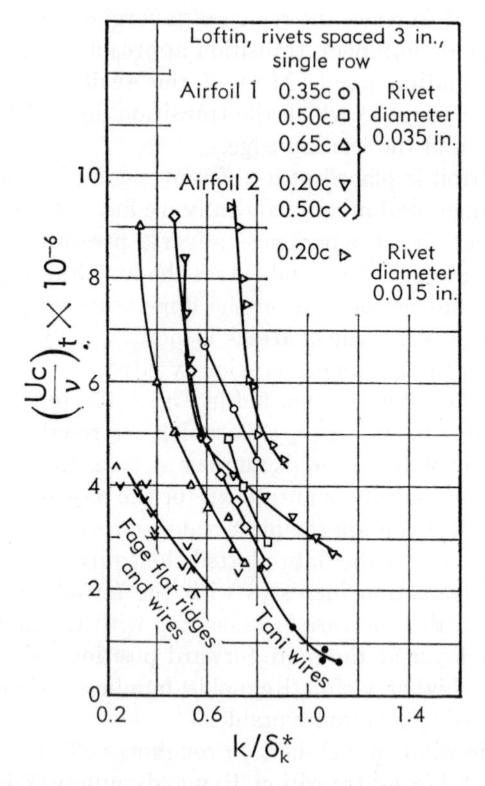


Fig. A,17c. Effect of roughness on transition Reynolds number of airfoils.

chord as a function of $k/\delta^*$. Varying techniques were used for measuring the transition Reynolds number, principally that of rise in total drag coefficient and surface tubes. The detector tubes were located in various positions and correction to a fixed position does not seem practicable. The effect of shape of the roughness elements is obvious as is the large influence of air stream turbulence.

Loftin's results [*62*] refer to three-dimensional roughness elements in the Langley two-dimensional low turbulence wind tunnel and were analyzed by him in terms of the Reynolds number of the roughness element $u_k k/\nu$. The observed value was a function of the ratio of the diameter $d$ of the cylindrical projections to the height $k$, varying from a value of about 1000 for $d/k = 0.5$ to 200 for $d/k = 7.0$. For $d/k = 1.0$, the value of $u_k k/\nu$ was 750. This compares with Klebanoff, Schubauer, and Tidstrom's value of 300 for spherical elements [*23*].

Von Doenhoff [*63*] studied the effect of sand grain roughness elements on airfoils in considerable detail. His results, also obtained in a low turbulence wind tunnel, give a critical Reynolds number of 250 based on nominal particle size, or 600 based on maximum particle size. The available data suggest that the critical Reynolds number of a roughness element is affected as much or more by the turbulence of the air stream in which the measurements are made as by the shape of the element (see Art. 5).

In the absence of sufficient data one can only conclude that the transition Reynolds number on airfoils is a function of air stream turbulence, pressure gradient, and surface roughness and that all variables have important effects.

The flight data on transition on airfoils presents as confusing a picture as the wind tunnel data. While the effects of air stream turbulence are presumably absent, the angle of attack changes with speed so that the Reynolds number cannot be systematically varied for a fixed angle of attack. The largest influence, however, appears to be that of surface waviness, for increased care to secure smooth and fair surfaces has given higher and higher values. In the last eighteen years the values of $(x_t/c)Re$ have increased from $3.5 \times 10^6$ for conventional airfoil sections in 1938 to $11.4 \times 10^6$ and $17.0 \times 10^6$ for low drag sections in recent years. Some of the more recent work is still classified but the highest observed values are those given in [*64*]. It seems impractical to secure the required freedom from surface waviness and roughness in normal construction and operation of aircraft to realize these high values.

**A,18. Transition on Airplane Configurations and on Airplanes in Flight.** Additional variables influence transition on three-dimensional airplane configurations in wind tunnels and on airplanes in flight. The pressure distribution at wing-body junctures and nacelle-wing fairings is often such as to bring transition close to the leading edge of the wing.

Moreover actual airplanes have unavoidable local roughness at access doors and elsewhere which generates local turbulence. Turbulence so generated spreads laterally, and this process has been studied by several authors [*65,66*]. In practical testing, using surface films for detecting transition [*67*], dust particles produce the typical wedges of turbulence behind them. The observed angle of spread (one half the vertex angle of the wedge) is 8.8°, the various determinations scattering over a range from about 8.5° to 11°. If there are a sufficient number of sources of disturbance and the wing chord is sufficiently large, the turbulence will cover the entire wing span.

A propeller generates turbulence in its wake and hence transition on that part of the wing lying within the slipstream will occur at a transition Reynolds number corresponding to a stream of large turbulence [*68*]. A tractor propeller produces a large effect; in the case studied its operation moved transition from midchord to less than 10 per cent of the chord from the leading edge. A pusher propeller was observed to have no measurable effect on transition on the wing ahead of it. Likewise the vibration due to an operating power plant appears to have little effect; wind tunnel measurements for vibrations of frequency of 27 cycles per second and amplitude of 0.1 inches gave no measurable change in the transition point.

The boundary layer on an airplane in flight is subjected to the noise emanating from its power plant. Wind tunnel measurements in a low turbulence wind tunnel [*2*] show that noise may affect transition under certain circumstances.

**A,19. Transition on Bodies of Revolution.** The simplest body of revolution is a sphere and the effect of the occurrence of transition before laminar separation in greatly reducing the drag coefficient has been known for 37 years. That transition on a sphere is greatly dependent on the turbulence of the air stream has been known for the same period and for many years the critical Reynolds number of a sphere was used as a measure of wind tunnel turbulence. The relationship is plotted in Fig. A,11a.

For reasons not fully understood the sphere is not a good indicator of turbulence when the turbulence level is less than a few tenths per cent. One hypothesis is that, because of the blunt shape, disturbances are set up at the forward stagnation point which mask the effects of low turbulence levels.

Görtler [*69*] has suggested that the concavity of the streamlines in the neighborhood of a stagnation point in two-dimensional flow leads to an instability of the type discussed in Art. 4, resulting in vortices with axes along the flow lines. Calculations for the two-dimensional case have been made by Hämmerlin [*70*]. Presumably a similar instability would be found near a stagnation point in three-dimensional flow.

Little work has been done in correlating the sphere data with flat plate data in terms of $Re_{\delta^*}$. Fage [*71*] gives $Re_{\delta^*} = 945$ at transition occurring well ahead of separation on a sphere in an air stream of 0.85 per cent turbulence. The equivalent flat plate Reynolds number of 298,000 is considerably below the curve of Fig. A,2b, but it must be noted that transition on the sphere occurred in a region of large adverse pressure gradient ($\lambda = -5$ to $-7$) in Fage's experiments.

Tomotika [*72*] computed the growth of the laminar boundary layer on the surface of a sphere in a uniform stream for an experimental pressure distribution obtained at a Reynolds number of 165,000. Separation occurred at an azimuth angle of 81° with $Re_{\delta^*}/\sqrt{Re} = 2.72$, hence at an equivalent flat plate Reynolds number of $2.5Re$. Thus if the Reynolds number at which transition occurs just ahead of the separation is known, the value of $Re_t$ may be computed. The critical Reynolds number of a sphere as usually defined corresponds to a considerably more forward position of transition and to a considerably modified pressure distribution. Examination of sphere drag coefficient and pressure coefficient curves shows a departure from an approximately constant value of the coefficient beginning at about $0.4Re_{cr}$. Hence the values of $Re_t$ are probably of the same order as $Re_{cr}$. The maximum value observed for a sphere is about $4 \times 10^5$ as compared with $28 \times 10^5$ for the flat plate in air streams of low turbulence. For a turbulence of 1.0 per cent the value of $Re_t$ from a sphere is about 200,000 as compared with 630,000 for a flat plate. For very high turbulence the values agree; for a turbulence of 3 per cent both sphere and plate give a value of $Re_t$ of about 100,000. The much lower values derived from the sphere at low turbulence are presumably due to the large adverse pressure gradient at the transition point on the sphere.

In this discussion the well-known but much smaller effect of the scale of turbulence has been omitted. The most suitable turbulence parameter for the generalized case is $(u'/u_e)(\delta_t^*/L)^{\frac{1}{5}}$ where $\delta_t^*$ is the displacement thickness of the boundary layer at transition.

The drag of streamline bodies of revolution as a function of wind tunnel turbulence was studied in 1929 [*73*] and the observed results were interpreted as due to the effect of turbulence on transition in the boundary layer. Computations were made on the crude assumption that the velocity distribution in the boundary layer was linear. It was assumed that transition occurred at values of $Re_\delta$ of 1250, 2000, and 2750 ($\delta$ being the thickness based on a linear distribution) for turbulence levels of 2.3, 1.6, and 1.2 per cent. The corresponding values of $Re_{\delta^*}$ are 625, 1000, and 1375, and of $Re_t$, 193,000, 333,000, and 630,000. In view of the crude approximations in the theoretical computations, and the experimental errors involved in early hot wire measurements of turbulence, these values are in satisfactory agreement with Fig. A,2b.

More recent studies have been made by Fage and Preston [74] in a water stream using the fluid motion microscope, but these do not agree so well with the two-dimensional values of Fig. A,2b. One of the bodies used was a long cylinder 3 inches in diameter with a semi-ellipsoidal nosepiece 6 inches long, and the water stream was 7 inches in diameter. Most of the observations were taken with turbulence screens about a foot ahead of the nose of the body. The turbulence varied considerably along the length of the body, and if the local value at the transition point is used as abscissa in Fig. A,2b, the values of $Re_t$ are of the order of $\frac{1}{2}$ to $\frac{1}{3}$ those observed for the flat plate. It is obvious that the higher turbulence levels upstream are influencing the location of transition. Even if the average turbulence level from the nose to the transition point is used, the values still fall below the flat plate values, although the pressure distribution is mildly favorable and should yield higher values. As in many early experiments on transition it is possible that effects of surface waviness may have been present. At any rate the values observed for $Re_t$ for a turbulence level of approximately one per cent were of the order of 300,000 to 400,000 as compared with the 600,000 to 700,000 for the flat plate shown in Fig. A,2b.

Fage and Preston also studied transition on a second body with the same semi-ellipsoidal nose shape, a 4-inch cylindrical mid-body section, and a tail tapering in diameter from 3 to 2 inches over a length of 16 inches. For this body, transition occurred following laminar separation and the phenomena observed were similar to those described in Art. 16.

The boundary layer on a body of revolution is of course not comparable with that on a plate at the same distance from the stagnation point because of the three-dimensional character of the flow. Mangler [75] has obtained a general relationship between two-dimensional and axially symmetrical boundary layers. When applied to compute the relation between the distance $x_1$ along the axis of the body of revolution and the distance $\bar{x}$ along a flat plate at which the boundary layer thickness is identical for the two bodies, we find

$$\bar{x} = \frac{1}{r^2(x_1)} \int_0^{x_1} r^2(x)dx$$

where $r(x)$ is the radius of the body of revolution at axial distance $x$. Thus $\bar{x}$ is less than $x_1$ over the forward part of the body, equal at some point beyond the maximum cross section, and exceeds it near the rear end where $r(x)$ is diminishing rapidly, causing a rapid thickening of the boundary layer from continuity considerations. The equivalent flat plate Reynolds number of transition differs from $Re_{x_1}$ in the same way.

Measurements of transition on a prolate spheroid of fineness ratio 9 and on a modified prolate spheroid of fineness ratio 7.5, modified to give more favorable pressure gradients over the nose, were made by Boltz,

Kenyon, and Allen [76] in a wind tunnel of low turbulence ($u' = 0.02$ per cent). The observed values of $Re_t$ ranged from 3.2 to 3.8 million for the body of fineness ratio 9 and from 3.6 to 4.3 million for the body of fineness ratio 7.5, the exact value being dependent on the axial location of transition.

The effect of local surface roughness in the form of a wire ring on the surface in a plane normal to the body axis was studied by Fage and Preston [74]. The results were similar to those already described for wires on a flat plate. As the speed was increased, transition moved forward from its original position in the absence of the wire until at some speed it reached the position of the wire where it remained at higher speeds. The Reynolds number formed from the wire diameter and the velocity in

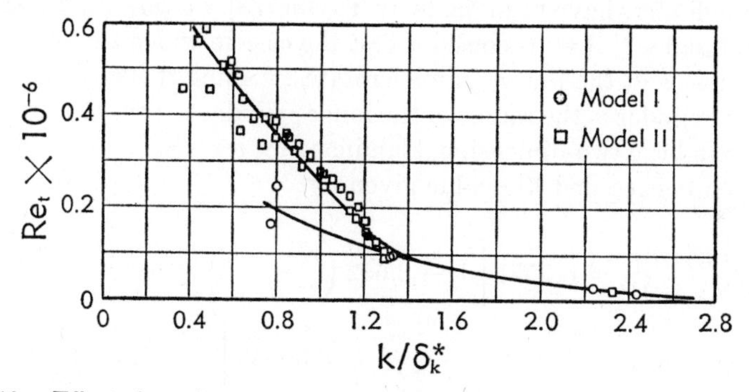


Fig. A,19. Effect of roughness on transition Reynolds number of bodies of revolution.

the boundary layer at a distance from the surface equal to the wire diameter varied from 205 to 450 with an average value of 390 for transition to just reach the wire. Values of $u_e x_t/\nu$ are plotted against $d/\delta^*$ in Fig. A,19.

To summarize, the available data on transition on bodies of revolution confirm the importance of pressure gradient, air stream turbulence, and surface roughness and waviness as important controlling variables in addition to Reynolds number, but do not permit a clear separation of the separate effects. Neither do the data give a conclusive demonstration that bodies of revolution give the same values of $Re_t$ as two-dimensional bodies with the same pressure distribution, air stream turbulence, and surface roughness. In the limited data available, the maximum value of $Re_t$ observed on bodies of revolution was about 4 million as compared with 14 million for airfoils.

**A,20. Transition in Flow between Rotating Cylinders.** Transition in the flow between rotating cylinders is a complex phenomenon but, as in the case of boundary layer flow, follows an instability of the laminar flow. Prandtl [77] discussed the stability of two-dimensional flows in which the streamlines were concentric circles in a general way as dependent on the velocity distribution; in particular, on the ratio of $du/dr$ to $u/r$. If this ratio is $-1$, the negative sign indicating a velocity decreasing with increasing radius, the resulting motion is a potential flow with constant circulation which exhibits neutral stability. If the ratio is less than $-1$, the flow is unstable with respect to three-dimensional disturbances, and the large cellular ring vortices studied by Taylor [*78*] make their appearance. If the ratio is $+1$, the fluid rotates as a rigid body. Laminar motion is stable for ratios between $-1$ and $+2$ as a result of the stabilizing action of the centrifugal field. For ratios greater than $+2$, turbulent motion is expected.

Experimental studies of instability and transition in the flow between rotating cylinders have been made by Taylor [*78*], Lewis [*79*], Wendt [*80*], and MacPhail [*81*]. Let us consider first the case in which the outer cylinder is at rest and the inner cylinder rotates. Calling the surface speed of the inner cylinder $u_i$ the radius of the inner cylinder $r_i$, that of the outer $r_o$, Taylor found the two-dimensional laminar flow replaced by steady vortex rings when $u_i$ exceeded the value given by

$$\frac{\pi^4\nu^2[1 + (r_o/r_i)]}{2u_i^2r_i^2[(r_o/r_i) - 1]^3} = 0.0571\left[1 - 0.652\left(\frac{r_o}{r_i} - 1\right)\right] + 0.00056\left[1 - 0.652\left(\frac{r_o}{r_i} - 1\right)\right]^{-1}$$

or if $(r_o/r_i) - 1$ is small, when

$$\frac{u_i(r_o - r_i)}{\nu} > 41.1\sqrt{\frac{r_o + r_i}{2(r_o - r_i)}}$$

The experimental values of the critical Reynolds number are in good agreement with this relation. However, the resulting motion is not turbulent in the accepted sense, consisting of large ring vortices regularly spaced along the length of the annulus. MacPhail found that transition to turbulence developed gradually. As the cylinder speed is increased the regular vortex rings break up and the fragment vortices travel round and round the inner cylinder. Their axes appear to oscillate about positions of rough alignment with the cylinder axis. The dimension of the eddies in the direction of the cylinder axis remains much greater than those in the other directions, and even at speeds far above that for a laminar breakdown, the turbulence spectrum contains a band of preferred frequencies. The whole behavior is reminiscent of that of the Kármán vortex street behind a circular cylinder at high Reynolds numbers.

When the inner cylinder is at rest and the outer cylinder is rotating, much higher transition Reynolds numbers are found, and a regular vortex system is not observed. To avoid disturbing secondary flows produced at the end walls, the ratio of height to width of annulus must be as great as 40, according to Wendt's measurements. The observed values of $u_o(r_o - r_i)/\nu$ vary from about 2000 for $2(r_o - r_i)/(r_o + r_i) = 0.016$ to about 65,000 for $2(r_o - r_i)/(r_o + r_i) = 0.3$ as shown in Fig. A,20. The velocity distribution indicates the presence of boundary layers at the surfaces of the cylinders, and it is probable that the transition mechanism is somewhat similar to that of the boundary layer on a plate. As $2(r_o - r_i)/(r_o + r_i)$ increases, the boundary layers occupy a smaller and

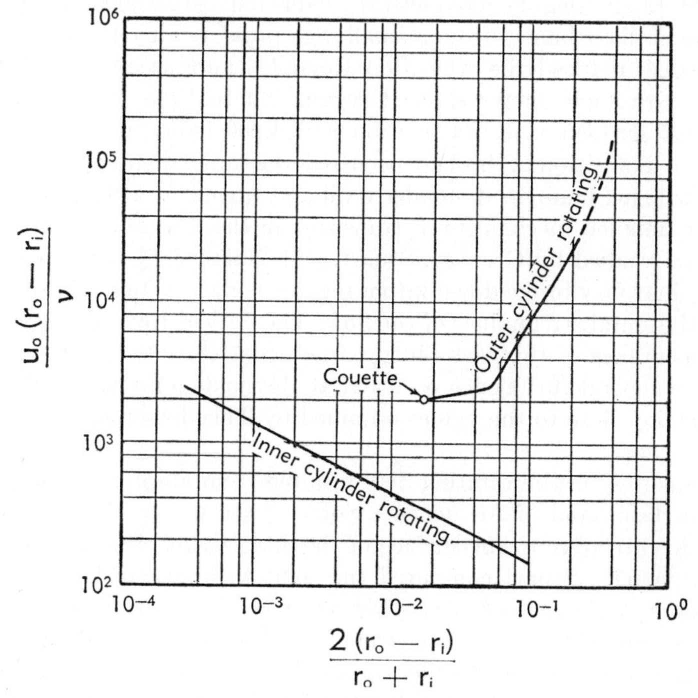


Fig. A,20. **Transition Reynolds numbers for flow between rotating cylinders.**

smaller fraction of the width of the annulus, and thus a transition Reynolds number based on the width of the annulus increases.

In the general case in which both cylinders rotate there are certain ranges of variables in which transition does not occur even at the highest Reynolds numbers. Here the stabilizing action of the centrifugal field is sufficient to prevent transition. The available data are not inconsistent with Prandtl's criterion that in such cases $(du/dr)/(u/r)$ should lie between $-1$ and $+2$. Since this ratio varies across the annulus, there are undoubtedly many cases in which the flow is partly laminar and partly turbulent, and it is not possible to state that the experiments yield precisely $+2$ as the limiting value.

**A,21. Transition in Flow near Rotating Disks.** If a smooth circular disk is rotated about an axis through its center and perpendicular to its plane in a large body of fluid, the flow near the disk may be laminar or turbulent, dependent on the Reynolds number $\omega r^2/\nu$ where $\omega$ is the angular velocity and $r$ is the radius. From Goldstein's analysis [*82*] of Schmidt and Kempf's measurements of the resisting moment, the critical Reynolds number is found to be about 80,000. Riabouchinsky [*83*] observed about 230,000.

Theodorsen and Regier [*84*] obtained a critical Reynolds number of 310,000. Large roughness reduced the value only to 220,000 but the introduction of disturbances from a small high pressure air jet near the center of the disk reduced the transition Reynolds number to about 125,000. A hot wire anemometer showed regular fluctuations in the transition region of frequency of 200 cps on a disk of 1-foot radius rotated at 525 rpm. Transition in this case occurred at a radial distance of 9.6 inches, the flow being laminar at smaller radii and turbulent at larger radii.

The detailed mechanism of transition in the flow near rotating disks has been studied by Gregory, Stuart, and Walker [*85*]. They found that the laminar flow broke down into a regular vortex system whose axes lay along the spiral streamlines of the flow. The critical Reynolds number for the appearance of this instability varied from 180,000 to 200,000; transition to general turbulence occurred at Reynolds numbers of 270,000 to 299,000, i.e. close to the values obtained by Theodorsen and Regier [*84*]. See also [*86*].

Transition on the rotating disk resulted from amplified waves covering a certain band of frequencies. Some of the waves were found to be stationary, relative to the surface of the disk, giving rise to the observed vortex pattern. Stuart computed the solution of the disturbance equation for disturbances of zero wave velocity on the rotating disk. The angle of the spiral was in extremely good agreement with experiment while the wave number, which gives the spacing of the vortices, was approximately four times too large. The discrepancy is believed to be due to the neglect of viscosity in the theoretical computations, only the inertial forces being considered. Transition in this case also is the end result of instability of the laminar flow and the Reynolds number for transition is a function of disturbances in the flow field.

**A,22. Transition in Flow at Boundary of a Jet.** We have previously discussed in Art. 7 the instability of the laminar mixing region at the edge of a jet or wake. Even when the motion within the jet and mixing region are fully turbulent, the secondary motions in the surrounding fluid are usually laminar in character, certainly so at large distances. Corrsin [*87*] has described the annular transition region and the laminar "collar" in an axially symmetrical heated jet of air. Hot wire anemometer oscillograms show the typical transition behavior. Nevertheless there is some question as to whether the phenomenon is analogous to other cases of transition described. It seems more likely that the outer boundary of a turbulent jet is very ragged and constantly changing with time as readily observed in the smoke stream from a factory chimney. The apparent transition is then to be interpreted as the intermittent striking of the hot wire by the turbulent jet.

**A,23. Transition at Subsonic Speed as Affected by Heat Transfer.** When a heated plate is placed vertically in still air, convection currents are set up. If the temperature difference between the plate and air is not too large, or more accurately if the Grashoff number $gh^3(T_w - T_\infty)/\nu^2 T_\infty$ is not too large, the motion will be laminar in character. Here $g$ is the acceleration of gravity, $h$ is the vertical height of the plate, $T_w$ is the plate temperature, $T_\infty$ the free air temperature, and $\nu$ the kinematic viscosity. According to Hermann [*88*], transition to turbulence occurs at a Grashoff number of about $10^9$ for which $Re_{\delta^*}$ is about 300.

The stabilizing and destabilizing effects of gravitational forces produced by density differences arising from heating and cooling in forced air flow are analogous to those of centrifugal forces in curved flow discussed in Art. 20. According to Prandtl [*77*] the controlling parameter is the ratio of $-gd\rho/dy$ to $2\rho(du/dy)^2$. When this parameter is greater than 1, the flow is very stable and the critical Reynolds number is infinite. Schlichting [*89*] found that the effect of gravity made all oscillations in a laminar boundary layer stable, provided $-gd\rho/dy$ exceeded $\frac{1}{25}\rho(du/dy)_0^2$ where $(du/dy)_0$ is the value of $du/dy$ at the wall. Reichardt's measurements [*90*] are in fair agreement with Schlichting's result.

Liepmann and Fila [*12*] investigated the effect of surface temperature on transition in incompressible flow, for heating only, and under conditions where the effects of gravitational forces were negligible. For the unheated plate the transition Reynolds number was only about 500,000, although the free stream turbulence was in one series 0.17 per cent and in another 0.05 per cent. The low value is attributed by the authors to lateral spreading of turbulence from the wind tunnel walls. The transition Reynolds number decreases as the surface temperature is increased, falling to about 400,000 at 100°C at a turbulence level of 0.05 and to about 250,000 at 100°C at a turbulence level of 0.17. The Reynolds numbers are based on the free stream value of the viscosity. If the viscosity at the wall is used, the transition Reynolds numbers at 100°C are 260,000 and 185,000, respectively. The observed effects are believed to be due to the effect of the variation of viscosity with temperature in producing inflection points in the velocity distribution curve; not to the influence of gravitational forces. Velocity profiles with inflection points are much more unstable than those without inflection points.

**A,24. General Remarks on Transition at Supersonic Speed.** When a body travels at supersonic speed through the air, its surface becomes heated above the temperature of the surrounding undisturbed air. If the body is insulated and there is no transfer of heat by radiation to or from it, the surface reaches a constant temperature $T_r$ equal to the temperature of the air adjacent to the surface. This temperature is somewhat less than the local adiabatic stagnation temperature $T_e^0$ and is known as the recovery temperature. If the local air temperature just outside the boundary layer is $T_e$, the ratio $(T_r - T_e)/(T_e^0 - T_e)$ is called the recovery factor $r$. For laminar flow the recovery factor is approximately equal to the square root of the Prandtl number $Pr$, the name given to the nondimensional parameter $\mu c_p/k$ formed from the viscosity $\mu$, specific heat at constant pressure $c_p$, and thermal conductivity $k$ of the air. For turbulent flow $r = \sqrt[3]{Pr}$ approximately.

For the circumstances described there is no heat lost from the body by convection. Art. 25 discusses the data on transition under these conditions. The indirect effect of aerodynamic heating appears as an effect of Mach number, since the changes in the density and velocity distribution accompanying the temperature rise in the boundary layer modify the stability of the layer.

Heat transfer to or from the body exerts a marked influence on transition as discussed later in Art. 26. Heat flow from the air to the body (cooling the body) increases the transition Reynolds number, whereas heat flow from the body to the air (heating the body) decreases it. These effects are quite substantial and sometimes overlooked. It is very difficult to realize experimentally the condition of complete absence of heat flow to or from the body, especially for experiments in which the relative speed cannot be maintained for long periods, as in firing ranges and blowdown wind tunnels. In a firing range, the body is usually initially at free air temperature. The recovery temperature is much higher and the experimental conditions are those of a cooled body. In a blowdown wind tunnel, the body is usually initially at or near the stagnation temperature which is only a little above the recovery temperature. The free stream temperature is very much lower and the experimental conditions are those of a heated body. These differences account for the commonly observed rise of transition Reynolds numbers with Mach number in firing range data (the effective cooling increasing with Mach number because of the rising stagnation temperature) and the fall with Mach number in blowdown wind tunnels (the effective heating increasing with Mach number because of the falling free stream temperature).

Effects of free stream turbulence, pressure gradient, nose shape, and roughness are found at supersonic as well as at subsonic speed. The effect of nose shape differs in that a bow shock wave is present at supersonic speed which modifies the viscosity, density, and speed of the flow near the surface. Shock waves influence transition in other ways. A weak shock wave striking a boundary layer produces a small disturbance analogous to that of a small roughness element. Stronger shock waves may induce boundary layer separation followed by transition or produce immediate transition. The observed values of the $x$ Reynolds number based on free stream properties range from about 0.5 million to about 90 million but the analysis of the experimental data to isolate the effects of the several variables is difficult.

The highest value, 90 million, was observed by Sternberg [*91*] on a cone of 20° included angle attached to the nose of a V-2 rocket in flight. The thickness of the laminar boundary layer on a cone in subsonic flow is $1/\sqrt{3}$ times that on a plate at the same $x$ Reynolds number; hence if transition is assumed to occur at a fixed value of the Reynolds number based on boundary layer thickness, the critical $x$ Reynolds number for the cone will be 3 times that for a plate. There is no reason to expect this relationship in supersonic flow, and the scanty experimental comparisons [*92*] of data taken on cones and plates in the same air stream show little differences between transition Reynolds number for plate and cone. In this and succeeding articles no attempt is made to adjust the values for cones and other bodies of revolution to give equivalent flat plate Reynolds numbers.

Various methods have been used to detect transition, the most common ones being Pitot-tube rakes, surface temperature measurements, schlieren, and shadow photographs. Transition at supersonic speed is intermittent [*93,94*] just as it is at subsonic speed. Hence the photographic methods require numerous pictures to obtain the average location of transition. Since the transition process extends over a certain range of Reynolds number, the choice of a single value is somewhat arbitrary. Wherever possible, the values quoted will refer to the beginning of transition, i.e. the point where turbulent bursts begin to appear for 5 or 10 per cent of the time or, eliminating the knee of the curve, where the pressure or the temperature begins to rise. Many authors adopt the value of the Reynolds number at which the pressure or temperature reaches its maximum value as that for transition; in these cases the values quoted herein will be less than those stated in the original papers.

**A,25. Effect of Mach Number on Transition for Bodies without Heat Transfer at Supersonic Speeds.** Art. 2 described the large effect of free stream turbulence on transition at subsonic speed. There is a similar large effect at supersonic speed up to a Mach number of 2, although there are few systematic experiments. The most useful test object at supersonic speed is a cone of small included angle. At supersonic speed there is no pressure gradient, the leading edge effects are small, and there is no contamination from tunnel wall boundary layers.

Laufer and Marte [*92*] made measurements on a 5° included angle cone in the JPL 20-inch wind tunnel, first with damping screens in the settling chamber of the tunnel, and then with a turbulence grid. The turbulence levels $u'/U$ in the settling chamber were 0.6 per cent and 6 per cent, respectively, with little change with Mach number and tunnel pressure. Unfortunately techniques for turbulence measurements in the test section at supersonic speeds are not well developed. Tests were run at Mach numbers of 1.79, 2.55, and 4.50. At $M = 1.79$, increasing the turbulence tenfold reduced the transition Reynolds number from 4.3 million to 3.3 million; at 2.55 there was no effect of turbulence, the transition Reynolds number being about 3.0 million. Similarly there was no effect at 4.50, the transition Reynolds number being about 2.7 million. Other measurements were made in the JPL 12-inch wind tunnel at $M = 2.6$ with similar results.

Measurements of transition on a 10° included angle cone have been made in numerous NACA wind tunnels [*95,96,97*]. The values vary from 400,000 to 8 million with no clear pattern of variation with Mach number or Reynolds number per foot. Turbulence measurements were not available. The design of the 1 × 1-foot variable Reynolds number wind tunnel at the NACA Lewis Laboratory has been twice modified to reduce its turbulence level, raising the maximum value of $Re_t$ for the 10° cone from 700,000 to 1.3 million and then to about 4 million. Apparently the lowest turbulence wind tunnel in which tests have been made on cones is the NACA 4-foot supersonic pressure tunnel [*97*]. Measurements on a 10° cone at Mach numbers of 1.41, 1.61, and 2.01 and over a Reynolds number range from 0.8 to 9.5 million per foot give values of $Re_t$ increasing from 7 to 8 million as the Reynolds number per foot increases from 4 to 9 million with no effect of Mach number. The schlieren technique was used.

Lange, Gieseler, and Lee [*98*] report values of $Re_t$ for a 5° cone in the NOL aeroballistics wind tunnel No. 2 decreasing from 3.4 million at a Mach number of 1.9 to one million at $M = 4.2$.

The effect of Mach number variation alone is indeterminate from the data available. According to stability theory [IV,F] as developed by Lees and Lin [*99,100*] the critical Reynolds number for instability of the laminar layer decreases slowly with increasing Mach number for a body without heat transfer. The experimental picture is complicated by possible variation of the turbulence level with Mach number, tunnel pressure, compressor staging, etc. The measurements giving the highest values of $Re_t$ show no appreciable effect for Mach numbers from 1.4 to 2.0, but this is a relatively small range of Mach number and the scatter of the measurements is large. The general trend over a wider range of Mach number [*92,101*] in wind tunnels for which the observed values are somewhat lower is a decrease with Mach number to a minimum value near $M = 3.7$, followed by an increase with Mach number. Typically from a value of $Re_t$ of 5 million at $M = 1.5$, $Re_t$ falls to 2 million at $M = 3.7$ and rises to about 3 million at $M = 5$.

Only a few scattered measurements have been made on flat plates at supersonic speeds. An incidental measurement [*102*] in the NACA Ames 6-inch heat transfer wind tunnel at a Mach number of 2.4 gave an $Re_t$ of 1.4 million. The authors interpret the data as showing values as low as 560,000 at the lowest tunnel pressure. In another study [*103*] a crude analysis of skin friction data gave extrapolated values from 2.6 to 4.4 million. Measurements in the JPL 20-inch supersonic wind tunnel by Coles [*104*] gave values decreasing from about 2.25 million at a Mach number of 2 to about 1.1 million at $M = 3.6$, increasing to about 1.2 million at $M = 4.5$, the position of minimum shear being taken as the beginning of transition. Other measurements in the same wind tunnel by Laufer and Marte [*92*] give somewhat higher values, but the damping screen configuration may have been different and the surface temperature method was used. A single measurement [*105*] in the GALCIT 5-inch hypersonic wind tunnel gave a value of at least 5 million at $M = 5.8$.

In addition to cones and flat plates, a hollow cylinder with sharp leading edge gives a boundary layer with zero pressure gradient. Brinich [*106*] made measurements on a hollow cylinder 5.31 inches outside diameter, 4.75 inches inside diameter, 33 inches long, with 5° beveled leading edge and 0.003-inch leading edge radius in the NACA Lewis 1 × 1-foot variable pressure wind tunnel at a fixed Mach number of 3.12. The transition Reynolds number varied with the pressure, increasing from 1.5 to 4 million as the pressure increased. Brinich attributes this to the variation of the Taylor turbulence parameter (Art. 11) with pressure at a constant turbulence level. As the pressure increases, the boundary layer thickness decreases. Thus the ratio of the scale of the turbulence to the boundary layer thickness increases and the turbulence has less effect in reducing the transition Reynolds number. On this view there would be both a Mach number and a density effect, since the thickness increases with increasing Mach number. In a wind tunnel of constant stagnation pressure increasing Mach numbers are accompanied by reduced density so that both effects would combine to reduce transition Reynolds number with increasing Mach number for a fixed turbulence level when turbulence effects on transition predominate in determining the location of transition.

Brinich discovered [*107*] a large downstream displacement of the transition point when the sharp leading edge was very slightly blunted. Moeckel [*108*] gave a theory of this effect, attributing it to the formation of an inviscid shear layer by the curved leading edge shock wave which reduces the local Reynolds number at the outer edge of the boundary layer. Bertram [*109*] made an analysis of the available data and suggested that the most suitable nondimensional parameter is a Reynolds number based on leading edge thickness. The transition Reynolds number (based on peak surface temperature) rises from about 1 million to about 4.5 million as the leading edge Reynolds number increases from 200 to 10,000.

There are no data on the effects of pressure gradient and surface curvature on two-dimensional boundary layers except for measurements [*110*] on airfoils, mainly at high subsonic speed. Fig. A,25a shows the position of transition as a function of Mach number for a slightly modified NACA 0012 airfoil. This figure indicates a large effect of compressibility, transition moving forward with increasing Mach number up to $M = 0.65$, then a slight rearward movement to $M = 0.7$, a forward movement to $M = 0.76$, and finally a continuing rearward movement up to the highest Mach number of about $M = 0.9$.

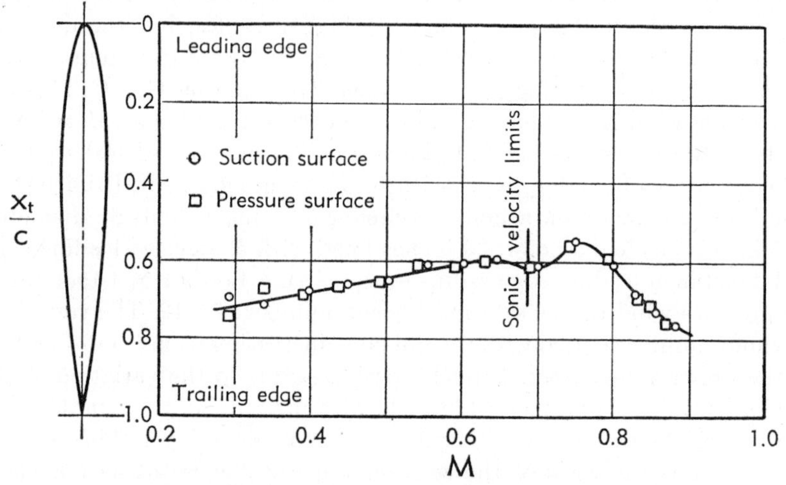


**Fig. A,25a. Transition position on modified NACA 0012 airfoil as a function of Mach number.**

The corresponding pressure distributions are shown in Fig. A,25b. It is seen that the final forward movement is associated with a change in the pressure distribution from a predominantly adverse gradient to a favorable gradient. It seems probable therefore that the principal effect of compressibility is the modification of the pressure distribution which in turn affects the position of transition. Whether identical pressure distribution in compressible and incompressible flow would yield the same position of transition has, however, not been determined.

Some observations of transition on airfoils at supersonic speeds have been made in connection with other investigations. Thus some of the photographs of Stalder and Slack [*67*] show wedges of turbulence behind dust particles, behind air jets from pressure orifices and from the side wall similar to those observed at low speeds. No systematic basic studies have been made.

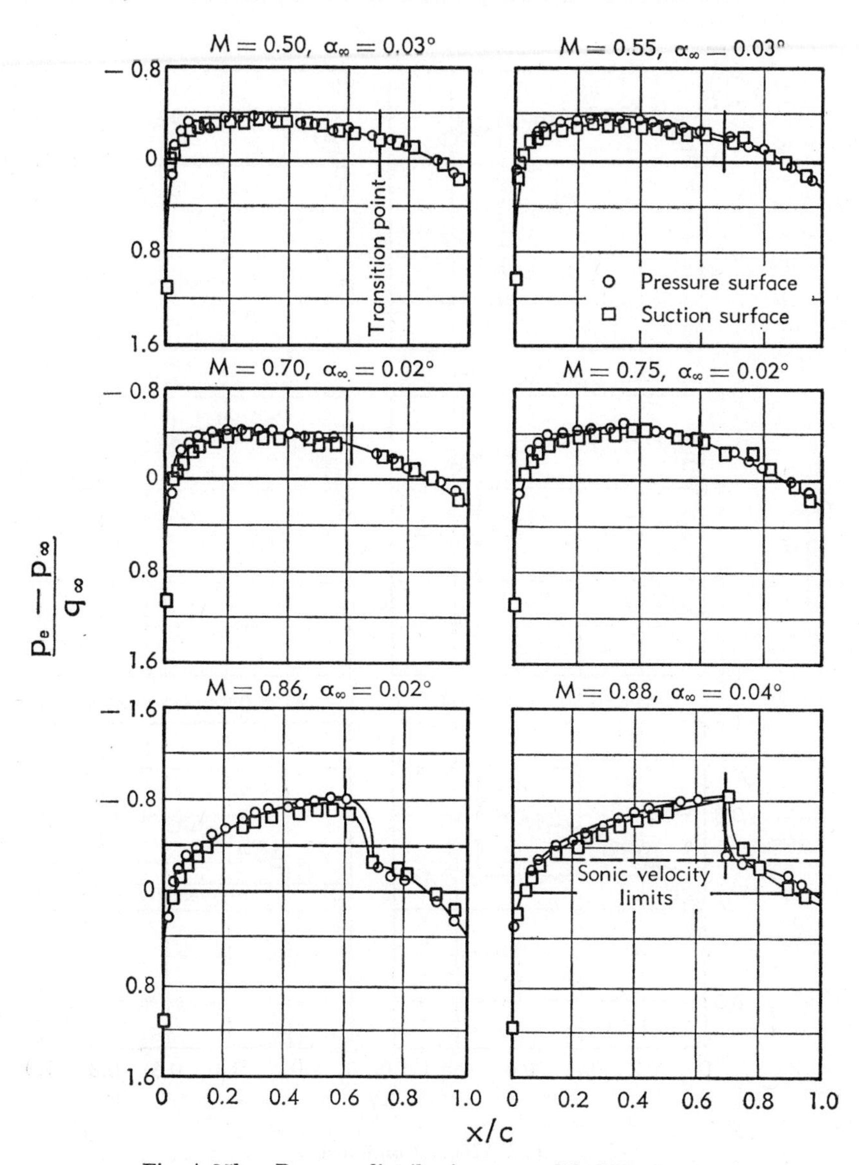


Fig. A,25b. Pressure distribution on modified NACA 0012 airfoil as a function of Mach number.

There are a few investigations of transition on bodies of revolution without heat transfer at supersonic speeds. Czarnecki and Sinclair [*111*] measured transition on the parabolic body of revolution RM-10 in the NACA Langley 4-foot wind tunnel. A transition Reynolds number of 11.5 million was observed. A further investigation [*112*] in the same wind tunnel was made on an ogive cylinder, a cone cylinder, and an RM-10

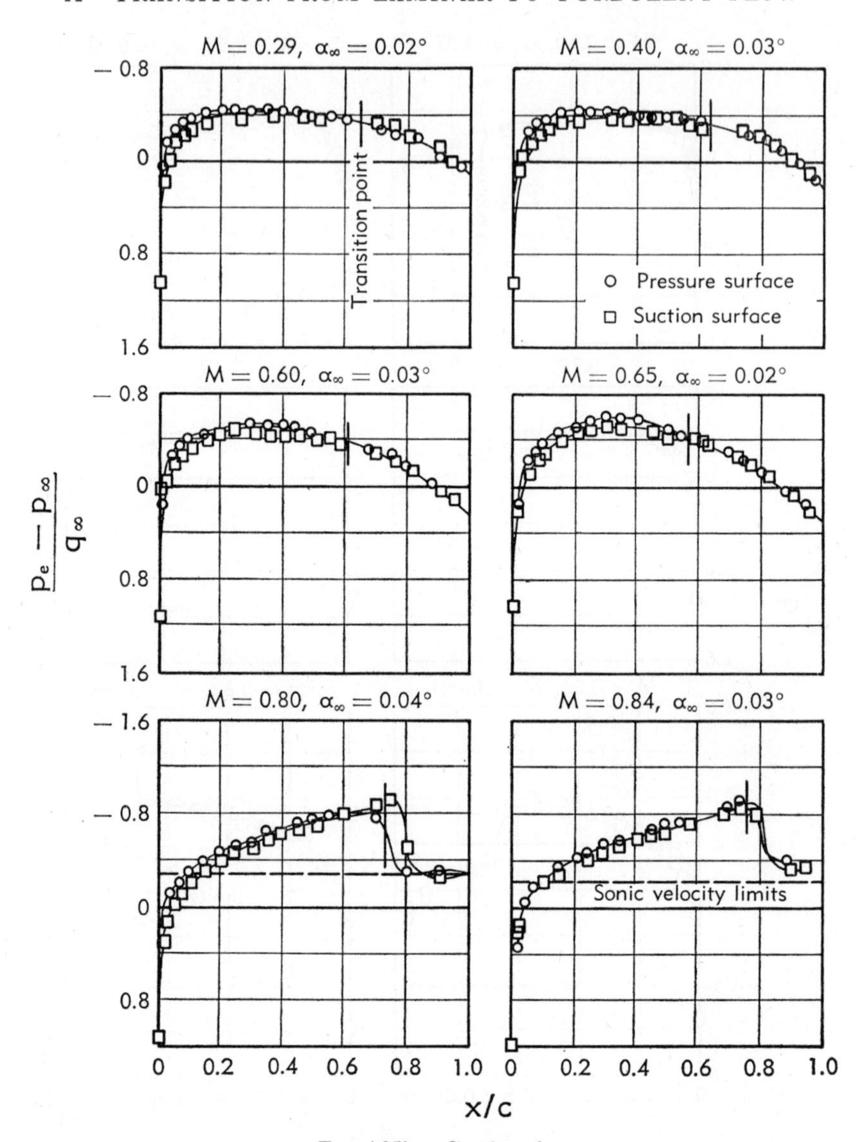


FIG. A25b. Continued.

model, all of fineness ratio 12.2. Measurements were made of transition and skin friction at Mach numbers from 1.2 to 2.2 and tunnel pressures from 0.125 to 2.25 atmospheres. The approximate Reynolds numbers for transition at the base were 2.5 million for the cone cylinder, 4.7 million for the ogive cylinder, and 11 million for the RM-10.

Data on a 20° cone cylinder obtained in the NOL 40 cm aerobalistics wind tunnel No. 2 at Mach numbers from 1.86 to 4.24 are reported by Potter [*113*]. The observed transition Reynolds number increased from

2.6 million at a Mach number of 1.86 to 4.4 million at a Mach number of 2.46, then decreased to 1.6 million at a Mach number of 4.51.

A systematic study of the effects of single roughness elements has been made by Brinich [*106*] at a Mach number of 3.12. The basic model was a hollow cylinder with axis along the stream direction as previously described and the roughness elements were wires encircling the cylinder. The diameter and location of the roughness element were varied. The results were analyzed along the lines discussed in Art. 5, the ratio of the transition Reynolds number for the rough cylinder to that for the smooth

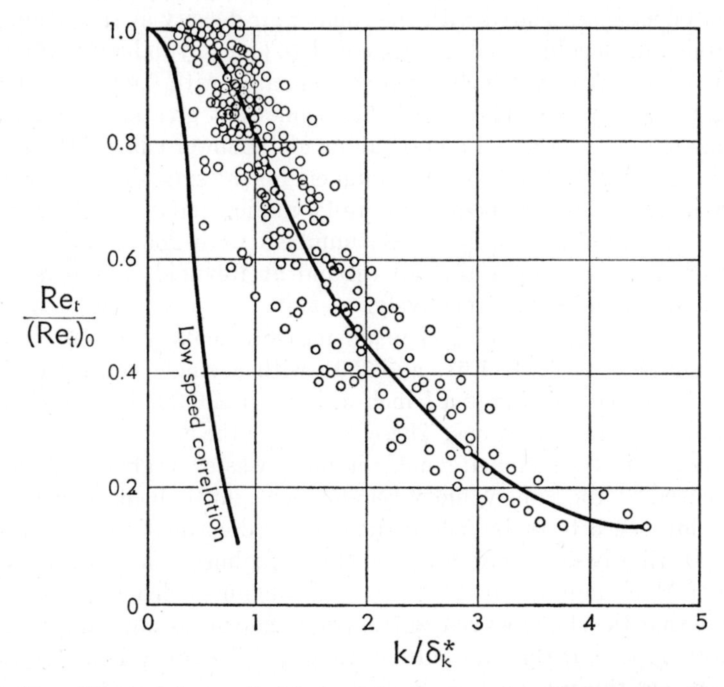


Fig. A,25c. Effect of single cylindrical roughness element on the transition Reynolds number of a smooth hollow cylinder at a Mach number of 3.12, the values for smooth and rough cylinder being compared for the same transition position.

cylinder being plotted against the ratio of the height of the element to the displacement thickness of the boundary layer. The displacement thickness was that computed by the compressible flow formula. The scatter band was very wide but it was clear that compressible boundary layers are much less sensitive to roughness than incompressible ones.

The transition Reynolds number of the smooth cylinder varied with the tunnel stagnation pressure. Brinich compared the rough cylinder value with the smooth cylinder value at the same pressure, which appears to be the natural basis for comparison. However, if the comparison is made with the smooth cylinder value for the same transition position, the scatter is greatly reduced. Fig. A,25c shows the recomputed data, omitting that for elements close to the leading edge (closer than 25 times the roughness height) and that for which transition is at the roughness element itself. There remain systematic variations with roughness location, but the anomalous features (regions in which the ratio *increases* with increasing roughness height) of Brinich's figure [*106*, Fig. 12] disappear.

The data for supersonic flow are displaced to values of $k/\delta_k^*$ about 3 times those for incompressible flow. This ratio is of the order of magnitude of the ratio of the free stream density to that of the air near the surface striking the roughness element. One might speculate that the smaller effect is associated with the smaller air density at the element.

Brinich made additional experiments [*107*] on a cylinder for which the leading edge radius was 0.001 inch as compared with 0.008 inch for the earlier measurements. These indicated somewhat greater sensitivity to roughness, the recomputed points falling at the lower edge of the scatter band in Fig. A,25c. The Reynolds numbers for the smooth cylinder based on maximum surface temperature were 1.7 million and 3.6 million, respectively. The leading edge Reynolds numbers were 286 and 2900. The minimum surface temperature was found at Reynolds numbers of 0.8 million and 1.2 million, respectively.

Sinclair and Czarnecki [*97*] made measurements on a 10° cone at Mach numbers of 1.41, 1.61, and 2.01 with a single two-dimensional roughness strip consisting of a $\frac{1}{2}$-inch wide band of 0.003-inch thick cellulose tape at various locations. These tests gave the surprising result that the decrease in transition Reynolds number was even greater than that experienced for the same value of roughness height to displacement thickness in low speed tests, i.e. below the low speed correlation curve of Fig. A,25c. Obviously more data are needed on roughness effects over a wider range of Mach number, body shape, and roughness element shape. It is possible that the shock wave configuration and shock-induced separation are more important than the ratio of roughness height to boundary layer displacement thickness.

The effects of roughness near the conical tip of cone-ogive-cylinder models on transition were studied by Luther [*114*]. He states that an attempted correlation on the basis of $k/\delta_k^*$ was unsuccessful. This is not surprising in view of the effects of pressure gradient produced by the body shape.

Luther was primarily interested in roughness as a means of fixing boundary layer transition. He used distributed roughness as well as trip wires to determine the minimum roughness height needed to produce transition at the element. Large Mach number effects were found, the critical heights for a Mach number of 4.09 being about 3 to 4 times that for a Mach number of 1.64. As in the case of Brinich's data the effect of the low density in reducing the value of the Reynolds number $u_k k/\nu$ seems to account for the Mach number effect.

narrow ranges of the variables. Data are included on a flat plate, cone cylinder, paraboloid cylinder, and the RM-10 body of revolution. The Mach numbers represented are 1.61, 2.40, 2.87, and 3.12.

The curves of Fig. A,26b suggest that three of the curves are approaching vertical asymptotes at sufficiently small values of $(T_w - T_r)/T_e^0$. The Reynolds numbers attainable are always limited by model size and tunnel characteristics so that complete stabilization to infinite Reynolds number can never be demonstrated. The asymptote values are compared with the

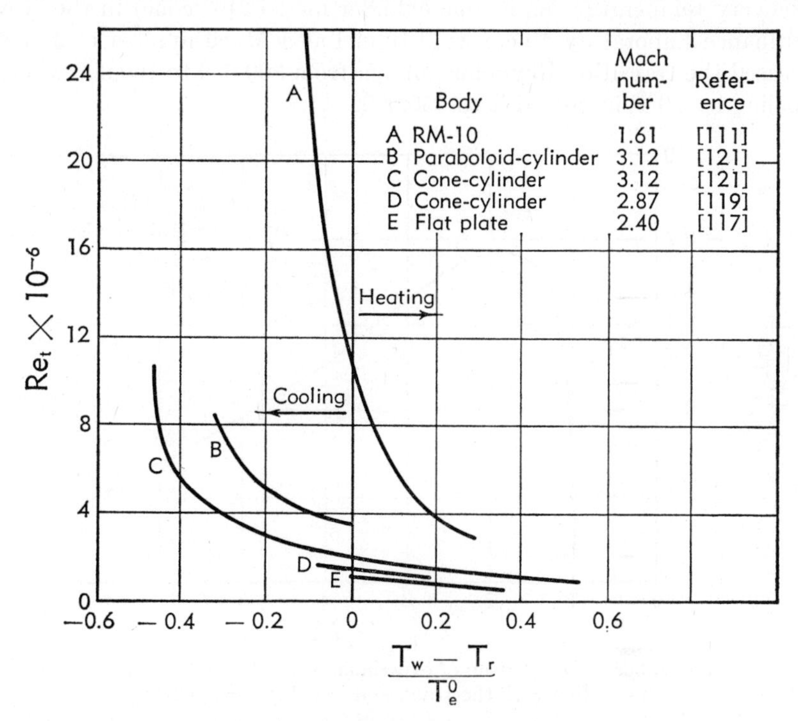


Fig. A,26b. Effect of heating and cooling on transition Reynolds number at supersonic speed.

Dunn and Lin theoretical curve in Fig. A,26c. The experimental values are of the same order of magnitude as those predicted by theory.

There are a number of individual papers giving additional data on the effects of heat transfer on transition at supersonic speeds. Higgins and Pappas [*117*] found that heating a flat plate to a wall temperature 200°F above the recovery temperature reduced the transition Reynolds number from 1.25 million to 600,000 in the NACA Ames 6-inch heat transfer wind tunnel at a Mach number of 2.4. Scherrer [*118*] studied the effect of heating and cooling on transition on a 20° cone in the Ames 1 × 3-foot wind tunnel No. 1 at Mach numbers of 1.5 and 2.0. In the absence of heating, the transition Reynolds number was 4.1 million. Heating to a value of $(T_w - T_r)/T_e^0$ of 0.14 reduced the transition Reynolds number to values of about 3 million. In order to study the effect of cooling, it was necessary to add artificial roughness in the form of grooves to move transition forward. Under these conditions the transition Reynolds number was about 2 million. Cooling to a value of $(T_w - T_r)/T_e^0$ of $-0.065$ at a Mach number of 2 increased $Re_t$ to 3.4 million and cooling to $-0.10$ at a Mach number of 1.5 to 3.8 million.

Eber [*119*] found that heating to a wall temperature 125°F above the recovery temperature on a cone cylinder model (40° cone) in the Naval Ordnance Laboratory 40-cm wind tunnel at a Mach number of 2.87 decreased the transition Reynolds number from 300,000 to 160,000 whereas cooling by 50°F increased it to 450,000.

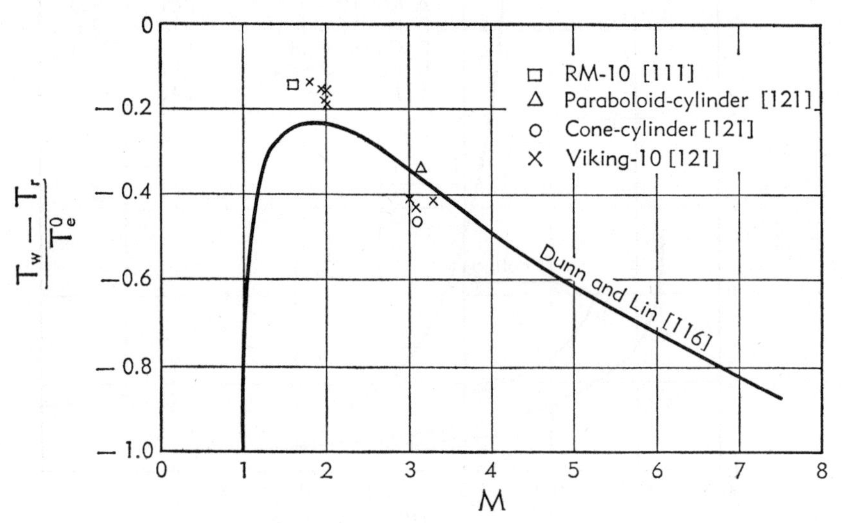


Fig. A,26c. Comparison of experimental results on stabilization by cooling with the Dunn and Lin theoretical curve.

Czarnecki and Sinclair [*111*] made measurements on the RM-10 body of revolution at a Mach number of 1.61 in the NACA Langley 4-foot wind tunnel for which the transition Reynolds number of the insulated body is 11.5 million. Heating to a value of $(T_w - T_r)/T_e^0$ of 0.3 reduced the transition Reynolds number to 3 million; cooling to $(T_w - T_r)/T_e^0$ equal to $-0.15$ increased it to 28.5 million. Roughening the surface by a cellophane tape at 3 and 25 per cent of the body length reduced the value from 11.5 to 5 and 7.5 million, respectively, and these values could not be increased by cooling the roughened body to $(T_w - T_r)$ equal to $-0.15$.

Jedlicka, Wilkins, and Seiff [*94*] investigated transition on small models fired from a 50 caliber smooth-bore gun at 4000 feet per second with the aid of a plastic sabot. While the principal object of the investigation was to study roughness effect, the short flight times mean that the model temperature remains nearly equal to the free-air temperature and thus the conditions are those of a cool body to which heat is transferred from the boundary layer. The models were long cylinders with tangent-ogival nose, the over-all fineness ratio being 30. They were stabilized by cruciform fins. Under the test conditions the critical Reynolds number for the smooth body at 0° angle of attack or on the windward side was greater than $11\frac{1}{2}$ million.

Van Driest and Boison [*120*] report that cooling a 20° cone in the North American Aviation $3\frac{1}{2}$-inch wind tunnel to $(T_w - T_r)/T_e^0$ of $-0.38$ increased the transition Reynolds number from about 2.7 million to a value greater than 5.4 million, the maximum permitted by the length of the cone.

Jack and Diaconis [*121*] made measurements on a cone-cylinder and a paraboloid-cylinder at a Mach number of 3.12 in the NACA Lewis 1-foot variable pressure wind tunnel. Heating the cone-cylinder to $(T_w - T_r)/T_e^0$ equal to 0.53 decreased the transition Reynolds number from 2 million to 0.86 million; cooling to $-0.45$ increased it to 10.6 million. For the paraboloid-cylinder the transition Reynolds numbers were approximately twice as great.

Snodgrass [*122*] reports the results obtained on a 10° nose cone on a Viking rocket in free flight. The individual observations of transition are plotted in Fig. A,26c. They are in fair agreement with the Dunn and Lin curve.

Bertram [*109*] reports an exploratory investigation of transition on a hollow cylinder in the NACA Langley hypersonic blowdown wind tunnel at a Mach number of 6.9. Because of the short duration of flow the body did not reach the recovery temperature. The value of $(T_w - T_r)/T_e^0$ is estimated to have been $-0.27$ and the observed transition Reynolds number was between 4 and 6 million.

The results described in this section include results in wind tunnels in which $Re_t$ for the body without heat transfer varies from 1.3 to 11.5 million, these differences presumably being due principally to effects of air stream turbulence. While the absolute changes in $Re_t$ with heat transfer are greatest in those wind tunnels where the highest values are observed for the insulated body, the relative changes for small rates of heat transfer are of the same order of magnitude. As the cooling is increased, the curves of $Re_t$ vs. $(T_w - T_r)/T_e^0$ indicate vertical asymptotes corresponding to values of $(T_w - T_r)/T_e^0$ which are in fair agreement with the values for complete stabilization computed by Dunn and Lin.

**A,27. Present Status and Future Direction.** It has been seen that transition is a phenomenon of wide occurrence in many types of flow and that its location in the flow is governed by a large number of variables. The problem of transition is the problem of the origin of turbulence and it is not yet clear whether we can recognize a single process as active in all the varied manifestations of beginning turbulence. Various approaches have been made by various investigators in the search for a key principle or idea which will unlock the door leading to understanding. Controversies have developed as to the adequacy of linear theories to contribute to a solution of the problem, especially as to the role of the linearized theory of the instability of laminar flow. Nevertheless it seems to me that, although a large amount of experimental and theoretical work remains to be accomplished, the principal outlines are reasonably clear and the apparently rival ideas are not contradictory but complementary. The phenomena are, however, far from simple.

For very small free stream turbulence, small surface roughness, and bodies of large fineness ratio, transition is preceded by the selective amplification of the small disturbances present. The process in the early stages, which is well described by a linear theory, is usually described as an instability. However, the linear theory describes only the amplification of disturbances, and if no disturbance is present, no oscillations result. The oscillations do not continue after their production if the disturbances are removed. The linear theory gives the result that viscosity produces a phase shift between the tangential and normal components of the velocity fluctuations which gives rise to shearing stresses which in turn modify the original velocity distribution. Hence, some of Munk's criticisms [*123*] of the linear theory are not justified; it is true, as will be seen later, that the linear theory cannot describe the transition process itself. The linear theory is well established both theoretically and experimentally as describing the beginning of the process leading to transition when the disturbances are small.

The initial disturbances to be introduced into the linear theory arise from several sources; collectively they may be described by a composite spectrum of intensity and frequency made up of several components, as follows: (1) the initial turbulence of the air stream, (2) acoustic waves, (3) the disturbance at the nose or leading edge, and (4) disturbances due to roughness and shock waves from external sources. Since the wavelengths of the most highly amplified waves are much larger than the thickness of the boundary layer, we may be justified in considering only the frequency region corresponding to wavelengths longer than the boundary layer thickness and to consider that all sources of disturbance yield a spectrum of velocity fluctuations superposed on the free stream velocity. Whether this simplification is justified or not is a matter for further investigation.

The initial turbulence of the air stream enters directly as a series of randomly varying disturbances of the free stream flow. Acoustic waves produce particle motions which in most cases are comparable with a very small initial turbulence (a few hundredths of one per cent) and, hence, are usually of importance only when all other disturbances are exceedingly small. As the free stream passes around the body under study it is subjected to a single disturbance corresponding to the mean velocity distribution around the body. This pulse can be analyzed into a spectrum, and if the body is of blunt shape yielding a sharp and large amplitude pulse, there may be sufficient energy in the region of amplified oscillations to be of importance. Similarly a single small roughness element yields a single pulse, even though it generates no turbulence directly, which contributes to the disturbance spectrum. Distributed roughness yields a random disturbance which can be analyzed in terms of its spectrum. Instability of the highly curved flow near a stagnation point and vorticity produced by intense shock waves at the leading edge also contribute to the spectrum at supersonic speed.

The region of spectrum which is amplified depends on the Reynolds number of the boundary layer and on the mean velocity distribution as discussed in IV,F. The linear theory then yields a growing disturbance. According to experiment the next step is the appearance of turbulent spots in the flow which grow in size. Since the disturbances arising from free stream turbulence and distributed roughness have a random character, these spots will appear at various points in the flow in a random manner as described by Emmons [*3*] and transition will be intermittent and extend over a considerable area.

The transition process or the real instability of the flow is the result of the nonlinear character of the equations describing the motion. Because of the nonlinear character the effects of several disturbances cannot be obtained by superposition, the concept of analysis into a spectrum is of limited utility, and it is difficult to conceive a simple typical process describing the essential features of the phenomenon. Munk [*123*] has tried to describe transition as an interplay between the selective aggregating action of shear flow on vorticity of one sign, the spreading-out of vorticity of the opposite sign, and the nonselective diffusion of vorticity by viscosity. Other pictures have previously been presented in Art. 10 in terms of the rolling-up of shear layers arising in flow separation or of the production of Görtler vortices in regions of highly curved streamlines. Betz [*124*] has recently described the origin of vortices in a fluid of small viscosity, pointing out several difficulties which can be avoided by assuming that vortices are formed by the rolling-up of vortex sheets. Progress in the development of a satisfactory conceptual picture and theory is dependent on progress in the study of nonstationary solutions of the Navier-Stokes equations.

When the disturbances are large the intermediate stage describable by linear theory is absent. Large disturbances in this sense are actually quite small; in the case of initial turbulence of 0.25 per cent or more, the laminar boundary layer oscillations are not observable, being masked, if present, by the large velocity fluctuations induced in the boundary layer flow by the external turbulence.

If this broad outline of the complex problem of transition is correct, it seems doubtful that the modified Schlichting approach based on the notion of a local transition Reynolds number can be anything more than an empirical engineering approximation. It may well be that its utility decreases as the disturbances are made smaller, if in fact it turns out to have any utility. Certainly there is ample room for further investigation of the transition problem.

## A,28. Cited References.


1. Dryden, H. L. Air flow in the boundary layer near a plate. *NACA Rept. 562*, 1936.
2. Schubauer, G. B., and Skramstad, H. K. Laminar-boundary-layer oscillations and transition on a flat plate. *NACA Rept. 909*, 1948.
3. Emmons, H. W. *J. Aeronaut. Sci. 18*, 490 (1951).
4. Mitchner, M. *J. Aeronaut. Sci. 21*, 350 (1954).
5. Schubauer, G. B., and Klebanoff, P. S. *NACA Tech. Note 3489*, 1955.
6. Wright, E. A., and Bailey, G. W. *J. Aeronaut. Sci. 6*, 485 (1939).
7. Schlichting, H., and Ulrich, A. *Jahrbuch deut. Luftfahrtforschung I*, 8 (1942).
8. Liepmann, H. W. Investigations on laminar boundary-layer stability and transition on curved boundaries. *NACA Advance Confid. Rept. 3H30*, 1943. Also issued as *NACA Wartime Rept. W-107*, 1943.
9. Feindt, E. G. Untersuchungen über die Abhängigkeit des Umschlages laminar-turbulent von der Oberflächenrauhigkeit und der Druck-verteilung. *D. F. L. Inst. Aerodynamik, Braunschweig, Bericht 56/10*, 1956.
10. Liepmann, H. W. Investigation of boundary layer transition on concave walls. *NACA Advance Confid. Rept. 4J28*, 1945. Also issued as *NACA Wartime Rept. W-87*, 1945.
11. Görtler, H. *Nachr. Ges. Wiss. Göttingen, Fachgruppen I (N.F.)2*, 1 (1940). Transl. *NACA Tech. Mem. 1375*, 1944.
12. Liepmann, H., and Fila, G. H. Investigations of effects of surface temperature and single roughness elements on boundary-layer transition. *NACA Rept. 890*, 1947.
13. Fage, A. The smallest size of a spanwise surface corrugation which affects boundary-layer transition on an aerofoil. *Brit. Aeronaut. Research Council Repts. and Mem. 2120*, 1943.
14. Holstein, H. Versuche an einer parallel angeströmten ebenen Platte über den Rauhigkeitseinfluss auf den Umschlag laminar/turbulent. *Zent. Wissensch. Berichtsw. über Luftfahrtsch, Berlin, Untersuch. u. Mitt. 3110*, 1944. See also *AVA Monograph Series, RT1005*.
15. Tani, I., Hama, R., and Mituisi, S. On the permissible roughness in the laminar boundary layer. *Rept. Aeronaut. Research Inst. Tokyo 199*, 1940.
16. Schiller, L. *Handbuch der Experimentalphysik*, Vol. 4, Part 4. Leipzig, 1932.
17. Dryden, H. L. *J. Aeronaut. Sci. 20*, 477 (1953).
18. Tani, I., and Hama, F. R. *J. Aeronaut. Sci. 20*, 289 (1953).
19. Stüper, J. The influence of surface irregularities on transition with various pressure gradients. *Dept. Supply Aeronaut. Research Consultative Comm. Rept. A59*, Melbourne, 1949. See also *Aerodynamics Tech. Mem. 77 and 78*, 1949; and *Z. Flügwiss. 4*, 30 (1956).
20. Quick, A. W. Einige Bemerkungen über Laminarprofile und über das Verhalten der laminaren Grenzschicht unter dem Einfluss von Störkörpern. *Lilienthal-Gesellschaft Bericht 141*, Supplement, 1941.
21. Tani, I., Hama, F. R., and Mituisi, S. On the effect of a single roughness element

82. Goldstein, S. *Proc. Cambridge Phil. Soc. 31, Part 2,* 232 (1935).
83. Riabouchinsky, D. *Bull. Koutchino, Fasc. V,* 1914.
84. Theodorsen, T., and Regier, A. Experiments on drag of revolving disks, cylinders, and streamline rods at high speeds. *NACA Rept. 793,* 1944.
85. Gregory, N., Stuart, J. T., and Walker, W. S. *Phil. Trans. Roy. Soc. London A248,* 155 (1955).
86. Smith, N. J. Exploratory investigation of laminar boundary layer oscillations on a rotating disk. *NACA Tech. Note 1227,* 1947.
87. Corrsin, S. Investigation of flow in an axially symmetrical heated jet of air. *NACA Wartime Rept. W*-94, 1943.
88. Hermann, R. Wärmeübergang bei freier Strömung am wagerechten Zylinder in zwei-atomigen Gasen. *Ver. deut. Ing. Berlin Forschungsheft 379,* 1936.
89. Schlichting, H. *Z. angew. Math. u. Mech. 15,* 313 (1935).
90. Prandtl, L., and Reichardt, H. Einfluss von Wärmeschichtung auf die Eigenschaften einer turbulenten Strömung. *Deut. Forschung, Part 21,* 110 (1934).
91. Sternberg, J. *J. Aeronaut. Sci. 19,* 721 (1952).
92. Laufer, J., and Marte, J. E. Results and a critical discussion of transition-Reynolds-number measurements on insulated cones and flat plates in supersonic wind tunnels. *Calif. Inst. Technol. Jet Propul. Lab. Rept. 20-96,* 1955.
93. Evvard, J. C., Tucker, M., and Burgess, W. C., Jr. Statistical study of transition-point fluctuations in supersonic flow. *NACA Tech. Note 3100,* 1954. See also *J. Aeronaut. Sci. 21,* 731 (1954).
94. Jedlicka, J. R., Wilkins, M. E., and Seiff, A. Experimental determination of boundary-layer transition on a body of revolution at $M = 3.5$. *NACA Tech. Note 3342,* 1954.
95. Ross, A. O. Determination of boundary layer transition Reynolds numbers by surface temperature measurements of a 10° cone in various NACA supersonic wind tunnels. *NACA Tech. Note 3020,* 1953.
96. Abbott, I. H. Some factors contributing to scale effect at supersonic speeds. *AGARD Mem. AG8/M4,* 1954.
97. Sinclair, A. R., and Czarnecki, K. R. Investigation of boundary-layer transition on 10° cone in Langley 4- by 4-foot supersonic pressure tunnel at Mach numbers of 1.41, 1.61, and 2.01. *NACA Tech. Note 3648,* 1956.
98. Lange, A. H., Gieseler, L. P., and Lee, R. E. *J. Aeronaut. Sci. 20,* 718 (1953).
99. Lees, L., and Lin, C. C. Investigation of the stability of the laminar boundary layer in a compressible fluid. *NACA Tech. Note 1115,* 1946.
100. Lees, L. The stability of the laminar boundary layer in a compressible fluid. *NACA Rept. 876,* 1947.
101. Probstein, R. F., and Lin, C. C. A study of the transition to turbulence of the laminar boundary layer at supersonic speeds. *Inst. Aeronaut. Sci. Preprint 596,* 1956.
102. Stalder, J. R., Rubesin, M. W., and Tendeland, T. A determination of the laminar-, transitional-, and turbulent-boundary-layer temperature-recovery factors on a flat plate in supersonic flow. *NACA Tech. Note 2077,* 1950.
103. Wilson, R. E., Young, E. C., and Thompson, M. J. 2nd interim report on experimentally determined turbulent boundary layer characteristics at supersonic speeds. *Univ. Texas Defense Research Lab. Rept. DRL-196,* 1949.
104. Coles, D. E. *J. Aeronaut. Sci. 21,* 433 (1954). See also *Calif. Inst. Technol. Propul. Lab. Rept. 20-71,* 1953.
105. Korkegi, R. H. *J. Aeronaut. Sci. 23,* 97 (1956). See also *Calif. Inst. Technol. Hypersonic Wind Tunnel Mem. 17,* 1954.
106. Brinich, P. F. Boundary layer transition at Mach 3.12 with and without single roughness elements. *NACA Tech. Note 3267,* 1954.
107. Brinich, P. F. Effect of leading-edge geometry on boundary-layer transition at Mach 3.1. *NACA Tech. Note 3659,* 1956.
108. Moeckel, W. E. Some effects of bluntness on boundary-layer transition and heat transfer at supersonic speeds. *NACA Tech. Note 3653,* 1956.
109. Bertram, M. H. Exploratory investigation of boundary-layer transition on a hollow cylinder at a Mach number of 6.9. *NACA Tech. Note 3546,* 1956.

110. Göthert, B. High speed tests in the DVL high speed wind tunnel on aerofoils of the same thickness distribution with different cambers (series NACA F3512-0.55 40). *Ministry Supply Repts. and Transls. 400*, 1947. (Transl. *Z. W. B. Forschungsbericht 1910*, 1944.)
111. Czarnecki, K. R., and Sinclair, A. R. Preliminary investigation of the effects of heat transfer on boundary layer transition on a parabolic body of revolution (NACA RM-10) at a Mach number of 1.61. *NACA Tech. Note 3165*, 1954. See also *NACA Tech. Note 3166*, 1954.
112. Hilton, J. H., Jr., and Czarnecki, K. R. An exploratory investigation of skin friction and transition on three bodies of revolution at a Mach number of 1.61. *NACA Tech. Note 3193*, 1954.
113. Potter, J. L., Jr. New experimental investigations of friction drag and boundary layer transition on bodies of revolution at supersonic speeds. *Nav. Ord. Rept. 2371*, 1952.
114. Luther, M. Fixing boundary-layer transition on supersonic-wind-tunnel models (II). *Calif. Inst. Technol. Jet Propul. Lab. Progress Rept. 20-287*, 1956.
115. Brinich, P. F. A study of boundary-layer transition and surface temperature distributions at Mach 3.12. *NACA Tech. Note 3509*, 1955.
116. Dunn, D. W., and Lin, C. C. *J. Aeronaut. Sci. 22*, 455 (1955).
117. Higgins, R. W., and Pappas, C. C. An experimental investigation of the effect of surface heating on boundary-layer transition on a flat plate in supersonic flow. *NACA Tech. Note 2351*, 1951.
118. Scherrer, R. Comparison of theoretical and experimental heat-transfer characteristics of bodies of revolution at supersonic speeds. *NACA Tech. Rept. 1055*, 1951.
119. Eber, G. R. *J. Aeronaut. Sci. 19*, 1 (1952).
120. van Driest, E. R., and Boison, J. C. *J. Aeronaut. Sci. 22*, 70 (1955).
121. Jack, J. R., and Diaconis, N. S. Variation of boundary-layer transition with heat transfer on two bodies of revolution at a Mach number of 3.12. *NACA Tech. Note 3562*, 1955.
122. Snodgrass, R. B. *Jet Propulsion 25*, 701 (1955).
123. Munk, M. *J. Aeronaut. Sci. 18*, 442 (1951).
124. Betz, A. *Naturwissenschaften 37*, 193 (1950).

# SECTION B

# *TURBULENT FLOW*

G. B. SCHUBAUER

C. M. TCHEN

## *CHAPTER 1. INTRODUCTION*

**B,1. Subject Treatment.** Since turbulent flows and their effects are encountered in nearly every case where fluid motion is involved, it becomes important to know their behavior. It is also important to understand the reason for their behavior, not only to formulate laws for practical use, but to satisfy our desire to know and to be able to explain the phenomena with which we deal.

These dual requirements have been kept in mind in writing this account, and some degree of balance has been attempted. However, greater emphasis is placed on the characteristics of mean flow resulting from the action of turbulence than on the turbulent motions themselves. Since the effects of compressibility and aerodynamic heating are assuming increasing importance in modern technology, these have been included wherever possible. The general equations of motion and energy are accordingly expressed in terms of a compressible fluid, and combined thermodynamic and aerodynamic formulations are presented in relation to boundary layer and skin friction effects at high speeds.

Due to the fact that most of the basic concepts by which we attempt to understand the behavior of turbulent flows are as yet conceived only in terms of incompressible flow, much of the subject must still be treated in these terms. Therefore the more penetrating treatment of wall-bounded flows on the one hand and free turbulent flows on the other are dealt with in terms of incompressible, isothermal flow. The specific subjects covered under these general headings are boundary layers, pipe and channel flows, jets, wakes, and mixing regions. In the case of jets the effects of compressibility and of temperature and density differences are treated.

It would be misleading to imply that complete coverage can be given to all of the varied aspects of turbulent flow in the space allotted to it here. Certain omissions are therefore inevitable. These include much of the structure of turbulent flow embracing the wealth of information derived from hot wire measurements and its theoretical interpretation. A bibliography of literature references is however supplied. This omission may be partially excused on the grounds that the reader may turn for such material to Townsend's book [*1*] on this general subject. Statistical theories of turbulence are likewise excluded, and justifiably so since they are the subject of Sec. C. Another fruitful source of information is the book by Batchelor [*2*].

**B,2. Nature of Turbulent Flow.** When entering into the subject of turbulent flow it is essential to understand that the kind of flows with which we shall be dealing belong to a particular class known as shear flows. These comprise flow fields in which relative velocities have been induced by shear stresses, and they are distinguished by having arisen in this way rather than by the action of pressures. They are therefore rotational flows as opposed to potential flows, and they are usually more restricted since their extent is governed by the range of action of the stresses. They may be bounded by solid walls or they may be free. Common examples are boundary layers, pipe and channel flows, jets, and wakes.

It is equally important that we know why we restrict ourselves to shear flow. The reason is that only in such flows can turbulent motions arise and sustain themselves. When turbulence is found in a stream that has no measurable mean shear, the turbulent motions themselves represent the decaying remnant of shear flows that existed somewhere upstream. Such a condition is not uncommon where upstream objects have created wakes. Grids or coarse screens placed across a stream are commonly used to create a homogeneous field of turbulence for experimental study. We shall not be concerned with this case.

Our main task will be to describe turbulent shear flows and to examine their laws of behavior. For the most part we shall be concerned with mean flows, but we shall have some opportunity as we go along to look into the flow itself, to find out what it contains, and to see reasons for certain behavior patterns. Some generalizations which apply to the mechanics of turbulent flows as a class can be made, and these we now take up. The more quantitative and precise aspects must be left to later articles on specific subjects. Since there is much about turbulent flow that has not been put on a firm theoretical basis, some amount of rationalization is involved, and this necessarily reflects individual viewpoints. It is hoped that the following discussion will stimulate thought and show that turbulent flow is a phenomenon that should arouse our curiosity.

We begin first with the somewhat controversial questions: What is turbulent flow, and why does it exist? When tangential stresses are applied to a fluid having internal friction, shearing motions are set up in line with the stresses and in conformity to the shape of the boundaries. Within this flow field, various kinds of secondary motions become possible. Regular ones, when they occur, are readily accounted for in terms of pressure gradients resulting from the curvature of the main flow, usually imposed by the shape of the boundaries. Irregular ones, called turbulence, are by far the more common, and their direct cause is less obvious. Their occurrence does not depend on the shape of the boundaries, but like all secondary flows, they must depend on a generating mechanism which produces motions in directions other than that of the applied shear. We must look for this mechanism within the flow itself. Our inquiry can be divided into two parts, the first having to do with how the motions begin, and the second being concerned with how the motions maintain themselves.

To consider the first part, it is necessary to recall the transition problem treated in Sec. A. In many important cases a shear flow is laminar over the initial part of its course and then becomes turbulent and remains so for the remainder of its course. According to present evidence the initial onset of turbulence occurs suddenly by a breakdown of the laminar flow in localized regions. The cause of the breakdown is attributed to instability of the laminar flow under the action of disturbances. While conditions may be altered by the roughness of a surface or pressure gradient, a characteristic feature is the completeness of the turbulent state in the patches which grow following the breakdown. It is now well known that turbulence is convected downstream in the manner of any other fluid property, and, except in special cases where the flow is impeded to such a degree that turbulence can hold its position, it is washed away from the point where it originates and is followed by laminar flow. Repeated breakdowns are therefore generally required to maintain a continuous supply of turbulence, and instability of laminar flow is an essential part of this process.

For the second part of the inquiry we turn our attention to some section downstream where all isolated patches have grown together and the flow is continuously turbulent. We now observe that turbulence which is convected on downstream is followed by other turbulence from upstream. A steady state is maintained if the turbulence leaving is as vigorous as that arriving. The question now is whether instability plays a similar role in this sustaining process as it played in initiating the turbulence originally. Evidently it does not if turbulent motions already present can reinforce themselves to counteract the damping action of viscosity. Since turbulent motions produce frictional stresses against which the mean flow does work, a mechanism does exist by which turbulent motions capture kinetic energy from the mean flow. This is expressed by the well-known production term in the energy equations, consisting of the turbulent shear stress times the mean local velocity gradient. In short, turbulence carries with it the mechanism for sustaining itself, and this is sufficient to balance losses or gains by diffusion and convection and losses by viscous damping and still maintain a steady state at each point.

Nothing has yet been said about the character of the motions themselves. Naturally we should like to know whether the sustaining mechanism dictates some particular form of motion. It is a known fact that even though the energizing of turbulence is expressible in terms of shear stresses, turbulent pressure gradients are required, and they must arise from interactions within the flow itself. These interactions can be imagined to take the form of collisions between fluid elements; but since all streams are connected, the interaction paths are curved and continuous. The resulting motions may best be described as a superposition of eddies with various orientations. The shearing action stretches the eddies with axes lying along directions in which the fluid is being strained and intensifies their vorticity. Some concentrated vortex motions can therefore be expected to exist in the complex jumble of motions.

Before we can proceed further we must consider the various scales of motion encountered in turbulent flow and examine their role. It is generally assumed that the largest scale is that characteristic of the size of the mean flow field, such as the thickness of a boundary layer. Next come the turbulent motions where the superimposed jumble of eddies have various sizes ranging from near that of the mean flow down to the so-called microscales. All turbulent motions are agents responsible for shearing stress in the presence of a mean shear, and therefore all extract energy from the mean flow to sustain themselves. However, this action decreases with decreasing scale, and from an over-all point of view it is generally assumed that the energy enters the turbulence by way of the larger eddies. Correspondingly, the damping action of viscosity is assumed to be negligible in the mean flow and among the larger eddies but to increase progressively with decreasing size until it finally becomes dominant among the smallest eddies. The effect of viscosity is the more removed from the larger eddies as the Reynolds number becomes higher.

It is obvious that if energy enters the turbulence more by way of the large eddies than by the small ones and leaves more by way of the small eddies than by the large ones, there must be a transfer of energy from larger scales to smaller scales. The succession of transfer is generally regarded as taking place from size to size down the scale, with the number of stages increasing with the Reynolds number.

Except for the laminar sublayer next to a wall and its immediate vicinity, it is an observed fact that if the Reynolds number is sufficiently high for transition to have occurred, the succession of transfer is already long. In the usual terms, the turbulent energy spectrum is broad. This signifies that turbulent flows as a class show comparatively minor effects of Reynolds number in their over-all character. The mean velocity distribution, for example, changes little with Reynolds number, and the mean flow field shows a tendency to remain similar in form as it grows to larger sizes. The turbulent velocities which contain the bulk of the turbulent energy likewise tend to maintain a constant ratio to the mean local velocity. This general condition is termed "Reynolds number similarity." This and the related property of preservation of form from section to section, commonly called "self preservation," are very important features of turbulent flow. They give to the flow a permanence of form and a continuity of behavior that simplify description and make possible certain general laws.

**B,3. Diffusiveness of Turbulence.** It is a well-known fact that frictional effects, mean velocity distributions, rate of spreading, and other features of turbulent flow bear little resemblance to those found in laminar flow. These differences can be attributed to a diffusiveness of turbulence that far exceeds molecular diffusion and has a more intimate connection with the mean flow. The mechanism of turbulent diffusion is commonly compared to that of molecular diffusion wherein a molecule moves and collides with another and so by a process of random walk migrates farther and farther from some initial point. Turbulent movements may also be likened to a random walk, and now bulk currents wander randomly in generally curved paths producing a cumulative increase in the distance from an initial point.

Except for the region near a wall where turbulent movements are inhibited, the bulk-lot transfers by turbulent motions so surpass transfer by molecular motions that the latter has little effect other than to smooth out the spotty condition of properties in their new neighborhood. Thus, molecular diffusion may often be neglected as far as the rate of transport is concerned. Where it cannot be neglected, molecular and turbulent diffusion are assumed to be additive.

When we concern ourselves with mean flow, we intentionally ignore the turbulent motions themselves and deal in effect with a fictitious "laminar flow" of a fluid behaving as though it had special properties. The analogy to laminar flow involves endowing the fluid with properties called "eddy viscosity" and "eddy heat conductivity," or more generally, "eddy diffusion coefficient." If we attempt to account for behavior in terms of an eddy viscosity, our fluid appears to be a very peculiar one. It might be described as non-Newtonian because of the dependence of the viscosity on rate of shear. We find further that the viscosity varies from point to point in one part of the flow and remains practically constant in other parts. Moreover, the numerical value is often hundreds of times larger than that of ordinary viscosity and bears no definite relation to it. What is even more unconventional is the fact that eddy viscosity increases with the size of the flow field and increases with over-all velocity. The fluid flow in a large pipe, for example, behaves as though it had a larger viscosity than the same fluid flowing in a small pipe. Furthermore, at high rates of flow the viscosity appears to be larger than at low rates of flow.

Our fictitious fluid properties are governed by an intimate connection to the flow itself, and the apparent anomalies arise because of this fact. As we know, the transporting agents are the turbulent motions, and taken as a whole their velocities are proportional to some velocity characterizing that of the mean flow. This connection between transporting motions and the flow field stands in marked contrast to the independence of molecular motions which do the transporting in laminar flow.

In every case we must refer back to the turbulence mechanisms in order ultimately to understand any kind of property with which we have endowed the fluid. Phenomenological theories have been employed for this purpose, of which one of the better known examples is the mixing length theory proposed by Prandtl. Ideally, of course, we should like to use the fundamental equations of motion for this purpose, but so far this has not been possible. These questions are discussed in more detail in Art. 10.

## *CHAPTER 2. GENERAL HYDRODYNAMICAL EQUATIONS FOR THE TURBULENT MOTION OF A COMPRESSIBLE FLUID*

**B,4. Equations of Continuity and Momentum.** The procedure introduced by Reynolds [*3*] and Lorentz [*4*], whereby equations of motion and energy balance for an incompressible turbulent flow are obtained, is well known. Briefly the turbulent motion is regarded as consisting of the sum of a mean part and a fluctuating part, and the sum is introduced into the Navier-Stokes equations. The resulting equations give considerable insight into the character of turbulent motions and serve as a basis for attacking mean flow problems and also for analyzing the turbulence into harmonic components.

We now follow the same procedure for compressible turbulent flow. The purpose in doing this is primarily to investigate the coupling between the mean motion and its fluctuations, and to establish the general fundamental equations from which some general properties become apparent. Later on, these equations may be simplified by approximations retaining the significant terms applicable in a particular problem, such as the customary boundary layer approximations.

The additional difficulties encountered in compressible turbulent flow are two-fold: First, the hydrodynamical equations are nonlinear, with the nonlinear terms not only containing the velocity components and their derivatives, such as was the case for incompressible flow, but also containing the product of velocity by density. The latter must moreover satisfy the conditions imposed by the equation of continuity and the equation of heat conduction. Second, in an incompressible flow the Reynolds equations have a form similar to the original Navier-Stokes equations, provided additional fictitious forces, called Reynolds stresses, are introduced. These stresses also characterize the turbulent friction and give the rate of production of turbulence when multiplied by mean velocity gradients. However, in a compressible flow, such fictitious stresses are more complicated and involve other roles in addition to the production of turbulence.

It is well to mention briefly why averages are used and what they mean. Turbulent motions of fluid elements are so complex that they cannot be treated individually. By averaging we can obtain mean motions which include turbulent properties statistically. The average can be taken at a given point over a certain interval of time, or over a certain region at a particular instant of time, or finally over a great number of realizations represented by identical fields at corresponding points and instants. These are the three kinds of Eulerian mean values, termed respectively, temporal, spatial, and statistical mean values. Finally we can follow the motion of an individual particle as a function of time and find the temporal and statistical mean value of any physical property associated with the particle. This would be the Lagrangian mean value. It is beyond our scope to discuss the different mean values. We shall adhere to the Eulerian description in which any one of the three averages may be used as far as the formalism is concerned. Commonly used methods of measurement and observation require the use of the temporal mean value, and this mean value will subsequently be inferred. The time interval does not need to be considered for present purposes, especially when we are concerned with steady motion.

The motion of the fluid is decomposed into a mean motion with velocity components $U_i$ parallel to the $x_i$ axis, with the running indices $i = 1, 2, 3$, and the superimposed turbulent motions or fluctuations, with velocity components $u_i$.[1] The velocity components of the total motion will be $U_i + u_i$. Likewise the scalar quantities, pressure, density, and temperature are also decomposed into their mean parts and fluctuating parts, and are respectively

$$\bar{p} + p', \quad \rho = \bar{\rho} + \rho', \quad T = \overline{T} + T'$$

where $\bar{p}$ denotes the mean pressure and $p'$ its fluctuations, and $\rho$ and $T$

[1] In this section as well as in Sec. C a departure from the usual notation of the Series wherein $\bar{u}$ is used to denote the mean velocity in the $x$ direction and $u'$ the fluctuation about its mean value has been necessary in order to eliminate the confusion that would result in referring to the fluctuations that might exist simultaneously at two points.

are respectively the instantaneous local density and the instantaneous local temperature. The bars denote mean parts, and the primes denote turbulent parts. Other physical quantities like viscosity, coefficient of heat condition, and specific heat are considered to have negligible fluctuating parts compared to their mean parts.

The Navier-Stokes equation for the total motion is written as follows:

$$(\bar{\rho} + \rho')\left[\frac{\partial}{\partial t} + (U_j + u_j)\frac{\partial}{\partial x_j}\right](U_i + u_i) = \frac{\partial}{\partial x_j}(\sigma_{ji} + \sigma'_{ji}) \tag{4-1}$$

Here $\sigma_{ji}$ is a stress tensor [5, p. 574] defined by

$$\sigma_{ji} = -\left(\bar{p} + \frac{2}{3}\mu\bar{\zeta}\right)\delta_{ij} + \mu\left(\frac{\partial U_j}{\partial x_i} + \frac{\partial U_i}{\partial x_j}\right) \tag{4-2}$$

where $\zeta = \partial(U_k + u_k)/\partial x_k$; $\bar{\zeta} = \partial U_k/\partial x_k$; $\zeta' = \partial u_k/\partial x_k$; $\mu$ is the viscosity supposed to be variable, but with a negligible fluctuating part; and $\delta_{ji}$ is the Kronecker delta having the value 1 for $i = j$ and 0 for $i \neq j$. In those equations a summation is understood for repeated indices.[2] A similar expression for $\sigma'_{ji}$ can be written but this is omitted here.

The variables $U_i$ and $u_i$ must moreover satisfy the equation of continuity

$$\frac{\partial}{\partial t}(\bar{\rho} + \rho') + \frac{\partial}{\partial x_j}[(\bar{\rho} + \rho')(U_j + u_j)] = 0 \tag{4-3}$$

With the aid of Eq. 4-3, the equation of motion (Eq. 4-1) may also be written in the following form:

$$\frac{\partial}{\partial t}[(\bar{\rho} + \rho')(U_i + u_i)] = \frac{\partial}{\partial x_j}[(\sigma_{ji} + \sigma'_{ji}) - (\bar{\rho} + \rho')(U_i + u_i)(U_j + u_j)] \tag{4-4}$$

One way of obtaining the momentum equations for the mean and fluctuating motions is to start from Eq. 4-4 instead of Eq. 4-1. By averaging we obtain the following momentum equation for the mean motion:

$$\frac{\partial}{\partial t}(\bar{\rho}U_i + \overline{\rho' u_i}) + \frac{\partial}{\partial x_j}(\bar{\rho}U_iU_j) = \frac{\partial \sigma_{ji}}{\partial x_j} - \frac{\partial}{\partial x_j}[\overline{\rho u_i u_j} + U_j\overline{\rho' u_i} + U_i\overline{\rho' u_j}] \tag{4-5}$$

Similarly by averaging Eq. 4-3, the continuity equation for the mean motion is

$$\frac{\partial \bar{\rho}}{\partial t} + \frac{\partial}{\partial x_j}(\bar{\rho}U_j + \overline{\rho' u_j}) = 0 \tag{4-6}$$

Corresponding equations could be written for the fluctuating motion, but this will not be done.

[2] The indicial notations are advantageous in the general discussion of the equations of motion. However, in the following articles when dealing with properties in two dimensions the indicial notations will usually be abandoned in favor of $x$, $y$, $U$, and $V$.

**B,5. Equation of Kinetic Energy.** The equation of kinetic energy for the mean motion is obtained by multiplying Eq. 4-5 by $U_i$. We obtain, after some transformation,

$$\frac{\partial}{\partial t}\left(\frac{1}{2}\bar{\rho}U_i^2\right) + \frac{\partial}{\partial x_j}\left(\frac{1}{2}\bar{\rho}U_i^2U_j\right) + U_i\left[\frac{\partial}{\partial t}(\overline{\rho' u_i}) + \frac{\partial}{\partial x_j}(\overline{\rho' u_i}U_j)\right]$$

$$= -\frac{\partial}{\partial x_j}[U_i(\bar{p}\delta_{ij} + \overline{\rho u_i u_j}) + \tfrac{1}{2}\overline{\rho' u_j}U_i^2]$$

$$+ \frac{\partial U_i}{\partial x_j}(\bar{p}\delta_{ij} + \overline{\rho u_i u_j}) - \varphi_0 \quad (5\text{-}1)$$

where

$$\varphi_0 = -U_i\frac{\partial}{\partial x_j}\left[-\frac{2}{3}\mu\bar{\zeta}\delta_{ij} + \mu\left(\frac{\partial U_j}{\partial x_i} + \frac{\partial U_i}{\partial x_j}\right)\right]$$

$$= \Phi_0 - \frac{\partial}{\partial x_j}\left\{U_i\left[-\frac{2}{3}\mu\bar{\zeta}\delta_{ij} + \mu\left(\frac{\partial U_j}{\partial x_i} + \frac{\partial U_i}{\partial x_j}\right)\right]\right\} \quad (5\text{-}2a)$$

and $\Phi_0$ is defined by

$$\Phi_0 = -\frac{2}{3}\mu\bar{\zeta}^2 + \frac{1}{2}\mu\left(\frac{\partial U_j}{\partial x_i} + \frac{\partial U_i}{\partial x_j}\right)^2 \quad (5\text{-}2b)$$

It is remarked that $\Phi_0$ is the Rayleigh dissipation function [*5*, p. 580]. In deriving Eq. 5-1, use has been made of Eq. 4-6. On the left-hand side of Eq. 5-1, we have the rate of change of kinetic energy,

$$\frac{\partial}{\partial t}\left(\frac{1}{2}\bar{\rho}U_i^2\right) + \frac{\partial}{\partial x_j}\left(\frac{1}{2}\bar{\rho}U_i^2U_j\right)$$

and the convection by density fluctuations,

$$U_i\left[\frac{\partial}{\partial t}(\overline{\rho' u_i}) + \frac{\partial}{\partial x_j}(\overline{\rho' u_i}U_j)\right]$$

On the right-hand side of Eq. 5-1, the term

$$\frac{\partial}{\partial x_j}[U_i(\bar{p}\delta_{ij} + \overline{\rho u_i u_j}) + \tfrac{1}{2}\overline{\rho' u_j}U_i^2]$$

accounts for the diffusion of energy by turbulence and pressure; the term $\overline{p'\zeta}$ represents the rate of change of energy due to expansion; the term $\overline{\rho u_i u_j}\partial U_i/\partial x_j$ is the rate of production of turbulent energy from the energy of the mean flow, as a result of Reynolds stresses $\overline{\rho u_i u_j}$; and finally the term $\varphi_0$, as given by Eq. 5-2a, is the action of viscosity, which takes the form of a dissipation $\Phi_0$, and a spatial transfer

$$-\frac{\partial}{\partial x_j}\left\{U_i\left[-\frac{2}{3}\mu\bar{\zeta}\delta_{ij} + \mu\left(\frac{\partial U_j}{\partial x_i} + \frac{\partial U_i}{\partial x_j}\right)\right]\right\} \equiv \varphi_0 - \Phi_0 \quad (5\text{-}3a)$$

It is remarked that the Reynolds stresses $\overline{\rho u_i u_j}$ which characterize the important nonlinear mechanism in the turbulent transfer, occur in two places, namely in the diffusion and in the production.

It is much easier to derive the equation of total kinetic energy, $K = \frac{1}{2}(U_i^2 + u_i^2)$. It suffices simply to multiply Eq. 4-4 by $(U_i + u_i)$ and obtain, after some transformation,

$$\frac{\partial}{\partial t}(\bar{\rho}\bar{K}) + \frac{\partial}{\partial x_j}(\bar{\rho}\bar{K}U_j) = -\frac{\partial}{\partial t}\overline{\rho' K'} - \frac{\partial}{\partial x_j}(\overline{\rho' u_j K'} + \bar{\rho}\overline{u_j K'} + U_j\overline{\rho' K'} + \bar{K}\,\overline{\rho' u_j}) - U_j\frac{\partial \bar{p}}{\partial x_j} - \overline{u_j\frac{\partial p'}{\partial x_j}} - \bar{\varphi} \tag{5-4}$$

where

$$\varphi = \Phi - \frac{\partial}{\partial x_j}\left\{(U_i + u_i)\left[-\frac{2}{3}\mu\zeta\delta_{ij} + \mu\left(\frac{\partial U_j}{\partial x_i} + \frac{\partial U_i}{\partial x_j} + \frac{\partial u_j}{\partial x_i} + \frac{\partial u_i}{\partial x_j}\right)\right]\right\} \tag{5-2c}$$

$$\Phi = -\frac{2}{3}\mu\zeta^2 + \frac{1}{2}\mu\left(\frac{\partial U_j}{\partial x_i} + \frac{\partial U_i}{\partial x_j} + \frac{\partial u_j}{\partial x_i} + \frac{\partial u_i}{\partial x_j}\right)^2 \tag{5-2d}$$

The quantities $\bar{\varphi}$ and $\bar{\Phi}$ can be easily obtained by taking the mean values of Eq. 5-2c and 5-2d. Reynolds stress terms are included in Eq. 5-4 but only as diffusion terms. There is no energy production term associated with these stresses such as we find in Eq. 5-1 for the kinetic energy of mean motion. This is not surprising since the Reynolds stresses, which transfer energy from the mean motion into turbulent motion, must have a vanishing balance in the production of the total kinetic energy by reason of conservation. The molecular motion contributes a pure dissipation $\bar{\Phi}$ and a spatial transfer $\bar{\varphi} - \bar{\Phi}$ which plays the role of viscous diffusion of energy. Its structure can be clarified by transforming either Eq. 5-2c or 5-3a. For the sake of abbreviation, let us take Eq. 5-3a and rewrite it as follows:

$$\Phi_0 - \varphi_0 = -\frac{2}{3}\mu\bar{\zeta}^2 + \frac{1}{3}U_j\frac{\partial \mu\bar{\zeta}}{\partial x_j} + \frac{\mu}{2}\left(\frac{\partial U_j}{\partial x_i} + \frac{\partial U_i}{\partial x_j}\right)^2 + U_i\frac{\partial}{\partial x_j}\left(\mu\frac{\partial U_i}{\partial x_j}\right) + U_i\frac{\partial \mu}{\partial x_j}\left(\frac{\partial U_j}{\partial x_i} - \bar{\zeta}\delta_{ij}\right)$$

$$= \frac{1}{3}\mu\bar{\zeta}^2 + \frac{1}{3}U_j\frac{\partial \mu\bar{\zeta}}{\partial x_j} + \mu\left(\frac{\partial U_i}{\partial x_j}\frac{\partial U_j}{\partial x_i} - \frac{\partial U_i}{\partial x_i}\frac{\partial U_j}{\partial x_j}\right) + \frac{\partial \mu}{\partial x_j}U_i\left(\frac{\partial U_j}{\partial x_i} + \frac{\partial U_i}{\partial x_j} - \bar{\zeta}\delta_{ij}\right) + \mu\frac{\partial^2}{\partial x_j^2}\left(\frac{U_i^2}{2}\right)$$

Let us introduce

$$\chi_0 = \Phi_0 - \varphi_0 - \mu\frac{\partial^2}{\partial x_j^2}\left(\frac{U_i^2}{2}\right) \tag{5-3b}$$

Then we obtain

$$\chi_0 = \frac{1}{3}\mu\bar{\zeta}^2 + \frac{1}{3}U_j\frac{\partial\mu\bar{\zeta}}{\partial x_j} + \mu\left(\frac{\partial U_i}{\partial x_j}\frac{\partial U_j}{\partial x_i} - \frac{\partial U_i}{\partial x_i}\frac{\partial U_j}{\partial x_j}\right)$$

$$+ \frac{\partial\mu}{\partial x_j}U_i\left(\frac{\partial U_j}{\partial x_i} + \frac{\partial U_i}{\partial x_j} - \bar{\zeta}\delta_{ij}\right) \quad \text{(5-3c)}$$

The last term vanishes if $\mu$ is taken as constant. The third term is not important, as can be shown by special examples, for instance, a boundary layer flow. The other terms are also not important if the effect of the compressibility is small. Hence $\Phi_0 - \varphi_0$ has predominantly the function of a spatial transfer. Similar formulas for $\Phi - \varphi$, $\bar{\Phi} - \bar{\varphi}$, or $\Phi' - \varphi'$ can readily be obtained, and so also can formulas for $\chi$, $\bar{\chi}$, and $\chi'$, for example,

$$\bar{\chi} = \frac{1}{3}\overline{\zeta'^2} + \frac{1}{3}\overline{u_j\frac{\partial\mu\zeta'}{\partial x_j}} + \mu\left(\overline{\frac{\partial u_i}{\partial x_j}\frac{\partial u_j}{\partial x_i}} - \overline{\frac{\partial u_i}{\partial x_i}\frac{\partial u_j}{\partial x_j}}\right) + \chi_0 \quad \text{(5-3d)}$$

**B,6. Equation of Energy and Enthalpy.** The production and transfer of heat in a turbulent flow is now considered. The derivation of the energy equation for the total motion is well known (see [*6*, p. 603] and also [*7*, p. 57]) and need not be repeated here. It is written as follows for constant specific heat and for variable thermal conductivity and viscosity:

$$(\bar{\rho} + \rho')\left[\frac{\partial}{\partial t} + (U_j + u_j)\frac{\partial}{\partial x_j}\right]\left[c_p(\bar{T} + T')\right]$$

$$- \left[\frac{\partial}{\partial t} + (U_j + u_j)\frac{\partial}{\partial x_j}\right](\bar{p} + p') = \Phi + \frac{\partial}{\partial x_j}\left[k\frac{\partial}{\partial x_j}(\bar{T} + T')\right] \quad \text{(6-1)}$$

where $c_p$ is the specific heat at constant pressure; $k$ is the thermal conductivity; $\bar{p}$, $p'$ are the mean and fluctuating pressures; $\bar{T}$, $T'$ are the mean and fluctuating temperatures; $\Phi$ is the dissipation function defined by Eq. 5-2d; and $c_p\bar{T}$ is the mean enthalpy. The energy equation (Eq. 6-1) can be separated into an equation for the mean motion and an equation for the fluctuating motion. Since the need for the latter equation is presently not apparent, only the energy equation for mean motion is developed and written as follows:

$$\frac{\partial}{\partial t}(\bar{\rho}c_p\bar{T}) + \frac{\partial}{\partial x_j}(\bar{\rho}c_p\bar{T}U_j) - \left[\frac{\partial\bar{p}}{\partial t} + \frac{\partial}{\partial x_j}(U_j\bar{p})\right] + \frac{\partial}{\partial t}(c_p\overline{\rho'T'})$$

$$+ \frac{\partial}{\partial x_j}(c_p\overline{\rho'T'}U_j) = - \frac{\partial}{\partial x_j}\left(c_p\overline{\rho T'u_j} + \overline{\rho'u_j}\bar{T} - \overline{u_jp'} - k\frac{\partial\bar{T}}{\partial x_j}\right)$$

$$- \left(\bar{p}\frac{\partial U_k}{\partial x_k} + \overline{p'\frac{\partial u_k}{\partial x_k}}\right) + \bar{\Phi} \quad \text{(6-2)}$$

Finally, by introducing the mean and fluctuating value of the total energy content per unit mass $E^0$, $E$, $\overline{E}$, and $E'$, such that

$$E^0 = c_p\overline{T} + \tfrac{1}{2}U_i^2$$

$$E = c_p(\overline{T} + T') + \tfrac{1}{2}(U_i + u_i)^2$$

$$\overline{E} = c_p\overline{T} + \tfrac{1}{2}(U_i^2 + \overline{u_i^2})$$

$$E' = E - \overline{E}$$

and adding Eq. 5-1 to Eq. 6-2, we obtain

$$\frac{D}{Dt}(\bar{\rho}E^0) + U_i\frac{D}{Dt}(\overline{\rho' u_i}) + \frac{D}{Dt}(c_p\overline{\rho' T'}) - \left(\frac{\partial\bar{p}}{\partial t} + \overline{u_j\frac{\partial p'}{\partial x_j}}\right)$$

$$= -\frac{\partial}{\partial x_j}\left(\overline{\rho' u_j}E^0 + U_i\overline{\rho u_i u_j} + c_p\overline{\rho T' u_j} - k\frac{\partial\overline{T}}{\partial x_j}\right) + \overline{\rho u_i u_j}\frac{\partial U_i}{\partial x_j} + \Phi_0 - \varphi_0 \tag{6-3a}$$

where the operator $D/Dt$ on any function $f$ denotes

$$\frac{Df}{Dt} = \frac{\partial f}{\partial t} + \frac{\partial}{\partial x_j}(fU_j)$$

The left-hand side of Eq. 6-3a expresses the rate of change of quantities $\bar{\rho}E^0$, $\overline{\rho' u_i}$, $\overline{\rho' T'}$, and $\bar{p}$. These rates are the result of diffusion and turbulent energy production expressed by the terms on the right-hand side. Here we find the production term $-\overline{\rho u_i u_j}\partial U_i/\partial x_j$ which decreases the energy of mean motion, and diffusion terms within the brackets which include Reynolds stress terms of transport of mass and temperature along with the better-known term $\overline{\rho u_i u_j}$. Here also is the molecular contribution expressed by $\Phi_0 - \varphi_0$, which we have already noted in Eq. 5-3 as a spatial transfer and not an energy dissipation. No molecular dissipation appears in Eq. 6-3a because the kinetic energy dissipated appears in the form of heat.

The corresponding equation for $\bar{E}$ may be obtained by adding Eq. 5-4 and 6-2. Thus

$$\frac{\partial}{\partial t}(\bar{\rho}\overline{E}) + \frac{\partial}{\partial x_j}(\bar{\rho}\overline{E}U_j) + \frac{\partial}{\partial t}(\overline{\rho' E'})$$

$$= -\frac{\partial}{\partial x_j}\left(\bar{\rho}\overline{u_j E'} + \overline{\rho' u_j}\overline{E} + \overline{\rho' u_j E'} + U_j\overline{\rho' E'} - k\frac{\partial\overline{T}}{\partial x_j}\right) + \overline{\Phi} - \overline{\varphi} \tag{6-4a}$$

As would be expected, Eq. 6-4a, which accounts for both the mean and the turbulent energy, is of simpler form and does not contain the production term $\overline{\rho u_i u_j}\partial U_i/\partial x_j$.

The diffusion terms in the energy equations (Eq. 6-3a and 6-4a) contain the thermal diffusion with flux $k\partial\overline{T}/\partial x_j$. This may be expressed as an energy diffusion $\partial E^0/\partial x_j$ or $\partial \bar{E}/\partial x_j$ if we introduce $\chi_0$ according to Eq. 5-3c and $\bar{\chi}$ according to Eq. 5 3d. In this way, Eq. 6-3a and 6-4a become respectively

$$\frac{D}{Dt}(\bar{\rho}E^0) + U_i\frac{D}{Dt}(\overline{\rho' u_i}) + \frac{D}{Dt}(c_p\overline{\rho' T'}) - \left(\frac{\partial \bar{p}}{\partial t} + \overline{u_j \frac{\partial p'}{\partial x_j}}\right)$$

$$= -\frac{\partial}{\partial x_j}\left(\overline{\rho' u_j}E^0 + U_i\overline{\rho u_i u_j} + c_p\overline{\rho T' u_j} - \frac{k}{c_p}\frac{\partial E^0}{\partial x_j}\right)$$

$$-\frac{\partial}{\partial x_j}\left[\mu\left(\frac{1}{Pr} - 1\right)\frac{\partial}{\partial x_j}\left(\frac{U_i^2}{2}\right)\right] + \chi_0 \quad \text{(6-3b)}$$

$$\frac{\partial}{\partial t}(\bar{\rho}\bar{E}) + \frac{\partial}{\partial x_j}(\bar{\rho}\bar{E}U_j) + \frac{\partial}{\partial t}(\overline{\rho' E'})$$

$$= -\frac{\partial}{\partial x_j}\left(\bar{\rho}\overline{u_j E'} + \overline{\rho' u_j}\bar{E} + \overline{\rho' u_j E'} + U_j\overline{\rho' E'} - \frac{k}{c_p}\frac{\partial \bar{E}}{\partial x_j}\right)$$

$$-\frac{\partial}{\partial x_j}\left[\frac{1}{2}\mu\left(\frac{1}{Pr} - 1\right)\frac{\partial}{\partial x_j}(U_i^2 + \overline{u_i^2})\right] + \bar{\chi} \quad \text{(6-4b)}$$

where $Pr = \mu c_p/k$ is the Prandtl number. The specific heat $c_p$ is taken as constant. Eq. 6-3b and 6-4b become much simpler if $Pr = 1$, and if $\chi_0$ and $\bar{\chi}$ are negligible.

Since in the incompressible case $\mu$ = const, $Pr = 1$ and $\chi_0 = \bar{\chi} = 0$, we can reduce Eq. 6-3b and 6-4b respectively to

$$\frac{D}{Dt}(\rho E^0) - \left(\frac{\partial \bar{p}}{\partial t} + \overline{u_j \frac{\partial p'}{\partial x_j}}\right) = -\frac{\partial}{\partial x_j}\left(U_i\rho\overline{u_i u_j} + c_p\rho\overline{T' u_j} - \frac{k}{c_p}\frac{\partial E^0}{\partial x_j}\right) \quad \text{(6-3c)}$$

$$\frac{D}{Dt}(\rho\bar{E}) = -\frac{\partial}{\partial x_j}\left(\rho\overline{u_j E'} - \frac{k}{c_p}\frac{\partial \bar{E}}{\partial x_j}\right) \quad \text{(6-4c)}$$

Eq. 6-4c is the well-known equation of turbulent heat transfer in an incompressible flow. Here $\rho\overline{u_j E'}$ is the flux of energy transported by turbulent diffusion.

# *CHAPTER 3. TURBULENT BOUNDARY LAYER OF A COMPRESSIBLE FLUID*

**B,7. Introduction.** When a fluid flows past the solid boundary of a body, a shear flow results. The condition of no-slip requires that the fluid immediately in contact with the wall be brought to rest. Next to it the fluid is retarded by the internal shear stresses. The retardation decreases with increasing distance from the wall and becomes vanishingly small in a relatively short distance. The layer in which this occurs is called the boundary layer. A knowledge of the flow behavior within this layer is of prime importance, especially when effects associated with compressibility and aerodynamic heating come into play.

The turbulent boundary layer occurs more generally than the laminar boundary layer, but is less well understood theoretically. The exceedingly complex character of turbulent flow and the inadequacy of theories of turbulence make an exact mathematical treatment of the flow impossible at present. Therefore a great number of approximations are necessary, and it is to be expected that the various proposed theories may turn out different results which are not always reconcilable. In order to clarify many obscure points in the theories, and to display in a simple manner the essential physical features governing boundary layer flow, it seems worthwhile to outline the main approaches of the analytical treatments, and especially to elucidate the bases and assumptions underlying the theories. Where possible the theoretical results will be compared with existing experimental results.

First the fundamental hydrodynamic equations, as developed earlier, will be simplified in Art. 8 under the special conditions of the boundary layer. Consequently some simple relations between pressure, temperature, and velocity can be derived in Art. 9. These will at once show some features of heat transfer in the boundary layer, and especially of the recovery factor, without going into the turbulent transport processes. For a deeper understanding of the problems, some statistical methods of transport phenomena become necessary. Existing theories make extensive use of the concept of mixing length as a parameter of the turbulent exchange of properties. Since several fundamental questions arise in connection with the application of mixing length to various types of transport (mass, momentum, and heat) governing the boundary layer, and in the analogy theories between heat transfer and skin friction (the so-called Reynolds analogy), the statistical foundation of the transport processes will be studied in Art. 10. As an immediate application, the Reynolds analogy can be better understood and will be treated in Art. 11.

Theories relating to velocity profiles in a compressible turbulent boundary layer do not seem to differ much from the corresponding theories for the incompressible boundary layer, especially concerning their basis and method of attack. Therefore we shall reserve these for Chap. 4 where incompressibility is assumed, and be content here to give only some experimental data on the velocity distribution.

The skin friction in a compressible boundary layer deserves special attention, because of its important compressibility effect and its practical significance. The basis of the theories will be described in Art. 12; the empirical formulas illustrating the essential behavior of skin friction will be given in Art. 13; and finally the comparison between theories and experiments will be given in Art. 14. Since no unique theory has evolved, the emphasis will be placed on the description and discussion of the bases and assumptions underlying the theoretical treatments rather than their detailed analysis. Experimental data will be compared with theories. This method of approach seems best to show the present state of the subject and to serve as a guide to future theoretical and experimental investigations.

**B,8. Fundamental Equations of Motion of a Compressible Boundary Layer.** When applying the hydrodynamic equations of Art. 4, 5, and 6 to the boundary layer developed on a flat plate with steady free stream velocity, certain simplifying approximations may be made. First of all, the mean flow is assumed two-dimensional with mean velocities denoted by $U$ and $V$ in the $x$ and $y$ directions respectively, where $x$ is the coordinate parallel to the plate, measured from the leading edge, and $y$ is normal to the wall. The turbulence is still three-dimensional, with components $u$, $v$, and $w$ in the $x$, $y$, and $z$ directions.

We now consider the order of magnitude of terms involved in the hydrodynamic equations. If $U$ is taken as a magnitude of standard order $0(1)$, and the thickness of the boundary layer $\delta$ is small compared to the distance $x$, it follows that $\partial/\partial t$, $\partial/\partial x$, $\partial^2/\partial x^2 \sim 0(1)$, and $\partial/\partial y \sim 0(\delta^{-1})$, $\partial^2/\partial y^2 \sim 0(\delta^{-2})$. Also we assume that $V \sim 0(\delta)$, the mean density $\bar{\rho}$ is $0(1)$, and the total energy content per unit mass $\bar{E}$ is $0(1)$. If the viscous term of Eq. 4-5 is to be at most of the same order as the remaining terms, then it follows that $\mu$ is at most of the order of $\delta^2$. By the same reasoning, the correlations involving $u, v, \rho', T'$, such as $\overline{uv}$, $\overline{uT'}$; $\overline{vT'}$; $\overline{\rho'u}$, $\overline{\rho'v}$, $\overline{\rho'T'}$, are at most of the order of $\delta$, while the triple correlation $\rho'uv$ will be at most of the order of $\delta^2$.

Retaining the predominant terms of the same order of magnitude, we can easily reduce the dynamic equations (Eq. 4-5, 4-6, and 6-4a) respectively to the following forms:

$$\frac{\partial}{\partial t}(\bar{\rho}U) + \frac{\partial}{\partial x}(\bar{\rho}U^2) + \frac{\partial}{\partial y}(\bar{\rho}UV) = -\frac{\partial \bar{p}}{\partial x} + \frac{\partial}{\partial y}\left(\mu\frac{\partial U}{\partial y} - \bar{\rho}\overline{uv} - U\overline{\rho'v}\right) \tag{8-1}$$

$$-\frac{\partial \bar{p}}{\partial y} - \frac{\partial}{\partial y}(\bar{\rho}\overline{v^2}) = 0 \tag{8-2}$$

$$\frac{\partial \bar{\rho}}{\partial t} + \frac{\partial}{\partial x}(\bar{\rho}U) + \frac{\partial}{\partial y}(\bar{\rho}V) + \frac{\partial}{\partial y}(\overline{\rho'v}) = 0 \tag{8-3}$$

$$\frac{\partial}{\partial t}(\bar{\rho}\bar{E}) + \frac{\partial}{\partial x}(\bar{\rho}\bar{E}U) + \frac{\partial}{\partial y}(\bar{\rho}\bar{E}V)$$

$$= \frac{\partial}{\partial y}\left(\frac{\partial \bar{E}}{\partial y} - \bar{\rho}\overline{vE'} - \overline{\rho'vE}\right) + \frac{\partial}{\partial y}\left[\left(\frac{1}{Pr} - 1\right)\mu\frac{\partial(c_p\bar{T})}{\partial y}\right] \tag{8-4}$$

Similarly from Eq. 6-3a with the same order of approximations we obtain

$$\frac{\partial}{\partial t}(\bar{\rho}E^0) + \frac{\partial}{\partial x}(\bar{\rho}E^0U) + \frac{\partial}{\partial y}(\bar{\rho}E^0V) = \frac{\partial}{\partial y}\left(\mu\frac{\partial E^0}{\partial y} - \bar{\rho}\overline{vE'} - \overline{\rho' v}E^0\right)$$
$$+ \frac{\partial}{\partial y}\left[\left(\frac{1}{Pr} - 1\right)\mu\frac{\partial}{\partial y}(c_p\bar{T})\right] + \bar{\rho}\overline{uv}\frac{\partial U}{\partial y} \quad (8\text{-}5)$$

Except for the production term $\bar{\rho}\overline{uv}\partial U/\partial y$, Eq. 8-4 and 8-5 have the same form. In the following we shall be concerned with Eq. 8-4 rather than Eq. 8-5.

Eq. 8-1, 8-2, 8-3, 8-4, and 8-5 form a system of basic equations of the compressible boundary layer. The effects of the density fluctuation are to contribute an additional Reynolds stress, an apparent source, and an additional eddy conductivity respectively in the equations of momentum, continuity, and energy.

**B,9. Relationships between Velocity, Pressure, and Temperature Distributions.** Some simple relations are now derived for velocity, pressure, and temperature by integrating the momentum and energy equations. This is done here without entering into the mechanism of turbulence in the boundary layer. We consider a steady boundary layer, with strictly parallel flow (all average quantities depend only on the coordinate $y$).

First by integrating the momentum equation (Eq. 8-2) from $y$ to $\delta$, where $\delta$ is the thickness of the boundary layer, we obtain

$$\bar{p} = \bar{p}_e + \bar{\rho}\overline{v^2}$$
$$= \bar{p}_e\left(1 + \gamma M_e^2 \frac{\bar{\rho}\overline{v^2}}{\bar{\rho}_e U_e^2}\right) \quad (9\text{-}1)$$

since $M_e^2 = \rho_e U_e^2/\gamma\bar{p}_e$. Here quantities without subscript are taken at the coordinate $y$, while subscript $_e$ denotes the quantity at the edge of the boundary layer. For future reference, superscript $^0$ denotes the total or stagnation value, and subscript $_w$ denotes the value at the wall ($y = 0$). The assumption of a constant pressure within the boundary layer is valid if the free stream Mach number is of the order of 0(1), and if the previous assumption of small turbulence level ($\overline{v^2}/U^2 \ll 1$) is made.

For the derivation of energy relations, the following conventional boundary conditions are used:

$$\text{At } y = 0: \quad U = 0,\ V = 0,\ u = 0,\ v = 0,\ w = 0,\ \bar{T} = T_w \quad (9\text{-}2a)$$

$$\text{At } y = \delta: \quad U = U_e,\ \bar{T} = T_e \quad (9\text{-}2b)$$

If $Pr = 1$ is assumed, the energy equation (Eq. 8-4) takes the form

$$\frac{\partial}{\partial y}\left(\mu \frac{\partial \bar{E}}{\partial y} - \bar{\rho}\overline{E'v} - \bar{E}\overline{\rho'v}\right) = 0 \tag{9-3a}$$

This is similar to the momentum equation (Eq. 8-1), rewritten as follows:

$$\frac{\partial}{\partial y}\left(\mu \frac{\partial U}{\partial y} - \bar{\rho}\overline{uv} - U\overline{\rho'v}\right) = 0 \tag{9-3b}$$

Further from the equation of continuity, Eq. 8-3, we have $\overline{\rho'v} =$ const. Therefore a comparison between Eq. 9-3a and 9-3b leads to the following linear relationship between $\bar{E}$ and $\bar{U}$:

$$\bar{E} = c_p\bar{T} + \frac{1}{2}U^2 + \frac{1}{2}(\overline{u^2} + \overline{v^2} + \overline{w^2}) = c_pT_e^0\left[(1-\eta)\frac{U}{U_e} + \eta\right] \tag{9-4}$$

where the constant $T_e^0$ and $\eta$, as determined by the boundary conditions (Eq. 9-2a and 9-2b), are

$$\eta = T_w/T_e^0$$

$$c_pT_e^0 = c_pT_e + \tfrac{1}{2}U_e^2$$

$T_e^0$ is the stagnation temperature at $y = \delta$. If we neglect as usual the turbulent intensity in Eq. 9-4, we obtain the approximate relation

$$c_p\bar{T} + \frac{1}{2}U^2 = c_pT_e^0\left[(1-\eta)\frac{U}{U_e} + \eta\right] \tag{9-5}$$

Eq. 9-5 gives a relation between $\bar{T}$ and $U$ on the basis that the *laminar* Prandtl number is unity. Some authors have derived the same relation requiring that the turbulent Prandtl number should also be unity (see e.g. [*8*]), but the latter condition is superfluous according to the above considerations.

Eq. 9-5 gives the temperature-velocity relationship including heat transfer. If the wall is insulated, we must have

$$\left(\frac{\partial \bar{T}}{\partial y}\right)_w = 0 \tag{9-2c}$$

but, according to Eq. 9-5,

$$\frac{\partial \bar{T}}{\partial y} + \frac{U}{c_p}\frac{\partial U}{\partial y} = \frac{T^0}{U_1}(1-\eta)\frac{\partial U}{\partial y} \tag{9-6}$$

and since in general $(\partial U/\partial y)_w \neq 0$, the condition (Eq. 9-2c) imposed upon Eq. 9-6 requires that

$$\eta = 1$$

hence Eq. 9-5 simplifies to the following form:

$$c_p\bar{T} + \tfrac{1}{2}U^2 = c_pT_w \; (= \text{const}) \tag{9-7}$$

with an insulated wall. We conclude that for $Pr = 1$, the relationships between temperature and velocity in the turbulent boundary layer are the same as those in the laminar boundary layer, which were first obtained by Crocco [9].

In an insulated boundary layer at low speeds, Squire [10] and Ackerman [11] have independently deduced the formula

$$c_pT_w = c_pT_e + \tfrac{1}{2}Pr^{\frac{1}{3}}U_e^2 \tag{9-8}$$

for $Pr \neq 1$ or $Pr = 1$. Here $T_w$ is the temperature at the wall. When there is no heat transfer, $T_w$ is sometimes called equilibrium temperature. This formula may be expected to be not seriously in error at high speeds, and includes Eq. 9-7 as a special case with $Pr = 1$. As $Pr < 1$ in general, the temperature at the wall is accordingly smaller than the total free stream temperature.

In the light of Eq. 9-4, a more general formula for the case of $Pr \neq 1$ can be written as follows:

$$c_pT_w = c_pT_e + \tfrac{1}{2}r_eU_e^2 \tag{9-9a}$$

by introducing a factor $r_e$, called the *recovery factor*. The recovery factor can then be considered as defined by Eq. 9-9a, and it then becomes

$$r_e = \frac{T_w - T_e}{T_e^0 - T_e} \tag{9-9b}$$

Using the adiabatic relation $T_e^0/T_e = 1 + (\gamma - 1)M_e^2/2$,

$$r_e = \frac{\left(\frac{T_w}{T_e^0}\right)\left(1 + \frac{\gamma - 1}{2}M_e^2\right) - 1}{\frac{\gamma - 1}{2}M_e^2} \tag{9-9c}$$

Here $M_e$ is the Mach number at the edge of the boundary layer, and $\gamma$ is the ratio of specific heats. According to Eq. 9-8 and 9-9, the recovery factor should not differ very much from the value

$$r_e = Pr^{\frac{1}{3}} \tag{9-10}$$

The turbulent recovery factor, which shows a close agreement with Eq. 9-10, has been measured by Mack [12] over the surface of a cone, in the range of free stream Mach number from 1.33 to 4.50, to be $0.88 \pm 0.01$, as compared with the calculated value of $Pr^{\frac{1}{3}} = 0.89$, based on the recovery temperature. Experiments for a flat plate have been made by Stalder, Rubesin, and Tendeland [13] ($r_e = 0.89 \pm 0.01$) at Mach number 2.4. Also the measurements of the laminar recovery factor show a close agreement with the theoretical value of $Pr^{\frac{1}{2}}$. The experimental results of various investigations are summarized in Fig. B,9a and B,9b.

In general the recovery factor depends on the Reynolds number. In

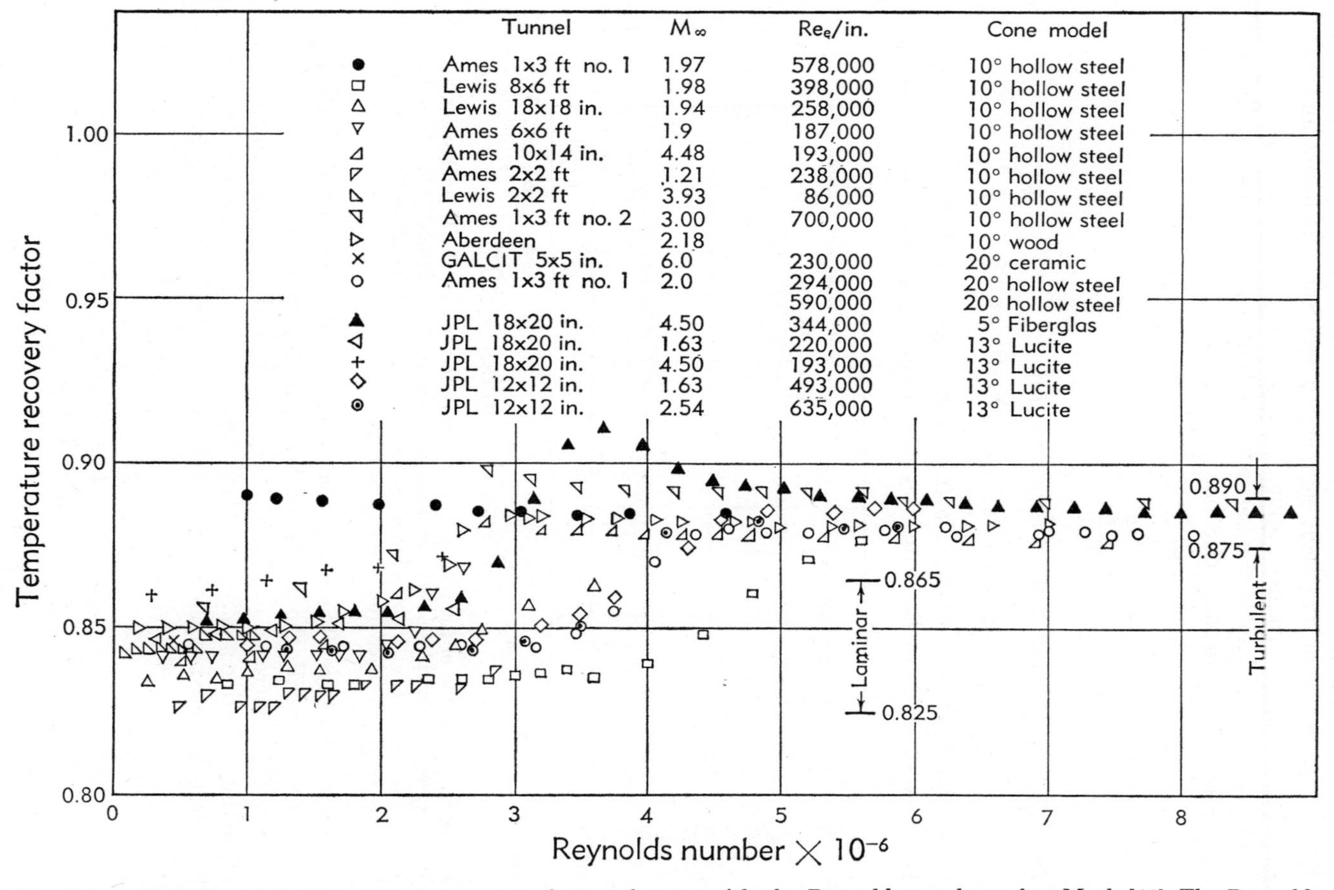


Fig. B,9a. Variation of the temperature recovery factor of cones with the Reynolds number, after Mack [12]. The Reynolds number $R_e$ is based upon the distance from the cone tip and on the conditions at the edge of the boundary layer.

the transition region, the recovery factor varies from the lower laminar value to the higher turbulent value. An increase of the turbulent recovery factor with the Reynolds number in the fully turbulent region predicted by the theoretical formula of Seban [14],

$$r_e = 1 - (4.71 - 4.11B - 0.601Pr)Re^{-0.2}$$

$$B = \frac{Pr}{2}\frac{5Pr + 7}{5Pr + 1}$$

and the theoretical formula of Shirokow [15],

$$r_e = 1 - 4.55(1 - Pr)Re^{-0.2}$$

is not systematically detectable from the experimental results of Fig. B,9a and B,9b. Here $Re$ is the Reynolds number based on the distance

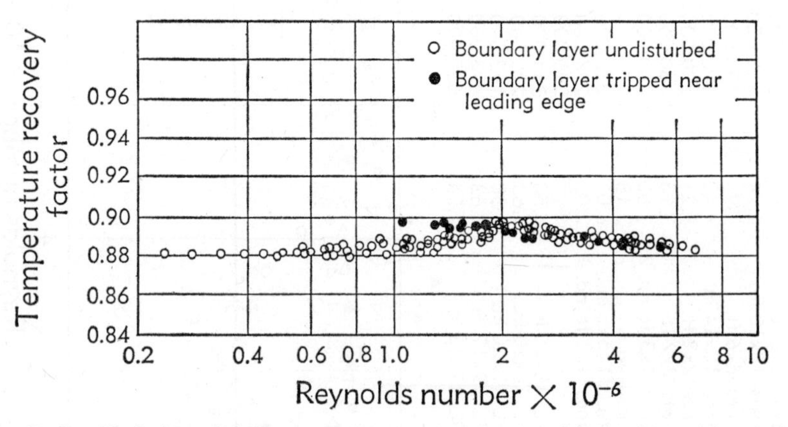


Fig. B,9b. Variation of the temperature recovery factor with the Reynolds number in the case of a flat plate, after Stalder, Rubesin, and Tendeland [13], $M_e = 2.4$. The Reynolds number $xU_e/\nu_e$ is based on the conditions at the edge of the boundary layer and on the distance from the leading edge.

from a leading edge. There is probably also some slight variation of the recovery factor with the Mach number. The measurements of Mack [12] show a slight increase of the recovery factor with the Mach number, while those of Stine and Scherrer [16] show no variation. The Mach number effect predicted by the theoretical formula of Tucker and Maslen [17],

$$r_e = Pr^m$$

$$m = \frac{N + 1 + 0.528M^2}{3N + 1 + M^2}$$

$$N = 2.6Re^{\frac{1}{7}}$$

is not yet verified by experiments. According to Fig. B,9a and B,9b, the turbulent recovery factors on cones and flat plates are of the same order, while the laminar recovery factors on plates are higher than those on cones and other models. These high values of the recovery factor can be attributed to heat conduction effects in the leading edge region of the flat plate.

The foregoing relations between temperature and velocity will be referred to in Art. 12 in connection with the relation between the temperature profile and the velocity profile. If $Pr = 1$, the relations become especially simple, as shown by Eq. 9-5 with heat transfer and by Eq. 9-7 without heat transfer. If $Pr \neq 1$, the viscous dissipation and the heat conduction render such a general relationship between temperature and

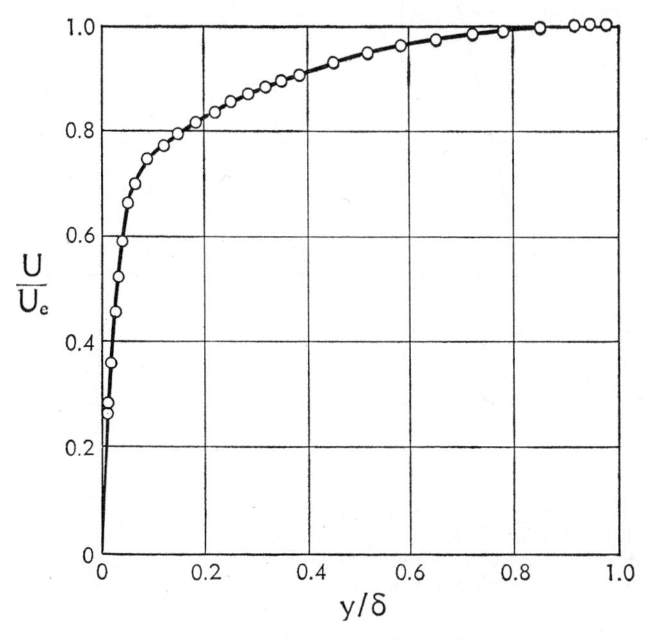


Fig. B,9c. Velocity profile across turbulent boundary layer. The free stream Mach number is 4.93 and there is no heat transfer. The data are drawn after Lobb, Winkler, and Persh [*18*] and private communications.

velocity very difficult, and a basic approach to the problem must involve the detailed mechanism of turbulence. However, without turning to this approach a relation between the temperature at the wall and the velocity and temperature at $y = \delta$ was made possible by introducing a recovery factor $r_e$. For no heat transfer such a relation was found to be that of Eq. 9-9a, and this agreed rather well with measurements. The question may be asked as to what form the relation might take if it were generalized to include the heat transfer and to cover all positions in the boundary layer. To this end and by similar reasoning, we could introduce a variable recovery factor $r(y)$ which satisfies Eq. 9-9a at the limit and becomes $r(y) = 1$ for $Pr = 1$. It is expected that a relation between $T^0$ and $T_w$

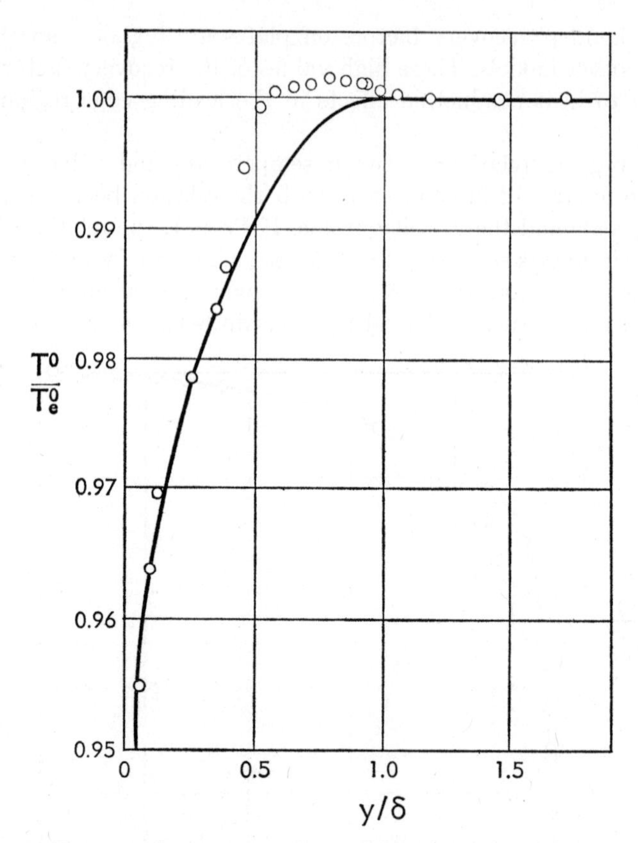


Fig. B,9d. Total temperature profile across turbulent boundary layer. The free stream Mach number is 4.93 and there is no heat transfer. The experimental data in circles are drawn after Lobb, Winkler, and Persh [*18*] and private communications. The curve is drawn according to Eq. 9-12, by assuming equal thickness of boundary layers for $U$ and $T$.

could then be formulated predicting that $T^0/T^0_e$ increases as $(U/U_e)^2$ increases. With this in view we shall introduce a variable recovery factor $r(y)$ and write by analogy to Eq. 9-7,

$$c_p\overline{T} + \tfrac{1}{2}r(y)U^2 = c_pT_e + \tfrac{1}{2}r_eU_e^2 \equiv c_pT_w \tag{9-11}$$

Here it is assumed that the heat conduction through the wall is absent, i.e. $(\partial\overline{T}/\partial y)_w = 0$, but $Pr$ may be arbitrary. Eq. 9-11 gives $T^0(y)$ in terms of $U(y)$ as follows:

$$\frac{T^0}{T^0_e} = \frac{T_w}{T^0_e} + \left(1 - \frac{T_w}{T^0_e}\right)\alpha\left(\frac{U}{U_e}\right)^2 \tag{9-12}$$

with

$$\alpha = \frac{r(y) - 1}{r_e - 1}$$

For a velocity distribution given by Fig. B,9c, the curve in Fig. B,9d shows the distribution of $T^0/T^0_e$ given by Eq. 9-12 when it is assumed as a rough approximation that $\alpha = 1$. On the same figure are shown the measurements of Lobb, Winkler, and Persh [*18*]. Fig. B,9e shows the measurements of van Driest [*19*] and Spivack [*20*]. Both figures suggest that $T^0/T^0_e$ passes through a maximum value in excess of unity, the indication of this being most pronounced in Fig. B,9e. This phenomenon cannot be explained from the above considerations unless a proper distribution of $r(y)$ is taken into account.

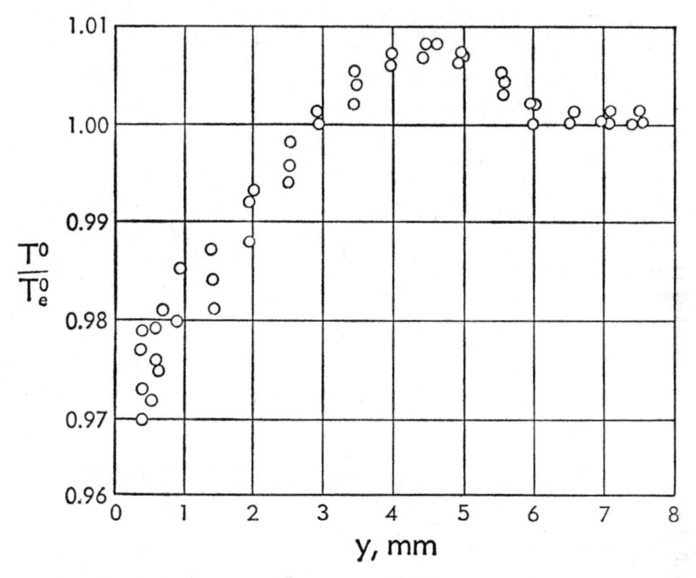


Fig. B,9e. Total temperature profile across turbulent boundary layer at free stream Mach number 2.8. The data are from Spivack [*20*] with an axial distance from throat of 12.96 inches.

**B,10. Phenomena of Transport of Properties in a Turbulent Fluid.** Up to the present we have dealt with the mean turbulent flow and certain simple relationships between mean quantities. For the latter, analogies were employed rather than procedures based on a mechanism of turbulence. Since the superficial nature of this approach is apparent, it becomes advisable to look into the physical transport processes of turbulence which are embodied in transport terms like $\overline{uv}$, $\overline{\rho' v}$, $\overline{T' v}$, etc., of the fundamental equations obtained in Art. 8. They represent the mean rate of transfer of $u$, $\rho'$, and $T'$ respectively, across a unit area perpendicular to $y$. One of the major aims of turbulent theory is to find a method of calculating these transport terms directly from the hydrodynamic equations governing the turbulent motion (Eq. 4-3, 4-4, and 6-1). At present the difficulties of the theories make such a program not yet possible.

The other approach is to regard the statistical effect of turbulence on the mean flow as being similar to that of molecular viscosity or heat conduction, so that the turbulent transport terms can be treated by the same statistical methods as those applied to transport processes in non-turbulent motions. To this end, and as a basis of the statistical theory of transport processes by molecular motions in a gas, we use the Boltzmann equation

$$\frac{\partial f}{\partial t} + \xi_j \frac{\partial f}{\partial x_j} + X_j \frac{\partial f}{\partial \xi_j} = \frac{\delta f}{\delta t} \tag{10-1}$$

where $\delta f/\delta t$ is a symbol representing the collision integral, $f(t, \mathbf{x}; \boldsymbol{\xi})d\mathbf{x}d\boldsymbol{\xi}$ is the number of particles in the space and velocity elements $d\mathbf{x}d\boldsymbol{\xi}$ at the instant $t$; $\mathbf{x}$ and $\boldsymbol{\xi}$ are the vectors of position and velocity, $\mathbf{X}$ is the external force per unit mass. The left-hand side of Eq. 10-1 represents the rate of increase in time of the number of particles in the phase element $d\mathbf{x}d\boldsymbol{\xi}$ when we move together with the particles in the phase space $\mathbf{x}$, $\boldsymbol{\xi}$. The right-hand side represents the effect of restoring and direct collisions which throw the particles respectively in and out of the phase element.

A consequence of the Boltzmann equation is the equation of evolution of a transferable property $\Phi(t, x)$ defined by

$$\Phi(t, \mathbf{x}) = \frac{\int d\boldsymbol{\xi}\phi(\boldsymbol{\xi})f}{\int d\boldsymbol{\xi}f} \tag{10-2}$$

where $\phi(\boldsymbol{\xi})$ is a function of the random velocity $\boldsymbol{\xi}$. As special cases it is interesting to put $\phi = 1, \xi_i, \frac{1}{2}\xi_j^2$, thus obtaining from Eq. 10-1 and 10-2 the general hydrodynamic equations

$$\left.\begin{aligned} \frac{\partial \bar{\rho}}{\partial t} + \frac{\partial}{\partial x_j}(\bar{\rho} U_j) &= 0 \\ \bar{\rho}\frac{DU_i}{Dt} \equiv \bar{\rho}\left(\frac{\partial U_i}{\partial t} + U_j \frac{\partial U_i}{\partial x_j}\right) &= \bar{\rho} X_i + \frac{\partial \sigma_{ij}}{\partial x_j} \\ \bar{\rho}\frac{DI}{Dt} - \frac{\partial q_j}{\partial x_j} &= \sigma_{ij}\epsilon_{ij} - \bar{\rho} U_j X_j \end{aligned}\right\} \tag{10-3}$$

Here the density $\bar{\rho}$, the speed $U_i$, and the internal thermal energy per unit volume $I$ are defined by the mean values

$$\bar{\rho} = m \int f d\boldsymbol{\xi} = mn$$

$$U_i = \frac{1}{n}\int \xi_i f d\boldsymbol{\xi} = \bar{\xi}_i$$

$$I = \tfrac{1}{2}\overline{C_i^2}$$

where $C_i = \xi_i - U_i$ is the thermal velocity and $m$ is mass. The mean values of high powers of $C_i$ are

$$\sigma_{ij} = -\bar{\rho}\overline{C_iC_j} = \text{stress tensor}$$

$$q_i = -\tfrac{1}{2}\bar{\rho}\overline{C_iC_j^2} = \text{thermal flux}$$

$I$ is the internal energy, which is equal to $C_v\overline{T}$ for an ideal gas, and finally

$$\epsilon_{ij} = \frac{1}{2}\left(\frac{\partial U_i}{\partial x_j} + \frac{\partial U_j}{\partial x_i}\right)$$

Eq. 10-3 express the conservation of mass, momentum, and energy respectively. In order to express the quantities $\sigma_{ij}$ and $q_i$ in terms of the macroscopic quantities $\bar{\rho}$, $U_i$, and $\overline{T}$ (or $I$) we have to investigate further the Boltzmann equation (Eq. 10-1). Because it is nonlinear in character, it can only be solved by approximations. For the detailed calculations, reference may be made to the textbook of Chapman and Cowling [*21*]. As a first approximation it is found that

$$\begin{aligned} \sigma_{ij} &= -p\delta_{ij} + 2\mu(\epsilon_{ij} - \tfrac{1}{3}\epsilon_{kk}\delta_{ij}) \\ q_i &= k\frac{\partial \overline{T}}{\partial x_i} \end{aligned} \tag{10-4}$$

where $\mu$ and $k$ are found as functions of $T$ and *depend on the collision cross section.* With this approximation, the second equation of Eq. 10-3 becomes the Navier-Stokes equation of motion.

In particular, for a transport in the $y$ direction of a property which either is a scalar, or has a component in the $x$ direction, Eq. 10-4 reduce to

$$\begin{aligned} \sigma_{xy} &= -\bar{\rho}\overline{\xi_xC_y} = \mu\frac{\partial U}{\partial y} \\ q_i &= -\bar{\rho}\frac{1}{2}\overline{C_x^2C_y} = \frac{k}{c_p}\frac{\partial I}{\partial y} \end{aligned} \tag{10-5}$$

or, in general, the laminar flux of the transport $J$ of a transferable property $\Phi$, which is the momentum or temperature in Eq. 10-5, can be written in the following form:

$$J_{\text{lam}} = D_{\text{lam}}\frac{\partial \Phi}{\partial y} \tag{10-6}$$

where $D_{\text{lam}}$ is a laminar phenomenological coefficient equal to the coefficient of viscosity in the case of transport of momentum, and to the coefficient of heat conduction in the case of the transport of heat.

When we deal with turbulent transport, it is necessary to replace the concept of the molecular collisions by the turbulent exchanges between fluid elements. Similarly the thermal velocity $C_i$ is replaced by the velocity $u_i$ of turbulent motions. If the property $\Phi$ is to be transferred by these motions, then it is to be expected, by analogy with Eq. 10-5 and 10-6, that a turbulent flux will result in the form

$$J = -\bar{\rho}\overline{\Phi v} = D\frac{\partial \Phi}{\partial y}$$

where $J$ is turbulent flux, $v$ is the turbulent velocity in the direction $y$, and $D$ is turbulent coefficient of transport. In general the transport coefficient $D$ may depend upon a number of unknown factors among which are the property to be transferred, and the intensity and scale of the turbulent motion. For example, its value may vary according to whether we have a transport of momentum, heat, or matter. A knowledge of its structure necessitates a detailed investigation of the basis of the turbulent exchange term by a procedure analogous to that which yielded the exchange coefficients $\mu$ and $k$ of Eq. 10-4 from the solution of the complete Boltzmann equation including the collision term. It is hoped that some insight into the essential structure of the turbulent transport can be gained by proceeding in this way on a somewhat simplified basis made possible by adopting an approximate form of the Boltzmann equation. When applied to turbulent motion, the right-hand side of Eq. 10-1 represents the effects of the turbulent exchanges on the distribution function. It can be regarded as a forcing term which distorts the distribution from its equilibrium. Therefore we can write Eq. 10-1 approximately as follows:

$$\frac{Df}{Dt} = -\kappa(f - f_{eq}) \tag{10-7}$$

where $f$ is the nonequilibrium distribution, $f_{eq}$ is the equilibrium distribution, and $\kappa$ depends on the efficiency of the turbulent mixing. The idea of writing such a simple relaxation type of exchange term in Eq. 10-7 in the place of the complete collision integral in Eq. 10-1 is not new. Lorentz [*22*], Van Vleck and Weisskoff [*23*] had initiated such a simplification in their study of microwave line shapes. Later Bhatnagar, Gross, and Krook [*24*] applied an essentially similar simplification for studying the collision processes in gases. According to Eq. 10-2 and 10-7, we can write

$$\frac{d\Phi}{dt} = -\kappa(\Phi - \bar{\Phi}) \tag{10-8}$$

Here $\Phi - \bar{\Phi}$ is the fluctuation of the transferable property. Eq. 10-8 can be used to find the evolution of the property $\Phi$ carried by a lump of fluid when the latter moves and mixes with its surroundings.

Being given $\bar{\Phi}$, the value of $\Phi$ at any instant $t$ is given by the integral of Eq. 10-8 as follows:

$$\Phi(t) = \kappa \int_0^\infty d\tau e^{-\kappa\tau}\bar{\Phi}(t - \tau) \tag{10-9a}$$

where $\bar{\Phi}(t - \tau)$ is the mean value of the property $\Phi$ when the lump of fluid carrying $\Phi$ found itself at the instant $t - \tau$. It can be expanded into series as follows:

$$\bar{\Phi}(t - \tau) = \bar{\Phi}(t) - \frac{\partial \bar{\Phi}(t)}{\partial y} \int_{t-\tau}^{t} dt' v(t') \tag{10-9b}$$

where the integral term is the displacement of the lump of fluid in the interval of time $\tau$. The expansion is valid when the lump of fluid makes only *small displacements* and when it is assumed that $\Phi$ is stationary, but nonuniform.

After substitution for $\Phi(t - \tau)$, Eq. 10-9a becomes

$$\Phi(t) = \bar{\Phi} - \frac{\partial \bar{\Phi}}{\partial y} \kappa \int_0^\infty d\tau e^{-\kappa\tau} \int_{t-\tau}^{t} dt' v(t')$$

The double integral is

$$\begin{aligned} \kappa \int_0^\infty d\tau e^{-\kappa\tau} \int_{t-\tau}^{t} dt' v(t') &= \kappa \int_0^\infty d\tau e^{-\kappa\tau} \int_0^{\tau} dt'' v(t - t'') \\ &= \kappa \int_0^\infty dt'' v(t - t'') \int_{t''}^\infty d\tau e^{-\kappa\tau} \\ &= \int_0^\infty dt'' e^{-\kappa t''} v(t - t'') \end{aligned}$$

Thus

$$\Phi(t) = \bar{\Phi}(t) - \frac{\partial \bar{\Phi}(t)}{\partial y} \int_0^\infty dt'' e^{-\kappa t''} v(t - t'')$$

Hence the flux for the transport of $\Phi$ is:

$$J \equiv -\bar{\rho}\overline{\Phi v} = \bar{\rho} \frac{\partial \bar{\Phi}(t)}{\partial y} \int_0^\infty dt'' e^{-\kappa t''} \overline{v(t - t'') v(t)} \tag{10-10a}$$

Consequently the turbulent coefficient of transport $D$ is found as follows:

$$D = \int_0^\infty dt'' e^{-\kappa t''} \overline{v(t - t'') v(t)} \tag{10-10b}$$

The transport coefficient $D$ in Eq. 10-10 depends on the autocorrelation function of velocities $\overline{v(t - t'')v(t)}$ and on $\kappa$. In its turn $\kappa$ depends on a number of factors among which is the property to be transferred. This entails that $D$ may differ according to the nature of properties to be transferred, i.e. heat, momentum, particles, etc.

Now we shall compare this result with the concept of mixing length, so often used in the study of the turbulent motion. By analogy with the kinetic theory of gases one may suppose that there is a length $l$, which represents the distance traveled by the lump of fluid between the instant when it was freed from its surroundings carrying with it the mean property of these surroundings, and the instant when it arrives in a new layer where it is supposed to mix with the new surrounding fluid. In this case, the transport coefficient is $\overline{vl}$, which can be written in the integral form

$$\overline{vl} = \int_0^\infty dt''\overline{v(t - t'')v(t)} \tag{10-11}$$

if the correlation of velocities converges. Eq. 10-11, based on the mixing length, does not distinguish between the transport of heat, momentum, and matter, because the same length is intrinsically implied in all cases.

As an illustration, Eq. 10-10 may be applied to the special case of transport of momentum and heat along the $y$ direction. We then obtain

$$\tau = -\bar{\rho}\overline{uv} = \bar{\rho}D_u\frac{\partial U}{\partial y} \tag{10-12}$$

$$q = -\bar{\rho}c_p\overline{T'v} = \bar{\rho}c_pD_h\frac{\partial \bar{T}}{\partial y}$$

where $\tau$ is the turbulent shear stress, $q$ is the rate of turbulent transport of heat, and $D_u$ and $D_h$ are respectively the transport coefficients of momentum and heat defined by Eq. 10-10b. The coefficients are commonly termed "turbulent exchange coefficients."

The results (Eq. 10-12) can be compared with the Boussinesq formulas of turbulent transport of momentum and heat, written usually in the following form:

$$\begin{aligned} \tau &= \epsilon_\mu\frac{\partial U}{\partial y} \\ q &= \epsilon_k\frac{\partial \bar{T}}{\partial y} \end{aligned} \tag{10-13}$$

where $\epsilon_\mu$ is the eddy viscosity and $\epsilon_k$ is the eddy heat conductivity, introduced by formal analogy to the corresponding laminar viscosity and heat conductivity of the Navier-Stokes and Fourier equations. Eq. 10-13 give neither the structure of the exchange coefficients nor the basis of the transfer. However, they can be made completely identical in form with Eq. 10-12, if the following expressions are assigned to $\epsilon_\mu$ and $\epsilon_k$

$$\epsilon_\mu = \bar{\rho}D_u$$

$$\epsilon_k = \rho c_pD_h$$

The ratio

$$\frac{D_u}{D_h} = \frac{\epsilon_\mu c_p}{\epsilon_k} \equiv Pr_t$$

is called the turbulent Prandtl number by analogy to the laminar Prandtl number introduced in Eq. 6-4b. We see that the mixing length theory

(Eq. 10-11), which implies $D_u = D_h$, predicts a turbulent Prandtl number of unity. However, experiments show that $Pr_t$ is about 0.7, a value very close, incidently, to the laminar Prandtl number for air.

The fact that the turbulent Prandtl number, as given by the ratio $D_u/D_h$, is different from unity is interesting and indicates that Eq. 10-10b, rather than the mixing length formula (Eq. 10-11), should be more correct. However, due to the simplification introduced in the transport equation (Eq. 10-7), the parameter $\kappa$ is not determined in terms of the transferable property, so that the numerical value of the ratio of the two exchange coefficients cannot be computed from Eq. 10-10b alone. An auxiliary equation is needed to determine the transfer of property, for example, heat or particles, under the action of a turbulent fluid. In the case of the transfer of particles, such an equation may govern the motion of a small spherical particle suspended in a turbulent fluid. On the basis of it, the velocity correlation for the particles can be computed in terms of the velocity correlation of the ambient fluid or vice versa, and hence the ratio of the two exchange coefficients can be obtained. This has been done by Tchen [*25*], and, for the case of $\kappa = 0$, it has been found that the exchange coefficient of particles is equal to that of the fluid (Eq. 10-11). This case is not surprising, since consistently the relaxation is neither involved in the motion of the fluid nor in the motion of the particles, and no difference in exchange coefficients should exist, as already revealed by the simple theory of Eq. 10-10b. The ratio of the two exchange coefficients for the case of $\kappa \neq 0$ has not yet been studied on this basis. Several authors are concerned with such difficulties of diffusion phenomena, see e.g. [*25*] and the Burgers lecture on the turbulent fluid motion [*26*].

In the integrand of Eq. 10-10b, the exponential term can be considered as a retarding effect of the relaxation between the equilibrium and nonequilibrium distribution in the transport phenomena (Eq. 10-8). Hence the complete integrand of Eq. 10-10b can be considered as a correlation corrected for the relaxation by means of the exponential factor. In the diffusion problem based on the model of a random walk, such an effect has been considered by Tchen [*27*] in the form of a more general memory, which could be either negative or positive, so that the corrected correlation will contain a factor respectively smaller or larger than unity.

Before leaving the discussion, it is important to remark that the diffusion phenomena, described by the above transport phenomena, are only valid for irregular movements of small scales, since we have used in Eq. 10-9b a series expansion in terms of a length and some gradient of the transferable property. Such a diffusion can be called diffusion of the gradient type. On the other hand, when the irregular movements are of coarse scales, the bulk property rather than its local gradient must be the governing factor. The latter diffusion can be called diffusion of the *bulk convective* type, and will be discussed in Art. 29 in connection with the coarse eddies of free turbulent flow.

The structure of the transport coefficients can be determined by means of kinetic equations more general than the Boltzmann equation. This attempt has been made in an article by Tchen published in the Proceedings of the International Symposium on Atmospheric Diffusion (1958).

**B,11. Reynolds Analogy between Heat Transfer and Skin Friction.** As an application of the transport processes treated in Art. 10, let us study the Reynolds analogy between heat transfer and momentum transfer. Let $q = -\bar{\rho}c_p\overline{vT'}$ be the rate of turbulent heat transfer in the $y$ direction across the unit area normal to this axis, and $\tau = -\bar{\rho}\overline{uv}$ be the rate of momentum transfer or turbulent shear stress. According to Eq. 10-6 we have

$$q = -\bar{\rho}c_p\overline{vT'} = \bar{\rho}c_pD_h\frac{\partial\bar{T}}{\partial y}$$

$$\tau = -\bar{\rho}\overline{uv} = \bar{\rho}D_u\frac{\partial U}{\partial y}$$

The following expressions written in nondimensional form may be compared:

$$-\frac{q}{\bar{\rho}c_p(U - U_e)(T - T_e)} \quad \text{and} \quad \frac{\tau}{\bar{\rho}(U - U_e)^2} \tag{11-1}$$

Here $U_e$ and $T_e$ are the velocity and temperature at a reference plane, which, in the present discussion, is taken at the edge of the boundary layer. The Reynolds analogy is a statement of equality of the two expressions of Eq. 11-1. Let us investigate this analogy in some detail. Of special interest are the heat and momentum transfers at the wall, where the two expressions of Eq. 11-1 become

$$St = \frac{q_w}{\bar{\rho}_w c_p U_e(T_w - T_e)}; \qquad \frac{1}{2}c_f = \frac{\tau_w}{\bar{\rho}_w U_e^2} \tag{11-2}$$

where the subscript $_w$ denotes the value at the wall, $St$ is the coefficient of heat transfer or Stanton number, and $c_f$ the coefficient of skin friction. Then the Reynolds analogy leads to

$$St = \tfrac{1}{2}c_f \tag{11-3}$$

This result was first obtained by Reynolds [*28*] and is also given by Squire [*7*, p. 819] and Goldstein [*6*, p. 654] in their study of heat transfer.

It is easy to see that Eq. 11-3 cannot be valid in general because, in the compressible case of an insulated boundary layer, we must have $St = 0$ and $c_f \neq 0$, which obviously violate Eq. 11-3. Therefore it is worthwhile to derive a more general relationship between the heat transfer and skin friction. For this purpose we make use of the relation (Eq.

9-5) between the temperature and velocity for the case of $Pr = 1$. By differentiating with respect to $y$, we obtain

$$\left(\frac{\partial \bar{T}}{\partial y}\right)_w = (T_e^0 - T_w)\frac{1}{U_e}\left(\frac{\partial U}{\partial y}\right)_w$$

Thus in terms of $(\partial U/\partial y)_w$, we can write $St$ and $c_f$ as defined by Eq. 11-2 in the following form:

$$St = D_h \frac{T_e^0 - T_w}{T_e - T_w}\frac{1}{U_e^2}\left(\frac{\partial U}{\partial y}\right)_w$$

$$\frac{1}{2}c_f = D_u \frac{1}{U_e^2}\left(\frac{\partial U}{\partial y}\right)_w$$

so that

$$\frac{St}{\frac{1}{2}c_f} = \frac{D_h}{D_u}\frac{T_e^0 - T_w}{T_e - T_w} = \frac{D_h}{D_u}\left[1 - \frac{\frac{\gamma - 1}{2}M_e^2}{\eta\left(1 + \frac{\gamma - 1}{2}M_e^2\right) - 1}\right] \tag{11-4}$$

where $\eta = T_w/T_e^0$, $M_e$ is the Mach number of the stream at $y = \delta$, and $\gamma$ is the ratio of specific heats. Eq. 11-4 can be considered as a generalization of the Reynolds analogy to include the effects of the heat transfer, compressibility, and the difference in the transport of heat and momentum. As $M_e > 0$, $\eta \neq 1$, and $D_u \neq D_h$ according to Art. 10, the right-hand side of Eq. 11-4 is in general not unity, and the Reynolds relation (Eq. 11-3) is not obtained. However, if we neglect the effect of compressibility, for example at low speeds, and if the transports of heat and momentum are similar ($D_h = D_u$), the right-hand side of Eq. 11-4 is approximately unity, and the Reynolds analogy (Eq. 11-3) is then found to be valid. In general those restrictive conditions are not present, and the Reynolds analogy will not hold. For example, in the case of a heated plate ($\eta > 1$), the factor between brackets in Eq. 11-4 is smaller than unity, so that in many circumstances we have

$$St < \tfrac{1}{2}c_f \tag{11-5a}$$

This inequality is verified by experiments. On the other hand, with intense cooling of the plate ($\eta < 1$) the term between brackets in Eq. 11-4 may become larger than unity so that we may get

$$St > \tfrac{1}{2}c_f \tag{11-5b}$$

In spite of its defects, the Reynolds analogy (Eq. 11-3) is often used in theories of boundary layers with heat transfer because of its simplicity, and sometimes the experiments show that the analogy is a surprisingly good approximation.

Instead of defining the shear stress and heat transfer on the basis of

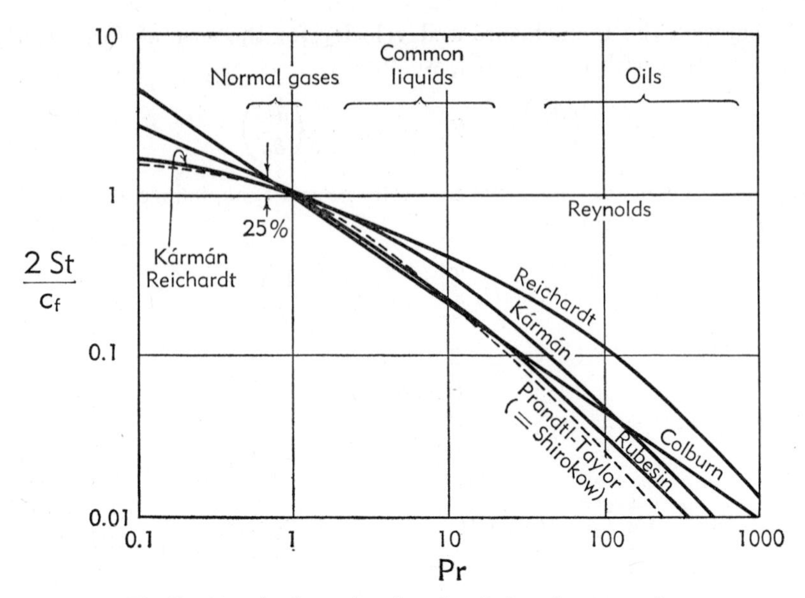


Fig. B,11a. Analogy theories of turbulent heat transfer; $M_e = 0$, $R_e = 10^7$ after Chapman and Kester [29].

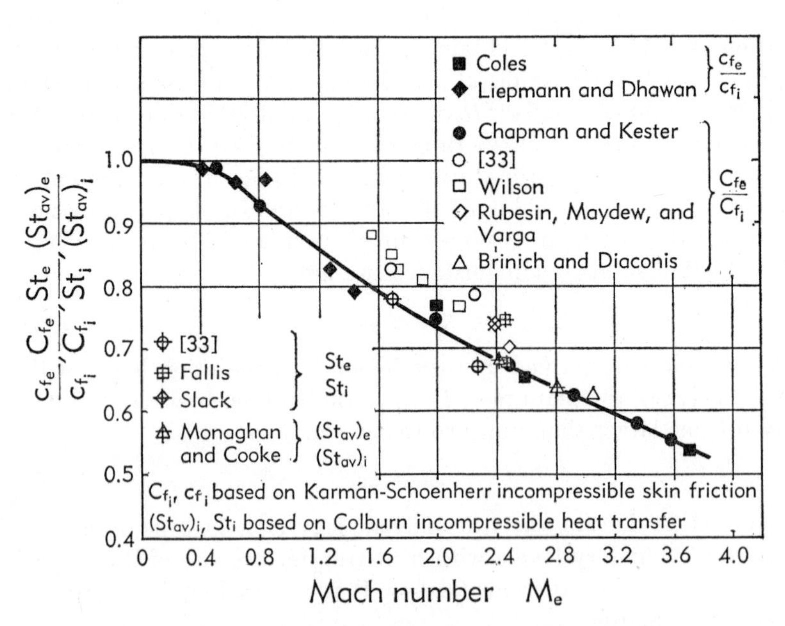


Fig. B,11b. Variation of skin friction and heat transfer coefficients with Mach number, after Pappas [33].

the elementary and fundamental transport phenomena by turbulence, as was done in Eq. 10-12, one could consider a more general shear stress and heat transfer, by defining them by the right-hand side of the boundary layer equations, Eq. 8-1 and 8-4 respectively. Then a new coefficient of skin friction and a new Stanton number are obtained with a rather complicated ratio between them. Such an analogy between shear stress and heat transfer is called in the literature "Modified Reynolds Analogy" [*8*]. While it is already hard to express a satisfactory analogy between two elementary transfers, one wonders sometimes whether an analogy between a complex transfer of different nature (turbulent and laminar combined) could be expected in a reasonably simple form. The results of some of those analogy theories and the effects of the Prandtl number are shown in Fig. B,11a, after Chapman and Kester [*29*]. The data mentioned in Fig. B,11a are found in [*15,30,31,32*]. Fig. B,11b, after Pappas [*33*] shows how the skin friction coefficient and the heat transfer coefficient vary with the Mach number. The data of Fig. B,11b refer to [*29,32,33,34,35,36,37,38, 39,40,41,42,43*].

**B,12. Basis of Skin Friction Theories.** For the analysis of the stresses acting on a body moving at high speeds, a study of the skin friction in a compressible fluid becomes important. Not only is it necessary for drag calculations, but it is useful for estimating heat transfer by means of the Reynolds analogy discussed in Art. 11.

Before discussing experimental results and their comparison with theories, it appears desirable to review in a simple and general way the main steps, concepts, and approximations underlying the theories which have been proposed.

According to Eq. 8-1, the turbulent shear stress for a compressible flow is

$$\tau = -\bar{\rho}\overline{uv} - U\overline{\rho' v} \qquad (12\text{-}1a)$$

The first term of the right-hand side of Eq. 12-1a represents a momentum transfer, and the second a mass transfer. The ratio of the second term to the first is estimated to be proportional to the square of the local Mach number. Now the theories of skin friction assume, as a first approximation, a value of $\tau = \tau_w$ for Eq. 12-1a, where $\tau_w$ is the total shear stress at the wall. Any variation of $\tau$ through the boundary layer is taken into account only in the higher order of approximations. Since the local Mach number is small near the wall, the second term of the right-hand side of Eq. 12-1a can be neglected, and we obtain

$$\tau = -\bar{\rho}\overline{uv} \qquad (12\text{-}1b)$$

The next step is to express the fluctuating quantities in terms of the mean quantities in accordance with the relations (Eq. 10-11 and 10-12) as follows:

$$\tau = \bar{\rho}\overline{vl}\,\frac{\partial U}{\partial y} \tag{12-2a}$$

where, following Prandtl, $\overline{vl}$ is expressed by

$$\overline{vl} = l^2\,\frac{\partial U}{\partial y} \tag{12-2b}$$

The mixing length $l$ is now to be expressed in terms of the local mean flow parameters. This can be done [*6*, Chap. 8] either by means of the Kármán similarity hypothesis

$$l = \kappa_1\,\frac{\partial U/\partial y}{\partial^2 U/\partial y^2} \tag{12-3}$$

or by means of the Prandtl hypothesis

$$l = \kappa_2 y \tag{12-4}$$

where $\kappa_1$ and $\kappa_2$ are numerical constants. With the Kármán hypothesis, Eq. 12-2a can be written as follows:

$$\tau = \kappa_1^2\bar{\rho}\,\frac{(\partial U/\partial y)^4}{(\partial^2 U/\partial y^2)^2} \tag{12-5}$$

In boundary layer theories the equations are usually rendered dimensionless by introducing a reference velocity

$$U_\tau = \sqrt{\frac{\tau_w}{\rho_w}} \tag{12-6a}$$

and a reference length

$$\frac{\mu_w}{\rho_w U_\tau} = \frac{\mu_w}{\sqrt{\rho_w \tau_w}} \tag{12-6b}$$

where the subscript $_w$ denotes the value at the wall.

Using the reference velocity and length, as defined by Eq. 12-6, we can write the following dimensionless quantities:

$$y^* = \frac{\rho_w U_\tau y}{\mu_w} = \frac{y\rho_w U_e}{\mu_w}\sqrt{\frac{c_{f_w}}{2}} \tag{12-7a}$$

$$U^* = \frac{U}{U_\tau} = \frac{U}{U_e}\sqrt{\frac{2}{c_{f_w}}} \tag{12-7b}$$

$$\rho^* = \frac{\bar{\rho}}{\rho_w} = \frac{T_w}{\bar{T}} \tag{12-7c}$$

and rewrite Eq. 12-5 in the dimensionless form as follows:

$$\kappa_1^2\rho^* = \frac{(\partial^2 U^*/\partial y^{*2})^2}{(\partial U^*/\partial y^*)^4} \tag{12-8}$$

where $c_{f_w}$ is the skin friction coefficient at the wall, defined by

$$c_{f_w} = \frac{\tau_w}{\frac{1}{2}\rho_w U_e^2} \tag{12-9a}$$

The expression (Eq. 12-7c) is based on the equation of state of a perfect gas and the constancy of pressure across a boundary layer (compare the assumptions underlying Eq. 9-1).

In order to formulate the differential equation for $U^*$, it is necessary to express $\rho^*$ in terms of $U^*$. This is possible by using relations between the temperature and velocity, such as those discussed in Art. 9. However, it is more proper to regard the boundary layer as a composite layer, consisting of a laminar sublayer very close to the wall with a superposed fully developed turbulent layer. Obviously the computation for such a condition becomes more elaborate, requiring matching of flow conditions at the interface and consideration of the heat transfer through it. But the final result of the temperature-velocity relation turns out to be rather simple and is of the form

$$\rho^{*-1} \equiv \frac{\overline{T}}{T_w} = A_0 + A_1 U^* + A_2 U^{*2} \tag{12-10}$$

as could be expected from the elementary considerations of Art. 9, although the coefficients $A_0$, $A_1$, and $A_2$ are more complicated functions of $Pr$, $c_{f_w}$, $T_e^0/T_w$, and $M_e$. For the details of the analysis by which these are found the reader is referred to [*44,45*].

When $\rho^*$ in Eq. 12-8 is replaced by Eq. 12-10 there is obtained an ordinary nonlinear differential equation of second order for $U^*(y^*)$, with $Pr$, $c_{f_w}$, $T_e^0/T_w$, $M_e$ as parameters. The integration gives two constants to be determined by two boundary conditions taken at the interface between the laminar sublayer and the turbulent layer. According to experimental data for incompressible flow [*46*], these are

$$\begin{aligned} U^* &= y^* = 11.5 \\ \frac{\partial U^*}{\partial y^*} &= 0.218 \end{aligned} \tag{12-11}$$

In principle, Eq. 12-8 and 12-10 with the boundary conditions (Eq. 12-11) can be solved, with the solutions of the following general form:

$$U^* = U^*\left(y^*; Pr, c_{f_w}, \frac{T_e^0}{T_w}, M_e\right) \tag{12-12}$$

In practice the solution is very elaborate and various numerical and approximate methods must be used.

Now we assume that all the parameters in Eq. 12-12 are constant, except $c_{f_w}$ which depends on $x$. Thus after integration of $U^*(y^*)$ given by

Eq. 12-12, according to the formula of momentum thickness,

$$\theta \equiv \int_0^\infty \frac{\bar{\rho}}{\rho_e} \frac{U}{U_e}\left(1 - \frac{U}{U_e}\right) dy \tag{12-13}$$

the momentum thickness $\theta(c_{f_w})$ must be a function of $x$. Since the solution (Eq. 12-12) is valid only in the turbulent boundary layer and not in the laminar sublayer, some error will be introduced in the integration of Eq. 12-13 by using Eq. 12-12. However, since the laminar sublayer is thin, the error must be very small.

We recall that the coefficient of skin friction $c_{f_w}$ is defined by Eq. 12-9a in terms of density $\rho_w$, and that the momentum equation in the integral form, for a flat plate with zero pressure gradient, is

$$c_{f_e} \equiv \frac{\tau}{\frac{1}{2}\rho_e U_e^2} = 2\frac{d\theta}{dx} \tag{12-9b}$$

where $c_{f_e}$ is the skin friction coefficient referred to $\rho_e$, which will be frequently used later on. It is to be noted that $c_{f_e}/c_{f_w} = T_e/T_w$. After integration with respect to $x$, Eq. 12-9b can be rewritten as follows:

$$\begin{aligned} x &= 2\frac{T_w}{T_e}\int_\infty^{c_{f_w}} \frac{d\theta(c_{f_w})}{dc_{f_w}} \frac{1}{c_{f_w}} dc_{f_w} \\ &= 2\left(1 + \frac{\gamma - 1}{2} M_e^2\right)\frac{T_w}{T_e^0}\int_\infty^{c_{f_w}} \frac{d\theta(c_{f_w})}{dc_{f_w}} \frac{1}{c_{f_w}} dc_{f_w} \end{aligned} \tag{12-14}$$

The value of the integrand of Eq. 12-14 is given by the differentiation of Eq. 12-13. In Eq. 12-14, the limits of integration are $(\infty, c_{f_w})$ for $c_{f_w}$, corresponding to $(0, x)$ for $x$, because at $x = 0$ the boundary is so thin that the velocity gradient and the skin friction become infinite. If we write $x$ in terms of the Reynolds number $\rho_w U_e x/\mu_w$, the integration of Eq. 12-14 gives a relation between the skin friction coefficient and the Reynolds number of the following form:

$$c_{f_w} = c_{f_w}\left(\frac{\rho_w U_e x}{\mu_w}, Pr, \frac{T_e^0}{T_w}, M_e\right) \tag{12-15}$$

Further the heat transfer coefficient may be found on the basis of the skin friction coefficient by means of the Reynolds analogy as examined in Art. 11.

Instead of using the Kármán similarity hypothesis (Eq. 12-3), which serves as the foundation of the differential equation (Eq. 12-5), we can use the Prandtl hypothesis (Eq. 12-4) so that Eq. 12-2a now becomes

$$y\frac{\partial U}{\partial y} = \frac{1}{\kappa_2}\sqrt{\frac{\tau_w}{\bar{\rho}}} \tag{12-16a}$$

Again by introducing the dimensionless quantities (Eq. 12-7), we can rewrite Eq. 12-16a in the following dimensionless form:

$$y^* \frac{\partial U^*}{dy^*} = \frac{1}{\kappa_2} \rho^{*-\frac{1}{2}} \tag{12-16b}$$

In Eq. 12-16 the assumption is again made that $\tau$ is constant across the boundary layer with the value $\tau_w$. For $\rho^*$, the expression given by Eq. 12-10 is again used, and all further steps to compute $U^*$ and the skin friction coefficient are similar to the treatment given above for the Kármán hypothesis. It is remarked that the differential equation (Eq.

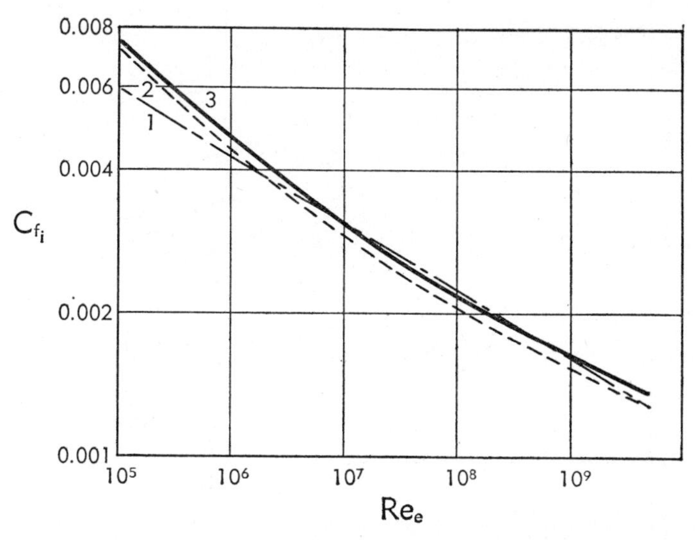


Fig. B,12a. Comparison of the mixing length and similarity hypotheses of skin friction. Curve 1 illustrates the Falkner law according to Eq. 13-15, curve 2 illustrates the Kármán law (Eq. 12-17), based on the similarity hypothesis, and curve 3 is the Prandtl law (Eq. 12-18) drawn with a coefficient 0.472, based on the mixing length hypothesis.

12-16b) from the Prandtl hypothesis corresponds to the differential equation (Eq. 12-8) from the Kármán hypothesis. However, Eq. 12-16b is of the first order and needs only one boundary condition, namely the interface condition

$$U^* = 11.5 \quad \text{at} \quad y^* = 11.5$$

It is interesting to compare the effect of the two hypotheses (Eq. 12-3 and 12-4) on the skin friction. For the sake of simplicity and in order to avoid as much as possible other assumptions which may obscure the issue, the comparison is made for skin friction coefficients of incompressible flow. Fig. B,12a shows that the Kármán and Prandtl hypotheses do not lead to an appreciable difference in skin friction coefficients. The curves are drawn according to the following formulas:

Kármán hypothesis [47],

$$\frac{0.242}{\sqrt{C_{f_i}}} = \log (C_{f_i} Re) \tag{12-17}$$

Prandtl hypothesis [48],

$$C_{f_i} = 0.472(\log Re)^{-2.58} \tag{12-18}$$

As an additional comparison, the power law of Falkner according to Eq. 13-5 with $A = 0.0262$, $n = \frac{1}{7}$ is also plotted, and agrees well with the

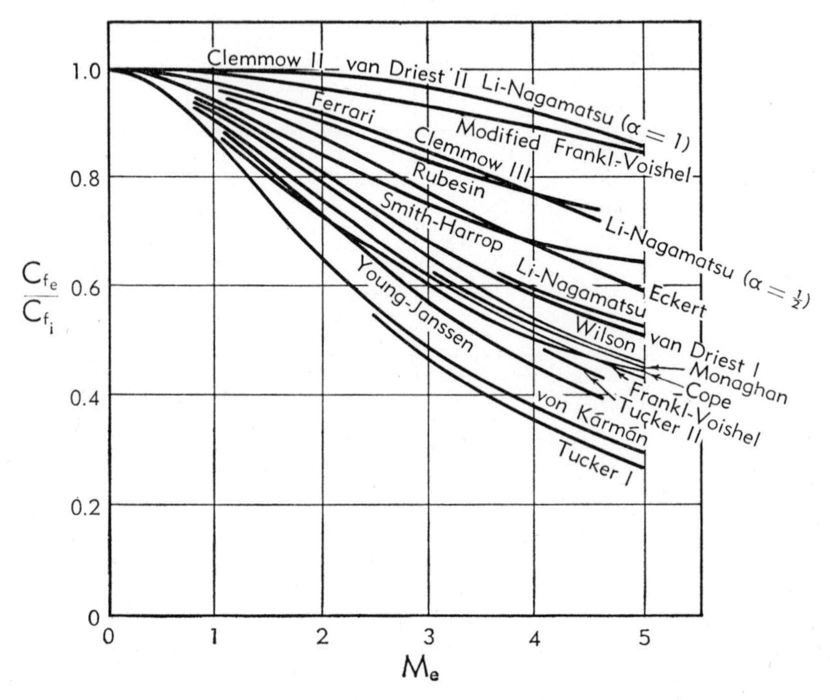


Fig. B,12b. Compressibility effect on skin friction (theories), after Chapman and Kester [29].

Kármán and Prandtl hypotheses. The Prandtl law has originally the coefficient 0.472 but Schlichting adopts a coefficient 0.455. Eq. 12-17 is sometimes called the Kármán-Schoenherr formula, and Eq. 12-18 the Prandtl-Schlichting formula.

Although the skin friction coefficient at low speeds does not depend very much on the Kármán or Prandtl hypotheses, with the application of those hypotheses to high speeds there arise many uncertainties. Now consideration must be given to new exchanges, such as density mixing and heat transfer, and to the variation of fluid properties across the boundary layer. An investigation of the theoretical basis of skin friction as given above will reveal many passages which are uncertain and arbitrary. Therefore it is not surprising that they yield a great number of different predictions of skin friction at high speeds. Fig. B,12b shows that the various theories differ appreciably at large $M_e$. They are based on the recovery factor $r_e = 1$, with the exception of the theory of Wilson which is based on $r_e = 0.89$. The viscosity-temperature exponent $\alpha$ covers the range of $\alpha = 0.75$ to 1, and the Reynolds number covers the range of $Re = 7$ to $10 \times 10^6$. The discrepancies between the values of skin friction predicted by the various theories increase as the Mach number increases. At a Mach number of 5, the theoretical values of the skin friction differ by a factor greater than 3. Only a small portion of the discrepancies can be attributed to the different values of $Re$, $r_e$, and $\alpha$ used in the various theories. Because of their uncertainties, we shall not enter into the detail of the theories, and the readers who are interested in such details are referred to [*19,38,49,50,51,52,53,54,55,56,57,58,59,60*]. In view of the difficulties of such theories of the skin friction coefficient, some empirical formula of skin friction coefficient may often be more useful in practice. These will be treated in Art. 13.

**B,13. Empirical Laws of Skin Friction.** Let us define again the various skin friction coefficients used in the theories and experiments. The local skin friction coefficient is defined in its general form by

$$c_f = \frac{2\tau_w}{\rho U_e^2} \tag{13-1a}$$

The wall and free stream values are obtained by writing in Eq. 13-1a, respectively, $\rho = \rho_w$ and $\rho = \rho_e$:

$$c_{f_w} = \frac{2\tau_w}{\rho_w U_e^2} \tag{13-1b}$$

$$c_{f_e} = \frac{2\tau_w}{\rho_e U_e^2} \tag{13-1c}$$

which have already been introduced in Eq. 12-13. The local skin friction coefficient $c_f$ is a function of $x$. Its average value is called the "average skin friction coefficient" $C_f$

$$C_f = \frac{1}{x}\int_0^x c_f(x)dx \tag{13-2}$$

or inversely

$$c_f(x) = C_f(x) + x\frac{\partial C_f}{\partial x} \tag{13-3}$$

Corresponding to $c_{f_w}$ and $c_{f_e}$, we can write their average values $C_{f_w}$ and $C_{f_e}$. In the dimensionless form $x$ can be replaced by the Reynolds numbers

$$Re = \frac{\rho U_e x}{\mu}, \quad Re_w = \frac{\rho_w U_e x}{\mu_w}, \quad \text{or} \quad Re_e = \frac{\rho_e U_e x}{\mu_e} \tag{13-4}$$

in respective cases.

The empirical laws of the skin friction coefficient for a compressible fluid start from incompressible laws, and the compressibility effects are incorporated by comparison with experiments. The power law

$$c_{f_i} = A Re^{-n} \tag{13-5}$$

is an example. Here $c_{f_i}$ is the skin friction coefficient for the incompressible boundary layer, $Re$ is defined by Eq. 13-4, $A$ and $n$ are numbers ($A = 0.0262$, $n = \frac{1}{7}$, according to Falkner [*61*]). In order to estimate the compressible skin friction coefficient (for example $c_{f_e}$), we assume that a reference temperature $T_r$ can be found so that the compressible skin friction coefficient $c_{f_r}$, defined by putting $\rho_r = \rho(T_r)$ into Eq. 13-1, satisfies the incompressible formula (Eq. 13-5). Then we can write

$$\begin{aligned} c_{f_r} &= c_{f_i}(Re_r) \\ &= c_{f_i}\left(Re_e \frac{\mu_e}{\mu_r} \frac{\rho_r}{\rho_e}\right) \\ &= c_{f_i}\left[Re_e \left(\frac{T_e}{T_r}\right)^{1+\alpha}\right] \end{aligned} \tag{13-6}$$

with $\rho_r/\rho_e = T_e/T_r$ and $\mu_e/\mu_r = (T_e/T_r)^\alpha$. Since $c_{f_i}$ follows the power law (Eq. 13-5), Eq. 13-6 can be rewritten in the following form:

$$c_{f_r} = c_{f_i}(Re_e)\left(\frac{T_e}{T_r}\right)^{-(1+\alpha)n}$$

Further, $c_{f_r}$ can be expressed in terms of $c_{f_e}$ by means of the definitions (Eq. 13-1) which can be rewritten as follows:

$$c_{f_r} = c_{f_e}\frac{\rho_e}{\rho_r} = c_{f_e}\left(\frac{T_e}{T_r}\right)^{-1}$$

so that Eq. 13-6 becomes

$$\frac{c_{f_e}(Re_e)}{c_{f_i}(Re_e)} = \left(\frac{T_e}{T_r}\right)^{1-(1+\alpha)n} \tag{13-7a}$$

The right-hand side of Eq. 13-7a gives the effect of compressibility (or $M_e$). In a compressible boundary layer $T$ varies between $T_e$ and $T_w$. It can be assumed that the compressibility effect is covered on the average, if the average temperature

$$T_r = \tfrac{1}{2}(T_e + T_w) \tag{13-8}$$

is taken as the reference temperature. Then $T_e/2T_r$ or $T_e/(T_e + T_w)$ can be computed in terms of $M_e$ on the basis of Eq. 9-9, so that finally Eq. 13-7a becomes

$$\frac{c_{f_e}(Re_e)}{c_{f_i}(Re_e)} = \beta^{1-(1+\alpha)n} \tag{13-7b}$$

where

$$\beta = \left(1 + r_e \frac{\gamma - 1}{4} M_e^2\right)^{-1} \tag{13-9}$$

$r_e$ is the recovery factor defined by Eq. 9-9b, $M_e$ is the free stream Mach number, and $\gamma$ is the ratio of specific heats.

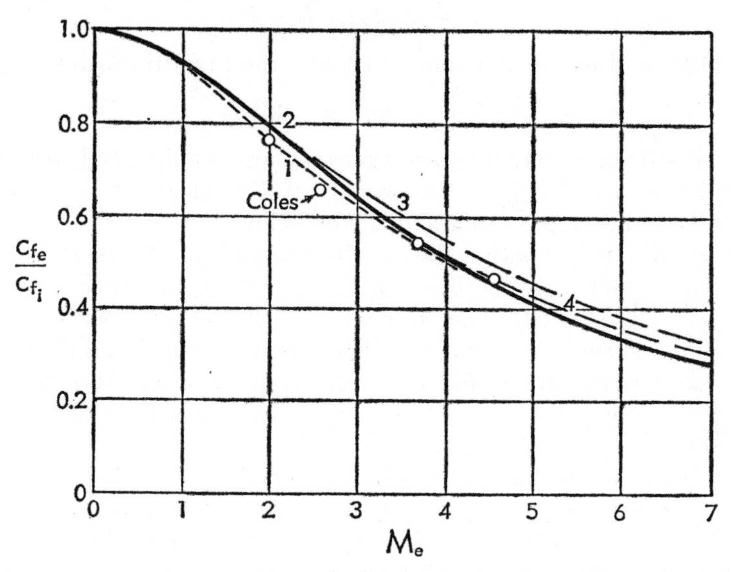


Fig. B,13. Compressibility effect on skin friction (empirical laws). $c_{f_e}/c_{f_i}$ is the ratio of average skin friction coefficients respectively at free stream Mach numbers $M_e \neq 0$ and $M_e = 0$. Curve 1 represents the theory of Frankl-Voishel [*44,45*]. Curves 2 and 3 represent Eq. 13-7b and 13-11, based respectively on the power law and the logarithmic law of incompressible skin friction coefficient. The experimental results of Coles [*34*] are shown in circles for comparison. A viscosity-temperature exponent $\alpha = 1$ is used in plotting curves 1, 2, and 3. Curve 4 is plotted with $\alpha = 0.75$, according to Eq. 13-11.

Instead of selecting the power law (Eq. 13-5) on which to base compressibility effect, we may take as an alternative example a logarithmic law of the form (decimal basis):

$$C_{f_i}(r) = A(\log Re)^{-n} \tag{13-10}$$

Then by the procedures of Eq. 13-6, 13-7, and 13-8 we find the following compressibility effect:

$$\frac{C_{f_e}(Re_e)}{C_{f_i}(Re_e)} = \left[1 + \frac{(1+\alpha)\log\beta}{\log Re_e}\right]^{-n} \beta \tag{13-11}$$

where $\beta = T_e/T_r$ is given by Eq. 13-9, when $T_r$ assumes the value given by Eq. 13-8.

It is interesting to note that the compressibility effect as given by Eq. 13-7b, on the basis of the power law (Eq. 13-5), is separated from the

Reynolds number effect, while the compressibility effect (Eq. 13-11), on the basis of logarithmic law (Eq. 13-10), includes a Reynolds number effect.

The two formulas (Eq. 13-7b and 13-11) are illustrated in Fig. B,13, by taking $\alpha = 1$, $r_e = 1$. The Falkner constants [*61*]

$$A = 0.0262, \quad n = \tfrac{1}{7}$$

have been used in Eq. 13-5 and 13-7b, and the Prandtl constants [*48*]

$$A = 0.455, \quad n = 2.58$$

in Eq. 13-10 and 13-11. It is seen that they are in quite good agreement. Also plotted are the theoretical results of Frankl and Voishel [*44,45*], originally in tabulated form, and the experimental results of Coles and Goddard [*35*]. It seems that the empitical formulas (Eq. 13-7*b* and 13-11) agree rather well with the theory of Frankl-Voishel and with the experiments of Coles. Although the experiments of Coles are run with a slightly different Reynolds number ($Re_e = 8 \times 10^6$) than the Reynolds number of the theoretical curves ($Re_e = 7 \times 10^6$), the correction for such a discrepancy is not significant. The viscosity-temperature coefficient $\alpha$ has the value between 0.75 and 1.

Eq. 13-11 is also plotted in Fig. B,14b with $C_{f_e}$ vs. $Re_e$, to be compared with experiments, by taking $\alpha = 0.75$, $n = 2.58$. $C_{f_i}$ is based on Eq. 13-10 with $A = 0.455$. It is seen that the theoretical formula (Eq. 13-11) is in good agreement with experiments.

**B,14. Comparison between Experiments and Theories.** There exists an extensive history of experiments on skin friction. Because of the importance of skin friction to naval architecture, experiments on skin friction were started as early as 1793 by Beaufoy. Schoenherr [*47*] gives a good review of experiments prior to 1932.

In Fig. B,14a are plotted the experimental values of skin friction in compressible flow. The ratio $C_{f_e}/C_{f_i}$ or $c_{f_e}/c_{f_i}$ is illustrated. Except for the measurements of Chapman-Kester and Liepmann-Dhawan, wherein the incompressible skin friction values are deduced experimentally, all data points shown are based on the incompressible skin friction formula (Eq. 12-17) of Kármán-Schoenherr. There are two methods of determining the skin friction coefficient. Liepmann-Dhawan, Coles, and Chapman-Kester determine the skin friction coefficient by direct force measurements. Others determine it by surveying the boundary layer and then calculating the friction coefficient by the usual momentum method. At the Mach number of 5, the two methods yield a discrepancy of about 5 per cent.

Since the empirical theories, as given in Art. 13, do not differ very much according to Fig. B,13, we have plotted the theoretical formula

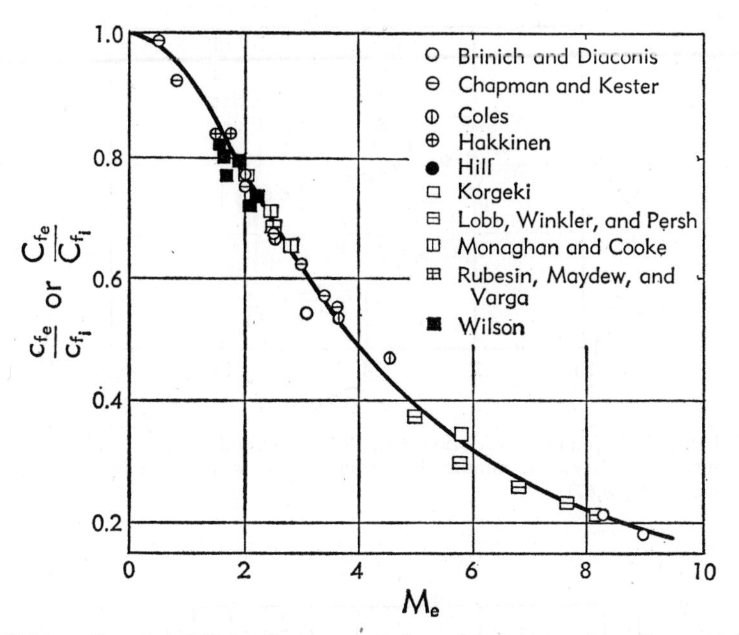


Fig. B,14a. Compressibility effect on turbulent skin friction (experimental). The experimental data are plotted according to [18,29,32,34,38,39,42,62,63]. The curve is drawn according to Eq. 13-9, with a viscosity-temperature coefficient of 0.75.

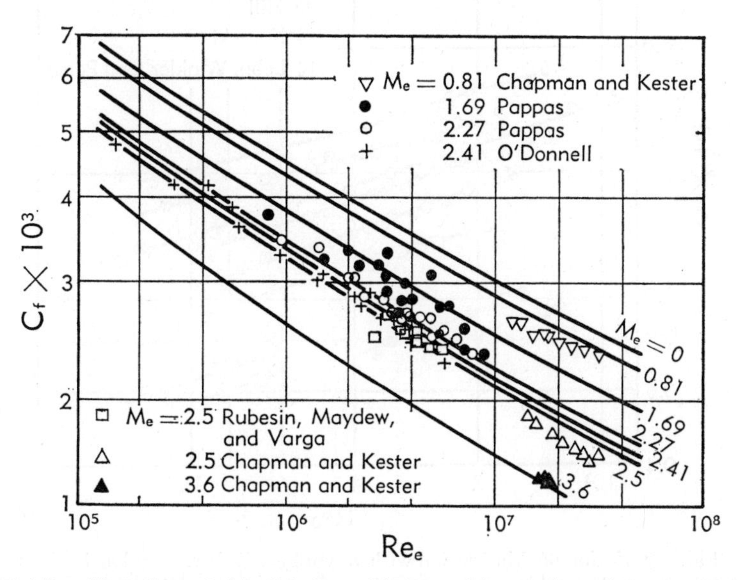


Fig. B,14b. Variation of skin friction with Reynolds number. $C_f$ = average skin friction coefficient. $Re_e = \rho_e U_e/\mu_e$, Reynolds number based on the free stream. The experimental data are drawn from [29,32,33,65] for the free stream Mach number $M_e = 0.81 - 3.6$. The theoretical curves ($M_e = 0 - 3.6$) are plotted according to Eq. 13-11, for $n = 2.58$, $A = 0.455$, $\alpha = 0.75$.

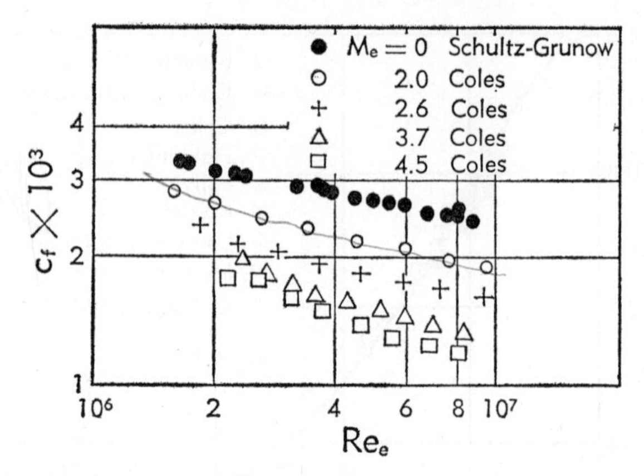


Fig. B,14c. Variation of skin friction with Reynolds number. $c_f$ = local skin friction coefficient, $Re_e$ = Reynolds number based on the free stream conditions. The data are drawn from [*66,67*].

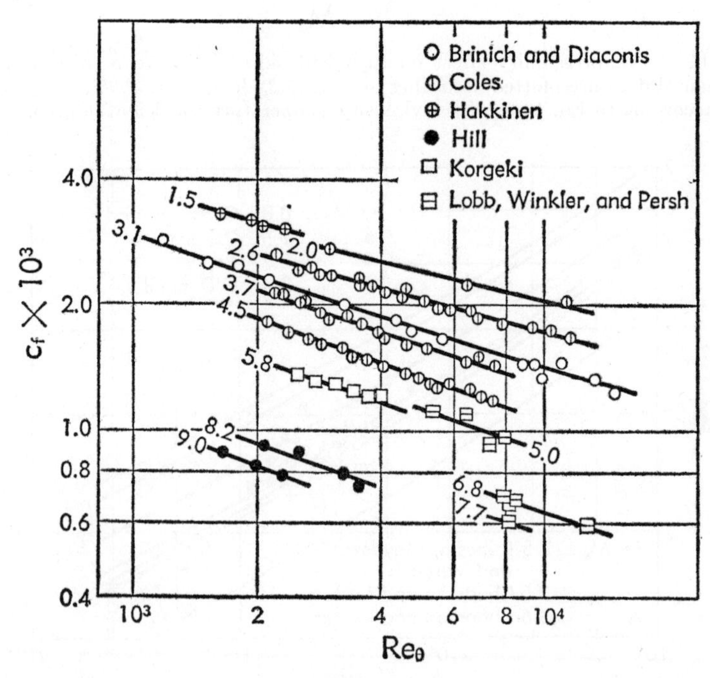


Fig. B,14d. Variation of skin friction with Reynolds number. $c_f$ = local skin friction coefficient, $Re_\theta$ = Reynolds number based on the momentum thickness. The experimental data are drawn from [*18,39,63,64,66*] for the free stream Mach number $M_e$ = 1.5 – 9.0.

(Eq. 13-9) with $\alpha = 0.75$, and $n = \frac{1}{7}$ based on the power law of incompressible skin friction to compare with experiments. It is seen that more experiments at higher Mach numbers are needed in order to understand skin friction better and to formulate better theories. The data of Fig. B,14a are plotted according to [*18,29,32,34,38,39,42,62,63,64*].

Fig. B,14b, B,14c, and B,14d illustrate the variations of the experimental skin friction coefficients $c_f$ and $C_f$ with the Reynolds numbers, based on the free stream conditions and the momentum thickness. It is interesting to see whether the experiments would follow some semi-empirical laws of skin friction. For this purpose, Eq. 13-11 is plotted for $n = 2.58$, $A = 0.455$, and $\alpha = 0.75$ in Fig. B,14b, and we see that Eq. 13-11 is in quite good agreement with experiments.

# *CHAPTER 4. GENERAL TREATMENT OF INCOMPRESSIBLE MEAN FLOW ALONG WALLS*

**B,15. Power Laws.** In attempting to deal with turbulent flows confined within pipes and channels or bounded on one side by a wall, much attention was given in the older literature to power laws. These were found to be very useful in that they could be made to approximate observed mean velocity distributions and to yield resistance laws that were reasonably correct over a limited Reynolds number range. These laws are, of course, purely empirical, but they have not lost their usefulness when one wishes to express the general character of a velocity profile in a pipe or boundary layer, or wishes to make an estimate of skin friction. We should, however, be mindful of their limitations.

The power laws stem from the Blasius resistance formula for smooth straight pipes of circular cross section [*68*]. They were found, however, to be transferable to two-dimensional channels with parallel walls and two-dimensional boundary layers, if the radius of a pipe, the half-width of a channel, and the thickness of a boundary layer were regarded as equivalent dimensions, and if velocities were referred to those at the center or free stream. In all cases the walls are assumed to be smooth. Since the detailed development is available elsewhere [*69*], only the main steps are given here. Because the condition of incompressibility has been imposed, the physical properties of the fluid are independent of the flow and constant for any set of conditions. Hence we may simply denote the density by $\rho$, the viscosity by $\mu$, and the kinematic viscosity by $\nu$.

Since it is not necessary to distinguish among the flows in pipes, channels, and boundary layers in bringing out the elemental aspects of power formulas, the distance from the wall is expressed by $y$, the velocity at the center or in the free stream by $U_e$, and the value of $y$ where the velocity is $U_e$ by $\delta$. The only constraint on the flow considered is the shear stress at the wall $\tau_w$. This means, of course, that the effect of a pressure gradient is neglected, and we must limit ourselves to cases where the pressure is constant or changing so slowly in the stream direction that its effect is minor compared to the effect of $\tau_w$. The coefficients involved are accordingly:

The local friction coefficient $$\frac{\tau_w}{\frac{1}{2}\rho U_e^2} = c_f \tag{15-1}$$

The friction velocity $$\sqrt{\frac{\tau_w}{\rho}} = U_\tau \tag{15-2}$$

Assuming that the local friction coefficient depends on the Reynolds number and may be expressed in powers of the Reynolds number, the relation may be written

$$c_f = \frac{\text{const}}{\left(\frac{U_e\delta}{\nu}\right)^m} \tag{15-3}$$

where $U_e\delta/\nu$ is a Reynolds number based on the maximum velocity and the distance from the wall to the point of maximum velocity. It follows from Eq. 15-3 and the definitions (Eq. 15-1 and 15-2) that

$$\frac{U_e}{U_\tau} = \text{const}\left(\frac{U_\tau\delta}{\nu}\right)^{\frac{m}{2-m}} \tag{15-4}$$

where $U_\tau\delta/\nu$ is a Reynolds number based on the friction velocity and $\delta$. Eq. 15-3 and 15-4 are both expressions for conditions near the wall. However, it may be argued that a formula similar to Eq. 15-4 may be used to express the velocity at any distance from the wall without appreciable error because the main increase in velocity takes place near the wall. Assuming this, the velocity distribution is written

$$\frac{U}{U_\tau} = \text{const}\left(\frac{U_\tau y}{\nu}\right)^{\frac{m}{2-m}} \tag{15-5}$$

where $U$ is the mean velocity at the distance $y$ from the wall.

We assume now that all mean velocity profiles are similar, and accordingly that $U/U_e$ is a function of $y/\delta$. While this assumption is exactly true for laminar flow, it is only an approximation for turbulent flow. The appropriate power-law form of the function is indicated by Eq. 15-5 and is written

$$\frac{U}{U_e} = \left(\frac{y}{\delta}\right)^{\frac{m}{2-m}} \tag{15-6}$$

By taking $m = \frac{1}{4}$ it is found that Eq. 15-3 expresses the variation of friction coefficients in pipes over the range $3000 < U_e\delta/\nu < 70{,}000$. With the constants also determined from pipe tests, Eq. 15-3, 15-4, 15-5, and 15-6 become

$$c_f = 0.0466 \left(\frac{U_e\delta}{\nu}\right)^{-\frac{1}{4}} \tag{15-3a}$$

$$\frac{U_e}{U_\tau} = 8.74 \left(\frac{U_\tau\delta}{\nu}\right)^{\frac{1}{7}} \tag{15-4a}$$

$$\frac{U}{U_\tau} = 8.74 \left(\frac{U_\tau y}{\nu}\right)^{\frac{1}{7}} \tag{15-5a}$$

$$\frac{U}{U_e} = \left(\frac{y}{\delta}\right)^{\frac{1}{7}} \tag{15-6a}$$

The foregoing formulas for pipes would not be expected to apply to other cases. However, they do apply to two-dimensional channels and flat plates over a limited range of Reynolds number for particular coefficients and exponents. Power-law velocity distributions fit the observed distributions in an over-all way but not in all detail.

When applied to the flat plate, Eq. 15-3a and 15-6a may be used to calculate $\delta$ and $c_f$ as functions of $x$ and of a Reynolds number based on $x$, provided the boundary layer begins as a turbulent layer at the leading edge. The loss of momentum flux through any section of the boundary layer is given by

$$\int_0^\delta \rho U(U_e - U)dy$$

The momentum thickness $\theta$, which when multiplied by $\rho U_e^2$ gives this quantity, is accordingly defined by

$$\theta = \frac{1}{\rho U_1^2} \int_0^\delta \rho U(U_e - U)dy = \int_0^\delta \frac{U}{U_e}\left(1 - \frac{U}{U_e}\right)dy \tag{15-7}$$

Since $\tau_w$ alone accounts for the loss of momentum, it follows that

$$\frac{d\theta}{dx} = \frac{\tau_w}{\rho U_e^2} = \frac{1}{2}c_f \tag{15-8}$$

With the velocity distribution given by Eq. 15-6a, $\theta = 7\delta/72$. By substituting this and Eq. 15-3a into Eq. 15-8, and integrating with the boundary condition $\delta = 0$ when $x = 0$, the result is

$$= 0.381x \left(\frac{U_e x}{\nu}\right)^{-\frac{1}{5}} \tag{15-9}$$

where $x$ is the distance from the leading edge and $U_e x/\nu$ is a Reynolds number based on $x$ and the velocity of the free stream. From Eq. 15-3a and 15-9 it follows that

$$c_f = 0.0592 \left(\frac{U_e x}{\nu}\right)^{-\frac{1}{5}} \tag{15-10}$$

Again taking $\theta = 7\delta/72$ and using Eq. 15-9,

$$C_f = 0.074 \left(\frac{U_e x}{\nu}\right)^{-\frac{1}{5}} \tag{15-11}$$

where $C_f$ is the mean friction coefficient from the leading edge to the point $x$. Eq. 15-11 checks the tests on smooth plates for $U_e x/\nu$ up to about $3 \times 10^6$.

Power formulas should be regarded as interpolation formulas, useful over a limited range of Reynolds number. For $U_e\delta/\nu$ over 100,000, Eq. 15-6a agrees better with measurements when the exponent $\frac{1}{7}$ is replaced by $\frac{1}{8}$, and even $\frac{1}{9}$ when the Reynolds number is sufficiently high. Skin friction formulas may likewise be improved for agreement with measurement over a greater range of Reynolds number by adjusting the exponent. For example, as we have seen in Art. 13, Falkner [*61*] uses an exponent of $-\frac{1}{7}$ instead of $-\frac{1}{5}$ and gives

$$c_f = 0.0262 \left(\frac{U_e x}{\nu}\right)^{-\frac{1}{7}} \tag{15-12}$$

$$C_f = 0.0306 \left(\frac{U_e x}{\nu}\right)^{-\frac{1}{7}} \tag{15-13}$$

It must be remembered that the foregoing considerations apply only to smooth walls. Except for Art. 23, where the effect of roughness is considered, and elsewhere where roughness is mentioned, the smooth-wall condition is implied throughout this chapter.

**B,16. Wall Law and Velocity-Defect Law.** Two laws that have gone far toward giving order and meaning to the seemingly confusing and conflicting data on flows bounded or partially bounded by walls are the "law of the wall" attributed to Prandtl (for example [*70*]) and the "velocity-defect law" introduced by von Kármán [*71*]. The first pertains to the region close to the wall where the effect of viscosity is directly felt and the second pertains to the bulk of the shear layer where viscous forces become negligible.

The law of the wall is based on the logical premise that the tangential stress at the wall $\tau_w$ must depend on the velocity $U$ at the distance $y$ from the wall and on the viscosity $\mu$ and density $\rho$. Assuming that the stress at the wall is the only constraint on the flow, we may write

$$F(\tau_w, U, y, \mu, \rho) = 0$$

This may be expressed in dimensionless form by

$$\frac{U}{U_\tau} = f\left(\frac{U_\tau y}{\nu}\right) \tag{16-1}$$

in terms of the characteristic friction velocity $U_\tau$ and the characteristic length $\nu/U_\tau$. The functional equation (Eq. 16-1) is the law of the wall. In the laminar sublayer it takes the special form

$$\frac{U}{U_\tau} = \frac{U_\tau y}{\nu} \tag{16-2}$$

which arises from the circumstance that the sublayer is so thin that $\tau$ therein is constant and equal to $\tau_w$. In Eq. 16-2 the density included in the terms automatically cancels out.

The range of $y$ over which Eq. 16-1 is valid must be established by experiment. It might be supposed that the range would be severely limited by pressure gradient effects when these are present, since, as we have seen, the pressure acting across an area of unit width and height $y$ has been neglected. Recent data, to be discussed in Art. 19, show that there remains a considerable range over which the law is valid for both rising and falling pressures and that the law is not so restricted as to be useless until conditions of near-separated flow are reached. Thus there is a range, even though possibly short, beyond the laminar sublayer, where the functional relation (Eq. 16-1) is universally of the same form. This is true only when there is a laminar sublayer, and therefore true only when the wall is aerodynamically smooth.

The argument leading to the velocity-defect law is that the reduction in velocity $(U_e - U)$ at distance $y$ is the result of a tangential stress at the wall, independent of how this stress arises but dependent on the distance $\delta$ to which the effect has diffused from the wall. We may then write

$$U_e - U = G(U_\tau, y, \delta)$$

and in terms of dimensionless ratios

$$\frac{U_e - U}{U_\tau} = g\left(\frac{y}{\delta}\right) \tag{16-3}$$

This is the velocity-defect law.

The law (Eq. 16-3), unlike Eq. 16-1, holds true for rough as well as smooth walls, provided the roughness elements are not so large that $y$ becomes indeterminate. Data for boundary layers with constant pressure are found to fall on a single curve within the precision fixed by the experimental scatter. This is shown by Fig. B,16 which presents various data collected by Clauser [*72*] for different Reynolds numbers and for smooth and rough walls. Aside from the fact that the law cannot apply in the vicinity of the laminar sublayer nor at distances comparable to the height of roughness elements, it appears to exhibit a universality for constant pressure boundary layers. Clauser has shown, however, by a formal argument that the law is fundamentally not universal when $U_\tau$ varies from one set of data to another, but that the dispersion will generally be small and scarcely outside the usual random scattering due to observational errors.

The function $g$ is affected to degrees that are far from negligible by conditions imposed on the flow from without. The effect of the pressure gradient, which will be considered in Art. 19, is of most importance. It is also affected by free stream turbulence and is therefore different in pipes and channels than in boundary layers. This sensitivity of the velocity-defect law to outer conditions stands in sharp contrast to the law of the wall which is remarkably insensitive in this respect.

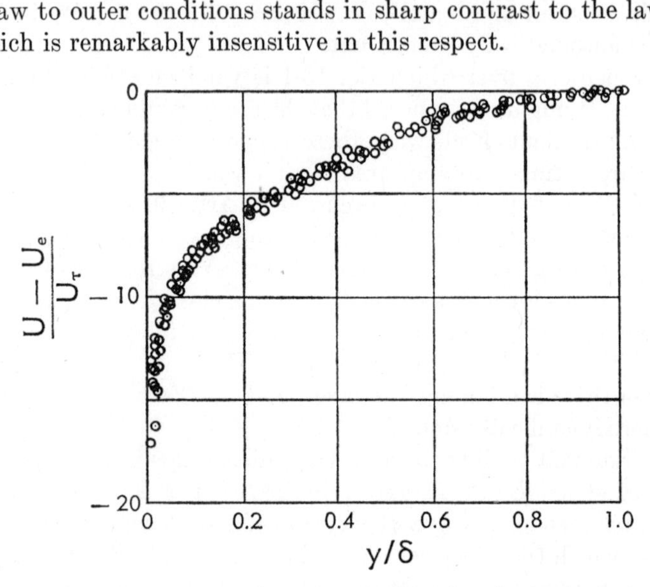


Fig. B,16. Data for smooth and rough walls plotted on basis of velocity-defect law. (Taken from Clauser [*72*] omitting data source and designation.)

**B,17. Logarithmic Formulas.** From time to time it has been inferred in the literature that the two laws, Eq. 16-1 and 16-3, are empirical laws, and in the sense that their adoption has depended on experimental confirmation, they are empirical. Certainly they draw but little on any knowledge of turbulent structure. About their only connection with the behavior of turbulence is the justification of the assumption that transfer processes are affected by viscosity very near a wall, but are independent of viscosity and dependent on the scale of the shear layer in the bulk of the flow. The principal empirical fact about these laws is that their regions of validity overlap one another. There is nothing in their makeup that requires an overlap, and the only apparent reason for it is a gradual change from wall conditions to outer-flow conditions.

Millikan [*73*] has shown that if there is any region of overlap, no matter how limited, in which both laws are valid, then the functions $f$ and $g$ must be logarithms. Since this is the same form which results from mixing length considerations, but which is arrived at without recourse to a physical model, the authors feel that this deduction must be ranked among the major contributions to the subject. A simple way of arriving at this result is to reexamine Eq. 16-1 and 16-3, written in the following forms:

$$\frac{U}{U_\tau} = f\left[\left(\frac{y}{\delta}\right)\left(\frac{U_\tau \delta}{\nu}\right)\right] \tag{17-1}$$

$$\frac{U}{U_\tau} = \frac{U_e}{U_\tau} - g\left(\frac{y}{\delta}\right) \tag{17-2}$$

Since these are two expressions for the same quantity, and since a multiplying factor inside a function must have the same effect as an additive factor outside a function, the functions $f$ and $g$ must be logarithms.

The two formulas are usually written in the form

$$\frac{U}{U_\tau} = \frac{2.3}{K}\log\left(\frac{U_\tau y}{\nu}\right) + c_1 \tag{17-3}$$

$$\frac{U_e - U}{U_\tau} = c_2 - \frac{2.3}{K}\log\frac{y}{\delta} \tag{17-4}$$

where $K$, $c_1$, and $c_2$ are experimentally determined constants. It follows from Eq. 17-1 and 17-2, when $f$ and $g$ are expressed as logarithms, that $K$ must be common to both Eq. 17-3 and 17-4. The constant $K$ is universal and the logarithmic form of the functions do fit the observations, but only over a limited range of the variables. More specifically they have the logarithmic form where they overlap, but not necessarily much beyond this region. This may be taken as evidence that the empirically established overlap is not a basic condition and therefore not a sufficiently strong one to impel a long range validity for the laws deduced from it. The extent to which these laws fit the data and are influenced by various conditions will be taken up in Art. 19, 20, and 21.

For the present we direct our attention to Eq. 17-4 in order to call attention to the fact that the constant $c_2$ is found to be the same for pipes and channels, but that it has a different value for boundary layers of flat plates. This is shown in Fig. B,17a in which pipe data have been omitted. The data are taken from [*67,74,75,76,77*]. The Reynolds number $Re_\delta$ is in all cases $U_e\delta/\nu$. The constant 5.75, corresponding to $K = 0.40$, is common to both, provided the curves are fitted near the wall. It is seen that the log law does not fit well for the full range of $y/\delta$. This means only that the logarithmic form of the defect law is at fault, not the functional form of the law itself. More significant is the fact that the function $g$ in Eq. 16-3 is different in boundary layers from that in channels. This difference is evidently due mostly to a sensitivity to conditions at the outer limit $y = \delta$ rather than to the presence of a small falling

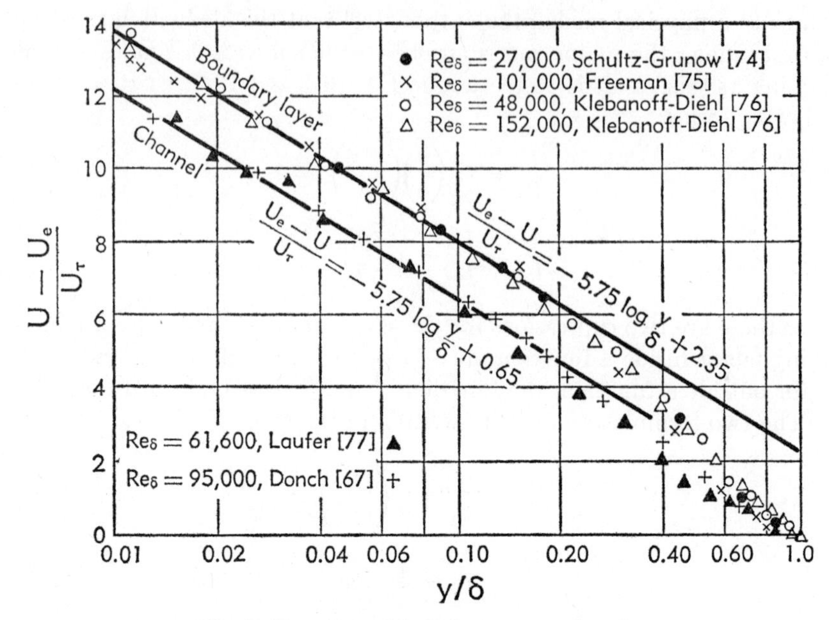


Fig. B,17a. Logarithmic law, comparison for channel and boundary layer of flat plate.

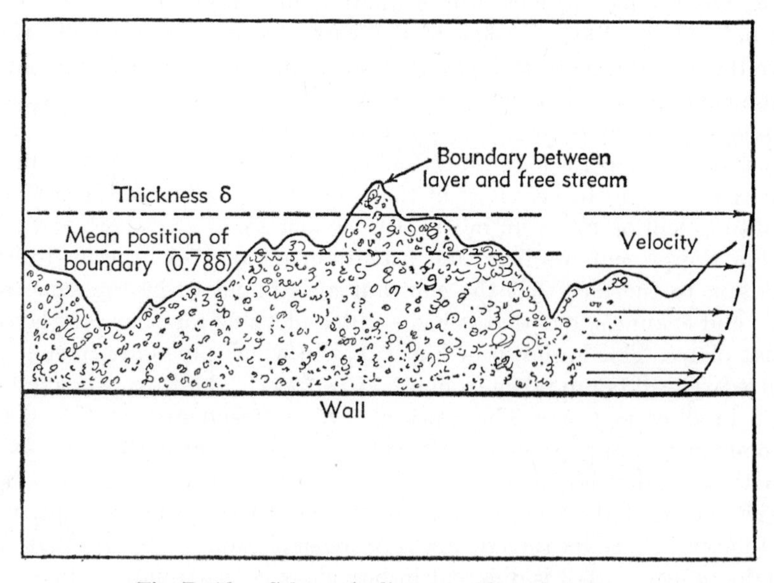


Fig. B,17b. Schematic diagram of boundary layer.

pressure in the case of a channel, and a constant pressure in the case of a boundary layer.

The boundary layer bounded by a free stream of negligible turbulence is known to have a sharp but very irregular outer limit. This is illustrated schematically in Fig. B,17b. The phenomenon is common to all turbulent shear flows which are limited only by the extent to which they have diffused into nonturbulent fluid. There is no such limit for fully developed turbulent flow in pipes and channels where turbulent motions may freely cross the center. To a limited extent a similar condition can be produced in boundary layer flows by introducing turbulence into the free stream by means of a grid. It has been noted that the profiles then deviate toward those for the pipe and channel.

**B,18. Smooth Wall Incompressible Skin Friction Laws.** So far our laws have been so general that pipes and channels on the one hand and boundary layers on the other could be treated as one subject. We may continue in this vein in expressing the general form of the skin friction law, but shortly it will be necessary to make a distinction.

Since skin friction depends on conditions near the wall, Eq. 17-3 and 17-4 are used to derive a formula for skin friction, as was first done by von Kármán [*71*]. If these equations are added, the result is

$$\frac{U_e}{U_\tau} = \frac{2.3}{K} \log\left(\frac{U_\tau \delta}{\nu}\right) + \text{const} \qquad (18\text{-}1)$$

By using Eq. 15-1 and 15-2 and introducing $Re_\delta = U_e\delta/\nu$, Eq. 18-1 becomes

$$\sqrt{\frac{2}{c_f}} = \frac{2.3}{K} \log\left(Re_\delta \sqrt{c_f}\right) + \text{const} \qquad (18\text{-}2)$$

Eq. 18-2 has been verified by a number of reliable measurements in pipes. With the constants for pipe flow as given by von Kármán [*78*], Eq. 18-2 becomes

$$\frac{1}{\sqrt{c_f}} = 4.15 \log\left(Re_\delta \sqrt{c_f}\right) + 3.60 \qquad (18\text{-}3)$$

where $Re_\delta$ is based on the velocity at the center $U_e$ and the radius of the pipe. The constant 4.15 corresponds to $K = 0.39$, this value having been chosen to give the best all-around agreement.

The Kármán skin friction formula for flat plates [*78,79*] results from conversion of Eq. 18-3 into terms involving $x$, where $x$ is the distance from the leading edge and the assumed beginning of the turbulent boundary layer. It is expressed as

$$\sqrt{\frac{2}{c_f}} = \frac{2.3}{K} \log\left(Re c_f\right) + \text{const} \qquad (18\text{-}4)$$

where $Re = U_e x/\nu$ and $c_f$ is again the local friction coefficient defined by Eq. 15-1. With the constants evaluated from Kempf's measurements on a flat plate [80], Eq. 18-4 becomes

$$\frac{1}{\sqrt{c_f}} = 4.15 \log (Re c_f) + 1.7 \tag{18-5}$$

Schoenherr [47] found the coefficient of mean friction over the distance $x$ to be given by

$$\frac{0.242}{\sqrt{C_f}} = \log (Re C_f) \tag{12-17}$$

and the relation between the local and the mean friction coefficients to be

$$c_f = \frac{0.558 C_f}{0.558 + 2\sqrt{C_f}} \tag{18-6}$$

Eq. 12-17 is one of the most widely used formulas for incompressible flow and, as previously mentioned in Art. 12 and 14, is sometimes called the Kármán-Schoenherr formula.

As reported by Prandtl [48], Schlichting proposed an interpolation formula of the form

$$C_f = 0.455 (\log Re)^{-2.58} \tag{12-18}$$

The comparison between Eq. 12-17 and 12-18 is shown in Fig. B,12a. The corresponding interpolation formula for $c_f$, also given by Schlichting [80], is

$$c_f = (2 \log Re - 0.65)^{-2.3} \tag{18-7}$$

Schultz-Grunow [74] adopted the Prandtl law with constants as follows:

$$c_f = 0.370 (\log Re)^{-2.584} \tag{18-8}$$

While the foregoing formulas are expressed in the form usually desired for engineering purposes, they suffer from the drawback that the boundary layer is often laminar for a significant distance before transition occurs. In such cases formulas based on $Re$ cannot be applied without assuming some fictitious origin for $x$. A formula like Eq. 18-3, based on the local parameter $Re_\delta$, does not involve this difficulty. Because of the indefiniteness of the outer limit of the boundary layer, the momentum thickness $\theta$ is commonly used in place of $\delta$, and $Re_\theta = U_e\theta/\nu$ takes the place of $Re_\delta$. Squire and Young [81] obtained from Eq. 18-4 the approximate relation

$$\frac{1}{\sqrt{c_f}} = A \log Re_\theta + B \tag{18-9}$$

with the constants $A$ and $B$ chosen to give the best agreement with Eq.

12-18. Their final expression, written in the form most commonly used, is

$$\frac{2}{c_f} = [5.890 \log (4.075 Re_\theta)]^2 \tag{18-10}$$

On the experimental side, measurements using the floating-element technique, wherein the shear stress on an element of the wall is determined from a direct force measurement, are now believed to be the most reliable. The best known examples of results employing this technique

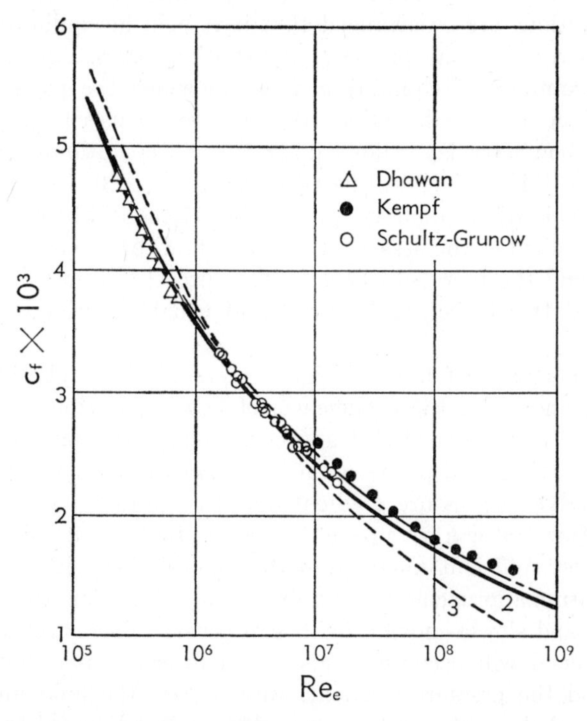


Fig. B,18. Local skin friction coefficient for smooth wall, zero pressure gradient. Experimental values represented by points. Curve 1: Eq. 18-5; curve 2: Eq. 18-8; curve 3: Eq. 15-10.

are those of Kempf [*82*] and the more recent results of Schultz-Grunow [*74*] and Dhawan [*37*]. These are given in Fig. B,18. Represented for comparison are the curves corresponding to the power formula (Eq. 15-10) and the logarithmic formulas (Eq. 18-5 and 18-8).

**B,19. Effect of Pressure Gradient.** When a body moves through a fluid, the pressure in the neighborhood of the body is different from that in the undisturbed fluid in ways that are too well known to be recounted here. It suffices merely to point out that pressure gradients are the rule rather than the exception. The present discussion will be limited to two-dimensional flow where pressure gradients in the $x$ and $y$ directions are encountered.

Boundary layers are usually so thin compared to the relatively large distances over which pressure changes occur that the changes across the layer are so small that they have insignificant effects. The pressure may change even more gradually in the $x$ direction, but here the boundary layer extends over the full range of the pressure changes, and cumulative effects become important. The thickness of the layer is always affected, and the mean velocity profile will change form as the flow progresses unless conditions are so arranged that it is held in equilibrium by the balance between inertial, pressure, and friction forces. Pipe and channel flows are examples of equilibrium flows in which the pressure drop is exactly balanced by wall friction. As shown by Clauser [*83*], a balance is possible in boundary layer flows under certain conditions, and his contributions to this subject will be taken up in Art. 20. In general, mean velocity distributions undergo progressive changes when subjected to pressure gradients—the less so when the flow proceeds toward lower pressures, and the more so when the flow proceeds toward higher pressures. The latter therefore deserves, and usually receives, the greater attention.

The importance of flow to higher pressures is emphasized by the possibility, and often the occurrence, of flow separation. Separation is the result of flow reversal and an accumulation of stagnant fluid over which the moving fluid passes without having to follow the contour of a body. An adverse pressure gradient opposes motion in the direction of the main flow and can set up motion in the reverse direction when the fluid has lost sufficient momentum through friction with a wall. Since the momentum approaches zero at a wall, only the shear stresses between the faster- and slower-moving fluids can prevent flow reversal. Whether or not reversal will occur depends on an interplay between the shear stresses and the pressure gradient. In any case the fluid movement is retarded, and shear stresses are expended against internal forces on the fluid arising from the pressure gradient. The maximum shear stress is no longer at the wall, as it is for constant pressure, but now occurs some fraction of the boundary layer thickness away from the wall depending on the state of retardation of the layer. These effects reduce skin friction and the momentum losses from this source, but only in exchange for even greater internal momentum losses resulting from shear stresses applied to pressure-retarded flow.

A classic example of the typical evolution of velocity profiles occurring when a boundary layer is subjected to a monotonically increasing pressure sufficient to bring about eventual flow separation is the set of curves compiled by von Doenhoff and Tetervin [*84*] shown in Fig. B,19a. Here $U_e$ is the local free stream velocity just outside the boundary layer, and

$\theta$ is the momentum thickness. Each curve of the set is characterized by a constant value of the form parameter $H$, where $H = \delta^*/\theta$ and in accordance with the usual definitions

$$\delta^* = \text{displacement thickness} = \int_0^\delta \left(1 - \frac{U}{U_e}\right) dy$$

$$\theta = \text{momentum thickness} = \int_0^\delta \frac{U}{U_e}\left(1 - \frac{U}{U_e}\right) dy$$

On the grounds that all suitable boundary layer data available up to 1943 could be made to fit one or another of these curves, von Doenhoff and

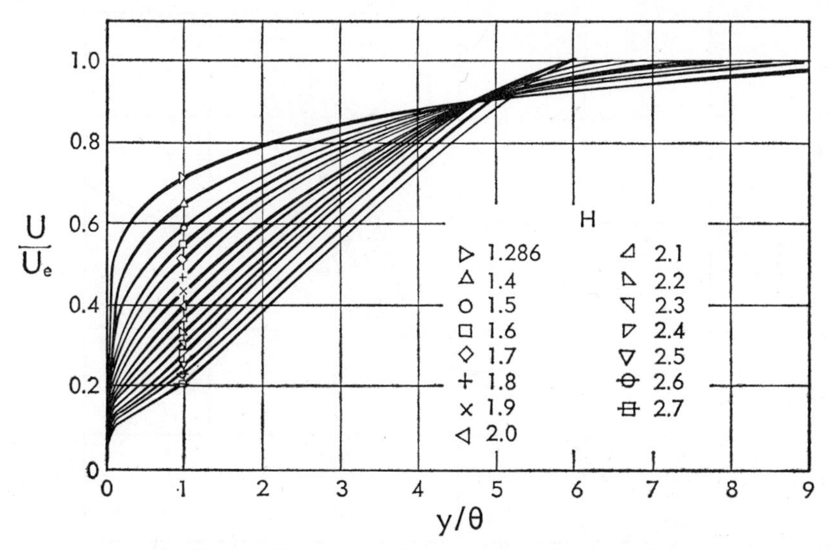


Fig. B,19a. Velocity profiles corresponding to various values of *H*, after von Doenhoff and Tetervin [*84*].

Tetervin concluded that $H$ was a suitable form parameter. When the pressure increases with increasing $x$ and the gradient is sufficient to bring about eventual separation, $H$ steadily increases, and each successive profile takes a shape similar to one of those in the figure. Separation is imminent when $H$ is above 2 and is likely to occur when $H$ is 2.6 or 2.7. Apparently this family characteristic is only true of nonequilibrium profiles, for Clauser has recently shown that equilibrium profiles, for which $H$ remains nearly constant with increasing $x$, do not align themselves with the typical forms of this family (see Art. 20). However, the general features are preserved.

There has been a great deal of speculation about the abrupt rise of the curves of Fig. B,19a near the origin. It will be noted that even when the flow is about to separate the steep initial rise is present. Thanks to the recent contributions of Coles [*85*], to be considered in Art. 21, and to facts pointed out earlier by Clauser about the law of the wall, this feature now has a simple explanation. If we regard the phenomenon as a sharp drop in velocity to zero at the wall instead of a rise from the wall outward, we see that this is simply the region where wall friction becomes predominant over the pressure effect. In other words, this is the region governed by the law of the wall. Typical of the agreement with the law of the wall and of the manner of departing from it are the examples shown in Fig. B,19b taken from Coles' paper [*85*]. When the Reynolds number is high and the pressure is either constant or the adverse gradients are not excessive, the agreement is more as shown in Fig. B,19c given by Clauser [*83*].

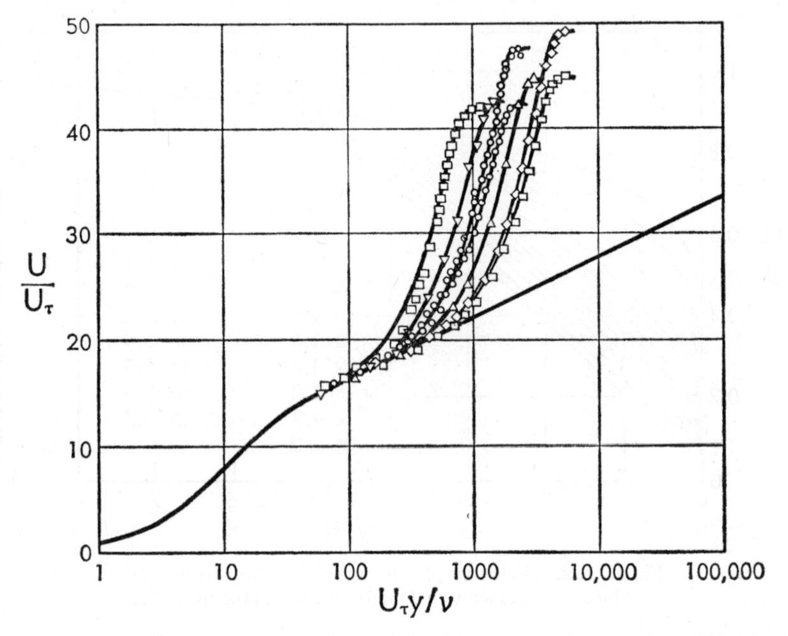


Fig. B,19b. Agreement and departures from the law of the wall, after Coles [*85*].

The region of the wall is a region for which we have a unique relationship between the velocity and the shear stress at the wall. Sometimes, slightly different working formulas evolve from the fitting to experimental data. We find, for example:

$$\text{According to Clauser} \quad \frac{U}{U_\tau} = 5.6 \log\left(\frac{U_\tau y}{\nu}\right) + 4.9 \qquad (19\text{-}1)$$

$$\text{According to Coles} \quad \frac{U}{U_\tau} = 5.75 \log\left(\frac{U_\tau y}{\nu}\right) + 5.10 \qquad (19\text{-}2)$$

It is difficult to specify where departures from the law occur, because this depends both on the Reynolds number and the pressure gradient. Departures occur at lower values of $U_\tau y/\nu$ and are greater as the effect of the adverse pressure gradient on the profile becomes more marked, i.e. as $H$ is greater. They also occur at lower values of $U_\tau y/\nu$ as the Reynolds number decreases. Landweber [*86*] has shown that the logarithmic part no longer exists if $U_e\delta^*/\nu$ is less than 725. At the wall side the law begins to merge into Eq. 16-2 somewhere around $U_\tau y/\nu = 50$. The outer limit of the laminar sublayer is usually taken as 11.5, representing the point where the curve of Eq. 16-2 and the logarithmic law intersect.

For a number of years there was considerable uncertainty about the effect of the adverse pressure gradient on the skin friction, and most methods of treating turbulent boundary layers assumed that the gradient had no effect. Estimates by means of the momentum equation were unreliable and in some cases showed an apparent increase in the skin friction

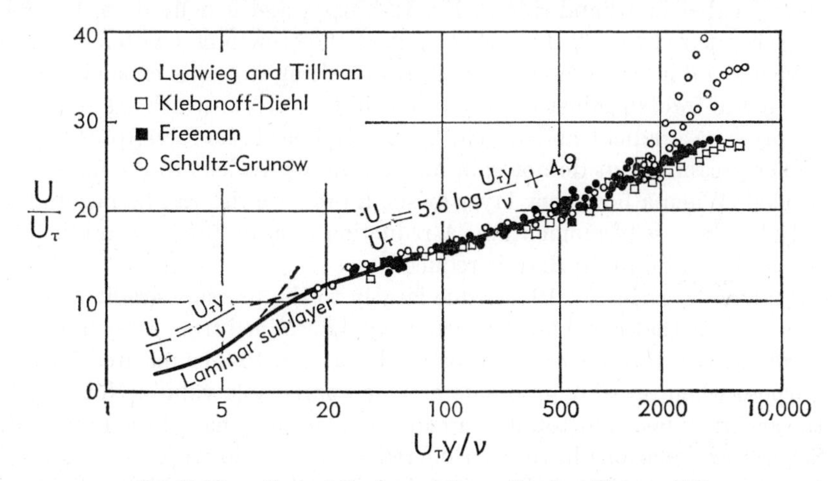


Fig. B,19c. Test of the law of the wall, after Clauser [*83*].

coefficient in regions of strongly rising pressure. When data based on more direct methods became available, such as those of Schubauer and Klebanoff [*87*] and Newman [*88*], based on hot wire measurements of shear stress, and those of Ludwieg and Tillmann [*89*], based on the heated-element method, it became clearly evident that $c_f$ was decreased by an adverse pressure gradient, and was steadily reduced toward zero as separation was approached, as logic dictates that it should be. The whole question has been considerably clarified by the universal character of the law of the wall which establishes a unique relation between velocity near the wall and skin friction without explicitly involving the pressure gradient. The effect of the pressure gradient on the skin friction is thereby seen to result from its reduction of velocity near the wall.

The relation between the integral characteristics of a two-dimensional boundary layer and the pressure gradient is obtained by integrating the equation of motion from $y = 0$ to $y = \delta$. The commonly used form, obtained from the equation of motion with only first order terms in the boundary layer approximation, is known as the Kármán momentum equation, and is expressed as

$$\frac{d\theta}{dx} = \frac{c_f}{2} + \frac{(H+2)}{2}\frac{\theta}{q}\frac{dp}{dx} \tag{19-3}$$

where $q$ is the dynamic pressure in the free stream where the pressure is $p$. This equation gives a synoptic description of boundary layer development and is independent of detailed processes. The relation between the various quantities in the equation does, however, depend on the mechanics of the turbulent diffusion process.

When the pressure gradient is positive (adverse) and large, the second term on the right-hand side of Eq. 19-3 may, and usually does, become large compared to $c_f/2$. For this condition the growth of $\theta$ with $x$ depends primarily on internal momentum losses resulting from the expenditure of tangential forces against those portions of the stream which are retarded by pressure gradient and which, by the action of the force, progress to higher pressures but do not gain momentum equivalent to the forces expended. When a boundary layer exists, a pressure rise can be negotiated only by the loss of momentum. A reduction of $c_f$ by pressure gradient is not an indication that drag is reduced.

When $d\theta/dx$ in Eq. 19-3 is due largely to the pressure gradient term, it is obvious that $c_f$ cannot be accurately determined from measurements of $d\theta/dx$. It is now generally recognized that Eq. 19-3 is unsuited for this purpose when pressure gradients assume appreciable values. Not only is the accuracy poor but totally unrealistic values of $c_f$ have been indicated. Several explanations have been offered having to do with the neglected terms in the equation of motion, but it now appears in the light of Clauser's experience [*83*] that departures of the flow from two-dimensionality are largely responsible.

The universal character of the law of the wall has suggested itself as a useful and reliable means of obtaining local skin friction coefficients from measured velocity distributions. It seems that the first published recognition of this occurs in the paper by Clauser [*83*], who devised the following procedure and used it in the analysis of his experimental results.

Using $U_\tau = U_e\sqrt{c_f/2}$, the following expressions are written:

$$\frac{U}{U_\tau} \equiv \frac{U}{U_e}\sqrt{\frac{2}{c_f}} \quad \text{and} \quad \frac{U_\tau y}{\nu} \equiv \frac{U_e y}{\nu}\sqrt{\frac{c_f}{2}}$$

With these and Eq. 19-1 he obtained the family of curves shown in Fig. B,19d having $c_f$ as the parameter. Application of the figure to a determination of $c_f$ merely requires the placing of a measured velocity distribution thereon and reading off the value of $c_f$, interpolating where necessary. It is still necessary to measure velocities within a short distance of a wall, but the requirement of nearness is considerably relaxed over that required to derive $c_f$ from the initial slope of a velocity distribution.

Ludwieg and Tillmann [*89*], who first confirmed the validity of the law of the wall in a region of adverse pressure gradient by means of their heated-element measurements of $c_f$, deduced the following formula for $c_f$:

$$c_f = \frac{0.246}{10^{0.678H} Re_\theta^{0.268}} \tag{19-4}$$

where $H$ is the form parameter and $Re_\theta = U_e\theta/\nu$. This formula gives $c_f$ reasonably well where the velocity profiles conform to the $H$-parameter family of Fig. B,19a.

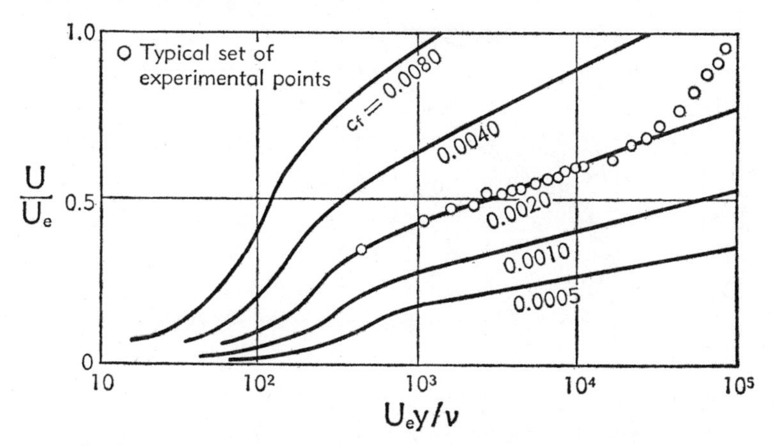


Fig. B,19d. Chart for experimental determination of turbulent skin friction coefficient, after Clauser [*83*].

## B,20. Equilibrium Boundary Layers According to Clauser.

Since the velocity profile beyond the immediate region of the wall is affected by the pressure gradient, a universal representation on the basis of the velocity-defect law, as shown by Fig. B,16, is not in general obtained. However, by means of an experiment in which long lengths of two-dimensional turbulent boundary layer could be subjected to various adverse pressure gradients, Clauser [*83*] showed that the pressure distribution could be adjusted to give similar boundary layer profiles when plotted on the basis of the defect law. The form of the function was different from that for constant pressure flow and also different for each separate pressure distribution, but the significant fact was that the same functional relation applied over an essentially arbitrary number of cross sections for any one pressure distribution. He termed the resulting boundary layer an "equilibrium boundary layer" on the grounds that the sameness of the function $g$ in the case of a pressure gradient implied the same similarity of major flow characteristics as was maintained in constant pressure flow. Constant pressure flows are then just one member of a family of flows developed under specific kinds of pressure distributions.

With regard to the kind of pressure distribution required to produce an equilibrium flow, Clauser points out that a gradient parameter like $(\delta'/\tau_w)dp/dx$, where $\delta'$ represents some effective face area over which the pressure acts, represents the ratio of forces acting on the layer; and if this is held constant, the flow should have a constant history and therefore be in equilibrium. The choice of the proper quantity, $\delta'$, was not known when the experiments were performed, and the attainment of equilibrium

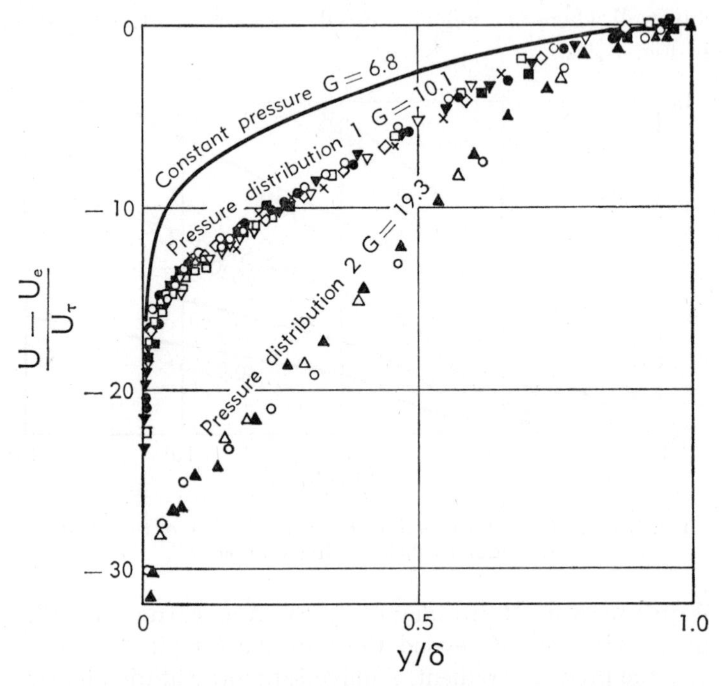


Fig. B,20a. Equilibrium boundary layer profiles on the basis of the velocity-defect law, after Clauser [*72*].

conditions proceeded on a cut-and-try basis. In a later article [*72*] Clauser concluded that the proper parameter was $(\delta^*/\tau_w)dp/dx$. Studies were conducted for two pressure distributions, designated as pressure distribution 1, corresponding to a mild adverse gradient, and pressure distribution 2, corresponding to a considerably stronger adverse gradient but not sufficient to cause separation. The resulting mean velocity profiles are shown in Fig. B,20a compared to a constant pressure profile.

Due to the uncertainty in defining $\delta$, Clauser sought a more suitable thickness parameter. Obviously it was required that this be proportional to $\delta$, since equilibrium profiles correlate on the basis of $y/\delta$. The customary $\delta^*$ and $\theta$ were not suitable because their ratio to $\delta$ could be shown to depend on $c_f$. Similarly the customary shape parameter $H$ was found to be unsuited to equilibrium profiles. He therefore adopted as the thickness parameter

$$\Delta = \int_0^\infty \frac{U_e - U}{U_\tau}\, dy \tag{20-1}$$

and as integral shape parameter

$$G = \int_0^\infty \left(\frac{U_e - U}{U_\tau}\right)^2 dy \Big/ \int_0^\infty \frac{U_e - U}{U_\tau}\, dy = \int_0^\infty \left(\frac{U_e - U}{U_\tau}\right)^2 d\left(\frac{y}{\Delta}\right) \tag{20-2}$$

Their relations $\delta^*$, $\theta$, and $H$ are

$$\delta^* = \sqrt{\frac{c_f}{2}}\,\Delta \tag{20-3}$$

$$\theta = \sqrt{\frac{c_f}{2}}\left(1 - G\sqrt{\frac{c_f}{2}}\,\Delta\right) \tag{20-4}$$

$$H = \frac{1}{(1 - G\sqrt{c_f/2})} \tag{20-5}$$

The reader is referred to the original paper for a more detailed discussion of these parameters. The logarithmic plot of the data in terms of

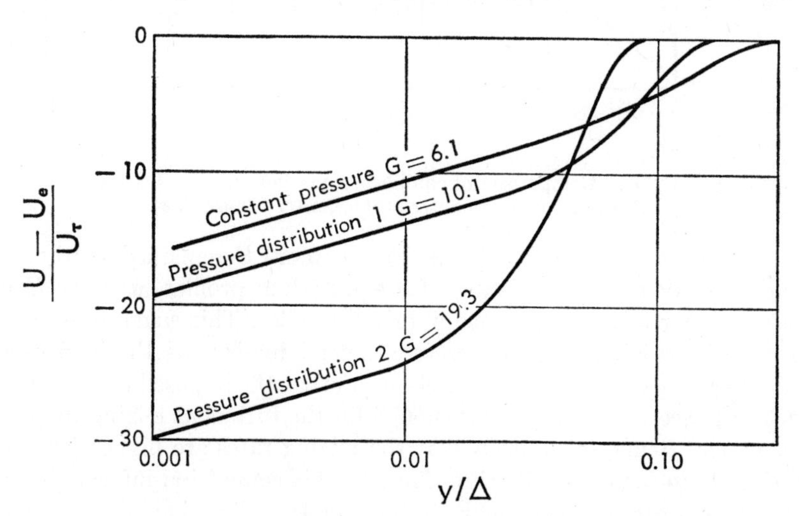


Fig. B,20b. Logarithmic plot of equilibrium velocity profiles using the Clauser thickness parameter Δ, after Clauser [83].

$y/\Delta$ is given here in Fig. B,20b. It is seen that near the wall the defect law conforms to the logarithmic law, as it must according to the arguments of Art. 17 if it overlaps the region in which the law of the wall is valid. This would be true, however, whether equilibrium existed or not, but without equilibrium a family of curves instead of a single curve would be obtained for any one pressure distribution. The parameters for these curves are:

| | $G$ | $\Delta/\delta$ |
|---|---|---|
| Constant pressure | 6.1 | 3.6 |
| Pressure distribution 1 | 10.1 | 6.4 |
| Pressure distribution 2 | 19.3 | 12.0 |

We shall return to Fig. B,20b in Art. 23 in connection with the universal skin friction law proposed by Clauser for equilibrium flows.

Another interesting fact brought out by Clauser's investigation is that equilibrium profiles do not conform to the $H$-parameter family of profiles shown in Fig. B,19a. Comparisons at two values of $H$ are shown in Fig. B,20c. It will be seen that nonequilibrium profiles are considerably more

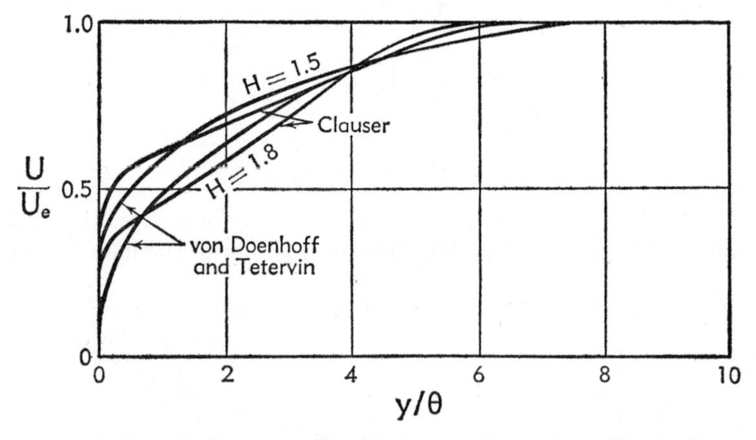


Fig. B,20c. Comparison of equilibrium profiles and von Doenhoff-Tetervin one-parameter profiles, after Clauser [*83*].

rounded than equilibrium profiles. Furthermore $H$ remained nearly constant with downstream distance for equilibrium profiles, whereas $H$ increases progressively for nonequilibrium profiles. This suggests that the increase in $\delta^*$ is slower and therefore that mixing is more thorough when equilibrium exists. This may merely mean that the imposed changes from section to section are now slow enough for the turbulent mixing to better keep pace. It may also mean that the mixing rates are higher for equilibrium than for nonequilibrium flow. In this connection information on turbulent structure is needed. A start in this direction was made by Ruetenik and Corrsin [*90*] who investigated equilibrium turbulent flow in a channel with a 1-degree half angle of divergence. Even for this small divergence, the average turbulent energy was found to be greater than that for a parallel channel by a factor of about 3. However, what is still needed is information of this sort to compare equilibrium and nonequilibrium flows.

The reader is referred to Clauser's paper [*83*] for a number of significant facts brought to light in his investigation. One of these concerned the downstream instability of a turbulent boundary layer with a large adverse pressure gradient. When the pressure gradient was small, no difficulty was experienced in adjusting the pressure distribution to obtain a desired equilibrium profile; but when it was large, great difficulty was experienced. He attributes the condition for large pressure gradients to a downstream instability, meaning that a change, say in the local gradient or in $\theta$, made at one point would produce further changes downstream as the layer developed, rather than become damped out. This is an instability in $x$, not in time.

**B,21. Law of the Wake According to Coles.** In the short space of this article it is impossible to cover adequately the careful and extensive study which led Coles [*85*] to propose the law of the wake as an extension to the law of the wall. After having examined practically all available experimental data on turbulent boundary layers in terms of the logarithmic form of the law of the wall, expressed by Eq. 19-2, and noting the universal agreement with the law near the wall and the characteristic departure from it away from the wall, he concluded that the flow had a wakelike character, modified in various degrees by wall constraints. He concluded further that the wakelike form could be reduced to a second universal similarity law which he called the "law of the wake." A linear combination with the law of the wall was then proposed as an over-all similarity law representing the complete profile for equilibrium and nonequilibrium flows alike.

Attempts to generalize the law of the wall and the defect law so as to fit experimental results are not new. Millikan [*73*], for example, proposed forms to fit the distribution in pipes and channels. Others have expressed and employed ideas bearing certain similarities to the present one, those known being Lees and Crocco [*91*], Ross and Robertson [*93*], and Rotta [*93*]. Coles, however, appears to have been the first to show evidence of a universal wake law and to give it a rational physical explanation.

In general form the mean velocity profile in turbulent shear flow may be expressed as

$$\frac{U}{U_\tau} = f\left(\frac{U_\tau y}{\nu}\right) + h(x, y) \tag{21-1}$$

For equilibrium flows it is found experimentally that Eq. 21-1 may be written

$$\frac{U}{U_\tau} = f\left(\frac{U_\tau y}{\nu}\right) + g\left(\pi, \frac{y}{\delta}\right) \tag{21-2}$$

where $\pi$ is a parameter which is independent of $x$ and $y$ for a specific situation and pressure distribution. The defect law is correspondingly expressed as

$$\frac{U_e - U}{U_\tau} = F\left(\pi, \frac{y}{\delta}\right) \tag{21-3}$$

Coles concluded from his survey of existing data that the central problem was not so much a study of the defect function $F$ as a study of the original function $g(\pi, y/\delta)$ which gives the departure of the mean velocity profile from the logarithmic law of the wall. Since the characteristic departure was obviously not confined to equilibrium flows, the mean-velocity profile was expressed in the form

$$\frac{U}{U_\tau} = f\left(\frac{U_\tau y}{\nu}\right) + \frac{\pi(x)}{K}\,\omega\left(\frac{y}{\delta}\right) \tag{21-4}$$

where $K$ is a constant, $\pi(x)$ denotes that $\pi$ is now in general a function of $x$, and $\omega(y/\delta)$ is a universal wake function common to all two-dimensional turbulent boundary layer flows.

The term

$$\frac{\pi(x)}{K}\,\omega\left(\frac{y}{\delta}\right)$$

in Eq. 21-4 gives the departure from the logarithmic law of the wall, i.e. from

$$\frac{U}{U_\tau} = \frac{1}{K}\ln\left(\frac{U_\tau y}{\nu}\right) + c$$

where, according to Coles, $K = 0.4$ and $c = 5.10$ (Eq. 19-2).

From an analysis of experimental data, Coles found the form of $\omega(y/\delta)$ as given in Fig. B,21a, in which $\omega(y/\delta)$ has been subjected to the normalizing conditions $\omega(0) = 0$, $\omega(1) = 2$, and $\int_0^2 (y/\delta)d\omega = 1$. When plotted against $y/\delta$ these curves have a nearly symmetrical S shape; and, due to the normalization, have the maximum value of 2 at $y/\delta = 1$. The curves obtained from Clauser's equilibrium profiles and the one obtained from Wieghardt's data, which Coles finds to be also an equilibrium flow, are plotted against the parameter $yU_\tau/(\delta^* U_e)$, which is equal to $y/\Delta$ in Clauser's notation. Included in this set are data from nonequilibrium profiles and the data of Liepmann and Laufer [*94*] for a region of turbulent mixing between a uniform flow and a fluid at rest.

The general working form of Eq. 21-4 may be written

$$\frac{U}{U_\tau} = \frac{1}{K}\ln\left(\frac{U_\tau y}{\nu}\right) + c + \frac{\pi(x)}{K}\,\omega\left(\frac{y}{\delta}\right) \tag{21-5}$$

where the constants $K$ and $c$ have the numerical values as given above. In order to use this formula, $\pi(x)$ must be known. It follows from Eq.

21-5, using the normalizing condition $\omega(1) = 2$, that

$$\frac{U_e}{U_\tau} = \frac{1}{K} \ln\left(\frac{U_\tau \delta}{\nu}\right) + c + \frac{2\pi(x)}{K} \tag{21-6}$$

where

$$\frac{U_e}{U_\tau} = \sqrt{\frac{2}{c_f}}$$

Thus Eq. 21-6 is an expression for $\pi(x)$ in terms of the skin friction coefficient $c_f$. For other relationships and a tabulation of $\omega(y/\delta)$ and related functions the reader is referred to Coles' original paper [*85*].

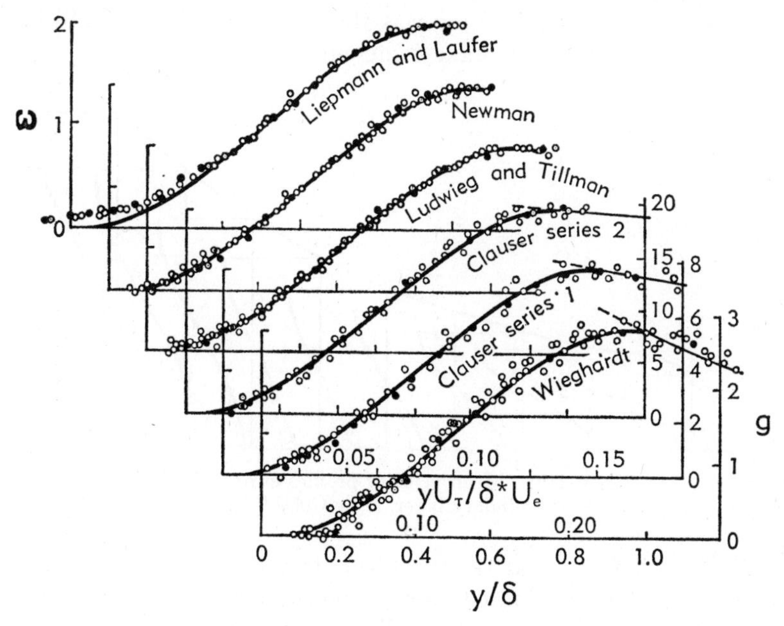


Fig. B,21a. The law of the wake, after Coles [*85*].

Coles found that in most cases (Eq. 21-5) fitted available experimental data on velocity distributions well and concluded, for unseparated flows at least, that the wake hypothesis appeared to be a useful concept. The analytic character of the method enabled him to express also the distribution of shear stress across the boundary layer. Computed distributions represented observations, except where the adverse pressure gradients were large. Here there were large discrepancies, reminiscent of those obtained by using the momentum equation.

The general success of the method led Coles to suggest that yawed or three-dimensional flows might be usefully represented by universal functions considered as vector rather than scalar quantities. For further discussions along these lines the reader is again referred to the original paper.

It is, of course, not uncommon to find empirical formulas with enough adjustable constants to fit experimental results. In the present case, however, the formula, with a specified function $\omega(y/\delta)$ and constants previously specified in the law of the wall, stands the test of a wide variety of conditions. In addition the present similarity law appears to be based on meaningful physical concepts, which may be described as follows.

It is easily seen that a wake is a natural consequence of earlier frictional constraints no matter how they may have arisen. There is therefore coming from upstream a flow of wakelike character, modified obviously by the remnant of upstream effects which caused it and by the local effects which distort the profile so that the velocity approaches zero at the wall. The remarkable thing was that Coles could extract S-shaped profiles typical of the pure wake component.

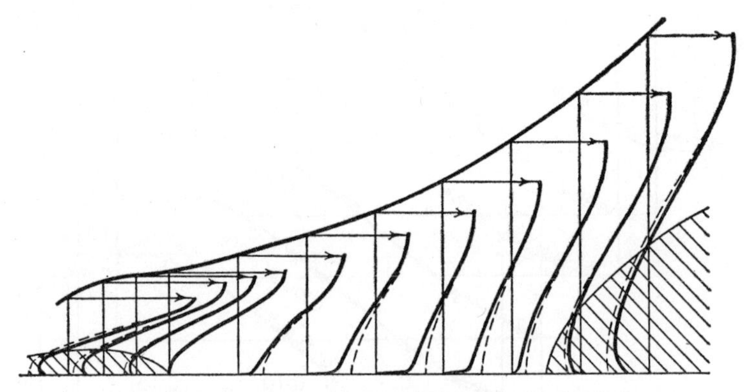

Fig. B,21b. Mean velocity profiles of hypothetical boundary layer, after Coles [*85*].

No claim is made that the turbulent structure is the same as that of a real wake. From the limited information available it appears that wake structure is coarser (has larger eddies) than boundary layer structure. However, the law of the wake may be interpreted as a manifestation of a large scale mixing process in which stress-controlling motions are independent of viscous effects. The wall effect, as we already know, superposes a viscous effect which increases in magnitude as the wall is approached.

The concept is best illustrated by the diagram of a hypothetical boundary layer used by Coles, reproduced here in Fig. B,21b. The figure shows velocity profiles for various values of $x$ in a flow proceeding from separation to separation through a region of attached flow. The dashed lines denote the wakelike component represented by the function $\omega(y/\delta)$. At points of separation or reattachment we find the wake component only. In regions of attachment we see the effect of the wall friction, and the requirement of vanishing velocity at the wall being met by a sharp drop to zero at the wall.

**B,22. Mixing Length and Eddy Viscosity in Boundary Layer Flows.** As mentioned in Art. 3 and 10, the transport of momentum by turbulent motions may be regarded as involving an eddy viscosity. We shall briefly reexamine the associated concepts in the light of certain known facts about the flow in various parts of the boundary layer.

In turbulent boundary layers three fairly distinct regions are easily recognized. First there is the laminar sublayer which is typically 0.01 to 0.001 of the total thickness of the layer. Beyond this is a turbulent region which extends to 0.1 to 0.2 of $\delta$ and comprises the inner part of the layer where the logarithmic law is valid and the mean flow is virtually unaffected by pressure gradient. A short time response and rapid adjustment to local conditions are also characteristic of this region (see discussion by Clauser [72]). Finally, there is the outer 0.8 to 0.9 of the layer where the eddies are limited in lateral extent only by the confines of the layer and mixing is relatively free. In the laminar sublayer molecular diffusion predominates, being exclusively this at the wall. Turbulent diffusion progressively increases as we enter the logarithmic region from the wall side and soon predominates over molecular diffusion. For virtually everything except the laminar sublayer the transfer processes should be governed by a property of the motion. We wish to see whether this property may be legitimately and usefully expressed in terms of an eddy viscosity, $\epsilon_\mu$.

Dimensionally, $\epsilon_\mu$ is a product of density, velocity, and length. According to the mixing length theory

$$\epsilon_\mu = \rho \overline{vl} \tag{22-1}$$

where $v$ is the $y$ component of turbulent velocity and $l$ is the reach of a turbulent motion while it has the velocity $v$ and is called the mixing length. Prandtl's assumption is that $v = l dU/dy$ and $l = c_2 y$ (see Art. 10). It is implied in this assumption that the correlation between $v$ and $l$ is absorbed into the value of $l$.

Using these assumptions and assuming further that $\tau$ is independent of $y$ and equal to $\tau_w$, the value at the wall, we find the well-known expression

$$\frac{\tau_w}{\rho} = c_2^2 y^2 \left(\frac{dU}{dy}\right)^2$$

or using $U_\tau^2 = \tau_w/\rho$

$$U_\tau = c_2 y \frac{dU}{dy} \tag{22-2}$$

This expression may be integrated to give the velocity distribution if we know the lower limits of $y$ and $U$. These are their values at the edge of the sublayer, which may be found from Eq. 16-2 and written in terms of a free constant: $y_l = c\nu/U_\tau$ and $U_l = cU_\tau$. If we now integrate Eq. 22-2 as follows:

$$\frac{1}{c_2}\int_{y_l}^{y}\frac{dy}{y} = \frac{1}{U_\tau}\int_{U_l}^{U} du$$

we obtain exactly the law of the wall

$$\frac{U}{U_\tau} = \frac{1}{c_2}\ln\frac{U_\tau y}{\nu} + \text{const}$$

where $c_2$ has the same numerical value as $K$.

If we assume at the outset, as Prandtl did also, that $v = U_\tau$ and again take $l = c_2 y$, we again obtain

$$U_\tau = c_2 y \frac{dU}{dy}$$

This is identical to Eq. 22-2 and again yields exactly the law of the wall.

It is time to examine the consequences of these results. Since the law of the wall is well founded and is one of the most universal features of turbulent flow, we cannot escape the conclusion that the above assumptions are valid for the region in which the logarithmic law is obeyed. We know, of course, that we must stay near the wall, if for no other reason than that $\tau$ changes with $y$. More specifically we may express the eddy viscosity

$$\frac{\epsilon_\mu}{\rho} = c_2 y U_\tau \tag{22-3}$$

in the region where the logarithmic law of the wall is valid.

Turning our attention to the outer 80 to 90 per cent of the layer, we find that both Townsend [*1*] and Clauser [*72*] have explored the possibility that $\epsilon_\mu$ is constant in this region. Townsend employed the rather straightforward procedure of solving the boundary layer approximation of the equation of mean motion, considering both constant pressure flow and equilibrium flow with pressure gradient. We call attention here only to his treatment of the constant pressure case. When the constants involving $\epsilon_\mu$ were chosen for the best fit of experimental results, fair agreement was found for $y/\delta > 0.05$. The principal defect was the usual one, namely that a constant $\epsilon_\mu$ yielded too slow an approach to the free stream velocity. Evidently $\epsilon_\mu$ effectively decreases near the outer edge, due no doubt to intermittency of turbulent flow. The extent and quality of the over-all agreement was, however, sufficiently good to show that an essentially constant and valid $\epsilon_\mu$ is a physical reality in the turbulent parts of the flow beyond the logarithmic region.

Clauser employed the novel approach of making laminar profiles resemble the outer portion of the constant pressure turbulent profile when the laminar profiles were reduced to the basis of $(U - U_e)/U_\tau$ vs. $y/\delta$.

He noted that the principal difference in appearance between constant pressure laminar profiles and turbulent profiles was that the turbulent profiles dropped so abruptly at the wall as to appear to extrapolate to a nonzero velocity at the wall, whereas laminar profiles went to zero much more gradually and did not give this impression. The characteristic shape of the turbulent profile arises from the circumstance that the laminar sublayer next to the wall and the flow adjacent to it has a lower viscosity than the eddy viscosity prevailing in the main body of the turbulent flow. Consequently a large part of the velocity change from the wall to the free stream occurs in this low viscosity region. If the same situation were made to prevail in a laminar layer, say by placing a layer of fluid of lower viscosity next to the wall, a laminar profile could be made to resemble a turbulent profile. Clauser therefore proceeded to simulate this condition in a family of laminar profiles obtained by solving the Blasius equation for slip velocities $U_w$ at the wall, $U_w/U_e$ amounting to 0, 0.2, 0.4, 0.5, 0.6, 0.7, and 0.8. He then attempted to collapse the family to a single curve by dividing $(U - U_e)/U_e$ and $y/\delta$ by suitable factors. Leaving details to the original paper [*72*], we merely point out the significant fact that exact coincidence proved to be impossible, but that two procedures each resulted in a narrow band of curves. Clauser concluded that the same basic dissimilarity would prevent turbulent profiles, which pertain to different values of $U_\tau$, from collapsing to a single curve on the basis of the velocity-defect law. Accordingly there is an almost-but-not-quite universal curve.

The next step was to relate the laminar profiles to turbulent profiles on a velocity-defect-law basis by an appropriate eddy viscosity, $\epsilon_\mu$. The appropriate velocity and length were chosen by the same reasoning process that leads to a reference velocity $U_\tau$ and a reference length $\delta$ in the velocity-defect law, and $\epsilon_\mu$ was expressed by

$$\frac{\epsilon_\mu}{\rho} = \alpha U_\tau \Delta$$

where $\alpha$ is a constant of proportionality to be determined. Since $\Delta$ is equal to $U_e\delta^*/U_\tau$ (see Art. 20)

$$\frac{\epsilon_\mu}{\rho} = \alpha U_e \delta^* \tag{22-4}$$

which is an expression for $\epsilon_\mu$ in readily available quantities.

The original article must be consulted for the details of the fitting process and the curves showing comparisons with data of Fig. B,16. Best agreement was obtained with $\alpha = 0.018$. Considering that a narrow band of laminar curves is obtained rather than a single curve and that experimental data are expected to show a similar dispersion, the agreement is excellent for the outer 80 to 90 per cent of the layer. The method proposed for connecting the outer and inner portions is left to the original article.

A treatment of the same character was applied to equilibrium flows involving adverse pressure gradients. Again a good fit was obtained by assuming a constant eddy viscosity given by Eq. 22-4 even for near-separation profiles. Some of the more significant results of this work were: (1) that $(\delta^*/\tau_w)dp/dx$ proved to be the proper pressure gradient parameter which must be constant throughout an equilibrium layer, (2) that $\alpha$ turned out to be practically independent of pressure gradient (independent of the parameter $(\delta^*/\tau_w)dp/dx$) and to have the value of approximately 0.018 in all cases tested.

An interesting outcome of a constant $\alpha$ is a constant eddy Reynolds number. If such a Reynolds number is defined by

$$Re_\epsilon = \frac{\rho U_e \delta^*}{\epsilon_\mu}$$

we find from Eq. 22-4 that $Re_\epsilon = 1/\alpha$. Taking $\alpha = 0.018$, $Re_\epsilon = 56$. A constant eddy Reynolds number is just another way of expressing the behavior trend of all turbulent shear flows, namely a tendency for the transferring agents to be proportional to the length and velocity scales of the flow.

Most important of all is the evidence from these sources that $\epsilon_\mu$ behaves in equilibrium flows toward mean-velocity distributions beyond the range of the logarithmic law as though it were constant. This cannot be taken as a sweeping generalization, but it furnishes good evidence that $\epsilon_\mu$ is likely to have a strong leaning in this direction generally and therefore will have only a weak dependence on local conditions. This being so, there is little foundation for a mixing length theory in such regions, and it renders of little significance the various arguments about how mixing length should be expressed. The degree to which $\epsilon_\mu$ is constant and the exactness with which a gradient type of diffusion is obeyed for coarse mixing are probably not sufficient to represent more sensitive quantities like shear stress distributions.

Near the wall the mixing length theory may be applied, and we see that a valid procedure starts with an expression for $\epsilon_\mu$ that has a striking resemblance to that for the outer flow. The comparison is:

Inner flow $\qquad \dfrac{\epsilon_\mu}{\rho} = c_2 y U_\tau; \quad c_2 = 0.4$

Outer flow $\qquad \dfrac{\epsilon_\mu}{\rho} = \alpha U_\tau \Delta; \quad \alpha = 0.018$

In the first case the mixing scale is proportional to the distance from the wall; in the second case it is proportional to the thickness of the shear layer.

The foregoing considerations regarding a constant eddy viscosity are given more for the physical ideas that they embody than for any possible expediency in methods of computation.

**B,23. Effect of Roughness.** The treatment of roughness and its effects is rendered difficult and somewhat inexact by the varied geometrical forms of roughness and the variety of ways in which it may be distributed. Again we are confronted with a subject that cannot be treated adequately in a short space, and the reader can profit by consulting additional sources of information, such as [*95,78,6,96,97*].

The pattern of roughness studies was set largely by the extensive work of Nikuradse [*95*] on sand-grain roughness in tubes. Sand-grain roughness has been adopted as a standard in skin friction studies, and is taken to mean roughness elements consisting of grains, either being sand or like grains of sand, of nearly uniform size but generally of irregular shape spread with maximum density on a plain surface. The significant dimensions then reduce to one, this one being the mean height of the roughness element, denoted by $k$. It is customary to express the effect of an arbitrary type of roughness in terms of an equivalent sand-grain roughness. For example, the effect of a given distribution of rivets of height $k_r$ is reduced to the effect of equivalent sand roughness of height $k$. A number of such equivalents are given by Schlichting [*96*].

It has been found that the onset of an effect of sand-grain roughness on skin friction and on the flow near the wall depends on $k$ relative to the thickness of the laminar sublayer. A more precise length, avoiding the arbitrariness of the sublayer thickness, is $\nu/U_\tau$. Using this, the criterion becomes a roughness Reynolds number

$$\frac{U_\tau k}{\nu}$$

It has been found that below some value of this number roughness has no effect. The surface is then said to be aerodynamically smooth. Above this value an effect sets in, at first as a mixture of smooth-wall and rough-wall behaviors, involving both the roughness and viscous effects. When $U_\tau k/\nu$ reaches a sufficiently large value, the behavior is characteristic of the roughness only, becoming independent of viscosity. The final condition is termed "fully rough." When the final condition is reached, the laminar sublayer no longer exists since the particles themselves induce turbulent mixing by the flow about them. Broadly speaking, the foregoing is true of all types of roughness but the limits are different for different types.

We shall shortly return to these limits and the importance of the parameter $U_\tau k/\nu$, but first we turn our attention to the fully rough condition where viscosity no longer enters explicitly into the picture. Here

$\tau_w$ depends on the velocity $U$ at some small distance $y$ from the wall and on $k$ and $\rho$. By dimensional reasoning similar to that leading to Eq. 16-1 we find

$$\frac{U}{U_\tau} = f\left(\frac{y}{k}\right) \tag{23-1}$$

As we have already noted, the velocity-defect law is unaffected by roughness. Since it again develops that there exists a region of overlap where both laws are valid, a logarithmic function is indicated in Eq. 23-1, and the law may be written

$$\frac{U}{U_\tau} = \frac{1}{K} \ln\left(\frac{y}{k}\right) + \text{const} \tag{23-2}$$

where $K$ is the same as that appearing in the smooth wall law and in the velocity-defect law.

Just as in the case of the smooth wall law there is a linear relationship between $U/U_\tau$ and $\ln (y/k)$ only for the region of the wall, not throughout the whole boundary layer. Obviously there is some question about a suitable reference point from which to measure $y$. If $y$ is not expressed correctly, the region that should be linear becomes curved. Experimentally this is used to find the origin of $y$. No cases are known where the origin did not lie somewhere between the top and bottom of the roughness elements.

The well-known skin friction law for fully rough walls is obtained by adding Eq. 23-2 and the defect law (Eq. 17-4) and using the relationship $U_e/U_\tau = \sqrt{2/c_f}$. The result is

$$\sqrt{\frac{2}{c_f}} = \frac{1}{K} \ln\left(\frac{\delta}{k}\right) + \text{const} \tag{23-3}$$

Since the defect law is affected by the pressure gradient, Eq. 23-3 applies only to cases where the effect of the pressure gradient is negligible. The effect of the free stream conditions is also present, but this effect is small and may be absorbed in the constant.

The effect of roughness is seen to depend on its height compared to the boundary layer thickness. The effect is independent of Reynolds number. These two circumstances illustrate in a very direct way an inherent characteristic of turbulent diffusion in shear flow, namely that the length scale in eddy diffusion processes tends to remain proportional to the thickness of the shear layer. In other words, mixing tends to take place on a scale of coarseness proportional to the boundary layer thickness, or the radius of a pipe. Ordinarily this rule cannot hold true in the immediate neighborhood of a wall where the turbulent motions are influenced by the presence of the wall; but if flow about roughness elements introduces a scale of mixing proportional to the scale of the shear layer, then the rule does hold true for the entire layer. This is true when $k$ is proportional to $\delta$, and at the same time $U_\tau k/\nu$ is sufficiently large to make viscous effects negligible. If we fully grasp the foregoing facts, it does not seem so strange that a small quantity like $k$ should be associated with a much larger quantity like $\delta$ and furthermore occupy a position of equal importance.

An important characteristic of the roughness effect, first pointed out by Nikuradse [*95*], is a downward shift of the velocity near the wall from that corresponding to the smooth wall condition at a given value of $U_\tau$. This is understandable in view of the fact that the mixing action of the roughness elements increases the rate of momentum transfer, and a lower velocity near the wall is required to keep $U_\tau$ the same. In connection with this downward shift it is necessary to recall that we now have two wall laws:

Smooth wall $$\frac{U}{U_\tau} = \frac{1}{K} \ln \left(\frac{U_\tau y}{\nu}\right) + \text{const}$$

Fully rough wall $$\frac{U}{U_\tau} = \frac{1}{K} \ln \left(\frac{y}{k}\right) + \text{const}$$

Both are dependent on conditions near the wall and both are independent of stream conditions, such as boundary layer thickness and pressure gradient. If we subtract the second equation from the first and call the difference $\Delta U/U_\tau$, the downward shift in velocity is found to be

$$\frac{\Delta U}{U_\tau} = \frac{1}{K} \ln \left(\frac{U_\tau k}{\nu}\right) + \text{const} \tag{23-4}$$

This equation applied only for values of $U_\tau k/\nu$ for which the surface is fully rough.

The behavior of $\Delta U/U_\tau$ over a wide range of values of $U_\tau k/\nu$ has been determined by a number of investigators. A representative summary of results given by Clauser [*72*] is reproduced in Fig. B,23a. This figure is very instructive. It shows the behavior of different kinds of roughness through the range smooth, partially rough, and fully rough conditions. The limits of such ranges can be judged from this figure. Where the roughness elements are of uniform size, as for example uniform sand, the limit below which the wall is smooth is reasonably definite. It appears to be $U_\tau k/\nu \cong 4$. However, when the roughness consists of a mixture of sizes or is not densely packed and a fictitious $k$ is chosen to bring the curves into coincidence in the fully rough regime, then the lower limit cannot be specified. The lower limit for the fully rough condition is seen to be somewhere between 50 and 100.

It is interesting to interpret these limits in terms of $k/\delta_{\text{lam}}$, where $\delta_{\text{lam}}$ is the thickness of the laminar sublayer on a smooth wall. The sublayer is inherently an indistinctly defined region, but taking the conventionally defined sharp limit given by

$$\delta_{\text{lam}} = 11.5 \frac{\nu}{U_\tau}$$

the effect of roughness begins when $k/\delta_{\text{lam}} \cong \frac{1}{3}$ and the fully rough regime sets in when $k/\delta_{\text{lam}}$ is between 4 and 8. These figures tell us little that could not be inferred, namely that the roughness elements must be well

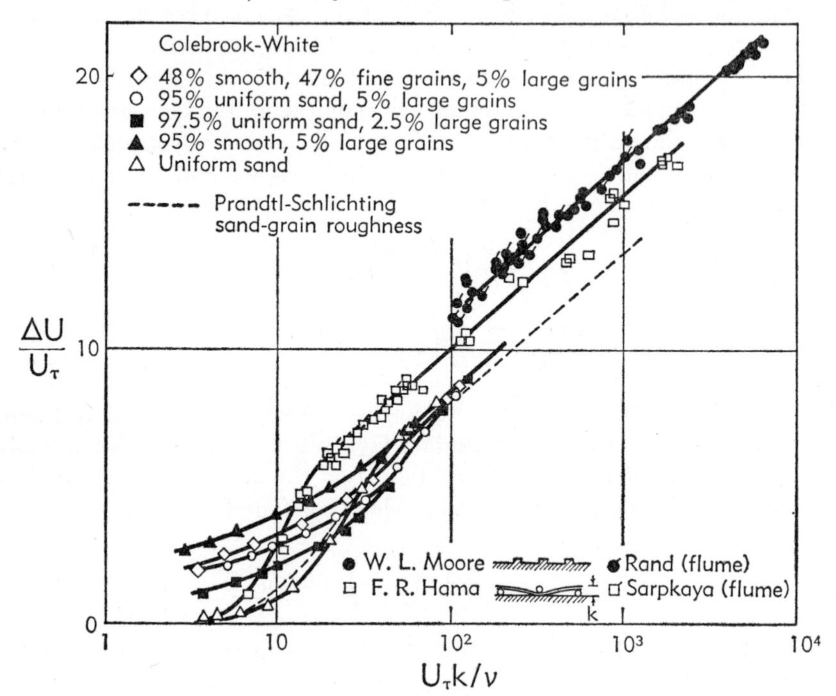


Fig. B,23a. Effect of roughness on universal turbulent velocity profile, after Clauser [72].

buried in the laminar sublayer to have no effect and must extend well above it to completely eradicate viscosity effects.

It may be shown rather simply that in order for a surface to remain aerodynamically smooth the roughness must decrease almost inversely with the free stream velocity. If the critical value is designated as $k_{\text{cr}}$ and the limit is taken as $U_\tau k_{\text{cr}}/\nu = 4$, then

$$k_{\text{cr}} = 4 \frac{\nu}{U_\tau} = 4 \left(\frac{\nu}{U_e}\right) \sqrt{\frac{2}{c_f}}$$

where $c_f$ is the smooth wall coefficient which varies with $U_e$ but only slowly. It is also apparent from the slow variation of $c_f$ that the requirements on $k_{\text{cr}}$ are nearly as stringent on a large body as on a small one.

Returning to Fig. B,23a it is significant that the data conform to the law (Eq. 23-4) for the fully rough condition. This means that the linear portion of the velocity distribution curve for a rough wall parallels that for a smooth wall but is stepped down by an amount $\Delta U/U_\tau$. With experimentally determined values of $\Delta U/U_\tau$, the velocity distribution for a fully rough wall may be expressed by the aid of the smooth wall formula. For this we use Eq. 19-1 containing the constants given by Clauser. The rough wall formula is then

$$\frac{U}{U_\tau} = 5.6 \log\left(\frac{U_\tau y}{\nu}\right) - \left(\frac{\Delta U}{U_\tau}\right) + 4.9 \qquad (23\text{-}5)$$

A skin friction formula results at once by subtracting Eq. 23-5 from the logarithmic form of the velocity-defect law. Clauser [*83*] has obtained a universal law applicable to equilibrium flows including the effect of the pressure gradient by noting, on the basis of Fig. B,20b, that a pressure gradient also has the effect of producing a step-down in the velocity, $\Delta U_2/U_\tau$. Accordingly he writes the generalized defect law for equilibrium flows

$$\frac{U - U_e}{U_\tau} = 5.6 \log\left(\frac{y}{\Delta}\right) - \left(\frac{\Delta U_2}{U_\tau}\right) + 0.6 \qquad (23\text{-}6)$$

Since Eq. 23-5 is unaffected by the pressure gradient, and Eq. 23-6 takes the effect of the pressure gradient into account, a universal skin friction law results by subtraction of Eq. 23-6 from Eq. 23-5. The end result may be written

$$\sqrt{\frac{2}{c_f}} = 5.6 \log Re_{\delta^*} - \frac{\Delta U}{U_\tau}\left(Re_k \sqrt{\frac{c_f}{2}}\right) + \frac{\Delta U_2}{U_\tau}(G) + 4.3 \qquad (23\text{-}7)$$

where $\sqrt{c_f/2} = U_\tau/U_e$, $\delta^* = \sqrt{c_f/2}\,\Delta$, $Re_k = U_e k/\nu$, $Re_{\delta^*} = U_e\delta^*/\nu$, and $(\Delta U/U_\tau)(Re_k \sqrt{c_f/2})$ and $(\Delta U_2/U_\tau)(G)$ denote functions of the arguments. The integral shape parameter $G$ is defined in Art. 20.

In order to put Eq. 23-7 into a more convenient form for engineering applications, Clauser proposes the introduction of two auxiliary factors

$$F_1 = 10^{\Delta U/5.6U_\tau}, \qquad F_2 = 10^{\Delta U_2/5.6U_\tau}$$

which permit Eq. 23-7 to be written

$$\sqrt{\frac{2}{c_f}} = 5.6 \log\left(Re_{\delta^*}\frac{F_2}{F_1}\right) + 4.3 \qquad (23\text{-}8)$$

Factors $F_1$ and $F_2$ have been determined by Clauser using Prandtl-Schlichting data for sand-grain roughness for the calculation of $F_1$ and his own data for equilibrium profiles for the calculation of $F_2$. These are presented in Fig. B,23b and B,23c. A plot of Eq. 23-8 for $F_1$ and $F_2$ equal to unity is given in Fig. B,23d. If a fictitious Reynolds number, $Re_\delta{}^* F_2/F_1$, is first obtained, $c_f$ may be found from this figure. Since values of $F_2$ are based on only two equilibrium pressure distributions, more data are to

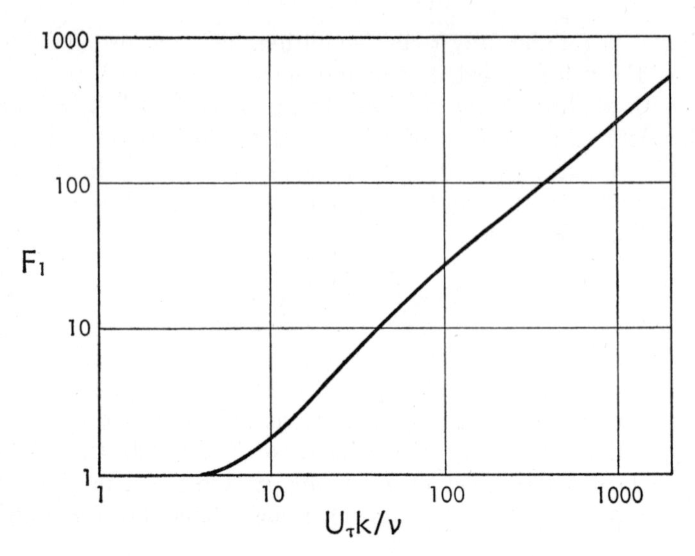


Fig. B,23b. Factor for effect of sand-grain roughness on local skin friction coefficient, after Clauser [*83*].

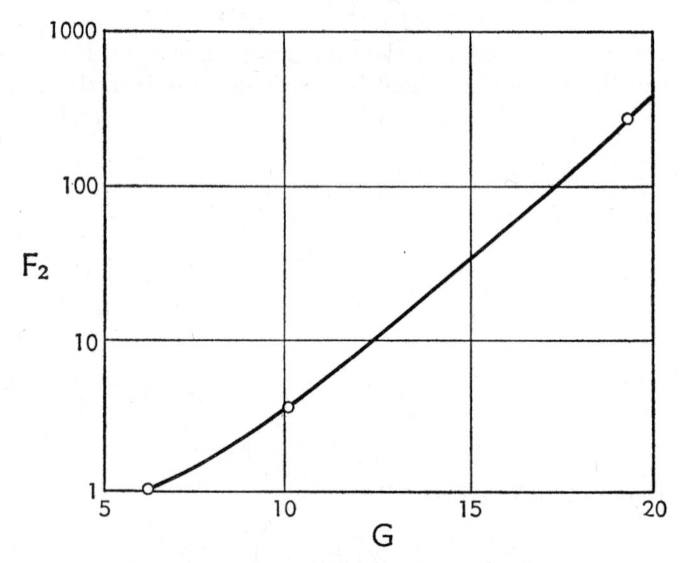


Fig. B,23c. Factor for effect of pressure gradient on local skin friction coefficient, after Clauser [*83*].

be desired in order to test the universality of the method. The term "universal" is here used in the restricted sense of applying only to equilibrium boundary layers.

The effect of roughness on velocity distribution is reflected in a raising of the shape parameter $H$. This effect has been shown by Hama [*97*] for a wide range of conditions. Since Clauser's integral shape parameter $G$ is not affected, the variation of $H$ may be expressed as a function of $c_f$ by Eq. 20-5 for both smooth and rough walls.

It is worth noting before we leave the subject that experimental determinations of roughness effect in terms of $\Delta U/U_\tau$ vs. $U_\tau k/\nu$ may be made optionally in boundary layers, pipes, or channels. Application of

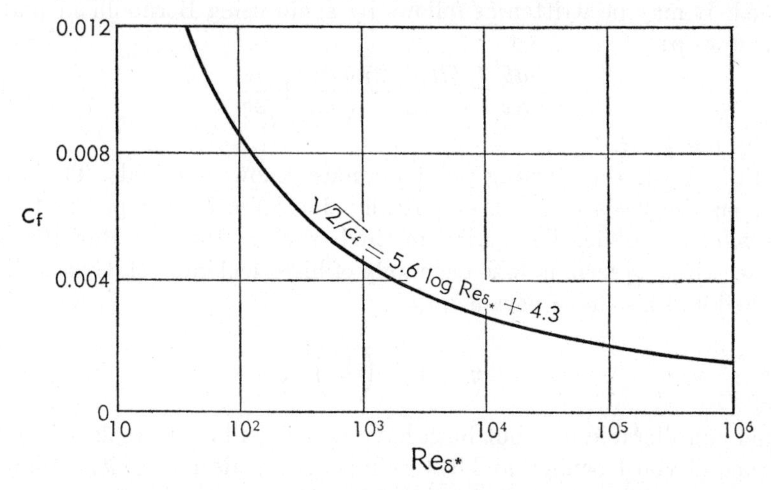


Fig. B,23d. Local skin friction coefficient for smooth plates with constant pressure, after Clauser [*83*].

the results then merely requires the introduction of $\Delta U/U_\tau$ into the appropriate smooth wall formula.

**B,24. Integral Methods for Calculating Boundary Layer Development.** A number of methods have been proposed for calculating boundary layer parameters and separation as functions of $x$ for boundary layers developed on a smooth wall in the presence of pressure gradients. Most of the attention has been given to cases involving adverse pressure gradients, and the methods are mostly restricted to two-dimensional flow, although sometimes the problem is set up so as to include axially symmetric flow for the conditions where the boundary layer is thin compared to the radius of the body about its axis.

It is generally assumed that the boundary layer is so thin that pressure changes across it may be neglected. Then the equations of motion and continuity for two-dimensional flow reduce to Eq. 8-1, 8-2, and 8-3. For incompressible flow, and by neglecting viscous stress and turbulent normal stresses, these become

$$U\frac{\partial U}{\partial x} + V\frac{\partial U}{\partial y} = -\frac{1}{\rho}\frac{\partial p}{\partial x} + \frac{1}{\rho}\frac{\partial \tau}{\partial y} \tag{24-1}$$

$$\frac{\partial U}{\partial x} + \frac{\partial U}{\partial y} = 0 \tag{24-2}$$

By integrating Eq. 24-1 from $y = 0$ to $y = \delta$, using Eq. 24-2 to eliminate $V$, and Bernoulli's equation to express $p$ in terms of the local free stream velocity $U_e$, the Kármán integral relation is obtained. The integrals turn out to be the well-known expressions for $\delta^*$ and $\theta$. By introducing these and their ratio $H$, the Kármán momentum equation is obtained. It may be written as follows by again using Bernoulli's equation to restore $p$:

$$\frac{d\theta}{dx} = \frac{(H+2)}{2}\frac{\theta}{q}\frac{dp}{dx} + \frac{\tau_w}{2q} \tag{24-3}$$

where $q = \frac{1}{2}\rho U_e^2$.

Eq. 24-3 is the starting point for most known methods. These proceed on the basis of some empirically determined form parameter for the velocity profile. The earlier methods such as those of Buri [*98*] and Gruschwitz [*99*] seem now to be mainly of historical interest. Gruschwitz's method and his shape parameter,

$$\eta = 1 - \left(\frac{U}{U_e}\right)^2_{y=\theta}$$

found considerable use, but both have now been largely replaced by the method of von Doenhoff and Tetervin [*84*], or variations of it, employing $H$ only.

Von Doenhoff and Tetervin [*84*] made what appears to be the most thorough search for a suitable form parameter. This resulted in the adoption of the parameter $H$ and the single parameter family of profiles shown in Fig. B,19a. It is now clear from evidence previously cited that all profiles do not fit this pattern, and that any method based on such an assumption cannot be expected to give correct results under all conditions. Nevertheless the method of von Doenhoff and Tetervin has had certain successes and has appeared sufficiently promising to lead others to attempt to improve upon it.

The method is based on the assumption that it is only necessary to determine $\theta$ and $H$ in order to establish the boundary layer characteristics. Since the momentum equation (Eq. 24-3) alone is not sufficient for this purpose, an auxiliary expression for $H$ was set up. Recognizing that a sudden change in pressure should not produce a discontinuity in the velocity profile, it was assumed that the rate of change of $H$ rather than $H$ itself would depend on local forces, $\tau_w$ and $dp/dx$. When the ratio of these forces was expressed by

$$\frac{\theta}{q}\frac{dq}{dx}\frac{2q}{\tau_w}$$

it was found that $\theta dH/dx$ was a function of this ratio and also, to some extent, of $H$ itself, but it was independent of Reynolds number. Using the Squire and Young formula (Eq. 18-10) for $\tau_w$, thereby ignoring any effect of pressure gradient on skin friction, von Doenhoff and Tetervin arrived at the following expression for $\theta dH/dx$:

$$\theta \frac{dH}{dx} = e^{4.680(H-2.975)} \left[ -\frac{\theta}{q} \frac{dq}{dx} \frac{2q}{\tau_w} - 2.035(H - 1.286) \right] \quad (24\text{-}4)$$

Given $dq/dx$, the two equations (Eq. 24-4 and 24-3) were solved by a step-by-step procedure for $\theta$ and $H$ as a function of $x$. Starting with some initial value, $\theta_0$ and $H_0$, $d\theta/dx$ and $dH/dx$ were found. Each when multiplied by an increment of $x$ and added to the initial values gave the next value of $\theta$ and $H$ to repeat the process.

Garner [*100*] undertook to improve on the method of von Doenhoff and Tetervin by using different auxiliary expressions for skin friction and $H$, again disregarding the effect of pressure gradient on skin friction. The method, however, remains basically the same.

Tests of this general method have shown a closeness of agreement with observations sufficient to make it worthy of consideration when conditions are not out of the ordinary; that is, when profiles can be expected to have the form of Fig. B,19a. Since adverse pressure gradient dominates the development of the layer, the use of an incorrect expression for the skin friction apparently has minor consequences.

Tetervin and Lin [*101*] initiated a fresh attack on the problem, again built around the $H$-parameter family. They set up integral expressions for momentum, moment of momentum, and kinetic energy in a form sufficiently general to include axially symmetric flow as well as two-dimensional flow, subject to the restriction that $\delta$ is small compared to the radius of curvature about the axis of symmetry. Their principal objective was to avoid an empirical expression for $H$ if possible. The moment of momentum equation was found to be best suited for this purpose, but it required auxiliary expressions for velocity and shear stress distributions across the layer. A power-law fitting of the $H$-parameter profiles was adopted as an approximate but reasonable procedure. More serious was insufficient information about the value and distribution of shear stress. While the work of Tetervin and Lin fell short of immediate success, it pointed the way to future progress.

It must be remembered that while $\tau_w$ may be reduced to small values by an adverse pressure gradient, $\tau$ may rise to large values away from the wall before falling to zero at the outer edge of the layer. Fediaevsky [*102*] proposed a method for calculating the distribution of $\tau/\tau_w$ with $y/\delta$ employing a polynomial expression that would satisfy boundary conditions at the wall and the outer edge of the layer. Certain large discrepancies were observed between shear stress distributions calculated by this method and those directly measured by the hot wire method by Schubauer and Klebanoff [*87*]. Ross and Robertson [*103*] modified the Fediaevsky method and obtained some improvement in accuracy.

Two contributions following the general method proposed by Tetervin and Lin are those of Granville [104] and Rubert and Persh [140]. Granville's work suggested that the difficulty in using the moment of momentum equation for $H$ might be overcome. By examining a limited amount of experimental data he showed that the integral of the shearing stress across the layer in terms of $y/\delta^*$ was the same in adverse pressure gradients as in constant pressure flow. Rubert and Persh chose the kinetic energy equation for the determination of $H$ and hence had to evaluate the integral of the dissipation across the layer. This they did empirically using experimental data for a variety of conditions. They also included the Reynolds normal stress in the momentum equation. Values of $\theta$ and $H$ calculated by Rubert and Persh showed reasonably close agreement with experiment for two-dimensional boundary layers and flow in diffusers. Both of these methods draw on the work of Ludwieg and Tillmann [89] for the shearing stress at the wall and the existence of the law of the wall in an adverse pressure gradient.

Two methods based on dividing the treatment between the inner part of the boundary layer and the outer part are those of Ross [141] and Spence [142]. Each uses a separate similarity for the inner and outer parts. Both use the law of the wall for the region next to the wall. Ross adopts a $\frac{3}{2}$-power velocity-deficiency expression for the outer region with a new parameter $D$, thus avoiding the use of the shape parameter $H$. Spence retains the $H$-parameter for the outer region, but evaluates it by means of an expression for the velocity at the distance $\theta$ from the wall, obtained from the equation of motion formulated for the distance $y = \theta$.

The several methods here mentioned show that progress is being made on this difficult problem. In some cases more tests are needed to judge the amount of progress. There is general agreement that more information is needed on the behavior patterns of turbulent flow before a universally valid method can come within reach.

**B,25. Three-Dimensional Effects.** It may seem that undue attention is given to two-dimensional mean flows when in their totality all flows are three-dimensional. The justification for the convenience of avoiding the complications introduced by a third dimension is that motion in the third dimension is in many cases locally absent or so insignificant that two-dimensionality is an acceptable assumption. This fortunate circumstance comes about because boundary layers are usually thin compared to the expanse and radius of curvature of a wall.

Obviously there are many cases where the edges are too close to the region in question or the boundary layers are too thick for three-dimensional effects to be ignored even under local inspection. Common examples are flow in noncircular pipes, flow near wing tips, and flow near the juncture between a wing and a body. Attention has already been called to the fact that three-dimensional effects are hard to avoid in regions of adverse pressure gradient. They become very pronounced in regions of flow separation. On low aspect ratio wings at large angles of attack, separation often manifests itself as a curving of the flow in a continuous fashion to form the large scale trailing vortices. Important as these cases are, we shall regard them as special problems beyond the scope of the present treatise.

Some mention will be made of a particular three-dimensionality known as yawed flow. This is the condition where the leading edge of a two-dimensional body is at an angle other than normal to the mean flow, such as might be represented by an infinitely long swept wing. In such cases deviations from the mean flow direction occur in the boundary layer. Among the first quantitative measurements to show the effects on swept wings are those of Kuethe, McKee, and Curry [*105*].

In the case of laminar yawed flow it is well known, and readily shown by the equations of motion, that the boundary layer development with distance normal to the leading edge and the velocity components associated with this direction are independent of yaw. In other words, boundary layer thickness and velocity profiles, based on the stream component normal to the leading edge are independent of the flow parallel to the leading edge. This is known as the "independence principle."

According to the best evidence at hand, the independence principle does not apply in turbulent flow. The experiments of Ashkenas and Riddell [*106*] conducted on yawed flat plates show that the thickness of the turbulent boundary layer at a given streamwise distance from the leading edge increases with the angle of yaw. A 1-inch strip of sandpaper glued to the surface near the leading edge made turbulent flow a certainty from that point on and gave an essentially fixed virtual origin for the boundary layer. In terms of distance $\xi$ from the virtual origin parallel to the free stream direction, the displacement thickness $\delta^*$ was found to be given by

$$\delta^* = \frac{0.046\xi}{(\cos\theta)^{\frac{2}{5}}}\left(\frac{U_e\xi}{\nu}\right)^{-\frac{1}{5}}$$

where $\theta$ is the yaw angle. Except for the factor $(\cos\theta)^{\frac{2}{5}}$, this is the ordinary expression for $\delta^*$ in terms of wall length traversed by the flow. According to Ashkenas and Riddell, yawing would have the effect of decreasing $\delta^*$ at a given streamwise distance if the independence principle were to apply. The arguments leading to this conclusion are left to the original paper.

The above result is in disagreement with that of Young and Booth [*107*] who concluded that the independence principle does apply in the turbulent boundary layer. Ashkenas and Riddell have noted this disagreement and have pointed out possible causes of error in the experiments of Young and Booth.

Even without putting this case to actual test, it may be seen that the independence principle would not be expected to apply in turbulent flow. Let us imagine a wind tunnel experiment in which we have a flat belt passing through slots in the tunnel walls and running diametrically across the stream with the stream crossing it edgewise. If the boundary layers on the two sides of the belt are laminar, running the belt has no effect on the boundary layer associated with the action of the stream, unless of course the belt is running so fast that heating effects change the viscosity and density of the air. If, on the other hand, the boundary layers are turbulent, then running the belt increases the turbulence because of the greater velocity relative to the surface. The eddy viscosity is thereby increased, and this increase affects all motions. To the flow component normal to the leading edge, the boundary layer now exhibits greater eddy viscosity. The friction to air flowing over the belt is thereby increased and the thickness of the boundary layer is increased correspondingly.

## *CHAPTER 5. FREE TURBULENT FLOWS*

**B,26. Types and General Features.** The term "free turbulent flows" refers to flows which are free of confining walls and exist in shear motion relative to a surrounding fluid with which they mix freely. The flows of common technical interest are jets, wakes, and mixing zones between two uniform streams moving with different relative velocity. Problems of technical interest are the rate of spreading with distance from a source of the flow, velocity distributions, and the manner in which other transported quantities such as heat and matter are distributed and mixed with a surrounding medium.

A characteristic common to this class of flows is a lack of viscous constraints on the mean motion in all parts of the field when the Reynolds number is sufficiently high. This condition is practically always fulfilled unless the Reynolds number is so low that the turbulent regime cannot exist at all. In the case of mixing zones, jets, and two-dimensional wakes this condition never degenerates; for no matter how feeble the relative motion may become with increasing distance from the source, the Reynolds number either remains constant or increases due to the increase in size. More specifically the Reynolds number increases with distance for mixing zones and two-dimensional jets, and remains constant for axially symmetric jets and two-dimensional wakes. The axially symmetric wake is the one exception, for here the rate of decay of mean motion (and turbulence) exceeds the growth in diameter, and the Reynolds number tends toward an eventual zero value.

We are therefore dealing with a class of flows in which the effects of viscosity are removed from those turbulent motions which control the mean motion and are relegated to the small scale eddies which take part in the final decay and the production of heat. In this respect the flow fields are subject to a controlling mechanism similar to that found in the outer regions of a turbulent boundary layer, but lacking the influence of a wall such as prevails to varying degrees in the boundary layer. Once the flows have attained a fully developed state, they remain similar throughout upon subsequent development, merely changing scales of length and intensive properties.

The fully developed state is an asymptotic condition reached only at some distance from a body in the case of a wake and from a nozzle in the case of a jet. Since the initial conditions in these two cases are vastly different, the distance for their effect to disappear is also different. Behind a body the flow is highly agitated by a succession of eddies comparable to the diameter of the body, and this coarse scale motion persists for a long distance. Townsend [*108*], in his investigation of the plane wake behind a cylinder, finds that the mean wake flow reaches similarity only after 100 cylinder diameters downstream, and that complete statistical equilibrium in the turbulent motions is not reached short of 1000 diameters. At a nozzle the initial jet consists of a potential core of relatively smooth flow, or a flow characteristic of the internal flow, bounded by a layer in which free mixing begins. Kuethe [*109*] finds that the potential core of a round jet is consumed between 4 and 5 nozzle diameters downstream of the plane of the nozzle, and that fully developed jet flow is established at 8 nozzle diameters.

We shall here be concerned mainly with fully developed characteristics and shall attempt to describe the principal ones, paying most attention to the plane wake (two-dimensional) and the round jet (axially symmetric) since these have been investigated in the most detail. Since little information is available on the wake of a self-propelled body, this case will not be considered. A discussion of its laws of spreading and decay may be found in [*110*].

**B,27. Laws of Mean Spreading and Decay.** A certain amount of useful information can be gathered from the equations of mean motion without requiring their actual solution. Using the condition that momentum, heat, and matter are conserved and that the flow when fully developed preserves similarity among mean motions and those turbulent motions which influence the mean motion, it is possible to obtain the laws of spreading and decay of mean properties.

The conventional procedure, which will be followed here, is to assume constant density. If heat is added or is generated by friction, or if another gas is added, it is assumed that the amounts are too small to affect the dynamical problem. The type of problem considered is that of fully developed rectilinear flow such as applies to the jet in a stationary surrounding medium and a wake at sufficient distance from a body.

The Reynolds equations in simple form become acceptable approximations under the conditions that (1) the viscous stresses may be neglected compared to the turbulent stresses, and (2) the mean pressure is so nearly constant that the gradients have a negligible effect on the axial motion and momentum. With regard to condition 2, it should be pointed out that the pressure in jets is slightly different from the ambient pressure [*111*], but this may be disregarded as far as our present interests are concerned.

Let $x$ be measured along the axis of mean flow from some suitable origin, and $U$ denote the mean velocity in the $x$ direction. Let $y$ be the lateral coordinate for two-dimensional flow and $r$ be the radial coordinate for flow symmetrical about the $x$ axis, and let $V$ represent the lateral or radial component of mean velocity in each case. Then for steady mean flow the equations of motion and continuity are respectively:

*Plane jet and mixing zone*

$$\begin{cases} U\dfrac{\partial U}{\partial x} + V\dfrac{\partial U}{\partial y} = \dfrac{1}{\rho}\dfrac{\partial \tau}{\partial y} & \text{(27-1)} \\ \dfrac{\partial U}{\partial x} + \dfrac{\partial V}{\partial y} = 0 & \text{(27-2)} \end{cases}$$

*Round jet*

$$\begin{cases} U\dfrac{\partial U}{\partial x} + V\dfrac{\partial U}{\partial r} = \dfrac{1}{r\rho}\dfrac{\partial (r\tau)}{\partial r} & \text{(27-3)} \\ \dfrac{\partial (rU)}{\partial x} + \dfrac{\partial (rV)}{\partial r} = 0 & \text{(27-4)} \end{cases}$$

Here $\tau$ is the shear stress.

For wakes, equations corresponding to Eq. 27-1 and 27-3 may be further reduced because of conditions which apply at the great distances from the object necessary for similarity to exist. These are that $V$ has become negligible, and $U$ is nowhere much less than the free stream velocity $U_e$. If we express the velocity reduction by

$$\Delta U = U_e - U$$

and substitute in Eq. 27-1, at the same time dropping the term $V\partial U/dy$, we obtain

$$-(U_e - \Delta U)\frac{\partial \Delta U}{\partial x} = \frac{1}{\rho}\frac{\partial \tau}{\partial y}$$

To a sufficient degree of approximation this may be written

*Plane wake*

$$-U_e\frac{\partial \Delta U}{\partial x} = \frac{1}{\rho}\frac{\partial \tau}{\partial y} \qquad \text{(27-5)}$$

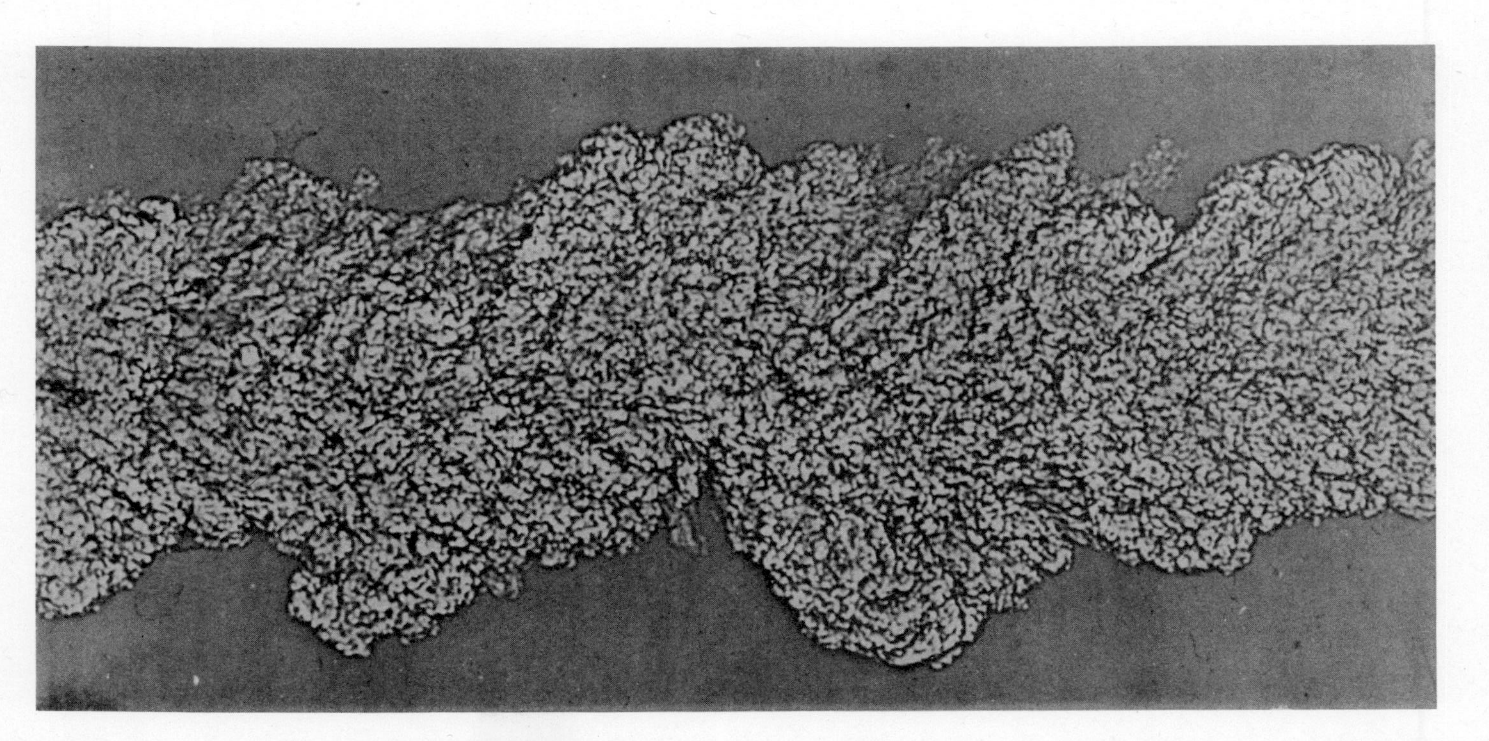

Plate B,28. Turbulent wake of bullet. (Courtesy Ballistic Research Laboratories, Aberdeen Proving Ground.) After Corrsin and Kistler [*117*].

Following a similar procedure for the round wake we obtain

*Round wake* $$-U_e \frac{\partial \Delta U}{\partial x} = \frac{1}{r\rho} \frac{\partial (r\tau)}{\partial r} \tag{27-6}$$

The equations for the conservation of momentum are:

$$\left.\begin{aligned}
&\textit{Plane jet} && \rho \int_{-\infty}^{+\infty} U^2 dy = \text{const} \\
&\textit{Round jet} && 2\pi\rho \int_0^{\infty} U^2 r dr = \text{const} \\
&\textit{Plane wake} && \\
&&& \rho \int_{-\infty}^{+\infty} U(U_e - U) dy = \text{const} \cong \rho U_e \int_{-\infty}^{+\infty} \Delta U dy \\
&\textit{Round wake} && \\
&&& 2\pi\rho \int_0^{\infty} U(U_e - U) r dr = \text{const} \cong 2\pi\rho U_e \int_0^{\infty} \Delta U r dr
\end{aligned}\right\} \tag{27-7}$$

The method of employing the foregoing relations to find the laws of spreading and decay will be illustrated by carrying through the steps for the plane jet. Then the end results for all cases will be stated. If $U_c$ is the velocity at the center of the jet and $b$ is any convenient measure of the width ($b$ may be the distance from the center to where $U$ is zero or some fraction of $U_c$), then similarity means

$$\frac{U}{U_c} = f\left(\frac{y}{b}\right) \tag{27-8}$$

and

$$\frac{\tau}{U_c^2} = g\left(\frac{y}{b}\right) \tag{27-9}$$

where $f$ and $g$ are any function whose form may remain unknown. We now set $b \sim x^m$ and $U_c \sim x^{-n}$. Then the terms in the equation of motion (Eq. 27-1) become of the following order in $x$:

$$U \frac{\partial U}{\partial x} \sim x^{-2n-1}; \quad V \frac{\partial U}{\partial y} \sim x^{-2n-m}; \quad \frac{\partial \tau}{\partial y} \sim x^{-2n-m}$$

In order that the equation shall be independent of $x$, we must have $2n + 1 = 2n + m$, or $m = 1$. The momentum relation

$$\rho \int_{-\infty}^{+\infty} U^2 dy = \text{const}$$

because of order

$$x^{-2n+m}$$

and since this must be independent of $x$, $-2n + m = 0$. Since $m = 1$, $n = \frac{1}{2}$. Thus it is found that the plane jet spreads linearly with $x$ and the velocity at the center decreases as $x^{-\frac{1}{2}}$. A similar procedure may be used for the other cases, and the results are summarized for all in Table B, 27.

*Table B,27*

| | Mixing zone | Plane jet | Round jet | Plane wake | Round wake |
|---|---|---|---|---|---|
| $m$ | 1 | 1 | 1 | $\frac{1}{2}$ | $\frac{1}{3}$ |
| $n$ | . . | $\frac{1}{2}$ | 1 | $\frac{1}{2}$ | $\frac{2}{3}$ |

Width parameter $x^m$.
Velocity at center $x^{-n}$.

The same results may be obtained by setting up integral relations for the energy and using these with the momentum relations to determine $m$ and $n$. This procedure is illustrated in [*94*].

The diffusion of heat and other scalar quantities is also of practical and theoretical interest. The equations of heat transfer, written for assumptions consistent with those made for the equations of motion, are as follows:

*Plane jet and mixing zone*
$$U\frac{\partial \bar{T}}{\partial x} + V\frac{\partial \bar{T}}{\partial y} = \frac{1}{\rho c_p}\frac{\partial q}{\partial y} \tag{27-10}$$

*Round jet*
$$U\frac{\partial \bar{T}}{\partial x} + V\frac{\partial \bar{T}}{\partial r} = \frac{1}{\rho c_p}\frac{1}{r}\frac{\partial (rq)}{\partial r} \tag{27-11}$$

*Plane wake*
$$U_e\frac{\partial \bar{T}}{\partial x} = \frac{1}{\rho c_p}\frac{\partial q}{\partial y} \tag{27-12}$$

*Round wake*
$$U_e\frac{\partial \bar{T}}{\partial x} = \frac{1}{\rho c_p}\frac{1}{r}\frac{\partial (rq)}{\partial r} \tag{27-13}$$

where $\bar{T}$ is the mean temperature, $q$ is the rate of heat transfer in the $y$ or $r$ directions per unit area (see Art. 10), and $c_p$ is the specific heat at constant pressure. In proper terms the same equations hold for the transfer of matter. Molecular diffusion is so slow compared to turbulent diffusion that the transfer can be regarded as due entirely to turbulent motions.

Again assuming similarity, and expressing it in analogous terms, Eq. 27-10, 27-11, 27-12, and 27-13, together with the fact that the same amount of heat and matter must flow through each cross section, serve to determine the form of spreading and the decrease of center temperature or concentration as a function of $x$. These are the same as for the velocity, but the absolute magnitudes are different.

In all cases the origin of $x$ is that point from which the flow appears to originate with the same law from the beginning. The point is usually found by extrapolating the experimental curves to a virtual origin. For the round jet this is usually between 0.5 and 1.5 orifice diameters downstream from the orifice. The virtual origin appears to be less well defined for the plane wake and is different for the extrapolated center velocity than for the extrapolated width (Townsend [*1*]).

The foregoing relations apply as long as the Reynolds number remains sufficiently high for similarity to exist. Since the Reynolds number is proportional to $x^{m-n}$, it is seen from Table B,27 that, if the condition is initially satisfied, it will continue to be satisfied with ever-increasing $x$ in all cases, with the exception of the round wake. For the latter the Reynolds number will eventually decrease to the point where the turbulent laws of spreading and decay merge into laminar laws with a new virtual origin. The distances for this change to occur can be expected to be very great, and in most cases any practical interest in the wake will have already been lost.

As already indicated, it is required in the foregoing analyses that similarity extend to the turbulent motions responsible for diffusion. The same rules must therefore apply to the scales of length and velocity entering into the diffusion process. If we adopt the concept of eddy viscosity, we may compare the behavior of a turbulent flow to that of a laminar flow in terms of the behavior of a viscosity. Denoting the mean eddy viscosity applicable to the flow by $\epsilon_\mu$, we have, since $\epsilon_\mu$ is proportional to a length times a velocity,

$$\epsilon_\mu \sim x^{m-n}$$

Referring to Table B,27, we find that $\epsilon_\mu$ is constant for the round jet and the plane wake. These flows should then behave as laminar flows with respect to their form of spreading and decay, as in fact they do. It must be borne in mind that we are here concerned only with the proportionality rule, not with absolute magnitudes. In the case of the plane jet, $\epsilon_\mu$ increases as $x^{\frac{1}{2}}$, and we find, as we should, that the spreading and decay follow faster laws than those governing laminar flow. In this case the laminar exponents are

$$m_{\text{lam}} = \tfrac{2}{3}, \qquad n_{\text{lam}} = \tfrac{1}{3}$$

In the case of the round wake, $\epsilon_\mu$ decreases as $x^{-\frac{1}{3}}$, and we find, again as we should, that the spreading and decay follow slower laws than those governing laminar flow. Here the laminar exponents are

$$m_{\text{lam}} = \tfrac{1}{2}, \qquad n_{\text{lam}} = 1$$

**B,28. General Form and Structure.** The boundary which separates the turbulent fluid, of say a jet or a wake, from the nonturbulent surrounding fluid is determined only by how far the motions have penetrated the surroundings. While it is self-evident that the boundary must be irregular, it was not until comparatively recent hot wire studies were made that the highly irregular and sharply defined character of the boundary was revealed. An intermittency in the turbulence recorded from a hot wire probe in the outer regions of a round jet was first observed and studied by Corrsin [*112*]. It soon became apparent that this effect was due to a sharp and irregular boundary convected past the hot wire. The phenomenon was studied in considerable detail by Townsend [*113,114, 115,116*] in connection with his studies of the plane wake. Corrsin and Kistler [*117*] later made an exhaustive study of free stream boundaries, and this together with studies in the boundary layer by Klebanoff [*118*] has resulted in a reasonably clear understanding of the character and meaning of the free boundary.

In Art. 17 attention has already been directed to the outer boundary of a turbulent boundary layer, and the situation has been depicted schematically in Fig. B,17b. The character of the free boundary and the sharp separation between turbulent and nonturbulent fluid is shown in actual reality by the photograph of the turbulent wake of a bullet, displayed by Corrsin and Kistler, and shown here as Plate B,28. No turbulence and no other property transported by the shear flow, except some energy associated with potential motions, has penetrated the surrounding medium beyond the boundary. Moreover, the boundary is a connected surface; there are no disconnected parcels of fluid. The billows and hollows are, of course, three-dimensional. All motion in the nonturbulent fluid outside the boundary is irrotational, and the velocity there is that accompanying the potential motion of a free stream.

These phenomena are reproduced at all free boundaries, differing only in degree. An "intermittency factor" has been adopted as one of the criteria of the irregularity of the boundary. If a hot wire probe, capable of following the fluctuations, is placed so that, as the flow passes by, it is alternately in and out of the turbulent fluid, a record of the signal will show intermittently turbulent and nonturbulent sections. From such a record, or by other instrumental means, the fraction of the time that the flow is found to be turbulent may be determined. This is defined as the intermittency factor. As the probe is moved from the center of the flow outward, the intermittency factor goes from unity to zero. The customary symbol for the intermittency factor is $\gamma$. This symbol when used here is not to be confused with the same symbol for the ratio of specific heats used earlier.

It is instructive to compare $\gamma$ distributions for several types of flow along with their mean velocity distributions. These are given for the boundary layer, the round jet, and the plane wake in Fig. B,28a and B,28b. In Fig. B,28a Klebanoff's data for a smooth wall and Corrsin's and Kistler's data for a very rough wall are compared. While there is considerable dispersion in the observations of intermittency, the difference between the curves for smooth and rough walls is believed to be real.

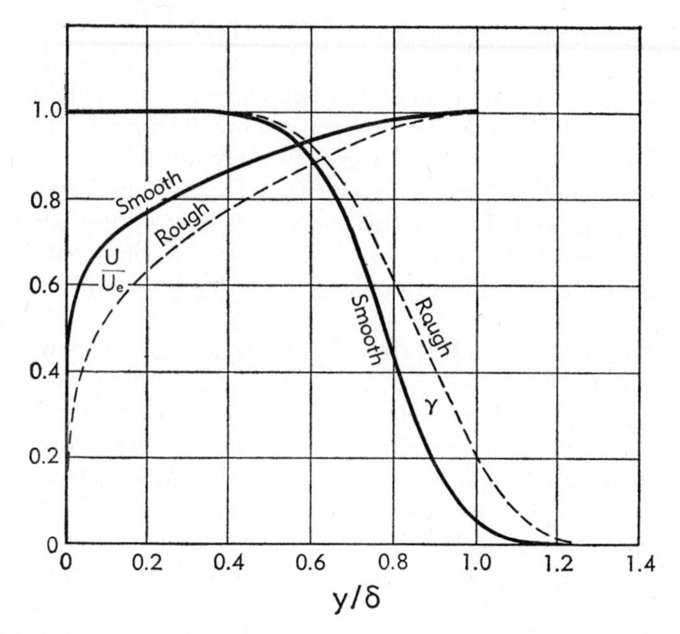


Fig. B,28a. Intermittency factor compared with velocity distribution in boundary layers for smooth and rough walls.

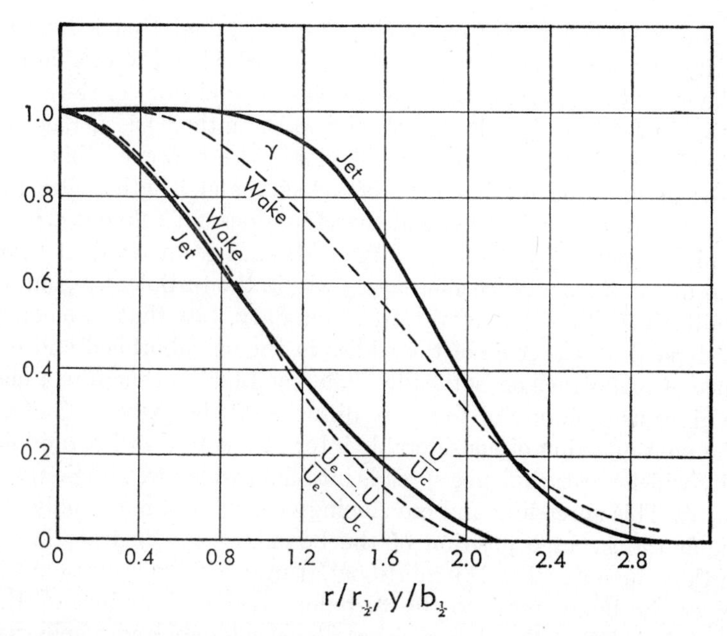


Fig. B,28b. Intermittency factor compared with velocity distribution for jet and wake. $r_{\frac{1}{2}}$, $b_{\frac{1}{2}}$ are distances from axis to where velocity ratios are $\frac{1}{2}$.

Comparing the boundary layer and free flow, it is seen that the region of intermittency occurs where the velocity is not much different from that of the free stream in the case of the boundary layer, whereas it penetrates more deeply into the jet and wake flows. The range of mean velocities occurring in the region covered by the various instantaneous positions of the boundary is therefore much less for the boundary layer than for jets and wakes; and while the boundaries may appear superficially similar in all cases, the bulges and hollows involve the greater portion of the mean velocity field in free flows. This applies particularly to the wake.

According to Townsend [*1*] free flows contain large eddies which have a relatively small amount of energy, but which nevertheless serve to convect the fluid about in large bulks. He postulates a double structure consisting of the large eddies containing little turbulent energy and a smaller scale of eddies containing most of the turbulent energy. This would seem to be a reasonable picture in view of the freedom of motion in the absence of a wall, but, to the degree that the outer boundary of a wall flow is also free, the same picture might also apply to the outer region of a boundary layer.

A statistical measure of the width of the intermittent zone is the standard deviation of the instantaneous boundary from its mean position given by $[\overline{(Y - \bar{Y})^2}]^{\frac{1}{2}}$, where $Y$ is the instantaneous position and $\bar{Y}$ is the average position.

From Townsend's point of view the standard deviation is determined primarily by the large eddies. Corrsin and Kistler [*117*] were able to predict the observed behavior (not the absolute magnitude) of the standard deviation in the boundary layer, jet, and wake on the basis of Lagrangian diffusion by continuous movements (Taylor [*119*]). However, this required only the assumption of similarity of velocity and length scales to one another and to the main flow, and therefore does not rule out a possibly predominant part played by the large eddies. It seems evident that the contour of a marked surface completely within the turbulent region would be qualitatively like that of the free boundary, but that its coarseness would depend on the scale of the eddies in the neighborhood and on the presence of turbulence on both sides. The boundary is therefore a marker which gives us a picture of the eddy diffusion at the extreme limits.

The next question of considerable interest has to do with the mechanism by which the turbulence spreads into fluid which was originally nonturbulent. This spreading and enveloping of new fluid is the only means by which the average position of the boundary can migrate laterally. Given that the outer flow is irrotational, it must become rotational when it crosses the boundary into the turbulent region. Corrsin and Kistler have concluded that the change takes place suddenly and wholly within a very thin laminar superlayer "plastered" over the boundary. Vorticity can be transmitted to an irrotational flow only by tangential forces due to viscosity. The layer in which this takes place is the laminar superlayer. Corrsin and Kistler have shown that this layer must be very thin, partly on the grounds that stability considerations would not permit it to be otherwise, and partly on the grounds that the turbulent stretching of vortex lines increases the vorticity and therefore sharpens up the velocity gradient. The thickness has been estimated to be less than the dissipation length $\lambda$. The presence of the laminar superlayer cannot be detected experimentally, but the observed sharp demarcation between turbulent and nonturbulent regimes tends to confirm the thinness of the layer.

The spreading of the turbulent region therefore takes place by viscous action at the immediate boundary, and the rate of encroachment depends on the steepness of the laminar gradient and on the surface area, both of which are increased by the larger-scale, eddy-diffusion process acting from within. Viscosity is the vorticity-propagating agent, but it plays no controlling role in the spread of the turbulent region. Corrsin and Kistler point out that heat and matter are transported across the boundary in exactly the same way; and if the Prandtl and Schmidt numbers are not much smaller than unity, these scalar quantities should be transported at the same rate as momentum. The processes at the immediate boundary therefore do not explain why heat and matter spread faster than momentum. We shall return to this question in Art. 29.

The phenomena just described require that the fluid everywhere beyond the boundary cannot have received any quantity by diffusion. If a jet is hot, all of the heat is confined within the sharp boundary. The same is true of all of the axial momentum. The only effect on the outer fluid is a pressure-induced flow toward the jet and pressure-induced fluctuations. Both are irrotational. The term, turbulence, cannot be applied to these fluctuations. Relatively slow, potential-type velocity fluctuations are in fact observed in the outer fluid. Jumps in mean velocity are also observed in passing from turbulent to nonturbulent regions. Apparently in some cases these are smaller than would be expected if free stream velocity prevailed in the nonturbulent regions. Townsend proposes that the fluid between two turbulent bulges is partially carried along as the bulges move downstream, but there is some disagreement on this point. Corrsin and Kistler find jumps in the intermittent region of a boundary layer of about the order to be expected if the outer fluid is not carried along.

The sharp boundary is not to be confused with the limits as usually expressed in terms of mean velocity distribution. It will be noted from the $\gamma$ curves that the fluctuations in the sharp boundary generally extend beyond the mean velocity boundary. A bulge protruding far out apparently carries so little mean velocity increment or defect that its effect cannot be detected by the usual methods.

**B,29. Transport Processes in Free Turbulent Flow.** In order to solve the equations of motion and heat transfer given in Art. 27 and thus obtain velocity and temperature distributions in $y$ or $r$, it is necessary to express the quantities on the right-hand side of the equations in terms that can be related to the derivatives of velocity and temperature with respect to $y$ or $r$. The auxiliary expressions for this purpose have been discussed in Art. 10. Specifically, Eq. 10-12 or 10-13 are used with the coefficients $D_u$, $D_h$, $\epsilon_\mu$, or $\epsilon_k$ specified either by general conditions of the problem or expressed in terms of local conditions.

The former usually takes the form of an assumption that the coefficients are constant over a given cross section of the flow but vary from one section to the next. In recent years the following expression proposed by Prandtl [*120*] has been extensively used:

$$D_u \text{ or } D_h = K(U_{\max} - U_{\min})b \tag{29-1}$$

where $b$ is the width of the region at a given cross section, $U_{\max}$ and $U_{\min}$ are the extremes of mean velocity across the section, and $K$ is an experimentally determined constant of proportionality whose value depends on the quantity $D_u$ or $D_h$.

Specification of transport in terms of local conditions takes the form of mixing length theory. This theory has already been discussed in Art. 12. Its application to free turbulent flows has been so widely discussed in the literature, for example [*6,111*], that only a few remarks are called for here. Much of the discussion has had to do with the relative merits of momentum transfer theory on the one hand and Taylor's vorticity transfer theory on the other. Vorticity transfer theory is generally favored on the grounds that it is consistent with a wider distribution of temperature than of velocity, but which of the two theories agrees the better with observed velocity distributions depends on cases.

We shall here concern ourselves with the broader question regarding the foundation of the foregoing procedures rather than with the details of their application. The basis for judgment rests largely on the work of Townsend with the plane wake and that of Corrsin with the round jet. As mentioned in Art. 28, there is evidence that large eddies operate in free turbulent flows to contort the whole flow field and thus transport fluid with smaller scales of turbulence over much of the width occupied by the flow. The next idea to be introduced is that mixing of all properties by large and small scale motions has gone on for a considerable time over the previous course of the flow. In this connection it is advisable to restrict the discussion to jets and wakes, for in these cases all of the properties in question have been put in at the beginning and through mixing have covered much of the cross section during their previous history. Eddies of any scale significant in diffusion will have existed for a considerable time, and their size and intensity found at a particular location will depend mainly on their past environment and will reflect the character of the flow as a whole rather than that of any particular locality. The large-eddy part of the structure helps greatly to promote this general averaging. The central idea here is that the lengths and velocities entering into a turbulent transport coefficient are not primarily determined by local conditions. What has been stated here is true to a degree of all turbulent flow, but the greater preponderance of large eddies and the exposure to mixing from the beginning enhance the effects in jets and wakes.

We have the picture, then, that any property that has been in the flow for a considerable length of time should be mixed to a fair degree of uniformity when it has arrived at a particular cross section. Dilution occurs at the sharp boundaries, and also new fluid has recently become turbulent there. Therefore we would not expect complete uniformity everywhere within the sharp boundaries. Experiments show that turbulent energy, temperature in the case of a heated jet or wake, and concentration of a tracer gas in a jet are nearly uniform over the fully turbulent core and decrease gradually in the turbulent bulges as the boundary is approached. The over-all average decrease toward the boundaries is faster than that in the turbulent parts alone due to the absence of any contribution from the nonturbulent parts.

The foregoing behavior does not apply in the same degree to the axial momentum. The mean velocity difference decreases considerably across the core and continues to decrease in the protruding turbulent bulges. This is obviously why the mean velocity distribution is less broad than the mean-temperature distribution, but it is only a superficial explanation since it leaves unexplained why the momentum should have been given preferential treatment in the mixing process.

We must now be concerned with the question of how to express the transfer processes. Mixing length theory and Eq. 29-1 both assume a gradient type of transfer in which the rate can be expressed in terms of the local gradient. This requires that the diffusing movements shall be small compared to the distance over which the gradient changes. This condition may be satisfied as far as the smaller eddies are concerned, but it is obviously not satisfied for eddies comparable in size to the width of the jet or wake. Townsend proposes that the total rate of transport is a combination gradient diffusion by the smaller eddies, which contain most of the turbulent energy, and bulk convection by the larger eddies. Since the gradients in scalar quantities, like heat, matter, and turbulent energy have been reduced due to the long continued mixing, it would appear that these quantities have been transported laterally more by the bulk convection than by gradient diffusion. On the other hand, since momentum has not been so thoroughly mixed, the prospects for gradient diffusion are better.

With regard to the theories in question, three main facts stand out: (1) only the smaller eddies of this double-structure picture can take part in the gradient diffusion on which the theories are based, (2) the smaller eddies are mixed to a state of near uniformity, and (3) the scale and intensity of all eddies responsible for transfer are determined by general conditions rather than local conditions.

Fact 1 means that we cannot predict to what extent the theories will apply. Fact 2 means that we can make a good case for Eq. 29-1 for that part of the transport which is of the gradient type. Fact 3 means that we must be skeptical of the kind of local dependence on which mixing length theory rests. This refers specifically to Eq. 12-2b and 12-13 of Art. 12 which expresses $v$ and $l$ in terms of local mean flow parameters. Some lessening of local dependence is achieved when $l$ is taken to be constant over a section of the flow and proportional to the width. This is commonly done in free turbulent flows. We see that even with this compromise, mixing length theory is scarcely tenable in free turbulent flows.

Turning to comparisons with measured distributions, we find that mixing length theory cannot be shown to be definitely wrong, although the agreement with observations is rather casual, with vorticity transfer turning out to be better in some cases and momentum transfer being better in others. The vorticity transfer version of the theory when combined with the heat transfer version does at least yield a broader temperature distribution than velocity distribution [*121*].

Hinze and van der Hegge Zijnen [*122*] conducted an exhaustive series of experiments in which they measured distributions of velocity, temperature, and concentration of small amounts of added gas in a round air jet. After comparing their results with mixing length theories they concluded that these theories were unsatisfactory, and so set out to explore the possibilities of constant turbulent exchange coefficient. From their measured velocity distributions and the equations of motion and continuity, $D_u$ was determined as a function of radius and axial distance. It was found to remain nearly constant with increasing $r$ from the center outward, and then to decrease in the intermittent zone. They concluded, however, that a constant $D_u$ was a sufficiently good assumption to justify the adoption of the well-known laminar solution. The resulting velocity distribution formula and the expression for $D_u$ are given in Art. 30.

Hinze and van der Hegge Zijnen found that temperature and concentration profiles indicated practically identical exchange coefficients. We shall denote these by the common symbol $D_h$ and refer to the ratio $D_u/D_h = Pr_t$ as the turbulent Prandtl number. (This ratio is known as the Schmidt number when referring to matter in place of temperature.) The value of $Pr_t$ on the axis of the jet was found to be 0.685. However, $Pr_t$ increased steadily with $r$ and became greater than unity for

$U/U_c < 0.2$. This means that $D_h$ decreased where $D_u$ remained constant and decreased more rapidly than $D_u$ in the outer regions.

Corrsin and Uberoi [*123*] calculated values of $Pr_t$ from their measurements in a heated round jet. Their mean values over the cross section of the jet were very close to the value 0.7. They also obtained an indicated increase from the center outward, but did not regard their accuracy as sufficient to be certain of a definite trend. They noted the striking agreement with the laminar Prandtl number for air at the mean temperature of the jet. Forstall and Shapiro [*124*] point out, however, that turbulent Prandtl numbers for jets are about 0.7 for various kinds of fluids irrespective of their laminar Prandtl number.

Townsend found in his investigations of the plane wake [*113*] that both $D_u$ and $l$ remained nearly constant in the central portion of the wake, but fell off rapidly in the outer part. However, $D_u$ divided by the intermittency factor $\gamma$ was not far from constant over the greater part of the wake.

These pieces of evidence tend to confirm what was conjectured earlier in this article, namely that insofar as theories based on gradient transfer can be applied at all, they should apply better to momentum than to temperature or concentration. The laminar-type solutions of the equations of motion based on some appropriate constant value of $D_u$ over the section have consistently given accurate descriptions of the velocity distribution. Discrepancies occur in the outer part of the flow due to the fact that $D_u$ decreases. Townsend has shown that improvement results for the plane wake if the eddy viscosity $\epsilon_\mu$ is allowed to decrease with the intermittency factor, i.e. as $\gamma\epsilon_\mu$.

The situation with regard to the diffusion of heat and matter is not so favorable, and transfer based on local gradients is little better than a crude approximation at best. For the round jet, and presumably for the plane jet also, $D_h$ is nowhere constant, but the assumption of constant $Pr_t$ is believed to be acceptable for practical purposes. When $Pr_t$ is constant, the relation between temperature distribution and velocity distribution for the round jet is

$$\begin{pmatrix}\text{temperature}\\ \text{ratio}\end{pmatrix} = \begin{pmatrix}\text{velocity}\\ \text{ratio}\end{pmatrix}^{Pr_t} \tag{29-2}$$

While there is some question about the appropriate value of $Pr_t$, a reasonable value is $Pr_t \cong 0.7$.

According to Reichardt [*125*] Eq. 29-2 should be more generally applicable in free turbulent flow. For a review of Reichardt's inductive theory of turbulence, reference is made to [*96*].

For plane wakes it does not seem possible to calculate temperature distribution on the basis of an exchange coefficient for heat. Paradoxically, mixing length theory gives reasonably good agreement with observed temperature and velocity distributions when $l$ is assumed constant over the cross section. Momentum transfer theory and vorticity transfer theory give the same results for velocity distribution, but vorticity transfer must be used in connection with the heat transfer equation to get the proper result for temperature distribution. The results are

$$\frac{U_e - U}{U_e - U_c} = \left[1 - \left(\frac{y}{y_e}\right)^{\frac{3}{2}}\right]^2$$

$$\frac{T - T_e}{T_c - T_e} = 1 - \left(\frac{y}{y_e}\right)^{\frac{3}{2}}$$

where $U_e$ and $T_e$ are respectively the velocity and temperature of the free stream, $U_c$ and $T_c$ are respectively the velocity and temperature at the center, and $y_e$ is the extreme limit in each case, $y_e$ being the greater for temperature distribution.

We may conclude this discussion by noting that recent findings have given us a clearer physical picture but little by way of a fundamental theory. It has not been possible to clarify the question as to why turbulent motions act differently toward heat and matter than toward momentum. Some discussion of this question is given by Townsend; and since this cannot readily be taken out of context, the reader is referred to [*1*, pp. 164, 165].

**B,30. Velocity Distribution Formulas for Jets and Wakes.** The advantage of a constant exchange coefficient is not so much in any marked improvement in accuracy over mixing length theory, but rather that it permits the adoption of laminar-type solutions. When similarity exists, the form of the dependence of the exchange coefficient on $x$ is known, but the absolute magnitude must be found from experiment. The purpose here is to give examples of final results based on this method. For the purpose of comparison a mixing length formula will be shown for one case. It is assumed that mixing length theory and the resulting formulas have been given sufficient attention in other literature, notably in [*6*,*111*].

A comparison of formulas for the plane wake, made by Townsend [*126*], is shown in Fig. B,30. Compared with an observed velocity distribution curve are

1. Mixing length theory, $l$ constant over the width:

$$f_1 = 1.835\left[1 - \left(\frac{\xi}{0.48}\right)^{\frac{3}{2}}\right]^2 \tag{30-1}$$

2. Constant exchange coefficient:

$$f_1 = 1.835 \exp\left[-\left(\frac{\xi}{0.253}\right)^2\right] \tag{30-2}$$

3. Modified theory: $\epsilon_\mu = (\epsilon_\mu)_t\gamma$, where $(\epsilon_\mu)_t$ = constant eddy viscosity in the turbulent region, $\gamma$ = intermittency factor:

$$f_1 = 1.835 \exp\left\{-14.4\xi^2\left[1 + \frac{1}{3}\left(\frac{\xi}{0.35}\right)^4\right]\right\} \tag{30-3}$$

In 1, 2, and 3, $f_1$ and $\xi$ are

$$f_1 = \frac{U_e - U}{U_e}\left(\frac{x - x_0}{d}\right)^{\frac{1}{2}}; \quad \xi = \frac{y}{[(x - x_0)d]^{\frac{1}{2}}}$$

$x_0$ = virtual origin ($x_0/d = +90$)

$d$ = diameter of cylinder producing the wake

In these cases

$$\frac{\epsilon_\mu}{\rho} \equiv D_u = 0.0173U_e d \tag{30-4}$$

It is seen that mixing length theory makes the distribution too narrow near the axis. The constant exchange coefficient fits in this region but

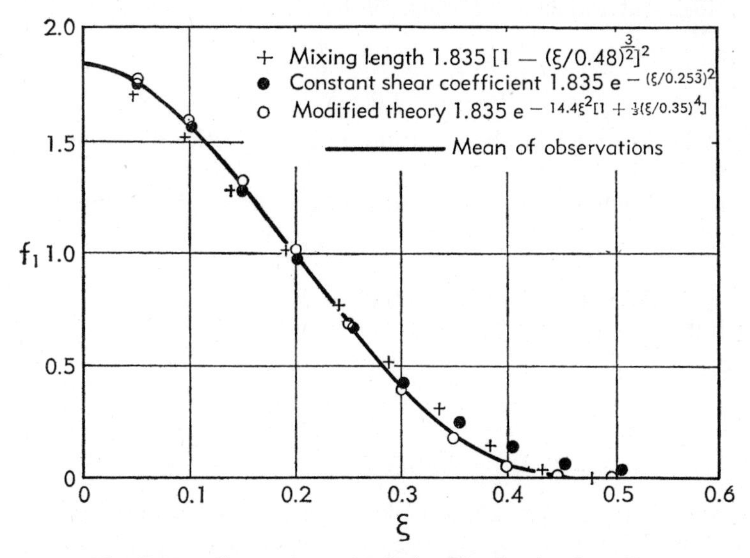


Fig. B,30. Comparison of velocity distribution formulas for plane wake, after Townsend [*126*].

makes the velocity difference approach zero too slowly in the outer region. In reality $\epsilon_\mu$ is not constant, and an all-over fit is obtained only by adjusting $\epsilon_\mu$, as in Eq. 30-3.

The distribution of axial velocity across the round wake may also be represented by a Gaussian error function. Such representations are characteristically faulty near the outer edges. The round wake has not been investigated so thoroughly as the plane wake.

The mixing zone between two uniform streams of velocities $U_1$ and $U_2$ and the plane jet were treated on the basis of constant exchange coefficient by Görtler [*127*]. Since this work has been well reviewed by Schlichting [*96*], only selected results are repeated here. The calculated velocity profile of the mixing zone is in very good agreement with experiment. The calculated distribution of axial velocity in the plane jet is also in good agreement with experiment except in the outer regions where the calculated profile approaches zero too slowly. The formula for the plane jet is

$$U = \frac{\sqrt{3}}{2}\sqrt{\frac{K\alpha}{x}}\,(1 - \tanh^2 \eta) \tag{30-5}$$

where $\alpha$ = a free constant to be determined by experiment,

$$\eta = \alpha \frac{y}{x}$$

$$K = \text{strength of jet} = \int_{-\infty}^{+\infty} U^2 dy$$

The velocity at the center $U_c$ is given by

$$U_c = \frac{\sqrt{3}}{2}\sqrt{\frac{K\alpha}{x}} \tag{30-6}$$

It must be assumed in these formulas that $x$ is the distance from the point where the jet appears to originate. Schlichting quotes Reichardt's experimental value of $\alpha$ as equal to 7.67 and $D_u$ as given by

$$D_u = 0.037 y_{\frac{1}{2}} U_c \tag{30-7}$$

where $y_{\frac{1}{2}}$ is the value of $y$ where $U/U_c = \frac{1}{2}$.

It follows from Eq. 30-5, 30-6, and 30-7 that

$$D_u = \frac{\sqrt{3}}{2}\, 0.037\, \frac{\eta_{\frac{1}{2}}}{\sqrt{\alpha}} \sqrt{Kx}$$

$$D_u = 0.0102 \sqrt{Kx} \tag{30-7a}$$

As mentioned in Art. 29, the adaptation of the laminar-type solution for the round jet was investigated by Hinze and van der Hegge Zijnen. Their expression is

$$\frac{U}{U_c} = \frac{1}{\left(1 + \frac{\eta_r^2}{8\alpha_0}\right)^2} \tag{30-8}$$

where $\eta_r = r/(x + x_0)$

$x_0$ = virtual origin which turned out to be 0.6 times the orifice diameter

$(x + x_0)$ = over-all distance from point where jet appears to originate

$\alpha_0$ = const = 0.00196

In this case

$$D_u = 0.00196(x + x_0)U_c \tag{30-9}$$

According to Schlichting [*96*] the velocity at the center may be expressed by

$$U_c = \frac{3}{8\pi} \frac{K_r}{D_u(x + x_0)} \tag{30-10}$$

Here

$$K_r = \text{strength of jet} = 2\pi \int_0^\infty U^2 r dr = \frac{\pi}{4} D^2 U_e^2 \tag{30-11}$$

where $D$ is the diameter of the nozzle and $U_e$ is the jet exit velocity. By means of Eq. 30-9 and 30-11, Eq. 30-10 may be written

$$\frac{U_c}{U_e} = \frac{6.92}{\frac{x}{D} + \frac{x_0}{D}} \tag{30-12}$$

According to Hinze and van der Hegge Zijnen the numerical constant in Eq. 30-12 turns out to be 6.39 on the basis of their observed axial distribution of velocity.

When $U_c$ given by Eq. 30-10 is substituted into Eq. 30-9,

$$D_u = 0.0153 \sqrt{K_r} \tag{30-13}$$

In jets, as in wakes, the constant exchange coefficient makes the calculated velocity approach zero too slowly in the outer regions. This discrepancy is tolerated partly because it is in the region where the velocity is low and partly because the reason for it is understood in terms of intermittency.

Since the exchange coefficient $D_u$ is the turbulent kinematic viscosity, it is interesting to compare it to ordinary kinematic viscosity $\nu$. For the plane wake from a cylinder the ratio $D_u/\nu$ is found from Eq. 30-4 to be

$$\frac{D_u}{\nu} = 0.0173 \frac{U_e d}{\nu} \tag{30-14}$$

where $U_e d/\nu$ is the Reynolds number of the cylinder. A similar expression may be found for the round jet by replacing $K_r$ in Eq. 30-13 by Eq. 30-11. The result is

$$\frac{D_u}{\nu} = 0.0153 \frac{\sqrt{\pi}}{2} \frac{U_e D}{\nu} = 0.0135 \frac{U_e D}{\nu} \tag{30-15}$$

If, in these two examples, $d$ and $D$ are both one inch and $U_e$ in both cases is 100 ft/sec, the Reynolds number for air at ordinary temperature and pressure is about $4.9 \times 10^4$. The two values of $D_u/\nu$ are then found to be 850 and 660 for the wake and jet respectively. These figures serve to convey an idea of the order of magnitude of the ratio of turbulent viscosity to ordinary viscosity.

When the spreading is linear, as it is for jets, the angle of spreading affords a convenient means of visualizing the size. This angle may be found from Eq. 30-5 and 30-8 in terms of some suitably defined width. If we take this to be the line along which $U/U_c = \frac{1}{2}$, we find that the plane jet is a wedge with a half angle of approximately $6\frac{1}{2}$ degrees and the round jet is a cone with a half angle of approximately 5 degrees. These angles are independent of the strength of the jet. The spreading of laminar jets, on the other hand, depends on the strength, becoming narrower as the strength increases. The plane laminar jet is not wedge-shaped; the width increases with $x^{\frac{2}{3}}$. These differences between turbulent flow and laminar flow are mentioned as additional illustrations of the effect of an eddy viscosity which is regulated by the flow itself.

**B,31. Effect of Density Differences and Compressibility on Jets with Surrounding Air Stationary.** In jet propulsion the jet is much hotter than the surrounding air and it issues at a high relative velocity. Density differences and compressibility are therefore expected to be of some importance. When we examine the situation realistically, however, we find that both temperature difference and relative velocity diminish rapidly with distance, and the jet soon behaves much like the constant-density, incompressible jet previously treated. When the jet issues rearward from a moving vehicle, it does not emerge into a surrounding medium at rest but rather into a medium with an axial velocity in the same direction. Under this condition the jet spreads more slowly, and the temperature and relative velocity diminish more slowly with distance from the orifice. The extent over which density and compressibility effects are possibly important therefore depends on the velocity of the outer stream. The effect of an outer velocity will be considered in Art. 32; here the problem is considered for the surrounding medium stationary with respect to the nozzle.

The work of Corrsin and Uberoi on the heated round jet [*123*] has contributed substantially to what is known about the hot jet issuing into still surrounding air. They studied the jet issuing from a 1-inch orifice with velocities ranging from 65 to 115 ft/sec. The initial temperature rise was made slight when it was desired to study the spread of momentum and heat without introducing significant effects of density difference, and was raised to about 300°C when the effect of density was to be studied. In the latter case the density ratio was $\rho_1/\rho_0 = 2$, where $\rho_0$ is the density of the jet at the nozzle and $\rho_1$ is the density of the surrounding air.

The principal effects are illustrated in Fig. B,31a and B,31b taken from the report of Corrsin and Uberoi. Fig. B,31a shows the velocity and temperature profiles 16 nozzle diameters downstream. From these it is clear that the reduced density corresponding to the higher temperature causes a more rapid spreading of both the velocity and temperature profiles. Again the temperature profile is wider than the velocity profile. Fig. B,31b shows the decrease of velocity and temperature along the axis.

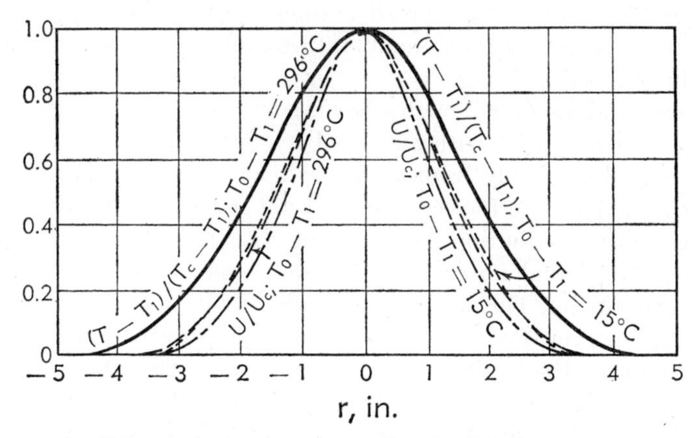


Fig. B,31a. Radial velocity and temperature distribution in round jet showing effect of density, after Corrsin and Uberoi [*123*]. Section 16 nozzle diameters from orifice. $T_0$ = initial temperature of jet, $T_c$ = temperature at center, $T_1$ = temperature of surrounding air.

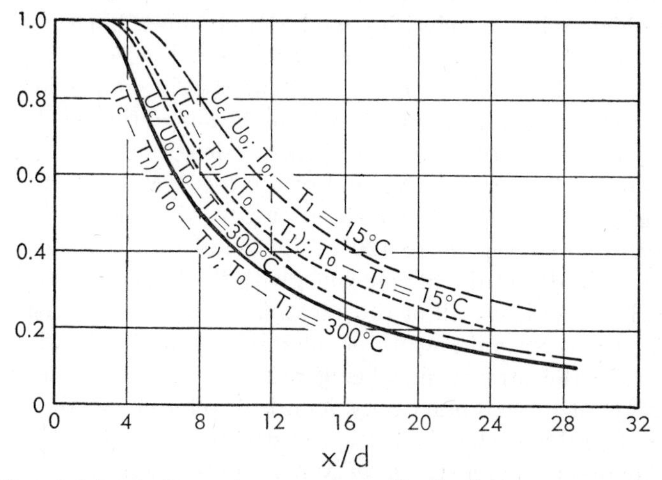


Fig. B,31b. Axial velocity and temperature distribution at center of round jet, after Corrsin and Uberoi [*123*]. $x$ = distance from orifice, $d$ = diameter of nozzle, $T_0$ = initial temperature of jet, $T_c$ = temperature at center, $T_1$ = temperature of surrounding air.

The decreased density causes both velocity and temperature to fall more rapidly than for constant density.

No appreciable change was noted in the shape of the profile in the fully developed jet for $\rho_1/\rho_0 = 2$. Corrsin and Uberoi showed definitely that there was no measurable change in the shape of the total head profiles. However, the density difference was not large after the distance of 7 or 8 nozzle diameters required for the flow to become fully developed. For example, at 15 diameters $\rho_1/\rho_c = 1.3$ when $\rho_1/\rho_0 = 2$. For a density ratio of this order there is no essential departure from similarity in any of the profiles, so that the spread is found to be proportional to $x$ and the decrease of velocity and temperature along the axis is found to be inversely proportional to $x$.

Cleeves and Boelter [*128*] made measurements of velocity and temperature in a round jet with an initial temperature difference of 650°C. The jet issued vertically from a pipe $1\frac{1}{8}$ inches in diameter at velocities ranging from 13 to 56 ft/sec. They did not detect any difference in the radial velocity distribution between the isothermal jet and the hot jet. In short, they found no effect of the decreased density on the rate of spreading of the jet. This disagrees with the results of Corrsin and Uberoi. They did, however, find the velocity on the axis decreased more for the hot jet than for the isothermal jet. The decrease was greater than that found by Corrsin and Uberoi, as would be expected from the higher temperature, but their isothermal results for the velocity on the axis do not agree with those of Corrsin and Uberoi. The Corrsin and Uberoi results should perhaps be given the greater weight in view of the accurate control over experimental conditions.

Since high relative velocities, and the compressibility and heating effects associated with them, are generally found close to a nozzle, the magnitude of these effects is of most interest in connection with the mixing-zone problem. Abramovich [*129*] investigated the effects by applying the vorticity transfer version of mixing length theory to the plane mixing zone between a stream of uniform velocity and a medium at rest, restricting the treatment to air speeds up to Mach number unity and temperature differences up to 120°C. He found that cooling the stream increased the width of the mixing zone, with the boundary on the stream side showing practically all of the effect. The effect of increasing the velocity was to decrease the width of the mixing zone, again with only the boundary on the stream side being affected. However, the predicted effects were such that practically identical velocity distributions were indicated if on the one hand a low speed stream is cooled to $\Delta T = -60$°C and on the other hand a stream of Mach number unity has a stagnation temperature equal to that of the stationary medium (static temperature, $\Delta T = -60$°C). Thus a jet cooled either by extraction of heat or by adiabatic expansion will have a more rapidly diverging mixing region than a jet having the same static temperature as the surrounding medium. This would not be consistent with the findings of Corrsin and Uberoi.

Gooderum, Wood, and Brevoort [*130*] measured the density distribution with an interferometer in the mixing zone of a jet issuing from a 3 by 3-inch nozzle at a Mach number of 1.6. The stagnation temperature of the jet was about the same as that of the surrounding air. The jet was therefore cold, the initial density being 1.5 times that of the surrounding air. The density and velocity were examined across the mixing zone from 2 inches to $7\frac{1}{2}$ inches from the nozzle. The distributions were similar at each cross section, and the velocity distribution could be represented by Tollmien's theoretical curve for incompressible flow [*131*] in the subsonic portion of the mixing region. Such distributions have the typical s-shape of the Gaussian integral curve, and they reduce to a common curve for different values of $x$ when plotted against $\sigma y/x$, where $\sigma$ is a scale factor. The width of the mixing region is thus inversely proportional to $\sigma$. The value for incompressible flow is generally around 12. Gooderum, Wood, and Brevoort found $\sigma = 15$. The rate of spreading into the jet core and into the surrounding air was therefore less than that for incompressible flow. This would appear to disagree with the trends found by Abramovich, which of course apply to subsonic flow, but is what would be expected from the density effect found by Corrsin and Uberoi in the round jet.

Similar results were reported by Bershader and Pai [*132*] from measurements on the discharge from a rectangular nozzle 1 by 2 cm at a Mach number of 1.7. Density measurements were made with an interferometer at several closely spaced stations within one nozzle width from the orifice. The density distributions were found to be similar, and $\sigma$ was found to be 17. The mixing zone was thus narrower than that for incompressible flow. The profile of density ratio is in reasonable agreement with a curve based on Pai's theory [*133*] which employs the concept of a constant coefficient of eddy kinematic viscosity of the form of Eq. 29-1.

These experimental results on supersonic jets do not distinguish between the effect of a denser jet and the heating effect resulting from internal dissipation. We might assume, however, as pointed out by Pai in relation to laminar flow, that the greater momentum associated with higher density causes the stream to carry farther and thus decrease the divergence of the mixing zone. Evidence to substantiate this assumption is afforded by the work of Keagy and Weller [*134*] who found wider velocity profiles for helium jetting into air and narrower profiles for carbon dioxide. It may be concluded from this that the observed effects are primarily density effects. Taken as a whole, the observations disagree with the theoretical predictions of Abramovich.

**B,32. Effect of Axial Motion of Surrounding Air on Jets.** When a jet is projected rearward from a vehicle moving through the air, it effectively emerges into a surrounding medium in motion in the same direction as the jet. Some attention is now given to the effect of this motion on the characteristics of the jet. We do not consider other cases, likewise of importance, where the jet is projected forward or at an angle to a moving stream.

It appears that no basic investigations have been carried out which would give us information on the turbulent structure and the boundary configuration when the surrounding medium is moving. Corrsin and Kistler [*117*] call attention to the limiting case where a turbulent and a nonturbulent stream are in contact with no mean relative velocity, and infer that the diffusing mechanism will be much the same as when a relative velocity exists. If this is so, it follows that mixing again depends on the velocity and scale of the mixing motions as determined by a relation of the type of Eq. 29-1. We know that travel of the surrounding stream along with the jet lessens the divergence and decay of jet velocity. In a very real sense the jet fluid rides along with the outer stream and reaches a distance $x$ from the nozzle in a shorter time. Fluid has had less time to diffuse and as a consequence has traveled a shorter distance laterally. Correspondingly, it has had less time to mix, and it would be expected that a greater distance is now required for the similarity regime to prevail. In the absence of any firm knowledge of the turbulent structure, the usual concepts are applied by investigators in this field, namely that either mixing length or turbulent exchange coefficient are constant over a cross section.

Using mixing length theory for momentum transfer, Kuethe [*109*] investigated the plane mixing region between streams moving in the same direction with different relative velocities and also treated the mixing zone of the round jet from the nozzle to the end of the potential core for the case where the outside medium is at rest. Görtler [*127*] later developed the relations for the plane mixing region between two streams on the basis of a turbulent exchange coefficient given in the form of Eq. 29-1. Szablewski [*135*] then extended this method to the core-containing region of the round jet for the case where the surrounding stream has different velocities. Squire and Trouncer [*136*], using mixing length theory, applied to momentum transfer developed relations for the characteristics of the round jet for various velocities of the surrounding stream, including both the initial core-containing region and the fully developed region. In addition they calculated the inflow velocity in the region surrounding the jet. All of the methods apply to incompressible, isothermal flow.

All of the methods agree, at least qualitatively, in showing a marked effect of velocity of the outer stream on the rate of jet spreading and decay of velocity differences. The effect depends on the ratio $U_1/U_0$, where $U_1$ is the outer stream velocity and $U_0$ is the jet exit velocity. As the ratio increases, the divergence decreases, the core region extends farther from the nozzle, and the velocity increments decrease more slowly with $x$. When $U_1/U_0 = 0$, the core region extends only to about 5 orifice diameters from the nozzle. When $U_1/U_0 = 0.5$, the distance is increased to 11 diameters according to Szablewski and to 8.1 diameters according to Squire and Trouncer. Each of these two methods requires that a single constant be evaluated by experiment, and for this purpose existing data for still surrounding air were used. Szablewski's method indicates somewhat greater effects, but it is difficult to judge the reliability of these methods due to the basic assumptions and approximations made in the solutions. No attempt will be made here to reproduce the developments and final formulas, all of which tend to be cumbersome. Squire and Trouncer achieved some simplification by arbitrarily adopting a cosine velocity profile which for the fully developed jet takes the form

$$\frac{U - U_1}{U_c - U_1} = \frac{1}{2}\left(1 + \cos \pi \frac{r}{r_1}\right) \tag{32-1}$$

where $U_1$ is the velocity of the surrounding stream, $U_c$ the velocity on the jet axis, $r$ the radial distance from the axis, and $r_1$ the radius of the jet boundary.

We turn next to experiment, and here we find a comprehensive investigation conducted by Forstall and Shapiro [*124*] aimed at testing the analytical formulation of Squire and Trouncer and additionally comparing mass transfer and momentum transfer. For obtaining the mass transfer 10 per cent by volume of helium was added to the jet as a tracer. Values of $U_0$ up to 225 ft/sec and values of $U_1$ up to 90 ft/sec were used. Velocity ratios $U_1/U_0$ ranged from 0.2 to 0.75.

Velocity and concentration profiles downstream from the end of the potential region could be closely represented by a formula of the type of Eq. 32-1. The assumption of this formula by Squire and Trouncer was therefore well justified. The profiles remained substantially similar at all values of $x$ and were independent of the velocity ratio $U_1/U_0$.

In order to avoid the uncertainty in specifying the extremes of the jet, the size parameters $r_{mv}$ and $r_{m\xi}$ were adopted, where $r_{mv}$ is the radius where the velocity is the mean of its value on the axis and in the outside stream, and $r_{m\xi}$ is the radius where the concentration is $\frac{1}{2}$ the concentration on the axis. Expressing these in terms of the diameter of the nozzle $D$ the rate of spreading with $x/D$ was found to be greater for concentration than for velocity. A turbulent Schmidt number of about 0.7 was indicated (compare Art. 29). The experiments checked the law of jet divergence derived by Squire and Trouncer.

Both concentration and velocity were found to decay inversely with $x/D$. In general, concentration showed more of a drop than did the velocity, but the difference in behavior was small. The inverse law amounts to a faster decrease with $x/D$ than that predicted by the Squire and Trouncer theory, although the theory gives the general order of magnitude of the center line properties.

Forstall and Shapiro give the following empirical formulas for the round jet in a surrounding stream of equal density to serve as rough rules for the velocity field:

*Formulas*

(i) $\dfrac{x_c}{D} = 4 + 12\lambda$

(ii) $\dfrac{U_c - U_1}{U_0 - U_1} = \dfrac{x_c}{x}$

(iii) $\dfrac{2r_{mv}}{D} = \left(\dfrac{x}{x_c}\right)^{1-\lambda}$

(iv) $\dfrac{U - U_1}{U_c - U_1} = \dfrac{1}{2}\left(1 + \cos\dfrac{\pi r}{2r_{mv}}\right)$

*Symbols*

$U_1$ = velocity of surrounding stream
$U_0$ = exit velocity of jet at nozzle
$\lambda = U_1/U_0$
$x$ = axial distance from end of nozzle
$x_c$ = distance to end of potential core
$U_c$ = center line velocity of jet for $x > x_c$
$D$ = diameter of nozzle
$r$ = radial distance from axis
$U$ = velocity at $r$
$r_{mv}$ = radius where $U = \dfrac{U_c + U_1}{2}$

It is noted that formula (i) for the case where $\lambda = 0$ does not agree with the one given by Hinze and van der Hegge Zijnen, which is

$$\frac{U_c}{U_0} = \frac{6.39}{\dfrac{x}{D} + 0.6}$$

Reference should be made to Pai's book [*111*, p. 120] for another form of (ii) and further discussion of the effect of a surrounding stream.

Turning next to the heated jet in a surrounding stream, we have the problem of the combined effects of a stream velocity and density differences on the velocity and temperature fields. Some experimental information on the temperature field of the round jet in a supersonic stream was obtained by Rousso and Baughman [*137*] in connection with an NACA program on jets aimed primarily at answering certain engineering problems. The only known account of work attempting to solve the transfer problem is the paper by Szablewski [*138*], in which a theoretical development is given, and the experimental work of Pabst [*139*] is displayed as a test of the theory. The analysis applies specifically to the round jet and includes large density differences. It does not include the case where the surrounding air is stationary.

It is left to the reader to consult [*138*] for the lengthy analytical development and the complete results. In brief, Szablewski bases his development on turbulent exchange coefficients given by the Prandtl expression (Eq. 29-1). These are introduced into the usual equations expressed in the form of continuity equations for mass, momentum, and heat. The ratio of the exchange coefficient for momentum to that for heat and mass (the turbulent Prandtl number, $Pr_t$) was taken to be 0.5 on the basis of Pabst's results. The computed examples cover the range

$$\frac{U_1}{U_0} = 0.5,\ 0.25,\ 0.05$$

$$\frac{T_0}{T_1} = 1,\ 1.75,\ 2.5$$

where $U_1$, $T_1$ = outer stream velocity and absolute temperature respectively

$U_0$, $T_0$ = jet exit velocity and absolute temperature respectively.

Pabst's measurements of velocity and temperature distributions in a round jet were made with $U_0 \cong 400$ m/sec, $U_1 = 18$, 101, and 188 m/sec, and $T_0 = 300°\text{C}$ ($T_0/T_1 \cong 2$). Since Szablewski's account of this work appeared to cover the significant points, the original work of Pabst was not consulted.

The following are the major conclusions:

1. The theoretical predictions for small density differences agree with other work regarding the direction of the effect of an outside stream, namely to decrease the rate of spreading of both velocity and temperature. The predicted asymptotic boundary (jet so far from nozzle that nozzle size has no effect) varies as $x^{\frac{1}{3}}$ for any value of $U_1$ except zero.
2. An outside stream reduces the rate of velocity and temperature fall along the axis. This is qualitatively confirmed by experiment, but there is some question about the accuracy of Pabst's temperature measurements. The asymptotic variation predicted by theory is $x^{-\frac{2}{3}}$ for any value of $U_1$ except zero.
3. When $U_1 \neq 0$ the asymptotic velocity profile is given by

$$\frac{U - U_1}{U_c - U_1} = \exp\left[-\left(c\frac{r}{r_1}\right)^2\right]$$

where $U_c$ is the velocity at the center, $r_1$ is the radius of the jet boundary, and $c$ is a shape factor. The temperature profile is

$$\frac{T - T_1}{T_c - T_1} = \left(\frac{U - U_1}{U_c - U_1}\right)^{Pr_t}$$

where $Pr_t$ is taken as 0.5. These distribution functions when fitted to Pabst's measurements at 16, 20, and 24 nozzle diameters downstream show reasonably good agreement.

4. Reduced jet density, due to elevated temperature, increases the rate of velocity and temperature fall along the axis. Apparently Pabst's work does not provide any test of this effect. However, this is consistent with the findings of Corrsin and Uberoi for $U_1 = 0$.
5. Reduced jet density, due to elevated temperature, decreases the rate

of spreading of both velocity and temperature. The effect of the temperature on the width is given as proportional to $[1 + (T_0 - T_1)/T_1]^{-\frac{1}{2}}$. Pabst's work, as quoted by Szablewski, does not provide any test of this effect. The effect is opposite to that found by Corrsin and Uberoi for $U_1 = 0$.

Conclusion 5 appears to be inconsistent with conclusion 4. Conclusion 5 can, however, be made to appear reasonable by following a suggestion by Squire and Trouncer to the effect that compressibility or heating might be dealt with in terms of an "equivalent jet." Since the momentum

$$\frac{\pi}{4} D^2 \rho U_0(U_0 - U_1)$$

is maintained at all sections, an equivalent incompressible jet should behave like a compressible jet when the momentum is the same. Heating a jet decreases $\rho U_0(U_0 - U_1)$ by decreasing $\rho$. We should obtain the same effect without heating by keeping $\rho$ the same and decreasing $U_0(U_0 - U_1)$. This can be done either by decreasing $U_0$ or by increasing $U_1$. By either means $U_1/U_0$ is increased, and this clearly has the effect of decreasing the divergence of the velocity field. Presumably the divergence of the temperature field would follow that of the velocity field.

The tentative conclusion drawn from the present information is that the effect of density on spreading characteristics reverses in going from the case where $U_1 = 0$ to the case where $U_1 > 0$. More experimental results covering a greater range of conditions are needed to clarify the situation.

Not all of the information on jets has been covered in this brief survey. Pai, for example, gives a mathematical procedure for dealing with turbulent jets by employing methods analogous to those for laminar flow. For this, the reader is referred to his book [*111*]. An extensive bibliography given by Forstall and Shapiro [*124*] will be helpful to readers wishing to pursue the subject of jets further.

# *CHAPTER 6. TURBULENT STRUCTURE OF SHEAR FLOWS*

**B,33. The Nature of the Subject.** Dating from about 1925 many investigators have applied the hot wire anemometer in aerodynamic experiments in an effort to learn something about turbulence through measurement. Over the years these efforts have borne fruit; consequently there are many separate pieces of information contributing to our present knowledge of turbulence and the turbulent structure of various flow fields.

For the most part the measured quantities are the velocity fluctuations, their mean square values, their time derivatives, space and time correlations, probability distributions, and energy spectra. In a few cases measurements have been made of temperature fluctuations, including correlations, spectra, and velocity-temperature correlations. Due to limitations inherent in the hot wire technique, very few measurements have yet been made in the compressible flow range. Low speed boundary layers, jets, and wakes have been the principal objects of investigation.

Theoretical studies on the turbulent structure of shear flows are not abundant because of the difficult nature of the statistical theories of turbulence and the additional complications arising from anisotropy and inhomogeneity associated with shear flows. Nevertheless, it becomes a lengthy task to present and discuss both the experimental and theoretical sides of the subject. We therefore restrict the present coverage to a listing of references. Qualitative aspects of structure have been discussed in previous articles, and the references there cited will be repeated here only by number. The list covers mainly relatively recent works which are available to us, and it can by no means pretend to be complete. Classification is by subject, each being headed by a brief discussion. Since many works cover topics belonging in different classes, the grouping must not be considered as rigid.

## B,34. References on Structure of Shear Turbulence.

*General considerations on vorticity and structure of turbulence.* The stretching of vorticity and the formation of vortex sheets play an important role in shear turbulence. Studies of these phenomena are generally theoretical, and often have to be based on a simple and isotropic model.

Agostini, L., and Bass, J. Les théories de la turbulence. *Publs. sci. et tech. Ministère air France 237*, 1950.

Betchov, R. An inequality concerning the production of vorticity in isotropic turbulence. *J. Fluid Mech. 1*, 497–504 (1956).

Burgers, J. M. The formation of vortex sheets in a simplified type of turbulent motion. *Proc. Acad. Sci. Amsterdam 53*, 122–133 (1950).

Corrsin, S. Hypothesis for skewness of the probability of the lateral velocity fluctuations in turbulent flow. *J. Aeronaut. Sci. 17*, 396–398 (1950).

Djang, F. G. A kinetic theory of turbulence. *Chinese J. Phys. 7*, 176 (1948).

Liepmann, H. W. Aspects of the turbulence problem. *J. Math. and Phys. 3*, 321–342, 407–426 (1952).

Lin, C. C. On Taylor's hypothesis in wind tunnel turbulence. *Mem. Nav. Ord. Lab. 10775*, 1950.

Lin, C. C. On Taylor's hypothesis and the acceleration terms in the Navier-Stokes equations. *Nav. Ord. Rept. 2306*, 1952.

Munk, M. M. *A Simplified Theory of Turbulent Fluid Motion.* Catholic Univ. of America, 1955.

Pai, S. I. *Viscous Flow Theory. II: Turbulent Flow.* Van Nostrand, 1957.

Theodorsen, Th. Mechanism of turbulence. *Proc. Second Midwestern Conf. Fluid Mech., The Ohio State Univ.*, 1952.

*Statistical theories of shear and inhomogeneous turbulence.* In statistical theories of turbulence, it is important to study the structure of correlations and spectral functions on the basis of hydrodynamical equations of motion. The spectral tensor in anisotropic turbulence has a much more complicated form than in isotropic turbulence. Exact mathematical theories are not yet possible. Dimensional arguments and simplifying reasoning are necessary. If a reasonably simple equation of motion of one-dimension is used, such as in Burgers' model, the solution can be obtained exactly, and many characteristics of turbulence can be studied without introducing simplifying assumptions at an early stage.

Burgers, J. M. Some considerations on turbulent flow with shear. *Proc. Acad. Sci. Amsterdam B56*, 125–136, 137–147 (1953).
Burgers, J. M., and Mitchner, M. On homogeneous non-isotropic turbulence connected with a mean motion having a constant velocity gradient. *Proc. Acad. Sci. Amsterdam B56*, 228–235, 343–354 (1953).
Kampé de Fériet, J. Le tenseur spectral de la turbulence homogène non isotrope dans un fluide incompressible. *Proc. Seventh Intern. Congress Appl. Mech., London*, 6–26 (1948).
von Kármán, Th. The fundamentals of the statistical theory of turbulence. *J. Aeronaut. Sci. 4*, 131 (1937).
Monin, A. S. Characteristics of anisotropic turbulence. *Doklady Akad. Nauk. S.S.S.R. 75*, 621–624 (1950).
Parker, E. N. The concept of physical subsets and application to hydrodynamic theory. *Naval Ord. Test Station Tech. Mem. 988*, China Lake, Calif., 1953.
Rotta, J. Statische Theorie nichthomogener Turbulenz I, II. *Z. Physik 129*, 547 (1951); *131*, 51 (1951).
Tchen, C. M. On the spectrum of energy in turbulent shear flow. *J. Research Natl. Bur. Standards 50*, 51 (1953).
Tchen, C. M. Transport processes as foundations of the Heisenberg and Obukhoff theories of turbulence. *Phys. Rev. 93*, 4 (1954).

*Structure of turbulence in wall-bounded flow (boundary layer, channel and pipe).* Turbulent measurements are made on energy, shear stresses, correlation, spectral functions of energy, and shear stress. In the case of the boundary layer, the flow is complicated by the fact that there exist a laminar sublayer near the wall and an irregular outer limit producing a region of intermittent turbulence near the free edge of the boundary layer. The intermittencies and the probability of their occurrence are important for the understanding of the boundary layer, and for the formulation of a realistic theory of the boundary layer structure. Phenomenological theories are based on transport concepts (such as mixing length) to express nonlinear turbulent terms. Other theories assume some definite relation between the fourth and second orders of correlations, and a third group of theories make some assumption involving physical and dimensional reasoning on the role of the turbulent pressure.

Chou, P. Y. On velocity correlation and the solutions of the equations of turbulent fluctuation. *Quart. Appl. Math. 3*, 38–54 (1945).
Chou P. Y. Pressure flow of a turbulent fluid between two infinite parallel plates. *Quart. Appl. Math. 3*, 198–209 (1945).

Chou, P. Y. On velocity correlations and the equations of turbulent vorticity fluctuation. *Natl. Tsing-Hua Univ. Sci. Rept. 5*, 1–18 (1948).

Chou, P. Y. The turbulent flow along a semi-infinite flat plate. *Quart. Appl. Math. 5*, 346–353 (1947).

Dryden, H. L. Recent advances in the mechanics of boundary layer flow. *Advances in Applied Mechanics*, pp. 1–40. Academic Press, 1948.

Eskinazi, S., and Yeh, H. An investigation on fully developed turbulent flows in a curved channel. *J. Aeronaut. Sci. 23*, 23–35 (1956).

Fage, A., and Townend, H. C. H. An examination of turbulent flow with an ultramicroscope. *Proc. Roy. Soc. London A135*, 656–677 (1932).

Favre, A., Gaviglio, J., and Dumas, R. Nouvelles mesure dans la couche limite d'une plaque plane, des intensités de turbulence, et des correlations dans le temps; spectres. *Recherche aéronaut. Paris 38*, 7–12 (1954).

Favre, A., Gaviglio, J., and Dumas, R. Couche limite turbulente: Corrélations spatiotemporelles doubles; spectres. *Recherche aéronaut. Paris 48*, 3–14 (1955).

Johnson, D. S. Turbulent heat transfer in a boundary layer with discontinuous wall temperature. *The Johns Hopkins Univ. Dept. of Aeronaut. Rept.*, 1955.

Klebanoff, P. S. Characteristics of turbulence in a boundary layer with zero pressure gradient. *NACA Tech. Rept. 1247*, 1955.

Laufer, J. Some recent measurements in a two-dimensional turbulent channel. *J. Aeronaut. Sci. 17*, 277–287 (1950).

Laufer, J. The structure of turbulence in fully developed pipe flow. *NACA Rept. 1174*, 1955.

Ludwig, H., and Tillman, W. Untersuchungen über die Wandschubspannung in turbulenten Reibungsschichten. *Ing.-Arch. 17*, 288–299 (1949).

Malkus, W. V. R. Outline of a theory of turbulent shear flow. *J. Fluid Mech. 1*, 521 (1956).

Mattioli, E. Una formula universale per lo spettro nella turbolenza di parete. *Atti accad. sci. Torino 90*, 1956.

Mattioli, E. Richerche teoriche e sperimentali sulla turbolenza di parete. *Aerotecnica 36*, (*2*), 1956.

Michel, R. Contribution à l'etude des couches limites turbulentes avec gradient de pression. *Publs. sci. et tech. Ministère air France 252*, 1951.

Newman, B. G. Skin friction in a retarded turbulent boundary layer near separation. *Dept. of Supply, Australia, Aeronaut. Research Lab. Rept.* A73, 1950.

Rotta, J. Beitrag zur Berechnung der turbulent Grenzschiehten. *Ing.-Arch. 19*, 31 (1953).

Rotta, J. Schubspannungsverteilungen und Energiedissipation bei turbulenten Grenzschichten. *Ing.-Arch. 20*, 195–207 (1952).

Sandborn, V. A., and Braun, W. H. Turbulent shear spectra and local isotropy in the low-speed boundary layer. *NACA Tech. Note 3761*, 1956.

Schubauer, G. B. Turbulent processes as observed in boundary layer and pipe. *J. Appl. Phys. 25*, 188–196 (1954).

Steketee, J. A. Some problems in boundary layer transition. *Univ. Toronto Inst. Aerophys. Rept. 38*, 1956.

Szablewski, W. Berechnung des turbulenten Strömung in Rohr auf der Grundlage der Mischungsweg-hypothese. *Z. angew. Math. u. Mech. 31*, 13–142 (1951).

Szablewski, W. Berechnung des turbulenten Strömung Langs einer ebenen Platte. *Z. angew. Math. u. Mech. 31*, 309 (1951).

Taylor, G. I. Correlation measurements in a turbulent flow through a pipe. *Proc. Roy. Soc. London A157*, 537–546 (1936).

Townsend, A. A. The structure of the turbulent boundary layer. *Proc. Cambridge Phil. Soc. 47*, 375–395 (1951).

Walz, A. Naherungstheorie fur kompressible turbulente Grenzschichten. *Z. angew. Math. u. Mech.*, 50–56 (1956).

Walz, A. Nouvelle méthode approchée de calcul des couches limites laminaire et turbulente en ecoulement compressible. *Publ. sci. et tech. Ministère air France 309*, 1956.

Yeh, H., Rose, W. G., and Lien, H. Further investigation on fully developed turbulent flows in a curved channel. *The Johns Hopkins Univ. Dept. Mech. Eng. Rept.*, 1956.
Cited references [*73,76,77,87,89,93*].

*Structure of turbulence in a free flow* (*jet, wake*). In a free flow, the intermittencies produced near the boundary of the flow play an important role in the characteristics of the flow and the structure of turbulence. The shear flow in the present case has a weak mean velocity gradient, so that the spectrum of energy is not far from the spectrum of an isotropic turbulence. However, here a spectrum of shear exists, in contrast to its absence in isotropic flow.

Chou, P. Y. On an extension of Reynolds' method of finding apparent stress and the nature of turbulence. *Chinese J. Phys. 4*, 1–33 (1940).
Corrsin, S., and Uberoi, M. S. Spectra and diffusion in a round turbulent jet. *NACA Rept. 1040*, 1951.
Hinze, J., and van der Hegge Zijnen, B. G. Heat and mass transfer in the turbulent mixing zone of an axially symmetrical jet. *Proc. Seventh Intern. Congress Appl. Mech., London*, 1948.
Kalinske, A. A., and Pien, C. C. Eddy diffusion. *Ind. Eng. Chem. 36*, 220–223 (1944).
Kovásznay, L. S. G. Hot-wire investigation of the wake behind cylinders at low Reynolds numbers. *Proc. Roy. Soc. London A198*, 174–190 (1949).
Laurence J. C. Intensity, scale, and spectra of turbulence in mixing region of free subsonic jet. *NACA Rept. 1292*, 1956.
Laurence, J. C., and Stickney, T. M. Further measurements of intensity, scale, and spectra of turbulence in a subsonic jet. *NACA Tech. Note 3576*, 1956.
Squire, H. B. Reconsideration of the theory of free turbulence. *Phil. Mag. 39*, 1–20 (1948).
Swain, L. M. On the turbulent wake behind a body of revolution. *Proc. Roy. Soc. London A125*, 647–659 (1929).
Tamaki, H., and Oshima, K. Experimental studies on the wake behind a row of heated parallel rods. *Proc. First Japan. Natl. Congress. Appl. Mech.*, 459–464 (1951).
Cited references [*94,112,113,114,115,116,121,123,124,126*].

*Structure of turbulence connected with turbulent diffusion and heat transfer.* In both the statistical and phenomenological theories of the structure of shear turbulence, of bounded or free flows, turbulent diffusion plays an important role. A thorough coverage of turbulent diffusion is not intended, and only those works dealing with the mechanism of diffusion which help in better understanding the structure of turbulence are listed below, leaving aside works mainly connected with applications of diffusion.

Batchelor, G. K., Binnie., A. M., and Phillips, O. M. The mean velocity of discrete particles in turbulent flow in a pipe. *Proc. Phys. Soc. London B68*, 1095–1104 (1955).
Batchelor, G. K., and Townsend, A. A. Turbulent diffusion. *Surveys in Mechanics*, pp. 353–399. Cambridge Univ. Press, 1956.
Beckers, H. L. Heat transfer in turbulent tube flow. *Appl. Sci. Research A6*, 147 (1956).
Brier, G. W. The statistical theory of turbulence and the problem of diffusion in the atmosphere. *J. Meteorol. 7*, 283–290 (1950).

Davies, D. R. The problem of diffusion into a turbulent boundary layer from a plane area source, bounded by two straight perpendicular edges. *Quart. J. Mech. and Appl. Math. 7*, 467–471 (1954).
Dryden, H. L. Turbulence and diffusion. *Ind. Eng. Chem. 31*, 416 (1939).
Ellison, T. H. Atmospheric turbulence. *Surveys in Mechanics*, pp. 400–430. Cambridge Univ. Press, 1956.
Frenkiel, N. F. On the statistical theory of turbulent diffusion. *Proc. Natl. Acad. Sci. 38*, 509–515 (1952).
Frenkiel, F. N. Application of the statistical theory of turbulent diffusion to micrometeorology. *J. Meteorol. 9*, 252–259 (1952).
Frenkiel, N. F. Sur la mesure de la diffusion de la chaleur. *Groupement franç. dévelop. recherches aéronaut.*, 1946.
Hinze, J. O. Turbulent diffusion from a source in turbulent shear flow. *J. Aeronaut. Sci. 18*, 565 (1951).
Inoue, E. On the temperature fluctuations in a heated turbulent field. *Geophys. Notes, Geophys. Inst., Tokyo Univ., 3*, 1950; *Geophys. Mag. 23*, (*1*), 1951.
Inoue, E. Some remarks on the dynamical and thermal structure of a heated fluid. *J. Phys. Soc. Japan 6*, 392 (1951).
Kitojima, K. On the mixing length of turbulence. *Kysyu Univ. Research Inst. Fluid Eng, Rept. 4*, 43–54 (1948).
Lee, T. D. Note on the coefficient of eddy viscosity in isotropic turbulence. *Phys. Rev. 77*, 842 (1950).
Levich, V. G. Diffusion. *Doklady Akad. Nauk. S.S.S.R. 78*, 1105–1108 (1951).
Liu, V. C. Turbulent dispersion of dynamic particles. *J. Meteorol. 13*, 399–405 (1956).
Monin, A. S. Equations of turbulent diffusion. *Doklady Akad. Nauk. S.S.S.R. 105*, 256–259 (1955).
Ribaud, G. Some remarks on the subject of heat and momentum transfer in the boundary layer. *C. R. Acad. Sci. Paris 240*, 1, 25–28 (1955).
Taylor, G. I. The dispersion of matter in turbulent flow through a pipe. *Proc. Roy. Soc. London A223*, 446 (1954).
Tchen, C. M. Enige Wiskundige Betrekkingen Welke een Rol Spelen in Diffusieproblemen. *Verhandl. Acad. voor Wet. 53*, 400–410 (1944).
Tchen, C. M. Stochastic processes and the dispersion of the configurations of linked events. *J. Research Natl. Bur. Standards 46*, 480–488 (1951).
Wieghardt, K. On diffusion phenomena in turbulent boundary layer. *Z. angew. Math. u. Mech. 28*, 346–355 (1948).
Cited references [*25,26,27,116,119,122*].

*Instrumentation for the measurement of turbulence.* What has been learned about the structure of turbulence from experiment has depended largely on the instruments available for making observations and measurements. Here the hot wire anemometer has played a predominantly important role. The number and accuracy of quantities measured have gone hand in hand with the development of hot wire probes and the adaptation of electronic circuits to amplify the signal, compensate for thermal lag of the hot wire, and perform a variety of operations such as adding, multiplying, and differentiating signals. The following references therefore pertain mainly to the hot wire and its auxiliary equipment.

Dryden, H. L., and Kuethe, A. M. The measurement of fluctuations of air speed by the hot-wire anemometer. *NACA Rept. 320*, 1929.
Fage, A. Studies of boundary-layer flow with a fluid-motion microscope. *50 Jahre Grenzschichtforschung*, pp. 132–146. (Ed: H. Görtler and W. Tollmien.) Vieweg, Braunschweig, 1955.

Kovásznay, L. S. G. Turbulence in supersonic flow. *J. Aeronaut. Sci. 20*, 657–675 (1953).

Kovásznay, L. S. G. Development of turbulence-measuring equipment. *NACA Rept. 1209*, 1954.

Laufer, J., and McClellan, R. Measurements of heat transfer from fine wires in supersonic flow. *J. Fluid Phys. 1*, 276–289 (1956).

Laurence, J. C., and Landes, L. G. Auxiliary equipment and techniques for adapting the constant-temperature hot-wire anemometer to specific problems in air-flow measurements. *NACA Tech. Note 2843*, 1952.

Mock, W. C., Jr. Alternating-current equipment for the measurement of fluctuations of air speed in turbulent flow. *NACA Rept. 598*, 1937.

Newman, B. G., and Leary, B. G. The measurement of the Reynolds stresses in a circular pipe as means of testing a hot wire anemometer. *Dept. of Supply, Australia, Aeronaut. Research Lab. Rept. A72*, 1950.

Ossofsky, E. Constant temperature operation of the hot-wire anemometer at high frequency. *Rev. Sci. Instr. 19*, 881–889 (1948).

Sansborn, V. A. Heat loss from yawed hot wires at subsonic Mach numbers. *NACA Tech. Note 3563*, 1955.

Schubauer, G. B. A turbulence indicator utilizing the diffusion of heat. *NACA Rept. 524*, 1935.

Spangenberg, W. G. Heat-loss characteristics of hot-wire anemometers at various densities in transonic and supersonic flow. *NACA Tech. Note 3381*, 1955.

Tchen, C. M. Heat delivery in a compressible flow at subsonic and supersonic speeds. *NACA Tech. Note 2436*, 1951.

Uberoi, M. S., and Kovásznay, L. S. G. Analysis of turbulent density fluctuations by the shadow method. *J. Appl. Phys. 26*, 1955.

Weske, J. R. A hot-wire circuit with very small time lag. *NACA Tech. Note 881*, 1943.

Willis, J. B. Review of hot-wire anemometry. *Council for Sci. and Ind. Research, Div. of Aeronautics, Australia, Rept. A34*, 1945.

Wise, B., and Schultz, D. L. Turbulent measurements in supersonic flow with the hot-wire anemometer. *Brit. Aeronaut. Research Council Rept. FM 2390*, 1955.


## B,35. Cited References.


1. Townsend, A. A. *The Structure of Turbulent Shear Flow*. Cambridge Univ. Press, 1956.
2. Batchelor, G. K. *The Theory of Homogeneous Turbulence*. Cambridge Univ. Press, 1953.
3. Reynolds, O. *Phil. Trans. A186*, 123 (1894), or *Papers 2*, 535.
4. Lorentz, H. A. *Abhandl. theoret. Physik 1*, 43 (1907).
5. Lamb, H. *Hydrodynamics*, 6th ed. Dover, 1945.
6. Goldstein, S. *Modern Developments in Fluid Dynamics*, 1st ed., Vol. 2. Clarendon Press, Oxford, 1938.
7. Howarth, L. Modern Developments in Fluid Dynamics, High Speed Flow, 1st ed., Vol. 2. Clarendon Press, Oxford, 1953.
8. Rubesin, M. W. A modified Reynolds analogy for the compressible turbulent boundary layer on a flat plate. *NACA Tech. Note 2917*, 1953.
9. Crocco, L. Sulla Transmissione del Calore da una Lamina Piana a un Fluido Scorrente ad alta Velocita. *Aerotecnica 12*, 181–197 (1932).
10. Squire, H. B. Heat transfer calculation for aerofoils. *Brit. Aeronaut. Research Council Repts. and Mem. 1986*, 1942.
11. Ackerman, G. *Forsch. Gebiete Ingenieurw. 13*, 226–234 (1942).
12. Mack, L. M. An experimental investigation of the temperature recovery factor. *Calif. Inst. Technol. Jet Propul. Lab. Rept. 20-80*, 1954.
13. Stalder, J. R., Rubesin, M. W., and Tendeland, T. A determination of the laminar-transitional, and turbulent-boundary-layer temperature-recovery factors on a flat plate in supersonic flow. *NACA Tech. Note 2077*, 1950.

14. Soban, R. A. *Analysis for the Heat Transfer to Turbulent Boundary Layers in High Velocity Flow. Ph.D. Thesis,* Univ. Calif., Berkeley, 1948.
15. Shirokow, M. *Tech. Phys. USSR 3,* 1020–1027 (1936).
16. Stine, H. A., and Scherrer, R. Experimental investigation of the turbulent-boundary layer temperature-recovery factor on bodies of revolution at Mach numbers from 2.0 to 3.8. *NACA Tech. Note 2664,* 1952.
17. Tucker, M., and Maslen, S. H. Turbulent boundary layer temperature recovery factors in two-dimensional supersonic flow. *NACA Tech. Note 2296,* 1951.
18. Lobb, K. R., Winkler, E. M., and Persh, J. *J. Aeronaut. Sci. 22,* 1–9 (1955).
19. van Driest, F. R. *J. Aeronaut. Sci. 18,* 145–160 (1951).
20. Spivack, H. M. Experiments in the turbulent boundary layer of a supersonic flow. *North Amer. Aviation Rept. AL-1052, APL/JHU CM-615,* 1950.
21. Chapman, S., and Cowling, T. G. *The Mathematical Theory of Non-Uniform Gases.* Cambridge Univ. Press, 1953.
22. Lorentz, H. A. *The Theory of Electrons.* Dover, 1952.
23. Van Vleck, J. H., and Weisskoff, V. G. *Rev. Mod. Phys. 17,* 227 (1945).
24. Bhatnagar, P. L., Gross, E. P., and Krook, M. *Phys. Rev. 94,* 511 (1954).
25. Tchen, C. M. *Mean Value and Correlation Problems Connected with the Motion of Small Particles Suspended in a Turbulent Fluid. Thesis,* Delft, 1947. Mededeeling No. 51 uit het Laboratorium voor Aero-en Hydrodynamica der Technische Hogeschool te Delft.
26. Burgers, J. M. On turbulent fluid motion. *Calif. Inst. Technol. Hydrodynam. Lab. Rept. E-34.1, Chap. 5,* 1951.
27. Tchen, C. M. *J. Chem. Phys. 20,* 214–217 (1952).
28. Reynolds, O. *Proc. Manchester Lit. Phil. Soc. 14,* 7–12 (1874); *Collected Papers 1,* 81–85.
29. Chapman, D. R., and Kester, R. H. *J. Aeronaut. Sci. 20,* 441–448 (1953).
30. Reichardt, E. Heat transfer through turbulent friction layers. *NACA Tech. Mem. 1047,* 1943.
31. Colburn, A. P. *Trans. Am. Inst. Chem. Engr. 29,* 174–210 (1933).
32. Rubesin, M. W., Maydew, R. C., and Varga, S. A. An analytical and experimental investigation of the skin friction of the turbulent boundary layer on a flat plate at supersonic speeds. *NACA Tech. Note 2305,* 1951.
33. Pappas, C. C. Measurement of heat transfer in the turbulent boundary layer on a flat plate in supersonic flow and comparison with skin-friction results. *NACA Tech. Note 3222,* 1954.
34. Coles, D. *J. Aeronaut. Sci. Readers' Forum 19,* 717 (1952).
35. Coles, D., and Goddard, F. E. Direct measurement of skin friction on a smooth flat plate at supersonic speeds. Paper presented at *8th Intern. Congr. Theoret. and Appl. Mech.,* Istanbul, 1952.
36. Liepmann, H. W., and Dhawan, S. *Proc. First U.S. Natl. Congr. Appl. Mech.,* Chicago, 869–874 (1951).
37. Dhawan, S. Direct measurements of skin friction. *NACA Tech. Note 2567,* 1952.
38. Wilson, R. E. *J. Aeronaut. Sci. 17,* 585–594 (1950).
39. Brinich, P. F., and Diacomis, N. S. Boundary-layer development and skin friction at Mach number 3.05. *NACA Tech. Note 2742,* 1952.
40. Fallis, W. B. Heat transfer in the transitional and turbulent boundary layers of a flat plate at supersonic speeds. *Univ. Toronto Inst. Aerophys., UTIA Rept. 19,* 1952.
41. Slack, E. G. Experimental investigation of heat transfer through laminar and turbulent boundary layers on a cooled flat plate at a Mach number of 2.4. *NACA Tech. Note 2686,* 1952.
42. Monaghan, R. J., and Cooke, J. R. The measurement of heat transfer and skin friction at supersonic speeds. Part III: Measurements of overall heat transfer and of the associated boundary layers on a flat plate at $M_1 = 2.43$. *Roy. Air Establishment Tech. Note Aero. 2129,* 1951.
43. Monaghan, R. J., and Cooke, J. R. The measurement of heat transfer and skin

friction at supersonic speeds. Part IV: Tests on a flat plate at $M_1 = 2.82$. *Roy. Air Establishment Tech. Note Aero. 2171,* 1952.
44. Frankl, F. Heat transfer in the turbulent boundary layer of a compressible gas at high speeds. Also Frankl, F., and Voishel, V. Friction in the turbulent boundary layer of a compressible gas at high speeds. *NACA Tech. Mem. 1032,* 1942.
45. Frankl, F., and Voishel, V. Turbulent friction in the boundary layer of a flat plate in a two-dimensional compressible flow at high speeds. *NACA Tech. Mem. 1053,* 1943.
46. von Kármán, Th. Mechanical similitude and turbulence. *NACA Tech. Mem. 611,* 1931.
47. Schoenherr, K. E. *Trans. Soc. Nav. Arch. and Marine Eng. 40,* 279–313 (1932).
48. Prandtl, L. *Göttingen Ergebnisse 4,* 27 (1932).
49. Clemmow, D. M. The turbulent boundary layer flow of a compressible fluid along a flat plate. *Brit. Directorate of Guided Weapons Research and Develop. Rept. 50/6,* 1950.
50. van Driest, E. R. Proceedings of the Bureau of Ordnance symposium on aeroballistics. Comments on paper by R. E. Wilson, *NAVORD Rept. 1961,* 264–267 (1950).
51. Li, T.-Y., and Nagamatsu, H. T. Effects of density fluctuations on the turbulent skin friction of an insulated flat plate at high supersonic speeds. *Calif. Inst. Technol. Guggenheim Aeronaut. Lab. Mem. 5,* 1951.
52. Ferrari, C. *Quart. Appl. Math. 8,* 33–57 (1950).
53. Smith, F., and Harrop, R. The turbulent boundary layer with heat transfer and compressible flow. *Roy. Aircraft Establishment Tech. Note Aero. 1759,* 1946.
54. Eckert, H. U. *J. Aeronaut. Sci. 16,* 573–584 (1950).
55. Monaghan, R. J. Comparison between experimental measurements and a suggested formula for the variation of turbulent skin friction in compressible flow. *Brit. Aeronaut. Research Council C.P. 45, 13260,* 1951.
56. Cope, W. F. The turbulent boundary layer in compressible flow. *NPL Eng. Dept., Brit. Aeronaut. Research Council 7634,* 1943.
57. Tucker, M. Approximate turbulent boundary-layer development in plane compressible flow along thermally insulated surfaces with application to supersonic-tunnel contour correction. *NACA Tech. Note 2045,* 1950.
58. Tucker, M. Approximate calculation of turbulent boundary-layer development in compressible flow. *NACA Tech. Note 2337,* 1951.
59. Young, G. B. W., and Janssen, E. *J. Aeronaut. Sci. 19,* 229–236 (1952).
60. von Kármán, Th. The problems of resistance in compressible fluids. *Mem. Reale Acad. D'Italia,* Rome, 1936.
61. Falkner, V. N. *Aircraft Eng. 15,* 65 (1943).
62. Hill, F. K. *J. Aeronaut. Sci. 23,* 35 (1956).
63. Korkegi, R. H. *J. Aeronaut. Sci. 23,* 97 (1956).
64. Hakkinen, R. J. *Measurements of Skin Friction in Turbulent Boundary Layer at Transonic Speeds. Ph. D. Thesis,* Calif. Inst. Technol., 1953.
65. O'Donnel, R. M. Experimental investigation at a Mach number of 2.41 of average skin-friction coefficients and velocity profiles for laminar and turbulent boundary-layers and an assessment of probe effects. *NACA Tech. Note 3122,* 1954.
66. Coles, D. *J. Aeronaut. Sci. 21,* 433–448 (1954).
67. Dönch, F. *Forsch.-Aro. Gebiete Ingenieurw-Wes. 282,* 1926.
68. Blasius, H. *Mitt. Forschung. Ver. deut. Ing. 131,* 1–34 (1913).
69. Prandtl, L. *Aerodynamic Theory,* Vol. 3, Durand, W. F. ed. Durand Reprinting Committee, Calif. Inst. Technol., 1943.
70. Prandtl, L. Recent results of turbulence research. *NACA Tech. Mem. 720,* 1933. (Transl. *Z. Ver. deut. Ing. 7,* (*5*), 1933.)
71. von Kármán, Th. *Nachr. Ges. Wiss. Göttingen,* 58–76 (1930).
72. Clauser, F. H. The turbulent boundary layer. *Advances in Appl. Mech. 4,* 1-51. Academic Press, 1956.

73. Millikan, C. B. A critical discussion of the turbulent flows in channels and circular tubes. *Proc. Fifth Intern. Congress Appl. Mech., Cambridge, Mass.*, 386–392 (1938).
74. Schultz-Grunow, F. New frictional resistance law for smooth plates. *NACA Tech. Mem. 986*, 1941. (Transl. *Luftfahrtforschung 17*, 239–246, 1940.)
75. Freeman, H. B. Force measurements on a $\frac{1}{40}$-scale model of the U.S. airship "Akron." *NACA Rept. 432*, 1932.
76. Klebanoff, P. S., and Diehl, Z. W. Some features of artificially thickened fully developed turbulent boundary layers with zero pressure gradient. *NACA Rept. 1110*, 1952.
77. Laufer, J. Investigation of turbulent flow in a two-dimensional channel. *NACA Rept. 1033*, 1951.
78. von Kármán, Th. *J. Aeronaut. Sci. 1*, 1–20 (1934).
79. von Kármán, Th. Mechanische Ähnlichkeit und Turbulenz. *Proc. Third Intern. Congress Appl. Mech., Stockholm, 1*, 85–93 (1930).
80. Schlichting, S. *Ing.-Arch. 7*, 1–34 (1936).
81. Squire, H. B., and Young, A. D. The calculation of the profile drag of airfoils. *Brit. Aeronaut. Research Council Repts. and Mem. 1838*, 1938.
82. Kempf, G. *Werft, Reederei, Hafen, 10*, (*11*), 234–239 (1929); (*12*), 247–253 (1929).
83. Clauser, F. H. *J. Aeronaut. Sci. 21*, 91–108 (1954).
84. von Doenhoff, A. E., and Tetervin, N. Determination of general relations for the behavior of turbulent boundary layers. *NACA Rept. 772*, 1943.
85. Coles, D. *J. Fluid Mech. 1, Part 2*, 191–226 (1956).
86. Landweber, L. *Trans. S.N.A.M.E. 61*, 5 (1953).
87. Schubauer, G. B., and Klebanoff, P. S. Investigation of separation of the turbulent boundary layer. *NACA Rept. 1030*, 1951.
88. Newman, B. G. Some contributions to the study of the turbulent boundary layer near separation. *Dept. Supply, Australia, Rept. ACA-53*, 1951.
89. Ludwieg, H., and Tillmann, W. Investigation of the wall-shearing stress in turbulent boundary layers. *NACA Tech. Mem. 1285*, 1950. Transl. from *Z. angew. Math. u. Mech. 29*, 15–16, 1949.
90. Ruetenik, J. R., and Corrsin, S. Equilibrium turbulent flow in a slightly divergent channel. *50 Jahre Grenzschichtforschung.* (Ed: H. Görtler and W. Tollmien), 446–459. Vieweg, Braunschweig, 1955.
91. Lees, L., and Crocco, L. *J. Aeronaut. Sci. 19*, 649–676 (1952).
92. Ross, D., and Robertson, J. *J. Appl. Mech. 18*, 95–100 (1951).
93. Rotta, J. On the theory of the turbulent boundary layer. *NACA Tech. Mem. 1344*, 1953. Transl. Über die Theorie der turbulenten Grenzschichten. *Mitt. Max-Planck-Inst., Gottingen, 1*, 1950.
94. Liepmann, H. W., and Laufer, J. Investigation of free turbulent mixing. *NACA Tech. Note 1257*, 1947.
95. Nikuradse, J. Laws of flow in rough pipes. *NACA Tech. Mem. 1292*, 1950. Transl. Strömungsgesetze in rauhen Rohren. *Ver. deut. Ing. Forschungsheft 361*, 1933.
96. Schlichting, H. *Boundary Layer Theory.* McGraw-Hill, 1955.
97. Hama, F. R. *Trans. Soc. Nav. Arch. and Marine Engrs. 62*, 333–358 (1954).
98. Buri, A. A method of calculation for the turbulent boundary layer with accelerated and retarded basic flow. *Brit. Ministry Aircraft Production R. T. P. Transl. 2073.* From *Thesis 652*, Federal Tech. College, Zurich, 1931. (Also available from *CADO, Wright-Patterson Air Force Base,* as *AT143493.*)
99. Gruschwitz, E. *Ing.-Arch. 2*, 321–346 (1931).
100. Garner, H. C. The development of turbulent boundary layers. *Brit. Aeronaut. Research Council Repts. and Mem. 2133*, 1944.
101. Tetervin, N., and Lin, C. C. A general integral form of the boundary-layer equation for incompressible flow with an application to the calculation of the separation point of turbulent boundary layers. *NACA Tech. Note 2158*, 1950.

102. Fediaevsky, K. Turbulent boundary layer of an airfoil. *NACA Tech. Mem. 822*, 1937. Transl. *Central Aero-Hydrodynam. Inst., Moscow, Rept. 282*, 1936.
103. Ross, D., and Robertson, J. M. *J. Appl. Phys. 21*, 557–561 (1950).
104. Granville, P. S. A method for the calculation of the turbulent boundary layer in a pressure gradient. *The David W. Taylor Model Basin Rept. 752*, 1951.
105. Kuethe, A. M., McKee, P. B., and Curry, W. H. Measurements in the boundary layer of a yawed wing. *NACA Tech. Note 1946*, 1949.
106. Ashkenas, H., and Riddell, F. R. Investigation of the turbulent boundary layer on a yawed flat plate. *NACA Tech. Note 3383*, 1955.
107. Young, A. D., and Booth, T. B. The profile drag of yawed wings of infinite span. *College of Aeronautics, Cranfield, Rept. 38*, May 1950.
108. Townsend, A. A. *Proc. Roy. Soc. London A190*, 551–561 (1947).
109. Kuethe, A. M. *J. Appl. Mech. 2*, (*3*), 1935. In *Trans. Am. Soc. Mech. Eng. 57*, A-87, A-95 (1935).
110. Birkhoff, G., and Zarantonello, E. H. Jets, wakes, and cavities. *Applied Math. and Mech.*, Vol. 2. Academic Press, 1957.
111. Pai, S.-I. *Fluid Dynamics of Jets*. Van Nostrand, 1954.
112. Corrsin, S. Investigation of flow in an axially symmetrical heated jet of air. *NACA Wartime Rept. ACR 3L23*, 1943.
113. Townsend, A. A. *Proc. Roy. Soc. London A190*, 551–561 (1947).
114. Townsend, A. A. *Australian J. Sci. Research, Series A 1*, 161–174 (1948).
115. Townsend, A. A. *Proc. Roy. Soc. London A197*, 124–140 (1949).
116. Townsend, A. A. *Phil. Mag. 41*, 890–906 (1950).
117. Corrsin, S., and Kistler, A. L. The free-stream boundaries of turbulent flows. *NACA Rept. 1244*, 1955.
118. Klebanoff, P. S. Characteristics of turbulence in a boundary layer with zero pressure gradient. *NACA Tech. Note 3178*, 1954.
119. Taylor, G. I. *Proc. London Math. Soc. 20*, 196–212 (1921).
120. Prandtl, L. *Z. angew. Math. u. Mech. 22*, 241–243 (1942).
121. Taylor, G. I. *Proc. Roy. Soc. London A135*, 685–702 (1932).
122. Hinze, J. O., and van der Hegge Zijnen, B. G. *Appl. Sci. Research A1*, 435–461 (1949).
123. Corrsin, S., and Uberoi, M. S. Further experiments on the flow and heat transfer in a heated turbulent air jet. *NACA Rept. 998*, 1950.
124. Forstall, W., and Shapiro, A. H. *J. Appl. Mech. 17*, 399–408 (1950). In *Trans. Am. Soc. Mech. Eng. 72*, 1950.
125. Reichardt, H. *Z. angew. Math. u. Mech. 24*, 268–272 (1944).
126. Townsend, A. A. *Australian J. Sci. Research, Series A, 2*, 451–468 (1949).
127. Görtler, H. Berechnung von Aufgaben der freien Turbulenz auf Grund eines neuen Naherungsansatzes. *Z. angew. Math. u. Mech. 22*, 244–254 (1942).
128. Cleeves, V., and Boelter, L. M. K. *Chem. Eng. Progr. 43*, 123–134 (1947).
129. Abramovich, G. N. The theory of a free jet of a compressible gas. *NACA Tech. Mem. 1058*, 1944. Transl. *Central Aero-Hydrodynam. Inst., Moscow, Rept. 377*, 1939.
130. Gooderum, P. B., Wood, G. C., and Brevoort, M., J. Investigation with an interferometer of the turbulent mixing of a free supersonic jet. *NACA Rept. 963*, 1949.
131. Tollmien, W. Calculation of turbulent expansion processes. *NACA Tech. Mem. 1085*, 1945. Transl. from *Z. angew. Math. u. Mech. 6*, 1926.
132. Bershader, D., and Pai, S. I. *J. Appl. Phys. 21*, 616 (1950).
133. Pai, S. I. *J. Aeronaut. Sci. 16*, 463–469 (1949).
134. Keagy, W. R., and Weller, A. E. A study of freely expanding inhomogeneous jets. *Heat Transfer and Fluid Mech. Inst., Univ. Calif.*, 89–98 (1949). Am. Soc. Mech. Eng., New York.
135. Szablewski, W. Contributions to the study of the spreading of a free jet issuing from a nozzle. *NACA Tech. Mem. 1311*, 1951. Transl. Zur Theorie der Ausbreitung eines aus einer Düse austretenden freien Strahls. *Untersuch. u. Mitt. Nr. 8003*, Sept. 1944.

136. Squire, H. B., and Trouncer, J. Round jets in a general stream. *Brit. Aeronaut. Research Council Repts. and Mem. 1974*, 1944.
137. Rousso, M. D., and Baughman, E. L. Spreading characteristics of a jet expanding from choked nozzles at Mach 1.91. *NACA Tech. Note 3836*, 1956.
138. Szablewski, W. The diffusion of a hot air jet in air in motion. *NACA Tech. Mem. 1288*, 1950. Transl. Die Ausbreitung eines Heissluftstrahles in Bewegter Luft. *GDC/2460*, Sept. 1946.
139. Pabst, O. Die ausbreitung heisser Gasstrahlen in bewegter Luft. *Untersuch. u. Mitt., Part II, UM 8007*, 1944.
140. Rubert, K. F., and Persh, J. A procedure for calculating the development of turbulent boundary layers under the influence of adverse pressure gradients. *NACA Tech. Note 2478*, 1951.
141. Ross, D. *Trans. Am. Soc. Civil Eng. Paper 2838*, *121*, 1219–1254 (1956).
142. Spence, D. A. *J. Aeronaut. Sci. 23*, 3–15 (1956).

# SECTION C

# *STATISTICAL THEORIES OF TURBULENCE*

C. C. LIN

## *CHAPTER 1. BASIC CONCEPTS*

**C,1. Introduction.** The general concepts of turbulent motion have been discussed in the previous section. It is recognized that the details of turbulent flow are so complicated that statistical description must be used. Indeed, only statistical properties of turbulent motion are experimentally reproducible. The purpose of the present section is to give a more comprehensive treatment of the statistical theory.

Current literature on the statistical theory of turbulence is mainly limited to the treatment of the case of homogeneous turbulence[1] without any essential mean motion. Superficially, one might think that there is little to be known about such fluid motions. Actually, the very absence of mean motion allows one to go more deeply into the inherent nature of the turbulent flow itself. Many basic concepts have been developed in the study of homogeneous turbulence, and these concepts now gradually find their way into the study of shear flow.

Since there is available an account of the theory of homogeneous turbulence [*1*] with a complete discussion of the mathematical background, a somewhat different presentation is adopted in the present section. Following the historical order, the isotropic case is taken up first. It is hoped that this will be helpful to those readers who wish to get an idea of the essentials without going through all the preliminaries required in a complete mathematical treatment.

In the later parts of this section, other aspects of the statistical theory and their applications will be treated.[2] We have, however, omitted several other approaches to the problem of turbulence. Among these, the work of Burgers [*3,4*] and Hopf [*5*] should especially be mentioned; nor is any attempt made to include a discussion of related mathematical studies, such as that of Hopf [*6*] and Kampé de Fériet [*7*].

[1] These concepts are explained more precisely in the following pages.
[2] For a brief survey of some aspects of the problem of turbulent motion, see [*2*].

**C,2. The Mean Flow and the Reynolds Stresses.** It is generally assumed that the motion can be separated into a mean flow whose components are $U_1$, $U_2$, and $U_3$ and a superposed turbulent flow whose components are $u_1$, $u_2$, and $u_3$, the mean values of which are zero. In taking average values, the following principles will be adopted. If $A$ and $B$ are dependent variables which are being averaged, and $S$ is any one of the space variables $x$, $y$, $z$, or the time $t$, then $\overline{\partial A/\partial S} = \partial \bar{A}/\partial S$ and $\overline{\bar{A}B} = \bar{A}\bar{B}$, where the bar denotes a mean value.

When the mean flow is not varying, that is, when the average value defined by

$$\bar{A}(x, y, z, t) = \lim_{\tau \to \infty} \frac{1}{2\tau} \int_{t-\tau}^{t+\tau} A(x, y, z, t')dt'$$

is independent of the time $t$, the time average is the natural mean value to use. Difficulties arise when the flow is variable, and other types of averages have to be introduced. For instance, in the problem of turbulent flow near an infinite plate moving with variable velocity, the mean values could be taken over planes parallel to the plate. In more general cases, neither the time nor the space mean values can be conveniently defined to possess all the desired properties. We then consider the statistical average over a large (infinite) number of identical systems (ensemble average).

The equation of continuity of an incompressible fluid, when averaged, becomes

$$\frac{\partial U_j}{\partial x_j} = 0 \tag{2-1}$$

The Navier-Stokes equations of motion are

$$\rho \frac{\partial v_i}{\partial t} = \frac{\partial}{\partial x_j} (\sigma_{ij} - \rho v_i v_j), \qquad v_i = U_i + u_i \tag{2-2}$$

where $\sigma_{ij}$ is the stress tensor due to pressure and viscous forces. If the mean value is taken, Eq. 2-2 becomes

$$\rho \frac{\partial U_i}{\partial t} = \frac{\partial}{\partial x_j} (\bar{\sigma}_{ij} - \rho U_i U_j - \rho \overline{u_i u_j}) \tag{2-3}$$

This equation has the same form as Eq. 2-2, if $v_i$ is replaced by $U_i$, and the stress $\sigma_{ij}$ is replaced by $\bar{\sigma}_{ij} - \rho\overline{u_i u_j}$. Thus, the equations of mean flow are the same as the ordinary equations of motion except that there are the additional virtual stresses

$$\tau_{ij} = -\rho\overline{u_i u_j} \tag{2-4}$$

which represent the mean rate of transfer of momentum across a surface due to the velocity fluctuations. These virtual stresses were first introduced by Reynolds [*8*], and are known by his name.

In the case of a turbulent flow with steady mean motion, the time average is taken at every point, and the above physical interpretation of the Reynolds stress is clear. In the case of variable mean motion, such as the case of the infinite plate mentioned above, where mean values are defined as the averages over parallel planes, the interpretation of $-\rho\overline{u_i u_j}$ as a local stress is not as direct. In the case of general variable motion, where the averaging process is the arithmetical mean taken over a large (infinite) number of unrelated identical systems (ensemble average), the physical interpretation of an average quantity as an apparent stress requires even more careful examination, since the average momentum transfer is not directly associated with any *one* particular system. Moreover, the time average is usually measured in the case of steady mean flow. Thus, if the general theory is developed on the basis of statistical averages, an ergodic hypothesis must be introduced to identify these two in that case. In this section, the statistical average shall be adopted, and the validity of such a hypothesis shall be implied. Further investigations of such basic problems are beyond the scope of the present treatment.

**C,3. Frequency Distributions and Statistical Averages.** One basic concept in the discussion of statistical averages is the frequency of occurrence, or the distribution function. For example, in the classical kinetic theory of gases, one considers a distribution function $f(u, v, w, x, y, z, t)$ such that

$$f(u, v, w, x, y, z, t)dudvdwdxdydz$$

gives the fraction of molecules at time $t$, having velocities in the range $u, u + du$; $v, v + dv$; $w, w + dw$ and lying in the element of volume $x, x + dx$; $y, y + dy$; $z, z + dz$. The kinetic theory of gases may then be based on the law governing the change of this function $f(u, v, w, x, y, z, t)$. For a homogeneous gas at rest, it is the well-known Maxwellian function.

In the case of turbulent motion, a similar (but different) function $F(u, v, w, x, y, z, t)$ can be introduced giving, for each point $(x, y, z)$ and each instant $t$, the probability that the turbulent velocity shall lie in the range $u, u + du$; $v, v + dv$; $w, w + dw$, or for shortness, $u_i, u_i + du_i$. If this function is known, then the Reynolds shear is given by formulas of the kind

$$-\rho\overline{uv} = -\rho\iiint_{-\infty}^{\infty} F(u, v, w, x, y, z, t)uvdudvdw \tag{3-1}$$

for each point $x, y, z$ at each instant $t$.

To analyze the structure of turbulence one also needs to know the joint probability distribution for quantities observed at several points. For example, if we are interested in the correlation of velocities at two points $P'$ and $P''$, then we must know a distribution function of the form

$F(u_1', x_1'; u_1'', x_1''; t)$. The correlation of the $x$ components of the velocities at these points is then given by

$$\overline{u(P')u(P'')} = \iint F(u', v'w'; x', y', z'; u'', v'', w''; x'', y'', z'', t) \\ u'u''d(u', v', w')d(u'', v'', w'') \quad (3\text{-}2)$$

Further generalization of joint probability distributions involves quantities observed at more than two points, and quantities other than velocity fluctuations.

Some experimental information is available regarding the distribution function $F(u_i, x_i, t)$. The Gaussian distribution has been found, in many cases, to be a fairly good approximation for each component (Fig. C,3a).[3] In the isotropic case, i.e. where the statistical properties of the motion

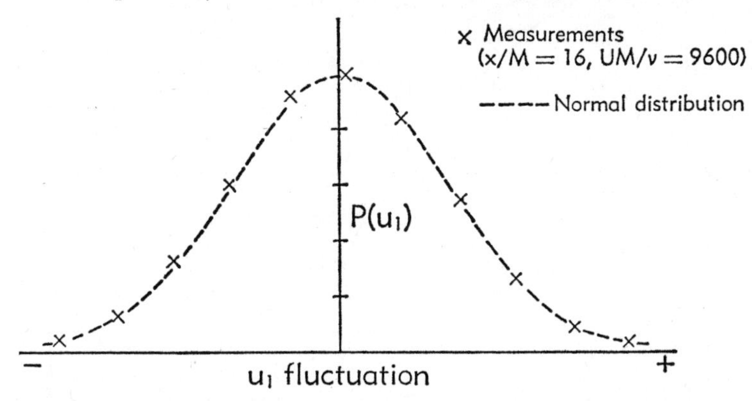


Fig. C,3a. Probability density function of the velocity component $u_1$ in the direction of the stream for the turbulence generated by a square-mesh grid in a wind tunnel (after [*1*]).

are essentially independent of direction, the Maxwellian distribution of velocity holds approximately [*9,10*].

There is also some indication that the joint probability distribution at two points in an isotropic field is approximately jointly Gaussian. However, this is known to be not accurate. To get a quantitative assessment of the departure from joint Gaussian distribution, one may introduce the quantities

$$S(r) = \frac{\overline{(u' - u)^3}}{[\overline{(u' - u)^2}]^{\frac{3}{2}}}$$

and (3-3)

$$F(r) = \frac{\overline{(u' - u)^4}}{[\overline{(u' - u)^2}]^2}$$

[3] In this and the following figures, $M$ denotes the width of the mesh of grid, $x$ denotes the distance of the observation point from the grid, $U$ denotes the velocity of air, and $\nu$ denotes the kinematic viscosity coefficient.

called respectively the skewness factor and the flatness factor. Fig. C,3b and C,3c show the experimental values of these factors as obtained by Stewart ([*11*], also as quoted in [*12*]). For exact joint-Gaussian distribution, the former should be zero, and the latter should have the value 3. Thus, the hypothesis of a joint-Gaussian distribution is not exact, but it may still be used for certain approximations (cf. Art. 16). One should

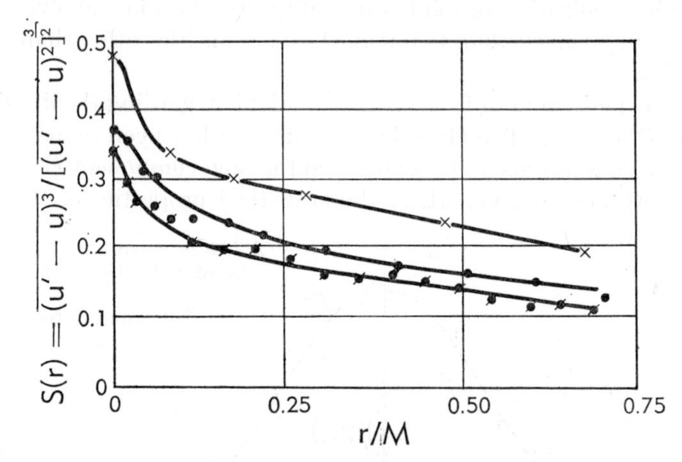


Fig. C,3b. Skewness factor for turbulent fluctuations behind a grid (after Stewart [*11*]).

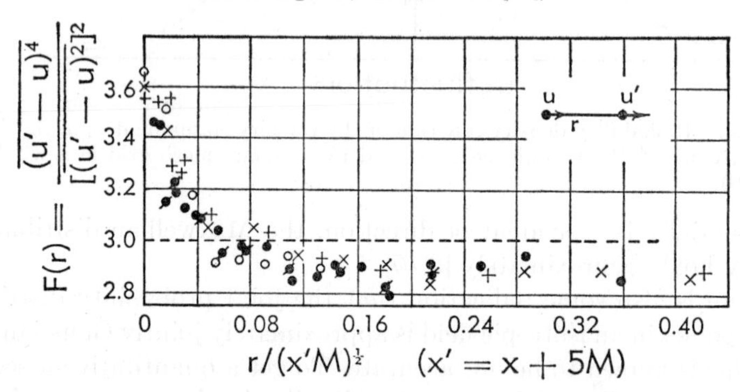


Fig. C,3c. Flatness factor for turbulent fluctuations behind a grid across a uniform air stream (after Stewart, as quoted in [*12*]).

especially note the departure of the experimental value of the flatness factor from the value 3 for a small value of $r$.

**C,4. Homogeneous Fields of Turbulence.** As noted in Art. 1, theoretical investigations of turbulent flow are often limited to the idealized case of an infinite field of turbulence which is statistically *homogeneous* or even *isotropic*, and devoid of mean motion. Homogeneity means that the *statistical* properties of the field are independent of the particular position in the field, and isotropy means that they are independent of direction.[4] For example, if we consider two points $P$ and $P'$ in such a field, the velocity components $u_r$ at $P$ and $u_r'$ at $P'$, both in the direction of $\mathbf{PP'}$, has a statistical correlation $\overline{u_r u_r'}$ dependent only on the distance $r$ between $P$ and $P'$, but independent of the coordinates of the point $P$ and the direction $\mathbf{PP'}$. In a *homogeneous anisotropic* field, this correlation would be unaltered by a translation of the vector $\mathbf{PP'}$ but would be altered by a rotation.

In particular, in a homogeneous isotropic field, the mean square value of the three components of the velocity are equal to each other and are the same throughout the field. Thus we have

$$\overline{u_1^2} = \overline{u_2^2} = \overline{u_3^2} = \underline{u}^2 \tag{4-1}$$

where $u_1$, $u_2$, $u_3$ are the velocity components along the coordinate axes $0x_1$, $0x_2$, and $0x_3$, and $\underline{u}$ is the root mean square value.

The statistical properties under consideration may be the spectrum, the joint probability distributions of velocity and pressure, etc. In many cases, we shall, however, be concerned with velocity correlations which are the easiest to measure with hot wire instruments.

The turbulent motion behind a grid in a wind tunnel has been found to be approximately homogeneous and isotropic in the above sense. Anisotropy is, however, generally found in the large scale eddies, and becomes prominent when the Reynolds number is relatively low.

**C,5. Conventional Approach to the Statistical Theory of Turbulence.** Since a basic theoretical treatment of the frequency distribution function has not yet been developed to an applicable stage (cf. [*5*]), current statistical theories of turbulence are usually concerned with readily measurable quantities. This has the advantage that experimental information can be easily resorted to when purely theoretical considerations become uncertain. Instead of dealing with the distribution functions, we consider correlation functions, which can be more readily measured by the hot wire technique. These are indeed the moments of the distribution functions, as one can readily see from the formulas (Eq. 3-1 and 3-2) and similar ones for correlations of higher orders. As higher and higher correlations are known the over-all properties of the distribution functions are known with increasing detail. Mathematically, the correlation representation can be shown to be equivalent to a spectral representation, considering energy distribution among various wave numbers or scales. The two types of descriptions, however, exhibit different aspects of the same physical phenomena. Both of them will therefore be used in the following developments of the theory.

[4] Indeed, general isotropy implies homogeneity, but the phrase "homogeneous isotropic turbulence" is usually preferred as more descriptive.

# CHAPTER 2. MATHEMATICAL FORMULATION OF THE THEORY OF HOMOGENEOUS TURBULENCE

**C,6. Kinematics of Homogeneous Isotropic Turbulence. Correlation Theory.** In this chapter, we shall develop the theoretical concepts used for the description of homogeneous turbulence. The main body of the discussion will be limited to the isotropic case. The general case of anisotropic turbulence will be taken up in Art. 11.

The statistical correlation of velocity fluctuations at two points is the most commonly used quantity for describing the structure of an isotropic field of turbulence. Clearly, the larger the size of the eddies, the further the correlation extends. Velocity correlations are used not only because they are the easiest to measure, but also because correlations involving pressure fluctuations are theoretically representable in terms of them. Experimentally, it is as yet difficult to determine correlations involving pressure fluctuations. In general, we shall be dealing with the correlation of quantities at several points and at different instants of time. For example, for three points $P$, $P'$, and $P''$ in a field of turbulent motion, we may wish to consider the correlation $\overline{u_1(P)u_2(P')p(P'')}$, where $u_1(P)$ and $u_2(P')$ are respectively the components of velocity in the direction of the $x_1$ axis at the point $P$ and in the direction of the $x_2$ axis at the point $P'$, and $p(P'')$ is the pressure at the point $P''$. Statistical correlations of the velocity components at one point are exemplified by the Reynolds stresses. In the order of increasing complexity, we next consider correlations at two points. As explained above, we now deal with the special case of isotropic turbulence.

*Double velocity correlations.* Since there is no preferred choice of the coordinate system in the isotropic case, it is clear that the correlations must be basically characterized by the directions of the velocity components relative to the vector **PP′** joining the two points at which the velocities are considered. It is therefore convenient to consider a *longitudinal correlation* coefficient $f(r)$ defined by (see Fig. C,6a)[5]

$$\overline{u_r u_r'} = \underline{u}^2 f(r) \tag{6-1}$$

Similarly, one may define a transverse correlation coefficient $g(r)$ by

$$\overline{u_t u_t'} = \underline{u}^2 g(r) \tag{6-2}$$

for two parallel velocity components perpendicular to **PP′**. It is obvious from isotropy that this correlation is independent of the particular pair

[5] Here the line $PP'$ lies in the direction of the $x_1$ axis, and the three mutually perpendicular components $u_r$, $u_t$, $u_p$ are $u_1$, $u_2$, $u_3$.

of parallel components taken. Now the velocity at a given point may be expressed as a linear combination of three mutually perpendicular components, taken along and perpendicular to **PP′**. The general velocity correlation between $P$ and $P'$ can therefore be expressed in terms of the nine correlations between $u_r$, $u_t$, $u_p$ and $u'_r$, $u'_t$, $u'_p$, where $u_p$ and $u'_p$ are components perpendicular to both $u_r$ and $u_t$. By isotropy, correlations like $\overline{u_r u'_t}$ and $\overline{u_t u'_p}$ are zero, and we see that an arbitrary velocity correlation can be expressed in terms of the two basic correlations $f(r)$ and $g(r)$. In fact, if $u_i (i = 1, 2, 3)$ are the components of velocity at $P(x_i)$, and

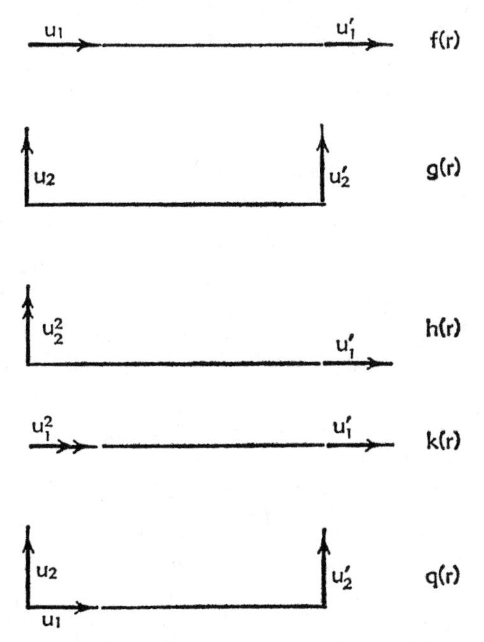


Fig. C,6a. Diagram illustrating the definition of the principal correlation functions in isotropic turbulence.

$u'_j (j = 1, 2, 3)$ are those at $P'(x'_i)$, von Kármán [*13*] has shown by direct calculation that

$$R_{ij} = \overline{u_i u'_j} = \underline{u}^2 \left[ \frac{f(r) - g(r)}{r^2} r_i r_j + g(r) \delta_{ij} \right] \tag{6-3}$$

where $r_i = x'_i - x_i$, and $\delta_{ij}$ is the Kronecker delta ($\delta_{ij} = 1$ if $i = j$, $\delta_{ij} = 0$ if $i \neq j$). The correlation coefficient $\overline{u_i u'_j}/\underline{u}^2$ will be denoted by $\tilde{R}_{ij}$, and is equal to the expression in the brackets in Eq. 6-3. A derivation of Eq. 6-3, following the method of Robertson [*14*] will be given at the end of this article.

By using the *correlation tensor* (Eq. 6-3), correlations involving velocity derivatives can be conveniently calculated. For example, if one wants to calculate the correlation between $u_i$ at $P$ and the derivatives $\partial u'_j/\partial x'_k$ at $P'$, one has only to use the following identity:

$$\overline{u_i \frac{\partial u'_j}{\partial x'_k}} = \overline{\frac{\partial}{\partial x'_k}(u_i u'_j)} = \frac{\partial}{\partial x'_k}\overline{u_i u'_j} = \frac{\partial}{\partial r_k}\overline{u_i u'_j} \tag{6-4}$$

The above transformations are made by using the general rule for averaging a derivative and the definition of $r_k$. Similarly

$$\overline{\frac{\partial u_i}{\partial x_l}\frac{\partial u'_j}{\partial x'_k}} = -\frac{\partial}{\partial r_l}\frac{\partial}{\partial r_k}\overline{u_i u'_j}$$

If we now make use of the equation of continuity $\partial u'_j/\partial x'_j = 0$, we may obtain from Eq. 6-4

$$\frac{\partial \tilde{R}_{ij}}{\partial r_j} = 0 \tag{6-5}$$

By using Eq. 6-3, this eventually gives rise to the single relation

$$g = f + \frac{r}{2}\frac{\partial f}{\partial r} \tag{6-6}$$

connecting the two correlation functions $f$ and $g$. Thus, *in homogeneous isotropic turbulence, all the correlation functions of the second order can be expressed in terms of a single correlation function, say* $f(r)$.

We shall now show that the correlation tensor (Eq. 6-3) is an even function of $r_i$. To do this, it is only necessary to show that $f(r)$ is an even function of $r$. It then follows from Eq. 5-6 that $g(r)$ is also an even function, and the desired result becomes obvious from the formula (Eq. 6-3).

Consider two points $P$ and $P'$ along the $x$ axis at a distance $r$ apart. Then

$$\underline{u}^2 f(r) = \overline{u(x)u(x+r)}$$

Expanding $u(x + r)$ into a Taylor series, we obtain

$$f(r) = 1 + \frac{\overline{uu_x}}{\underline{u}^2} r + \frac{1}{2!}\frac{\overline{uu_{xx}}}{\underline{u}^2} r^2 + \cdots$$

The coefficients of this power series can be simplified as follows by using the condition of homogeneity:

$$\overline{uu_x} = \tfrac{1}{2}\overline{(u^2)_x} = 0$$

$$\overline{uu_{xx}} = \overline{(uu_x)_x} - \overline{u_x^2} = -\overline{u_x^2}$$

It can be easily seen that all coefficients of the odd powers of $r$ are zero. Thus,

$$f(r) = 1 - \frac{1}{2}\frac{\overline{u_x^2}}{\overline{u^2}} r^2 + \cdots \tag{6-7}$$

is an even function of $r$.

The idea of using the correlation function for isotropic turbulence was first introduced by Taylor [*15*], who also gave the above proof that they are even functions. The correlation tensor was first introduced by von Kármán [*13*], who also deduced Eq. 6-6. Detailed experimental verification of this relation (Eq. 6-6) seems to have first been made by Macphail [*16*], and reconfirmed by later experimenters (see Fig. C,6b).

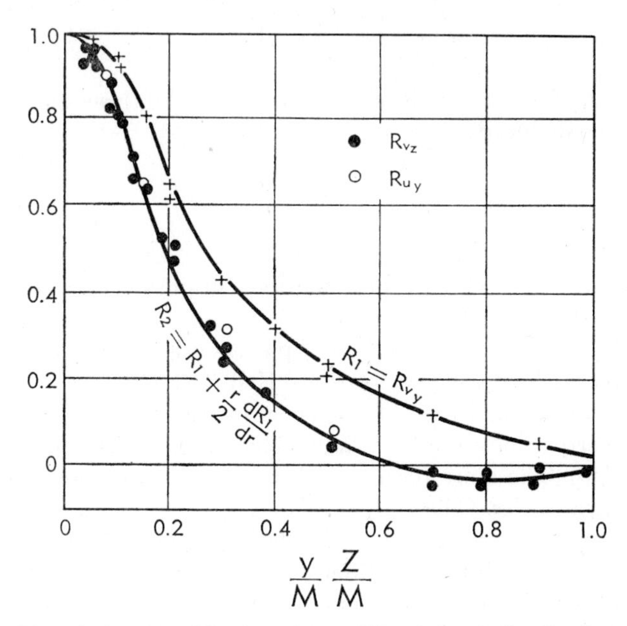


Fig. C,6b. Experimental verification of von Kármán's relation for isotropic turbulence, after Macphail [*16*]. $R_1 = f(r)$, $R_2 = g(r)$. $M$ denotes mesh width, $y$ and $z$ are distances parallel to the grid.

*Triple velocity correlations.* Continuing the study of velocity correlation, one would naturally be led to correlations for velocity components at three points $P$, $P'$, and $P''$:

$$T_{i,j,k} = \underline{u}^3\tilde{T}_{i,j,k} = \overline{u_i(P)u_j(P')u_k(P'')} \tag{6-8}$$

This triple correlation tensor is a function of the two vectors $\mathbf{PP'}$ and $\mathbf{PP''}$, say, and shows clearly that we are dealing with multiple-point tensors. Often one needs only the correlation tensor $T_{ij,k}$ for two points $P$ and $P'$:

$$T_{ij,k} = \underline{u}^3\tilde{T}_{ij,k} = \overline{u_i(P)u_j(P)u_k(P')} \tag{6-9}$$

It then becomes a function of the vector $\mathbf{PP'}$. Such a two-point triple correlation tensor was first studied by von Kármán and Howarth [*17*], who showed that, because of isotropy, it can be expressed in terms of three scalar triple correlation coefficients $h$, $k$, and $q$ in the following manner:[6]

$$\tilde{T}_{ij,k} = \frac{k - h - 2q}{r^3} r_i r_j r_k + \delta_{ij} r_k \frac{h}{r} + \delta_{ik} r_j \frac{q}{r} + \delta_{jk} r_i \frac{q}{r} \tag{6-10}$$

The definitions of $h$, $k$, and $q$ are shown in Fig. C,6a. Again, the equation of continuity leads to

$$\frac{\partial \tilde{T}_{ij,k}}{\partial r_k} = 0 \tag{6-11}$$

From this, the following two relations between the three quantities $h$, $k$, and $q$ may be deduced:

$$k = -2h$$
$$q = -h - \frac{r}{2} \frac{\partial h}{\partial r} \tag{6-12}$$

expressing all triple correlation functions in terms of a single scalar function.

It can be shown, by the method of power-series expansion used above for the study of the double correlations, that $h$, $k$, and $q$ are odd functions of $r$, and that their series expansions begin with the *third* powers of $r$.

Triple correlations seem to have been first measured directly by Townsend [*10*]. The more recent results of Kistler, O'Brien, and Corrsin [*18*] are shown in Fig. C,6c.

*Higher velocity correlations.* Correlation tensors involving one velocity component each from $n$ different points are multiple-point tensors involving $n - 1$ positional vectors.

*Correlations involving pressure.* Correlations involving pressure are exemplified by

$$(1)\ \overline{p(P)p(P')} \quad \text{and} \quad (2)\ \overline{p(P)u_i(P')}$$

The first one is obviously a scalar quantity, which, from kinematical considerations alone, is not connected with velocity correlations. However, by making use of dynamical relations, it can be connected with velocity correlations of the fourth order. This will therefore be taken up in later sections (Art. 7 and 16). On the other hand, von Kármán and Howarth [*17*] showed that

$$\overline{pu_i'} = 0 \tag{6-13}$$

from the requirements of isotropy and incompressibility alone.

*Robertson's invariant theory.* As the need for developing more complicated correlations arises, one must employ some systematic methods

[6] Derivation of Eq. 6-10 can be carried out by direct transformation of coordinates and application of the condition of continuity. That is the original method used by von Kármán and Howarth. The method of Robertson described below yields the result more readily.

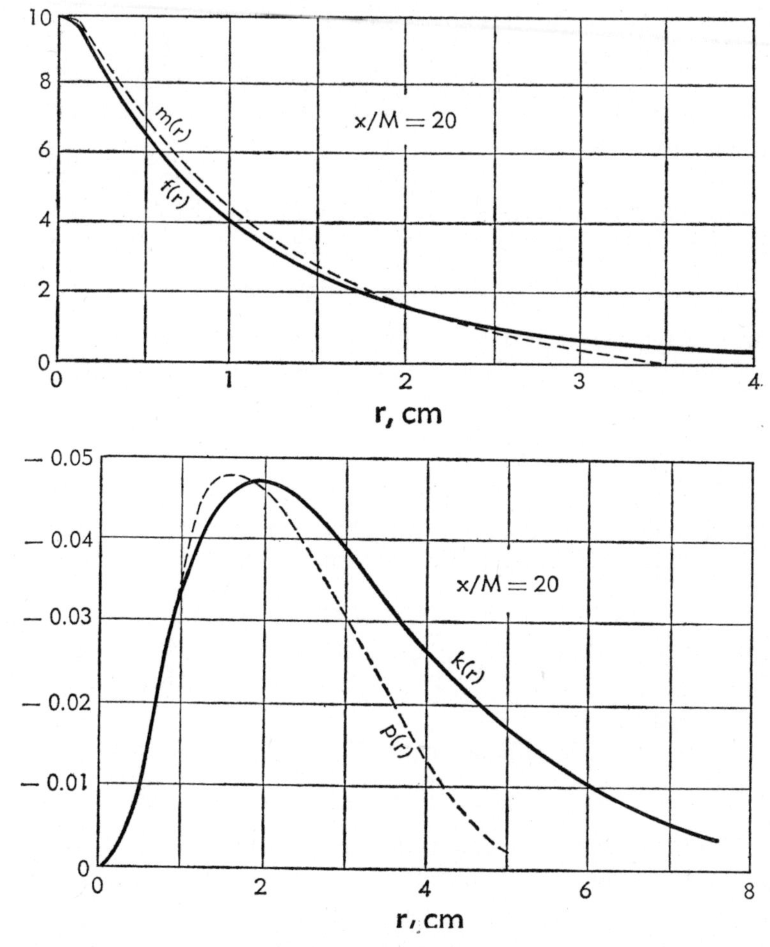


Fig. C,6c. Top, double correlation functions involving velocity and temperature fluctuations $u$ and $\theta$ behind a heated grid set perpendicular to a uniform air stream.

$$m(r) = \frac{\overline{\theta(x)\theta(x + r)}}{\theta'(x)\theta'(x + r)}$$

$$f(r) = \frac{\overline{u(x)u(x + r)}}{u'(x)u'(x + r)}$$

where $x$ and $r$ denote distance in the direction of the stream and a dash indicates the root mean square value. $M$ is the mesh width of the grid (after Kistler, O'Brien, and Corrsin [*18*]).

Bottom, triple correlation functions obtained by the same authors under the same conditions as those in Fig. C,6c, top.

$$k(r) = \frac{\overline{u^2(x)u(x + r)}}{u'^2(x)u'(x + r)}$$

$$p(r) = \frac{\overline{u(x)\theta(x)\theta(x + r)}}{u'(x)\theta'(x)\theta'(x + r)}$$

for their deduction. Robertson [14] gave such a method based on a consideration of invariants. It proved very useful in later developments, particularly in the study of homogeneous anisotropic turbulence. We shall give below the development for the double velocity correlation tensor as an illustration of the method.

Consider two arbitrary unit vectors $a_i$ and $b_i$. Then the correlation between the velocity components $u_i a_i$ at $P$ and $u'_j b_j$ at $P'$ is a scalar quantity $Q$, independent of rotation of the coordinate system:

$$Q = \overline{u_i a_i u'_j b_j} = \underline{u}^2 \tilde{R}_{ij} a_i b_j \tag{6-14}$$

It must therefore be a scalar function of all the scalar quantities involved in the problems, namely, all the scalar quantities formed with the vectors $a_i$, $b_j$, and $r_k$. These invariants are the following:

(i) $$a_i a_i = 1, \quad b_j b_j = 1, \quad r_k r_k = r^2$$

(ii) $$a_i b_i, \ a_i r_i, \ b_i r_i$$

In addition, the determinant formed of these vectors is an invariant under rotation. This may be written in the form

(iii) $$\epsilon_{ijk} a_i b_j r_k$$

where $\epsilon_{ijk}$ is the alternating symbol: $\epsilon_{ijk} = 1$ if $(i, j, k)$ is $(1, 2, 3)$ or its cyclic permutation, $\epsilon_{ijk} = -1$, if $(i, j, k)$ is $(1, 2, 3)$ or its cyclic permutation, and $\epsilon_{ijk} = 0$ otherwise.

We note that $Q$ is a bilinear expression in the vectors $a_i$ and $b_i$. Hence,

$$Q = Q_1(r) a_i b_i + Q_2(r) a_i r_i b_j r_j + Q_3(r) \epsilon_{ijk} a_i b_j r_k$$

since this is the most general bilinear form in $a_i$ and $b_i$ that can be formed from the invariants cited above. If one now imposes the further condition that $Q$ must also be invariant under a reflection, which changes $r_k$ into $-r_k$, it is clear that $Q_3 = 0$, and hence

$$Q = (Q_1 \delta_{ij} + Q_2 r_i r_j) a_i b_j$$

Since $a_i$ and $b_j$ are arbitrary unit vectors, it is at once clear that

$$\underline{u}^2 \tilde{R}_{ij} = Q_1 \delta_{ij} + Q_2 r_i r_j \tag{6-15}$$

This may be identified with Eq. 5-3 if $Q_1$ and $Q_2$ are related to $f(r, t)$ and $g(r, t)$ as follows:

$$Q_1 = \underline{u}^2 g, \quad Q_2 = \underline{u}^2 \frac{f - g}{r} \tag{6-16}$$

**C,7. Dynamics of Isotropic Turbulence.** The dynamics of isotropic turbulence is governed by the Navier-Stokes equations of motion

$$\frac{\partial u_i}{\partial t} + u_j \frac{\partial u_i}{\partial x_j} = -\frac{1}{\rho} \frac{\partial p}{\partial x_i} + \nu \Delta u_i \tag{7-1}$$

where $\rho$ is the density of the fluid, $p$ is the pressure, $\nu$ is the kinematic viscosity coefficient, and $\Delta$ is the Laplacian operator. It might be expected that one could, from Eq. 7-1, derive the equations governing the behavior of all the statistical properties of turbulent motion, such as the level of turbulence, the correlation functions, etc. However, as one proceeds to construct the equations for such purposes, it becomes at once clear that we are always faced with the difficulty of having fewer equations than unknowns, caused primarily by the nonlinear terms in the differential equations. Unless additional assumptions are introduced, deductions from such an approach are quite limited. In this article, we only discuss the results following the formal construction of the equations for the change of the correlation functions. The necessary additional assumptions will be taken up later (Art. 16 and 17).

To obtain the equation for the change of the double correlation function, one may multiply Eq. 6-1 by $u_k'$ and add to it a similar equation obtained by the interchange of the role of the points $P$ and $P'$. The leading term of the combined equation is then

$$u_k' \frac{\partial u_i}{\partial t} + u_i \frac{\partial u_k'}{\partial t} = \frac{\partial}{\partial t} (u_i u_k')$$

Upon averaging, this yields an equation for the time rate of change of the double correlation tensor $\underline{u}^2 \tilde{R}_{ik}$.

However, there are clearly terms of other types appearing in the equation. The nonlinear term on the left of Eq. 7-1 gives rise to triple correlations and the pressure term gives rise to a pressure-velocity correlation. It can be easily verified by using Eq. 6-13 that the pressure term vanishes identically, and the equation finally reduces to

$$\frac{\partial}{\partial t} (\underline{u}^2 \tilde{R}_{ik}) - \underline{u}^3 \frac{\partial}{\partial r_j} (\tilde{T}_{ij,k} + \tilde{T}_{kj,i}) = 2\nu \underline{u}^2 \Delta \tilde{R}_{ik} \tag{7-2}$$

The appearance of the triple correlation in Eq. 7-2 would suggest the attempt to establish a relation governing *its* time rate of change. This can be done by combining three equations with leading terms

$$u_k' u_l'' \frac{\partial u_i}{\partial t}, \quad u_i u_l'' \frac{\partial u_k'}{\partial t}, \quad u_i u_k' \frac{\partial u_l''}{\partial t}$$

obtained by multiplying the equations of motion at $P$, $P'$, and $P''$ respectively by suitable factors. Upon averaging, an equation for $(\partial/\partial t)(\underline{u}^3 \tilde{T}_{i,k,l})$ is obtained, but this equation also involves correlations of the fourth order and pressure-velocity correlations. The latter can be eliminated in terms of velocity correlations by the following process. From Eq. 7-1, one may obtain, by taking its divergence, a Poisson equation

$$\Delta p = \frac{\partial u_i}{\partial x_j} \frac{\partial u_j}{\partial x_i} \tag{7-3}$$

relating the pressure to the instantaneous velocity. One may then obtain, for example, $\Delta\overline{pu'_k u''_l}$ in terms of velocity correlations and attempt to calculate $\overline{pu'_k u''_l}$ by integration.

Thus, one may expect that, in general, a system of differential equations can be obtained for the correlation coefficients of different orders, each involving velocity correlations of one order higher. To obtain a deductive theory, it would be necessary to interrupt this process by some judicious assumption (suggested by experimental information or other theoretical considerations) connecting higher order correlations with ones of lower orders. (See Art. 16 and 17.)

Many of the existing investigations involve only the dynamical equation (Eq. 7-2) for double correlations. The equations for higher correlations have been exploited only recently. Now, Eq. 7-2 represents a system of six equations. However, since $R_{ik}$ and $T_{ij,k}$ are each determined by a single scalar function (Eq. 6-3 and 6-10), it should be possible to reduce Eq. 7-2 to a single equation. In fact, von Kármán and Howarth [*17*] found it to be

$$\frac{\partial}{\partial t}(\underline{u}^2 f) + 2\underline{u}^3\left(\frac{\partial h}{\partial r} + \frac{4h}{r}\right) = 2\nu\underline{u}^2\left(\frac{\partial^2 f}{\partial r^2} + \frac{4}{r}\frac{\partial f}{\partial r}\right) \tag{7-4}$$

A direct experimental verification of this equation has been made by Stewart [*11*].

If one expands both $f$ and $h$ as power series of $r$, one obtains a series of relations among the derivatives of those functions. The first of these is commonly written in the form

$$\frac{d\underline{u}^2}{dt} = -10\nu\frac{\underline{u}^2}{\lambda^2} \tag{7-5}$$

where $\lambda$ is Taylor's vorticity scale defined by

$$\frac{1}{\lambda^2} = -\left(\frac{\partial^2 f}{\partial r^2}\right)_{r=0} \tag{7-6}$$

The relation (Eq. 7-5) essentially gives the rate of decrease of kinetic energy. It was first established by Taylor [*15*], both theoretically and experimentally. The equations corresponding to the higher powers of $r$ will be discussed in connection with the small scale structure of turbulence (Art. 13).

**C,8. The Spectral Theory of Isotropic Turbulence.** The early adoption of statistical correlations for the description of isotropic turbulence is at least partly due to the fact that they are relatively easy to measure. Another powerful method for describing a fluctuating field is to analyze it into Fourier components, i.e. to adopt the spectral approach. It is well known that the spectral theory and the correlation theory are intimately connected with each other by simple mathematical transformations. Physically speaking, however, the two methods of description put different emphasis on the different aspects of the same phenomena. The spectral theory is often found to give a clearer description of the basic mechanism of turbulence.

Spectral analysis has long been used for the study of electromagnetic waves, such as the radiation of heat and light. It was first introduced into the study of turbulence by Taylor [*19*]. Taylor made spectrum measurements, behind a grid in a wind tunnel, of the velocity fluctuation as registered by a hot wire fixed in the wind tunnel. This is a fluctuation in time. But Taylor assumed[7] that "the sequence of changes in $u$ at the fixed point are simply due to the passage of an unchanging pattern of turbulent motion over the point." The variation is then essentially the same as that in space, and the spectrum he observed corresponds to a one-dimensional Fourier analysis of the field of turbulence in the direction of the wind.

The field of turbulence in the wind tunnel is obviously not homogeneous in the direction of the wind. However, in developing the theory, we shall consider a homogeneous field and its Fourier analysis. In isotropic turbulence, the analysis would be the same in all directions, provided we are always dealing with the component of velocity in the direction chosen for the analysis. The transverse component in general has a different spectrum whether the turbulence is isotropic or not.

In the case of turbulent motion, we may formulate the Fourier transform relations between the power spectrum and the correlation function as follows. If $\frac{1}{2}F_1(\kappa)d\kappa$ is the amount of kinetic energy per unit mass, associated with the longitudinal component of the velocity, and lying in the range of wave numbers $(\kappa, \kappa + d\kappa)$, then $F_1(\kappa)$ is related to the longitudinal correlation function $f(r)$ by the pair of Fourier transform relations:

$$\begin{aligned} \underline{u}^2 f(r) &= \int_0^\infty F_1(\kappa) \cos \kappa r d\kappa \\ F_1(\kappa) &= \frac{2\underline{u}^2}{\pi} \int_0^\infty f(r) \cos \kappa r dr \end{aligned} \tag{8-1}$$

It is clear from the first formula in Eq. 8-1 that

$$\underline{u}^2 = \int_0^\infty F_1(\kappa) d\kappa \tag{8-2}$$

recapitulating the original physical interpretation of $F_1(\kappa)$. To clarify our concepts, a derivation of Eq. 8-1 will be given in the next section.

[7] A theoretical analysis justifying Taylor's assumption was given by Lin [*20*]. A thorough experimental investigation, including measurements of velocity correlations involving both time and space separations, was made by Favre, Gaviglio, and Dumas (see [*21*] and the references quoted).

Taylor made use of Eq. 8-1 to connect the observed *time* spectrum with the *spatial* correlation function by way of his assumption. To do this, the spatial distance $r$ is replaced by $Ut$ and the time frequency $n$ is related to $\kappa$ by

$$\kappa U = 2\pi n$$

Then,

$$\begin{aligned} \underline{u}^2 f(r) &= \int_0^\infty F(n) \cos \frac{2\pi n r}{U}\, dn \\ F(n) &= \frac{4\underline{u}^2}{U} \int_0^\infty f(r) \cos \frac{2\pi n r}{U}\, dr \end{aligned} \tag{8-3}$$

These relations were actually well verified, justifying his assumption experimentally. (See Fig. C,8; after Stewart and Townsend [*22*].)

From Eq. 8-3 we can calculate the rate of energy dissipation in terms of the spectrum. It is easy to show that

$$\underline{u}^2 f''(0) = \frac{4\pi^2}{U^2} \int_0^\infty F(n) n^2 dn \tag{8-4}$$

which is proportional to the rate of energy dissipation (cf. Eq. 7-5). This formula shows that the high frequency components are more important for the dissipation of energy. In fact, Taylor found from an analysis of his measurements of spectrum that *the dissipation of energy is practically all associated with such high frequency components which contain a negligible amount of energy.* This has a very important bearing on later developments (see Art. 13 on Kolmogoroff's theory).

The above spectral considerations do not give a proper representation of the energy distribution among various scales. For theoretical purposes, one should then consider spectral functions obtained by a three-dimensional harmonic analysis. As it will be shown in Art. 10, the three-dimensional spectrum $F(\kappa)$ is connected with the one-dimensional spectrum $F_1(\kappa)$ by the relation [cf. Eq. 10-3],

$$F(\kappa) = \tfrac{1}{3}[\kappa^2 F_1''(\kappa) - \kappa F_1'(\kappa)] \tag{8-5}$$

The kinetic energy per unit volume, for each component of the motion, lying in the range of spacial frequencies $(\kappa, \kappa + d\kappa)$ is now given by $\frac{1}{2}\rho F(\kappa) d\kappa$, the functions $F(\kappa)$ and $F_1(\kappa)$ being both normalized to give

$$\underline{u}^2 = \int_0^\infty F(\kappa) d\kappa = \int_0^\infty F_1(\kappa) d\kappa \tag{8-6}$$

It is now easy to obtain the equation for the change of spectrum. We take the cosine transform of the Kármán-Howarth equation and then apply the operation

$$\frac{1}{3}\left(\kappa^2 \frac{\partial^2}{\partial \kappa^2} - \kappa \frac{\partial}{\partial \kappa}\right)$$

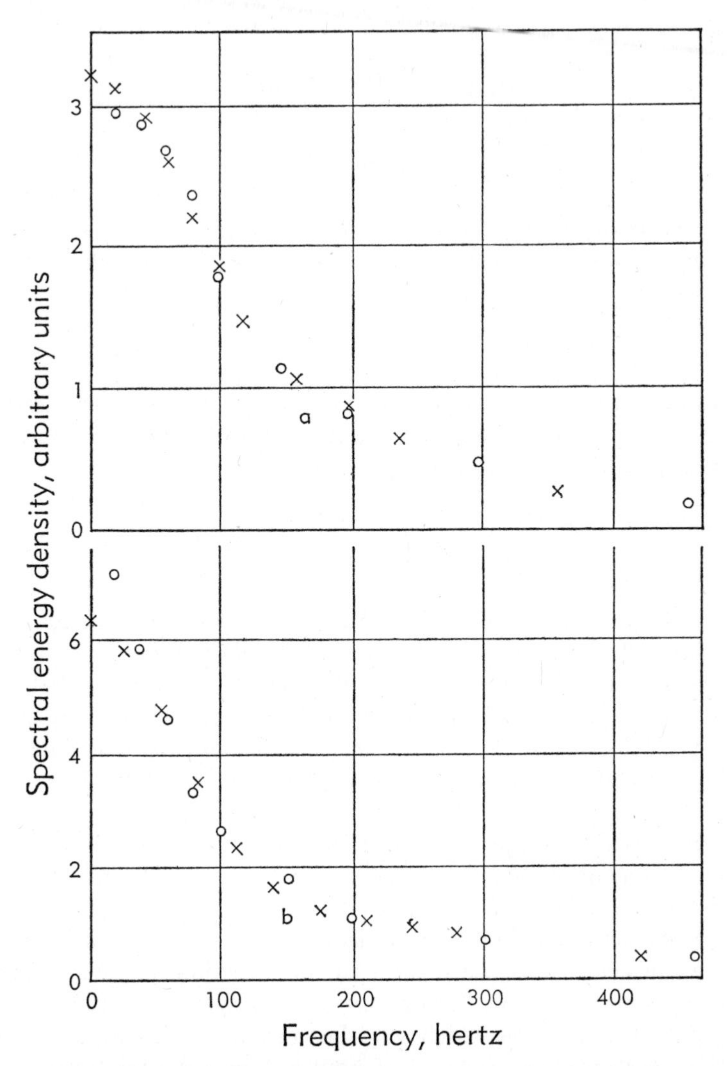


Fig. C,8. Experimental verification of the Fourier transform relation between space correlation and time spectrum for turbulent fluctuations behind a grid in a wind tunnel (after Stewart and Townsend [22]).

This leads to an equation of the form

$$\frac{\partial F}{\partial t} + W = -2\nu\kappa^2 F \tag{8-7}$$

In the above equation, $W(\kappa, t)$ is connected with the triple correlation function $h(r, t)$ by the following relations:

$$W(\kappa, t) = \frac{2\kappa^2}{3}\,[\kappa^2 H_1''(\kappa) - \kappa H_1'(\kappa)] \tag{8-8}$$

where

$$\begin{aligned} \kappa H_1(\kappa) &= \frac{\underline{u}^3}{\pi} \int_0^\infty h(r) \sin \kappa r dr \\ h(r) &= \int_0^\infty \kappa H_1(\kappa) \sin \kappa r d\kappa \end{aligned} \tag{8-9}$$

It is clear that the quantity $W(\kappa, t)$ in Eq. 8-7 represents the transfer of energy among various frequencies. The above formula for $W(\kappa, t)$ also shows that

$$\int_0^\infty W d\kappa = 0 \tag{8-10}$$

which means that no energy is generated or lost while it is redistributed among various scales. The rate of dissipation is obtained from Eq. 8-7 by integrating it with respect to $\kappa$ from $\kappa = 0$ to $\kappa = \infty$:

$$\epsilon = -\frac{d\underline{u}^2}{dt} = -\int_0^\infty \frac{\partial F}{\partial t} d\kappa = -2\nu \int_0^\infty \kappa^2 F d\kappa \tag{8-11}$$

Exactly as in the case of the correlation theory, one cannot proceed much further with the basic equation (Eq. 8-7) without a more specific knowledge of $W$. However, with the physical interpretation that $W(\kappa, t)$ represents the transfer of energy among various frequencies, it has been found possible to obtain certain plausible formulas connecting $W(\kappa, t)$ with $F(\kappa, t)$ and to make reasonable deductions. (Cf. Art. 17.)

**C,9. Spectral Analysis in One Dimension.** We shall now develop briefly the one-dimensional spectral analysis of a field of turbulence and derive the Fourier transform relations (Eq. 8-1).

In a *homogeneous* (not necessarily isotropic) field of turbulence, let $u(x)$ be the velocity at the point $x$ in the direction of the $x$ axis. It remains finite as $x \to \pm\infty$. This makes its Fourier analysis more difficult than that of a function which vanishes rapidly at infinity. For such a function, $\phi(x)$, we have the pair of Fourier transform relations

$$\begin{aligned} \phi(x) &= \int_{-\infty}^\infty a(\kappa) e^{-i\kappa x} d\kappa \\ a(\kappa) &= \frac{1}{2\pi} \int_{-\infty}^\infty \phi(x) e^{i\kappa x} dx \end{aligned}$$

where $a(-\kappa)$ is equal to the complex conjugate $a^*(\kappa)$ for real $\phi(x)$, and $|a(\kappa)|^2$ is a measure of the energy content associated with the wave number or spatial frequency $\kappa$. However, since the velocity fluctuation $u(x)$ in a homogeneous field of turbulence does not approach zero as $x \to \pm\infty$, we cannot put $u(x)$ in place of $\phi(x)$ in the above relation. Instead we first consider

$$a(\kappa, X) = \frac{1}{2\pi} \int_{-X}^{X} u(x) e^{i\kappa x} dx \tag{9-1}$$

and then try to adopt a suitable limiting process as $X \to \infty$. In fact, we want to consider first the amplitude not *at* $\kappa$ but associated with a *finite range* of values of $\kappa$. We integrate Eq. 9-1 between $\kappa$ and $\kappa + \Delta\kappa$, obtaining

$$\begin{aligned} \Delta A(\kappa, X) &= \int_{\kappa}^{\kappa+\Delta\kappa} a(\kappa, X) d\kappa \\ &= \frac{1}{2\pi} \int_{-X}^{X} \frac{u(x)}{x} e^{i\kappa x} dx [e^{i(\Delta\kappa)x} - 1] \end{aligned}$$

Here, we may take the limit as $X \to \infty$, and obtain

$$\Delta A(\kappa) = \frac{1}{2\pi} \int_{-\infty}^{\infty} \frac{u(x)}{x} e^{i\kappa x} dx [e^{i(\Delta\kappa)x} - 1] \tag{9-2}$$

since the integral is now convergent.

We now form the expression for the measure of energy $\Delta A(\kappa) \cdot \Delta A^*(\kappa)$ and calculate its statistical average. Then

$$\overline{\Delta A(\kappa) \cdot \Delta A^*(\kappa)} = \frac{1}{4\pi^2} \int_{-\infty}^{\infty} \frac{e^{i\kappa x}}{x} [e^{i(\Delta\kappa)x} - 1] dx \int_{-\infty}^{\infty} \frac{e^{-i\kappa x'}}{x'} \overline{u^2} R(x' - x) [e^{-i(\Delta\kappa)x'} - 1] dx'$$

where $R$ is the statistical correlation between $u(x)$ and $u(x')$. The inner integral can be transformed by replacing $x' - x$ by $\xi$. Then it becomes

$$e^{-i\kappa x} \int_{-\infty}^{\infty} \frac{e^{-i\kappa\xi}}{x + \xi} \overline{u^2} R(\xi) [e^{-i(\Delta\kappa)x - i(\Delta\kappa)\xi} - 1] d\xi$$

and we obtain

$$\overline{\Delta A(\kappa) \Delta A^*(\kappa)} = \frac{\overline{u^2}}{4\pi^2} \int_{-\infty}^{\infty} \frac{dx}{x} [e^{i(\Delta\kappa)x} - 1] \int_{-\infty}^{\infty} \frac{e^{-i\kappa\xi}}{x + \xi} R(\xi) d\xi [e^{-i(\Delta\kappa)x - i(\Delta\kappa)\xi} - 1]$$

We shall now divide both sides by $\Delta\kappa$ and replace $(\Delta\kappa)x$ by a new variable $\zeta$. Then we obtain a measure of the "density of energy":

$$\frac{\overline{\Delta A(\kappa) \Delta A^*(\kappa)}}{\Delta\kappa} = \frac{\overline{u^2}}{4\pi^2} \int_{-\infty}^{\infty} \frac{d\zeta}{\zeta} [e^{i\zeta} - 1] \int_{-\infty}^{\infty} \frac{e^{-i\kappa\xi}}{\zeta + \xi(\Delta\kappa)} R(\xi) d\xi [e^{-i\zeta - i\xi(\Delta\kappa)} - 1]$$

It is easy to see that the right-hand side has a limit as $\Delta\kappa \to 0$. We therefore have the interesting situation that $\overline{\Delta A(\kappa) \cdot \Delta A^*(\kappa)}$ is of the order of $\Delta\kappa$ and not of the order of $(\Delta\kappa)^2$. Let the limit be denoted by $F_1(\kappa)/2$. Then

$$\frac{F_1(\kappa)}{2} = \frac{1}{2\pi} \int_{-\infty}^{\infty} R(\xi) e^{-i\kappa\xi} d\xi$$

and

$$\underline{u}^2 R(\xi) = \frac{1}{2} \int_{-\infty}^{\infty} F_1(\kappa) e^{i\kappa\xi} d\kappa$$

It is clear that $F_1(\kappa)$ must be even when $R(\xi)$ is real, and the above equations become the same as Eq. 8-1.

**C,10. Spectral Analysis in Three Dimensions.** The one-dimensional spectrum, however, does not give an exact representation of the distribution of energy among the scales. Consider a simple harmonic variation with wave number $\kappa$ in a direction making an angle $\theta$ with the $x$ axis

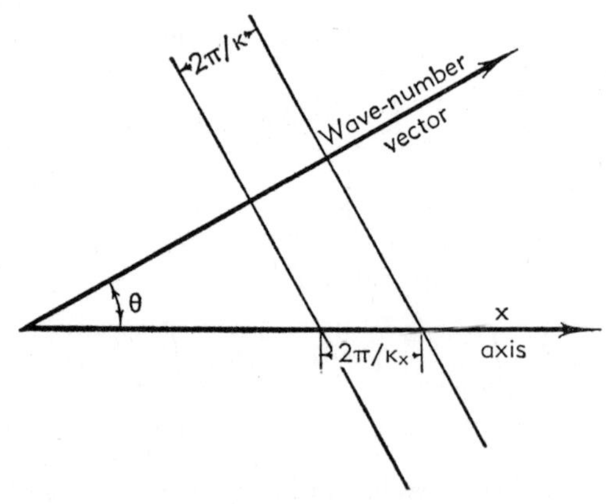


Fig. C,10. Diagram illustrating the relationship between one-dimensional and three-dimensional Fourier analysis of a field of turbulence.

(Fig. C,10). Its period in the $x$ direction would be longer and the wave number in a harmonic analysis in the $x$ direction is

$$\kappa_x = \kappa \cos \theta \tag{10-1}$$

Thus a modified picture is obtained of the energy distribution among the various scales. In the case of isotropic turbulence, as we shall demonstrate below, it is easy to establish the relation between the one-dimensional spectrum $F_1(\kappa)$ and the spectrum function $F(\kappa)$ corresponding to a three-dimensional Fourier analysis. The relation is

$$F_1(\kappa) = \frac{3}{2} \int_{\kappa}^{\infty} \frac{d\kappa'}{\kappa'^3} (\kappa'^2 - \kappa^2) F(\kappa') \tag{10-2}$$

or, upon differentiation,

$$F(\kappa) = \frac{1}{3}[\kappa^2 F_1''(\kappa) - \kappa F_1'(\kappa)] \tag{10-3}$$

Note that $\underline{u}^2 = \int_0^\infty F(\kappa) d\kappa = \int_0^\infty F_1(\kappa) d\kappa$.

The analysis of the $y$ component of the motion in the $x$ direction leads to a spectrum

$$F_2(\kappa) = \frac{3}{4}\int_\kappa^\infty \frac{d\kappa'}{\kappa'^3}(\kappa^2 + \kappa'^2)F(\kappa') \tag{10-4}$$

by combining Eq. 10-2 and 10-4, we obtain, after a little calculation,

$$F(\kappa) = -\frac{2}{3}\kappa\frac{d}{d\kappa}\left[F_2(\kappa) + \frac{1}{2}F_1(\kappa)\right] \tag{10-5}$$

This relation is more convenient for obtaining $F(\kappa)$ from experimental data. It is numerically more accurate than Eq. 10-3 since only one differentiation is involved.

To establish the relations (Eq. 10-2 and 10-4) let us write[8] the three-dimensional Fourier analysis of the velocity in the following form:

$$u_i = \sum A_i(\kappa_j)e^{i(\kappa_n r_n)} \tag{10-6}$$

Then, for a wave in the direction of the vector $\kappa_j$, the equation of continuity gives

$$\kappa_j A_j = 0 \tag{10-7}$$

This means that all the motion associated with the vector wave number $\kappa_j$ must be perpendicular to this vector.

Consider now the contribution to the spectrum of a Fourier analysis in the $x$ direction of a component of turbulent motion with vector wave number $\kappa_j$. In the first place, the motion appears to have a space frequency $\kappa_x$ defined by Eq. 10-1. Secondly, the motion has in general all three components. The $x$ component is (cf. Eq. 10-2 and Fig. C,10).

$$u_1(\kappa_j) = -A(\kappa_j)\cos\phi\sin\theta, \quad A^2 = A_iA_i$$

where $\theta$ is the angle between $\kappa_j$ and the $x$ axis, and $\phi$ is the angle which the velocity vector $A_i$ makes with the plane containing $\kappa_j$ and the $x$ axis. Thus, averaging over the angle $\phi$, we have (cf. Eq. 10-1)

$$|u_1(\kappa_j)|^2 = |A(\kappa_j)|^2\frac{\sin^2\theta}{2} = |A(\kappa_j)|^2\frac{1}{2}\left(1 - \frac{\kappa_1^2}{\kappa^2}\right)$$

Consider now a distribution of energy in the $\kappa$ space. Let the total kinetic energy per unit mass and per unit volume of the $\kappa$ space be $\frac{1}{2}\Phi(\kappa_j)$; i.e. $\frac{1}{2}\Phi(\kappa_j)d\kappa_1 d\kappa_2 d\kappa_3$ is the energy contained in the range $\kappa_i$, $\kappa_i + d\kappa_i$. To obtain the energy per unit mass $\frac{1}{2}F_1(\kappa_1)$ lying between $\kappa_1$, $\kappa_1 + d\kappa_1$ and associated with one component of the motion, one must multiply this expression with the factor $(1 - \kappa_1^2/\kappa^2)/2$ and then integrate for all values of

[8] The reasoning here is essentially that used by Heisenberg [*23*].

$\kappa_2$ and $\kappa_3$ while keeping $\kappa_1$ constant. Thus, the one-dimensional spectrum is

$$F_1(\kappa_1) = \iint\limits_{-\infty}^{\infty} \frac{1}{2}\left(1 - \frac{\kappa_1^2}{\kappa^2}\right) \Phi(\kappa_j) d\kappa_2 d\kappa_3$$

Now, the three-dimensional spectrum is isotropic, so that

$$F(\kappa) = \frac{4\pi\kappa^2}{3}\Phi(\kappa)$$

considering all $\kappa_j$'s with the same magnitude $\kappa$. We have finally

$$F_1(\kappa_1) = F_1(\kappa_1) + F_1(-\kappa_1) = \iint\limits_{-\infty}^{\infty} \left(1 - \frac{\kappa_1^2}{\kappa^2}\right) \frac{3F(\kappa)}{4\pi\kappa^2} d\kappa_2 d\kappa_3$$

This is easily transformed into Eq. 10-2 by carrying out the integration in a polar coordinate system in the plane of $\kappa_2$, $\kappa_3$.

**C,11. General Theory of Homogeneous Anisotropic Turbulence.** The above development of the theory of homogeneous isotropic turbulence can be generalized to remove the restriction of isotropy. Such a generalization is necessary because anisotropy of turbulence, particularly in the largest eddies, does occur in practice. We shall outline here only the main features of the developments and conclusions, pointing out especially the difference between the isotropic and anisotropic cases.

The concept of correlation functions requires very little modification, although it is now obviously impossible to represent the double correlation functions, for example, in terms of a single scalar function. The spectral function must be replaced by a spectral tensor, which may be defined as the three-dimensional Fourier transform of the double correlation tensor. Thus,

$$\Phi_{ik}(\kappa_j) = \frac{1}{8\pi^3} \iiint R_{ik}(r_m) e^{i(\kappa_n r_n)} d\tau(r_m) \tag{11-1}$$

and

$$R_{ij} = \underline{u}^2 \iiint \Phi_{ij}(\kappa_m) e^{-i(\kappa_n r_n)} d\tau(\kappa_m) \tag{11-2}$$

It can be shown that $\Phi_{jj}$ represents the energy density in the wave number space. In the case of isotropic turbulence,

$$F = 4\pi\kappa^2\Phi_{jj} \tag{11-3}$$

Because of the condition of vanishing divergence of the correlation tensor, we obtain

$$\Phi_{ij}\kappa_j = 0 \tag{11-4}$$

and $\Phi_{ij}$ can be expressed in the form

$$\Phi_{ij} = \psi(\kappa_m)(\kappa^2 - \kappa_i\kappa_j) + \chi_i(\kappa_m)\chi_j^*(\kappa_m) \tag{11-5}$$

where $\psi(\kappa_m)$ is a scalar function of the vector $\kappa_m$, $\chi_i(\kappa_m)$ is a vector perpendicular to $\kappa_m$, and $\chi_j^*$ is its complex conjugate. When the turbulence is isotropic, $\chi_j = 0$, and $\psi(\kappa_m)$ is a function of the magnitude $\kappa$ only. The form (Eq. 11-5) is due to Kampé de Fériet [*24*].

The dynamical equations for anisotropic turbulence are more complicated than those for isotropic turbulence, among other things, by the presence of the pressure terms in the equations of the change of double correlations. In the correlation form, the equations are

$$\frac{\partial R_{ik}}{\partial t} = P_{ik} + T_{ik} + 2\nu\Delta R_{ik} \tag{11-6}$$

where

$$P_{ik} = \frac{1}{\rho}\left(\frac{\partial}{\partial r_i}\overline{pu_k'} - \frac{\partial}{\partial r_k}\overline{p'u_i}\right) \tag{11-7}$$

$$T_{ik} = \frac{\partial}{\partial r_p}\left(\overline{u_iu_pu_k'} - \overline{u_iu_p'u_k'}\right) \tag{11-8}$$

In the spectral form, we have

$$\frac{\partial \Phi_{ik}}{\partial t} = \Pi_{ik} + \Theta_{ik} - 2\nu\kappa^2 F_{ik} \tag{11-9}$$

where $\Pi_{ik}$ and $\Theta_{ik}$ are respectively the Fourier transforms of $P_{ik}$ and $T_{ik}$. Obviously $P_{ii} = 0$, so that $\Pi_{ii} = 0$. Thus the pressure fluctuations have no effect on the total energy density $F_{kk}$; their influence produces a redistribution of energy among the various directions. It is not immediately evident whether the net effect is to make the turbulent field more or less isotropic, but general evidence seems to indicate that the former is the case.

The above developments are mostly due to Batchelor [*25*]. Other detailed studies of anisotropic turbulence have been by Batchelor [*26*], Chandrasekhar [*27*], and others. The reader is referred to the original papers.

# *CHAPTER 3. PHYSICAL ASPECTS OF THE THEORY OF HOMOGENEOUS TURBULENCE*

**C,12. Large Scale Structure of Turbulence.** In the following articles, we shall make use of the methods developed above—the correlation and spectral theories—to study the nature of turbulent motion. As pointed out above, the theory by itself allows us to reach only partial results. Some theoretical speculation and assumptions will therefore be introduced in the following discussions for the purpose of reaching definite conclusions. We shall begin by considering the large scale structure of turbulence, which is associated with small values of $\kappa$ in the spectral representation and large values of $r$ in the correlation representation. Let us now consider the second equation in Eq. 8-1,

$$F_1(\kappa) = \frac{2\underline{u}^2}{\pi} \int_0^\infty f(r) \cos (\kappa r) dr \tag{12-1}$$

and expand $\cos (\kappa r)$ into a power series. We obtain

$$F_1(\kappa) = \frac{2\underline{u}^2}{\pi} \left( J_0 - \frac{J_2}{2!} \kappa^2 + \frac{J_4}{4!} \kappa^4 - \cdots \right) \tag{12-2}$$

where

$$J_n = \int_0^\infty f(r) r^n dr \tag{12-3}$$

Such a step is justified only when the function $f(r)$ vanishes sufficiently rapidly at infinity (e.g. as a negative exponential function) so that the integrals $J_n$ are convergent. In that case, one may derive from Eq. 12-2 a power series expansion for the three-dimensional spectrum $F(\kappa)$ by using Eq. 10-3. This gives

$$F(\kappa) = \frac{2\underline{u}^2}{\pi} \left( \frac{J_4}{3} \kappa^4 - \cdots \right) \tag{12-4}$$

Similarly, assuming that $h(r)$ also vanishes sufficiently rapidly at infinity, one can show that the transfer function $W(\kappa, t)$ behaves as $\kappa^6$ for small values of $\kappa$. The spectral equation (Eq. 8-7) then shows that

$$\frac{d}{dt} (\underline{u}^2 J_4) = \frac{d}{dt} \left[ \underline{u}^2 \int_0^\infty f(r) r^4 dr \right] = 0 \tag{12-5}$$

It then follows that

$$\underline{u}^2 \int_0^\infty f(r) r^4 dr = J, \text{ a constant} \tag{12-6}$$

Thus, the large scale motions are permanent in the sense that the principal part of $F(\kappa)$ for small values of $\kappa$ remains unchanged.

The above derivation (including explicit statements of the necessary convergence assumptions) was given by Lin [*28*] for the spectral interpretation of the parameter $J$, which was first obtained by Loitsiansky [*29*] from the Kármán-Howarth equation. Indeed, if one multiplies that equation by $r^4$ and then integrates it with respect to $r$ from zero to infinity, one obtains

$$\frac{d}{dt} \left[ \underline{u}^2 \int_0^\infty f(r) r^4 dr \right] = 2\underline{u}^3 \lim_{r \to \infty} (r^4 h) \tag{12-7}$$

provided the integral involved is convergent. If, in addition, $h(r, t)$ vanishes sufficiently rapidly at infinity so that

$$\lim_{r \to \infty} r^4 h = 0 \tag{12-8}$$

the relation (Eq. 12-5) is obtained.

It must be noted that there is no a priori reason[9] for the convergence of the integrals (Eq. 12-3) and the validity of Eq. 12-8. As a matter of fact, recent investigations of Batchelor and Proudman [*31*] show that even if $f(r)$ is exponentially small at infinity at an initial instant, because of the influence of the long range pressure forces, one can only be sure that it will be no larger than $0(r^{-6})$ when $r$ is large, although the possibility of an exponentially small behavior is by no means excluded. We are therefore only assured of the leading term in Eq. 12-4 and the existence of the Loitsiansky *parameter*,

$$J = \underline{u}^2 \int_0^\infty f(r) r^4 dr \tag{12-9}$$

However, the constancy of $J$ depends on the relation (Eq. 12-8), which is shown to be not generally true by the analysis of Batchelor and Proudman. On the other hand, for low Reynolds numbers based on the turbulence level $\underline{u}$, the term on the right-hand side of Eq. 12-7 becomes negligible, and the Loitsiansky parameter is indeed approximately constant. (Cf. Art. 14 and 15 for the part dealing with the final period of decay.)

From a physical point of view, any prediction of the behavior of the largest eddies must be regarded with some reserve, since it is expected to be dependent on the experimental apparatus. If the general scale of turbulence is much smaller than the dimensions of the experimental apparatus, it would appear that this complication may be avoided by a proper interpretation of the above results. The integrals (Eq. 12-3) may, for example, be considered as extending over a distance much larger than the scale of turbulence but still much smaller than the scale of the apparatus.

Generalization of the above discussions to the anisotropic case has been made by Batchelor [*25*]. The earlier conclusions are again modified by the work of Batchelor and Proudman [*31*]. In fact, in the anisotropic case, the correlation tensor $R_{ij}$ is shown to be in general of the order of $r^{-5}$, so that even the existence of a Loitsiansky parameter is in doubt.

**C,13. Small Scale Structure of Turbulence. Kolmogoroff's Theory.** We now turn to consider the small scale structure of turbulence. Here the formal relations analogous to Eq. 12-1, 12-2, 12-3, and 12-4 are obtained by expanding cos ($\kappa r$) into a power series in the first equation in Eq. 8-1:

$$\underline{u}^2 f(r) = \int_0^\infty F_1(\kappa) \cos(\kappa r) d\kappa \tag{13-1}$$

[9] Cf. Birkhoff [*30*].

We then obtain a power series for $f(r)$ in the form

$$f(r) = 1 + \frac{f''(0)}{2!} r^2 + \frac{f^{iv}(0)}{4!} r^4 + \cdots \tag{13-2}$$

with

$$(-1)^n \underline{u}^2 f^{(2n)}(0) = I_{2n} = \int_0^\infty \kappa^{2n} F_1(\kappa) d\kappa, \qquad n = 0, 1, \ldots \tag{13-3}$$

In terms of the three-dimensional spectrum, these integrals become

$$I_{2n} = \frac{3}{(2n+1)(2n+3)} \int_0^\infty \kappa^{2n} F(\kappa) d\kappa \tag{13-4}$$

Here it is useful to recall that $I_0$ is proportional to the energy, and that $I_2$ is proportional to the rate of energy dissipation.

Consider now the dynamical relations in the correlation theory. We expand both $f(r, t)$ and $h(r, t)$ in power series of $r$,

$$\begin{aligned} f(r, t) &= 1 + \frac{f''(0)}{2!} r^2 + \frac{f^{iv}(0)}{4!} r^4 + \cdots \\ h(r, t) &= \frac{h'''(0)}{3!} r^3 + \cdots \end{aligned} \tag{13-5}$$

and substitute them into the Kármán-Howarth equation (Eq. 7-4). As observed before (Art. 7) the terms independent of $r$ give the energy relation. The terms in $r^2$ give the vorticity equation in the form

$$\frac{d\omega^2}{dt} - 70 h_0''' \underline{u}^2 = -10 \frac{\omega^2}{\lambda_\omega^2} \tag{13-6}$$

or

$$\frac{d\omega^2}{dt} - \overline{2\omega_i \omega_k \frac{\partial u_i}{\partial x_k}} = -10 \frac{\omega^2}{\lambda_\omega^2} \tag{13-7}$$

where $\omega_i$ is the vorticity vector, $\omega^2$ is the mean square value of one component of the vorticity, and $\lambda_\omega^2$ is defined by

$$\frac{1}{\lambda_\omega^2} = \frac{7}{15} \lambda^2 f_0^{iv}, \qquad f_0^{iv} = \left(\frac{\partial^4 f}{\partial r^4}\right)_{r=0} \tag{13-8}$$

The second term on the left side of Eq. 13-7 represents the change of vorticity due to stretching or contraction of the vortex tube without the action of viscosity. It is well known that, in a perfect fluid, the circulation around a vortex tube is permanent and hence the vorticity increases at a rate in proportion to its rate of stretching. The right-hand side represents the dissipation of viscosity by viscous forces.

Taylor [*32*] suggested that this relation represents one of the basic mechanisms in the process of turbulent motion. The rotation of the fluid is being slowed down by the effect of viscosity. This loss is partly compensated, or even over-compensated, by the stretching of the vortex tubes, due to the diffusive nature of turbulent motion. (Hence one may expect more stretching of the vortex tubes than compression.) Taylor calculated the relative magnitudes of the various quantities by determining $f_0''$ and $f_0^{iv}$, and he found that all the three terms in Eq. 13-6 are of the same order of magnitude for his experiments. Such measurements were more accurately made later by Batchelor and Townsend [*33*] and by Stewart [*11*].

As noted before (Art. 8), in many experiments the dissipation of energy is practically all associated with the high frequency components which contain a negligible amount of energy. Combining this fact with the mechanism of vortex-stretching just discussed, one can form a reasonable picture of the process of turbulent motion. There are the large energy-containing eddies which contribute very little to the viscous dissipation directly. By their own diffusive motion, small eddies are formed, i.e. the kinetic energy of turbulent motion goes down to smaller scales. It is at these small scales that viscous forces become most effective and the predominant part of the energy dissipation occurs. Thus one forms the picture of an energy reservoir in the large eddies, and a dissipation process in the small eddies which may be presumed to depend very little on the structure of the large eddies except to the extent of the amount of energy supplied to them. This forms the physical basis of Kolmogoroff's theory of locally isotropic turbulence [*34*].

Before we go on with the discussion of his theory, it should be emphasized that the picture is correct only when the diffusive mechanism is strong; i.e. when the inertial forces are large compared with the viscous forces. In other words, the Reynolds number of the turbulent motion must be relatively large. This is well illustrated by the detailed calculations made by Taylor and Green [*35*] on a model of isotropic turbulence.[10] Indeed, they found that for very low Reynolds numbers of turbulence, defined by

$$R_\lambda = \frac{u\lambda}{\nu}$$

the stretching mechanism is not strong enough, so that the magnitude of the vorticity decreases steadily. On the other hand, if the motion starts out at a fairly high $R_\lambda$, the mean square vorticity (and hence also the rate of energy dissipation) first increases to several times its original value due to the stretching mechanism. The kinetic energy of the motion, however, decreases steadily. Eventually, it becomes very low, and the stretching process is so weakened that the vorticity of the motion also decreases steadily.

*Kolmogoroff's theory.* In line with the above ideas, Kolmogoroff postulates that, at large Reynolds numbers of turbulent motion, the *local*

[10] See also Goldstein [*36*].

property of turbulent motion should have a universal character described by the following concepts. First, it is locally isotropic whether the large scale motions are isotropic or not.[11] Second, the motion at the very small scales is chiefly governed by the viscous forces and the amount of energy which is handed down to them from the larger eddies. The large eddies tend to break down into smaller eddies due to inertial forces. These in turn break down into still smaller eddies, and so on. At the same time, viscous forces dissipate these eddies at very small scales into heat. In the long series of processes of reaching the smallest eddies, the turbulent motion adjusts itself to some definite state. The further down the scale, the less is the motion dependent on the large eddies.

Furthermore, in line with Taylor's experimental findings, Kolmogoroff essentially postulates that practically *all* the dissipation of energy occurs at the smallest scales when the Reynolds number of turbulent motion is sufficiently high.

To formulate these concepts mathematically, he introduced the correlation functions of the type

$$\overline{(u - u')^2} = \underline{u}^2[1 - f(r)]$$

which is the mean square value of the *relative* velocity of turbulent motion. The introduction of the relative velocity stresses the *local* nature. The moments $\overline{(u - u')^n}$ would then be emphasized instead of the usual correlations at two points. (In fact, the third moment $\overline{(u - u')^3}$ is proportional to $k(r)$.)

The second step in the formulation of the theory is to introduce the assumption that, for small values of $r$, these correlation functions depend only on the kinematic viscosity $\nu$ and the total rate of energy dissipation $\epsilon$. This is in accordance with the previously discussed physical concepts. One can then make some dimensional analysis and construct universal characteristic velocity and length for motion at very small scales. Indeed, from $\epsilon$ and $\nu$, one can only construct the length scale

$$\eta = \left(\frac{\nu^3}{\epsilon}\right)^{\frac{1}{4}} \tag{13-9}$$

and the velocity scale

$$v = (\nu\epsilon)^{\frac{1}{4}} \tag{13-10}$$

We may then write

$$\overline{(u' - u)^2} = (\nu\epsilon)^{\frac{1}{2}}\beta_{dd}\left(\frac{r}{\eta}\right) \tag{13-11}$$

$$\overline{(u' - u)^3} = (\nu\epsilon)^{\frac{3}{4}}\beta_{ddd}\left(\frac{r}{\eta}\right) \tag{13-12}$$

where $\beta_{dd}$ and $\beta_{ddd}$ are *universal* functions for small values of $r$.

[11] See Sec. B on shear flows for the experimental confirmation of this fact.

For very high Reynolds numbers, Kolmogoroff visualizes that, at the larger end of the universal range, there is a range of $r$ for which the viscosity coefficient does not play an explicit role. This range may be conveniently referred to as an *inertial* subrange. The above relation then implies that

$$\overline{(u' - u)^2} \sim (\epsilon r)^{\frac{2}{3}} \tag{13-13}$$

A definite form of the correlation function is thereby obtained.

The concept of Kolmogoroff can also be introduced into the spectral formulation. Thus, at high Reynolds numbers the spectrum $F(\kappa)$ at very high frequencies can be expressed as

$$F(\kappa) = v^2 \eta f(\kappa\eta) \tag{13-14}$$

where the function $f(x)$ has a universal form for large values of $x$.

For the inertial subrange, the spectral function can again be determined completely from dimensional arguments. This gives

$$F(\kappa) \sim \epsilon^{\frac{2}{3}} \kappa^{-\frac{5}{3}} \tag{13-15}$$

This form was first given by Obukhoff [*37*]. It has received some experimental support at high Reynolds numbers.[12] With a spectrum of this form, it can be explicitly demonstrated that the dissipation of energy lies essentially in the universal range of Kolmogoroff (cf. [*39*]).

The actual form of the spectrum in the universal range is obviously of basic theoretical interest. By following the general ideas discussed in this section, Townsend [*38*] developed a more concrete model giving a definite form for the spectrum of the small eddies. The results are in general agreement with experimental observations.

The scales $\eta$ and $v$ defined above also occur in the study of the small scale structure even when the Reynolds number is not high. This cannot be interpreted on the basis of Kolmogoroff's theory, but follows from considerations of self-preservation during the process of decay (see next article).

**C,14. Considerations of Similarity.** As noted above, the general theory of turbulent motion, as developed in Chap. 2, cannot lead to specific predictions without auxiliary considerations. For this reason, von Kármán and Howarth [*17*] introduced the idea of self-preservation of correlation functions.[13] In terms of the spectral language, this states that the spectrum remains similar in the course of time. Since the energy distribution among the various frequencies is changing through the transfer mechanism, this may be reasonably expected provided that there is enough time for the necessary adjustments. In this article, we shall con-

[12] Cf. [*99*] and [*101*] for detailed discussions. A different form of the spectrum has been recently obtained by Kraichnan [*100*].

[13] This article follows closely the treatment of von Kármán and Lin [*39*, p. 1].

sider the theoretical aspects. Comparison with experiments will be made in the next article.

Let us consider the equation (Eq. 8-7) for the change of spectrum

$$\frac{\partial F}{\partial t} + W = -2\nu\kappa^2 F$$

and try to find a similarity solution. If $V$ is a characteristic velocity, and $l$ is a characteristic length, then, from dimensional arguments,

$$F = V^2 l\psi(\xi), \quad W = V^3 w(\xi), \quad \xi = \kappa l \tag{14-1}$$

Thus, the above equation becomes

$$\frac{1}{V}\frac{dl}{dt}[\xi\psi'(\xi) + \psi(\xi)] + \frac{2l}{V^2}\frac{dV}{dt}\psi(\xi) + w(\xi) = -\frac{2\nu}{Vl}\xi^2\psi(\xi) \tag{14-2}$$

If the similarity solution is to be valid, one must have

$$\frac{1}{V}\frac{dl}{dt} = a_1 \tag{14-3}$$

$$\frac{2l}{V^2}\frac{dV}{dt} = a_2 \tag{14-4}$$

$$\frac{\nu}{Vl} = a_3 \tag{14-5}$$

where $a_1$, $a_2$, and $a_3$ are all constants. Eq. 14-2 becomes

$$a_1\xi\psi'(\xi) + (a_1 + a_2)\psi(\xi) + 2a_3\xi^2\psi(\xi) + w(\xi) = 0 \tag{14-6}$$

Besides Eq. 14-3, 14-4, and 14-5, it is evident that the mean square value $\underline{u}^2$ and the rate of energy dissipation have to satisfy the relations (cf. Eq. 8-6 and 8-11)

$$\underline{u}^2 = V^2 \int_0^\infty \psi(\xi)d\xi \tag{14-7}$$

$$-\frac{d\underline{u}^2}{dt} = 2\nu\frac{V^2}{l^2}\int_0^\infty \xi^2\psi(\xi)d\xi \tag{14-8}$$

Finally, if the convergence criteria for Loitsiansky's relation (Eq. 12-6) are assumed to be valid, we have

$$V^2\xi^5 \lim_{\xi\to 0}\frac{\psi(\xi)}{\xi^4} = J \tag{14-9}$$

This system of equations presumes that the transfer term in Eq. 14-2 is considered generally of equal importance with the term expressing the viscous dissipation. It has been shown by Dryden [*40*] in the equivalent problem of self-preserving correlation functions that such a solution is connected with the statement that the square of the characteristic length is proportional to the time $t$ and the law of decay is expressed by $\underline{u}^2 \sim t^{-1}$.

Heisenberg [*41*] indicated an equivalent solution for the spectral problem. It is easily seen that these solutions are at variance with Eq. 14-9. In other words, full similarity is only possible when we reject Loitsiansky's theorem. In addition, experimental evidence clearly indicates that the law of decay and the behavior of the characteristic length during decay exclude the possibility of adopting full similarity as a generally valid assumption for *all* decay processes.

Let us now consider two opposite approaches. In the first approach, we assume that Loitsiansky's invariant exists and that it plays a role in the similarity of the spectrum. In the second approach, we assume that similarity of the spectrum is occurring only in the eddies contributing appreciably to the dissipation process, and that the largest eddies play no role in determining the similarity of the spectrum. Clearly, the first approach will not yield valid results unless Loitsiansky's invariant does exist. This is definitely known only in the decay of *isotropic* turbulence at very low Reynolds numbers (case (a) below). The second approach is naturally independent of Loitsiansky's invariant.

Let us consider now two opposite specific cases in the first approach: (a) the transfer term is negligible for all frequencies, and (b) the influence of viscous dissipation is restricted to high frequencies whereas for low frequencies the transfer term is the prevailing factor.

*Case (a)*, $w(\xi) = 0$, leads to a solution of Eq. 8-7 which has full similarity for all frequencies and also satisfies Loitsiansky's relation. One obtains with $\xi = \kappa l$ and $l = \sqrt{\nu t}$

$$F = \text{const } V^2 l \xi^4 e^{-2\xi^2} \tag{14-10}$$

or

$$F = \text{const } V^2 l^5 \kappa^4 e^{-2\kappa^2 \nu t} \tag{14-11}$$

By using the definition of $J$ in Eq. 14-9, we write

$$F = J\kappa^4 e^{-2\nu\kappa^2 t} \tag{14-12}$$

The corresponding correlation function can be easily shown to be

$$f(r, t) = e^{-r^2/8\nu t} \tag{14-13}$$

by using Eq. 8-1 and 10-3. This correlation function was noted by von Kármán and Howarth [*17*], and discussed by Millionshchikov [*42*], Loitsiansky [*29*], and Batchelor and Townsend [*43*]. Kármán and Howarth also obtained a more general self-preserving solution in terms of the Whittaker function, with a spectral form $F = C\kappa^n e^{-2\nu\kappa^2 t}$. It can be easily shown that the solution must specialize into Eq. 14-13 if the Loitsiansky invariant is to be finite. The law of decay in this case is the five-fourths power law:

$$\underline{u}^2 \sim (t - t_0)^{-\frac{5}{4}}, \qquad \lambda^2 = 4\nu(t - t_0) \tag{14-14}$$

This law of decay and the corresponding correlation function have been verified experimentally by Batchelor and Townsend for the final stage of decay (see Art. 15 for further details).

*Case* (*b*) has also been treated in the theory of self-preserving correlations by von Kármán and Howarth [*17*] and later by Kolmogoroff [*44*]. The former authors came to the conclusion that any power law for the decay-time relation may prevail in the decay process. Kolmogoroff pointed out that if one assumes the validity of Loitsiansky's theorem the relations

$$\underline{u}^2 = \text{const}\, t^{-10/7} \quad \text{and} \quad \lambda^2 = 7\nu t \tag{14-15}$$

must apply.[14] Von Kármán [*45,46*] dealt with the corresponding spectral problem in two communications assuming the specific decay law (Eq. 14-15). It should be reiterated, however, that this first approach, especially in case (b), can only be regarded as tentative because of the uncertainty in the constancy of the Loitsiansky integral.

Consider now the second approach. Clearly, the idea of complete similarity, with the rejection of Loitsiansky's relation, belongs to this case. However, there are physical and mathematical reasons for believing that the large eddies do not play a significant role in the determination of the similarity characteristics in the smaller eddies. We therefore consider cases where the similarity requirement is relaxed for an increasing range of frequencies at the end of largest eddies.

*Case* (*c*). We first consider the assumption that similarity extends over the whole frequency range, with the exception of the lowest. More specifically, we assume that the deviation from similarity shall occur for such small values of $\kappa$ that, whereas the contribution of the deviation is negligible for computation of $\epsilon$ (Eq. 8-11), it enters in the calculation of energy (Eq. 8-6).

It is easy to see the corresponding assumption in the correlation formulation by using Eq. 13-2 and 13-4 in the following form:

$$\underline{u}^2[1 - f(r)] = -\sum_{n=1}^{\infty} \frac{(-r^2)^n}{(2n+1)(2n+3)} \frac{1}{(2n)!} \int_0^{\infty} F(\kappa)\kappa^{2n} d\kappa \tag{14-16}$$

The above assumptions imply that all the higher moments of $F(\kappa)$ are not appreciably influenced by the deviation from similarity. Hence, they are all proportional to $V^2 l^{-2n}$. Similarity is therefore assumed for $u^2[1 - f(r)]$.

This form of the similarity hypothesis was introduced by Lin [*48*]. Assuming the self-preservation of

$$\overline{(u - u')^2} = \underline{u}^2[1 - f(r)]$$

and

$$\overline{(u - u')^3} = 12\underline{u}^3 h(r)$$

[14] See Frenkiel [*47*] for some discussion of the comparison of Eq. 14-15 with some experiments.

he derived the law of decay

$$\underline{u^2} = a(t - t_0)^{-1} + b \tag{14-17}$$

where $a$ and $b$ are constants, with $a > 0$. This law can be easily obtained from the general relations (Eq. 14-3, 14-4, 14-5, and 14-8), which are valid for any similarity hypothesis. One obtains the positive and negative half-power laws for the change of the characteristic length and the characteristic velocity $V$, and the inverse square law for the rate of dissipation $\epsilon$. To be more specific, one finds that $l$ and $V$ may be identified with Kolmogoroff's characteristic quantities (cf. Eq. 13-9 and 13-10)

$$\eta = \left(\frac{\nu^3}{\epsilon}\right)^{\frac{1}{4}} \quad \text{and} \quad v = (\nu\epsilon)^{\frac{1}{4}} \tag{14-18}$$

It can easily be seen by introducing these relations into Eq. 14-3, 14-4, and 14-5 that the law of decay is of the form of Eq. 14-17.

It is convenient to rewrite the results as follows, with definite physical interpretations attached to the constants. The law of decay is given by

$$\epsilon = \left(\frac{D_0}{10}\right)t^{-2}, \quad \underline{u^2} = \left(\frac{D_0}{10}\right)t^{-1} - u_D^2, \quad \text{or } \lambda^2 = 10\nu t\left(1 - \frac{10u_D^2}{D_0}\,t\right) \tag{14-19}$$

where $u_D^2$ is the additive constant giving the departure of the energy content from that in the case of similarity, and $D_0$ is the initial diffusion coefficient

$$D_0 = \lim_{t\to 0} \frac{\underline{u^2}\lambda^2}{\nu} \tag{14-20}$$

defined according to a formula of the kind suggested earlier by von Kármán [*13*]. The changes with time of the characteristic velocity and scale, and of the Reynolds number of turbulence are given by

$$v^2 = (10)^{-\frac{1}{2}}R_{\lambda 0}\nu t^{-1}, \quad \eta^2 = (10)^{\frac{1}{2}}R_{\lambda 0}^{-1}\nu t, \quad R_\lambda = R_{\lambda 0}\left(1 - \frac{10u_D^2}{D_0}\,t\right) \tag{14-21}$$

where $R_{\lambda 0}$ is the initial Reynolds number of turbulence

$$R_{\lambda 0} = \lim_{t\to 0} \frac{u\lambda}{\nu} \tag{14-22}$$

It is evident from Eq. 14-19 and 14-21 that the solutions obtained can only be applied to an early stage of the decay process, in which $10u_D^2t/D_0$ remains small.

*Case* (*d*). The above assumption is based on the idea that the low frequency components do not have the time to adjust themselves to an equilibrium state. (An investigation of such a concept was made by Lin, and will be briefly presented in Art. 17.) It is specifically assumed that $\epsilon$ may be calculated by a similarity spectrum. Goldstein [*49*] further relaxed the requirement and assumed that the similarity spectrum might be adequate only for the calculation of higher moments of $F(\kappa)$. If the similarity spectrum is accurate only for the calculation of $\int_0^\infty \kappa^4 F(\kappa)d\kappa$ and higher moments, Goldstein shows that the law of decay becomes

$$\underline{u}^2(t - t_0) = a + b(t - t_0) + c(t - t_0)^2 \qquad (14\text{-}23)$$

This includes one more constant than Eq. 14-17. Further generalization involving higher powers of $t - t_0$ is immediate.

Comparison of the laws of decay with experiments will be made in the next article.

**C,15. The Process of Decay.** We shall now examine the whole process of decay and compare the above theoretical laws with experiments, whenever such evidence is available.

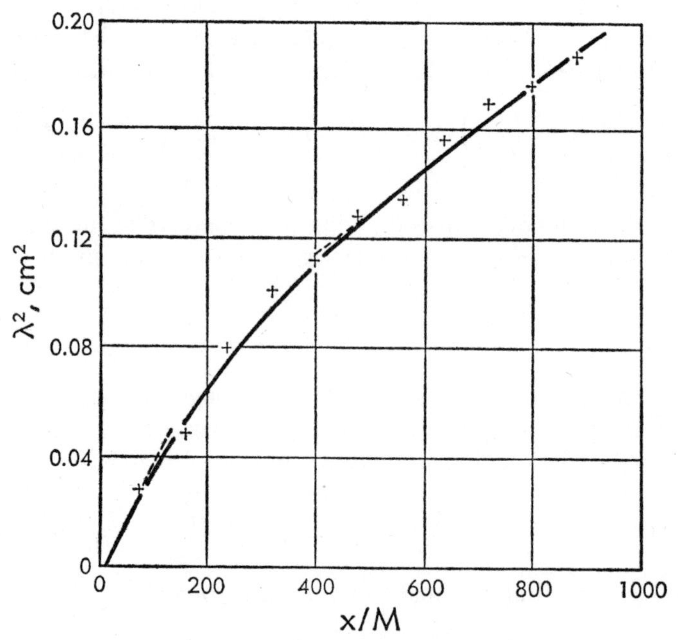


Fig. C,15a. Change of vorticity scale during a decay process at low Reynolds numbers.

For small Reynolds numbers of turbulence, the nonviscous range cannot be expected to occur. The process of decay may be described by adopting the law (Eq. 14-17) for the first part of the decay process and the law (Eq. 14-14) for the last part. This is shown by the experimental results[15] of Batchelor and Townsend (Fig. C,15a). The slope of the curve ($\lambda^2$, $\nu t$) begins with a value 10 and ends with a value 4.

[15] The experimental agreement in this case should be accepted with some reservation, since so little data are available. See [30,31] for detailed discussions.

For large initial Reynolds numbers of turbulence, von Kármán and Lin [*39*] made a tentative proposal to divide the process of decay into three stages: (1) the early stage in which the law (Eq. 14-17) holds, (2) the intermediate stage, in which the law (Eq. 14-15) holds, and (3) the final stage in which the Reynolds number is very low and the law (Eq. 14-14) holds. For estimates of the length of the three periods, we refer to the original article. Here it suffices to say that there is as yet no experimental result available to check the theory for the intermediate stage, and that the recent doubt cast on Loitsiansky's invariant tends to change the basis for such an assumption.

Detailed discussions will therefore be given only for the early and the final stages.

*Final period of decay.* When the Reynolds number of the turbulent motion is very low, as it must eventually happen in the final period of decay of a homogeneous field of turbulence, without external supply of energy, the inertial forces are negligible and only the viscous forces are effective. Case (a) discussed in Art. 14 then applies. On the other hand, the problem now admits of an explicit solution. In fact, if the quadratic terms are neglected from the equations of Navier-Stokes, we have

$$\frac{\partial u_i}{\partial t} = -\frac{1}{\rho}\frac{\partial p}{\partial x_i} + \nu \Delta u_i \tag{15-1}$$

By the equation of continuity, this leads to

$$\Delta p = 0$$

Now the only solution of a Laplace equation which is finite throughout the whole space is a constant. Thus the pressure must be independent of position, and the equation for $u_i$ becomes the equation for heat conduction[16]

$$\frac{\partial u_i}{\partial t} = \nu \Delta u_i \tag{15-2}$$

The solution of the initial value problem of this equation is well known to be

$$u_i(x, y, z, t) = \frac{1}{(4\pi\nu t)^{\frac{3}{2}}} \int_{-\infty}^{\infty}\int_{-\infty}^{\infty}\int_{-\infty}^{\infty} u_i(X, Y, Z, 0)$$
$$\exp\left[-\frac{(x-X)^2 + (y-Y)^2 + (z-Z)^2}{4\nu t}\right] dXdYdZ \tag{15-3}$$

From this, the properties of the motion can be explicitly calculated. In

[16] Reissner [*50*] was the first to attack the problem of turbulence by using the explicit solution of Eq. 15-2. He obtained results analogous to the observed laws of decay. They are, however, more adequate for the discussion of temperature fluctuations, and will be taken up again in that connection. The following development is due to Batchelor [*51*].

particular, it is found that the correlation function is

$$R(\xi, \eta, \zeta, t) = \frac{1}{(8\pi\nu t)^{\frac{3}{2}}} \iiint_{-\infty}^{\infty} R(a, b, c, 0)$$

$$\exp\left[ -\frac{(\xi - a)^2 + (\eta - b^2) + (\zeta - c)^2}{8\nu t} \right] dadbdc \quad (15\text{-}4)$$

This last formula can be used to evaluate the asymptotic behavior of the correlation function for large values of $t$.

A simpler approach to the problem is to use the spectral tensor. In fact, Eq. 15-2 shows that the pressure terms $P_{ik}$ must be dropped when the nonlinear effect represented by $T_{ik}$ is negligible in the spectral equation (Eq. 11-6), which becomes simply

$$\frac{\partial F_{ij}}{\partial t} = -2\nu\kappa^2 F_{ij} \quad (15\text{-}5)$$

The general solution of this equation is

$$F_{ij}(\kappa_m, t) = F_{ij}(\kappa_m, t_0)e^{-2\nu\kappa^2(t-t_0)} \quad (15\text{-}6)$$

From this, we may calculate the correlation tensor by a Fourier transformation. For large values of $t - t_0$, only small values of $\kappa$ are important. Thus one may try to expand $F_{ik}$ in powers of $\kappa_m$ and retain only the lowest terms.

Following this method, Batchelor and Proudman [*31*] found that the longitudinal correlation coefficient $f(r, t)$ is of the form (Eq. 14-13) for isotropic turbulence and certain very special cases of anisotropic turbulence. Previous to this investigation, Batchelor and Townsend [*43*] compared the experimental curve for $f(r, t)$ with the Gaussian curve (Eq. 14-13) and found good agreement. At that time, this agreement was explained by assuming $F_{ij}(\kappa_m, t)$ to be essentially expandible as a Taylor series in $\kappa_m$. Since this assumption is now found to be not true in general, other tentative explanations are suggested by Batchelor and Proudman [*31*]. A critical examination of this problem is clearly warranted.

*Early period of decay.* Much experimental information is available during the early part of the decay process. Recently, Stewart and Townsend [*22*] summarized their results and compared them with some of the above self-preserving hypotheses. They cautioned against the assumption of complete self-preservation, but did not include case (c) in their discussion, which seems to fit all their experimental findings.

In Fig. C,15b, the law of decay observed by Stewart and Townsend [*22*] is presented. Although the variation of $\lambda^2$ and $\underline{u}^{-2}$ both follow the linear law, as they would in the case of complete similarity, the *origin of time* (or $x$ axis) *must be taken differently* for the two straight lines. It can easily be seen that the Reynolds number of turbulence $R_\lambda$ steadily *decreases* in the case shown in the figure, contrary to the law of decay for complete similarity. The earlier experiments of Batchelor and Townsend [*33*] also show a definite trend for the decrease of $R_\lambda$. It should be noted that the curves for $\lambda^2$ and $\underline{u}^{-2}$ versus time both have fairly large slopes, and it is therefore more difficult to detect any slight deviation

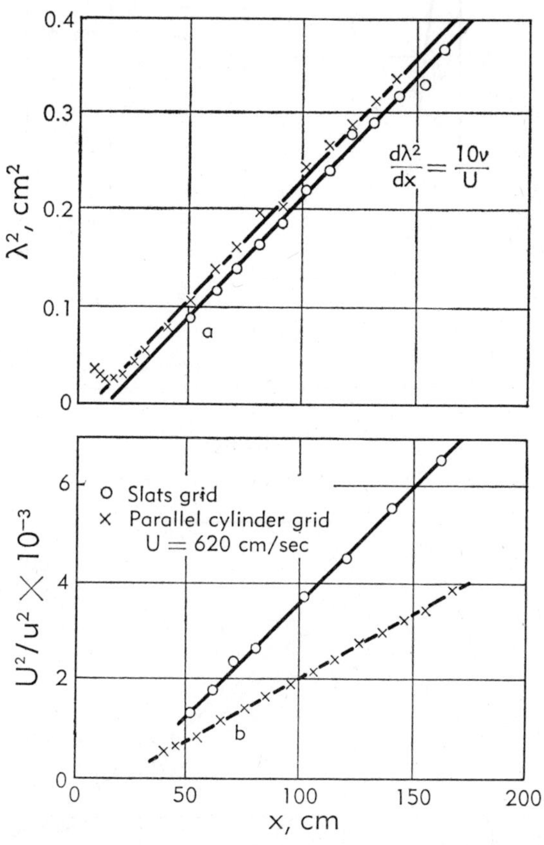


Fig. C,15b. Decay of turbulence behind grids of differing shapes. (After Stewart and Townsend [*22*].)

from a straight line. On the other hand, $R_\lambda$ should remain constant according to the assumption of complete similarity and is more sensitive for detecting the departure from such laws. The comparison of the intercepts of the straight lines in Fig. C,15b is also a very sensitive method for detecting the same effect. On the basis of the discussions of case (c) of Art. 14, it may be expected that $R_\lambda$ should decrease linearly in $t$, if $u_D^2 > 0$, i.e. if the energy in the large eddies is smaller than that corresponding to full similarity. The observed decrease of $R_\lambda$ indicates that this is indeed the case.

A more definite verification of case (c) is provided by their measurement of the spectrum, which is reproduced in Fig. C,15c and C,15d. Fig. C,15c gives the one-dimensional spectrum $F_1(\kappa)$ which shows a large departure from similarity at low values of $\kappa$. Fig. C,15d shows that, for

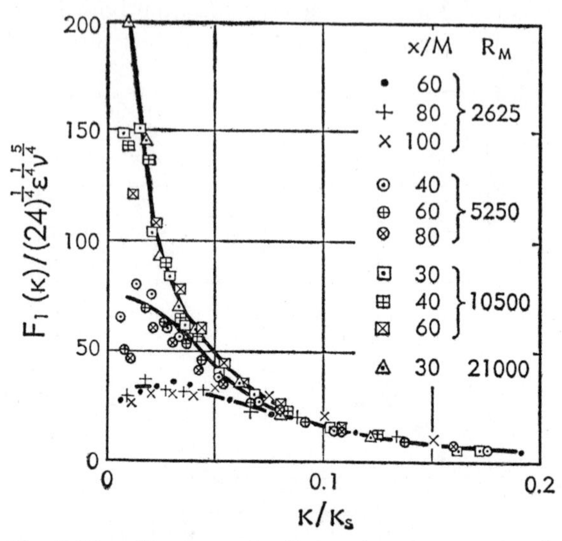


Fig. C,15c. Spectrum of $u$ fluctuations $[\kappa_s = (3\epsilon/2\nu^3)^{\frac{1}{4}}]$.

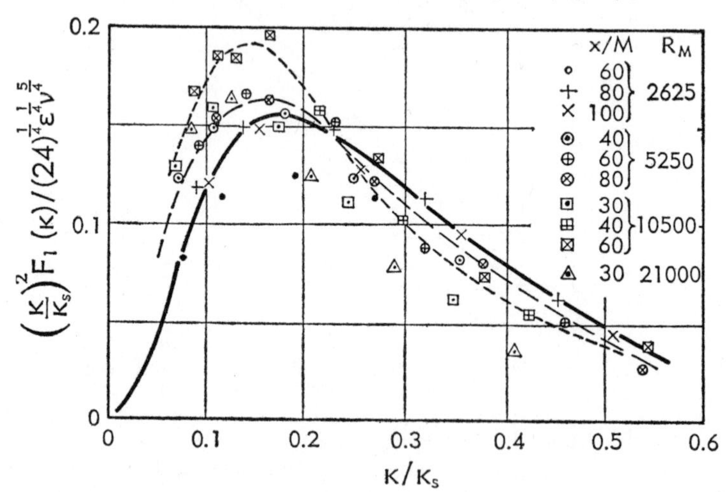


Fig. C,15d. Spectrum of $\partial u/\partial t$ fluctuations.

each experiment, all the points for $\kappa^2F_1(\kappa)$ fall on a single curve. Similar results are obtained for $\kappa^4F_1(\kappa)$ and $\kappa^6F_1(\kappa)$ by Stewart and Townsend [*22*]. Thus, all the moments

$$\int_0^\infty \kappa^{2n}F_1(\kappa)d\kappa, \qquad n \geqq 1$$

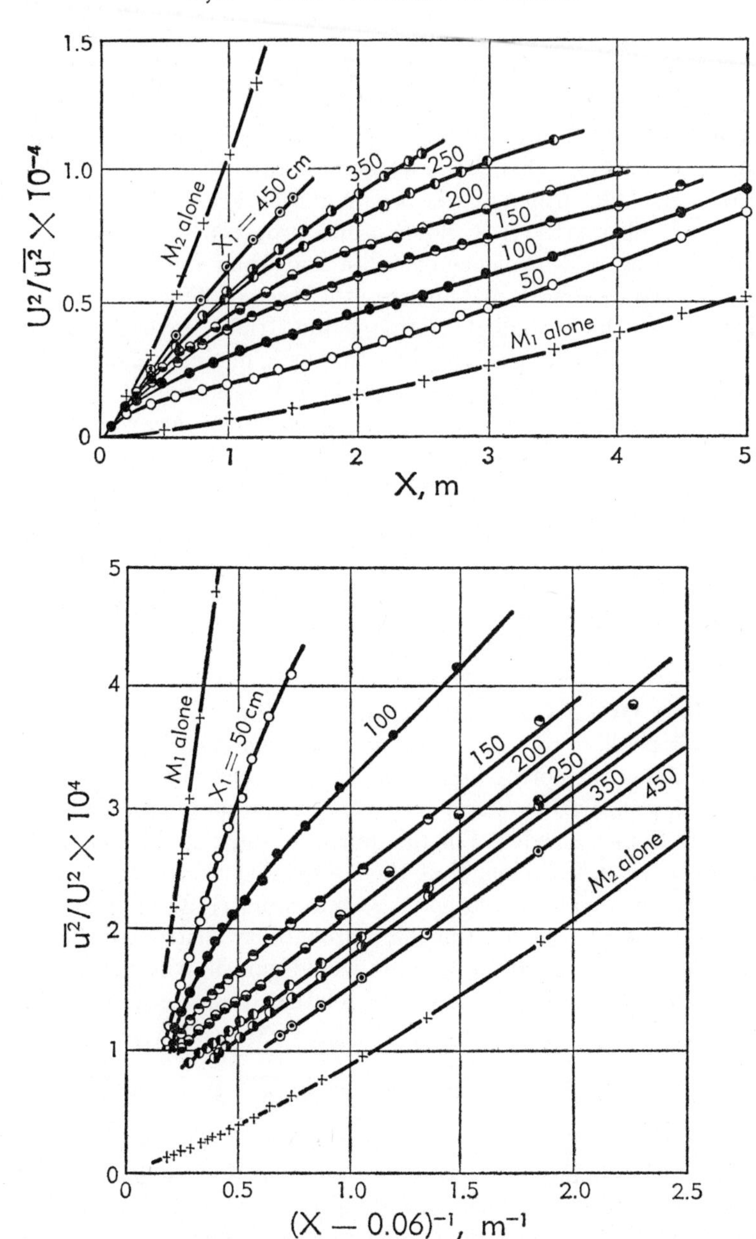


Fig. C,15e. Top, decay of turbulence behind two grids $M_1$ and $M_2$ with mesh widths 5 cm and 1 cm, respectively ($M_2$ downstream from $M_1$). $x$ is the distance behind the second grid $M_2$, $x_1$ is the distance between the grids, $U$ is the mean velocity, and $\overline{u^2}$ is the mean square turbulence. (After Tsuji and Hama [*52*].) Data show departure from the simple law of decay $\overline{u^2} \sim t^{-1}$.

Bottom, same data as presented in Fig. C,15e, upper, replotted to show conformity with Eq. 14-7 (after Tsuji and Hama [*52*]).

can be calculated from a hypothesis of self-preservation. This provides an experimental basis for Lin's earlier hypothesis [*48*] which was obtained from general considerations influenced by the theory of Kolmogoroff.

It may be noted here that, at least in these experiments, there is as yet no need for generalizing the hypothesis further in the line indicated by Goldstein [*49*], although the need for such generalization is not excluded. (See also Art. 17.) Goldstein also proposed the measurement of the law of decay of turbulence behind a grid when another grid of larger mesh is placed upstream. In this case, the large eddies from the first grid tend to cause the turbulent motion behind the second grid to depart greatly from similarity. Such experiments were made by Tsuji and Hama [*52*], showing strong departure from the law of decay $\underline{u}^2 \sim t^{-1}$ (Fig. C,15e, upper). On the other hand, the more general law of decay (Eq. 14-17) is verified with the additive term $b \neq 0$ (Fig. C,15e, lower). More recently, Tsuji [*53*] examined the spectral distribution of the turbulent motion behind the second grid and obtained results in agreement with the above concepts. When the second grid is 70 mesh widths behind the first grid, the similarity of the vorticity spectrum is not found to be accurate, as one may also expect from the fact that a well-developed turbulent motion is not yet formed behind the first grid.

**C,16. The Quasi-Gaussian Approximation.** As pointed out in Art. 7, it is possible to obtain an infinite system of differential equations for determining the correlation functions of all orders. In order to obtain a "deductive theory," a closed system of a finite number of partial differential equations is needed. For this purpose, some approximation has to be made. Now it is known that the probability distribution of the velocity components at a given point is approximately the normal distribution. If this were true for the joint probability distribution at several points, the triple correlation function would vanish, while the correlation functions of the fourth order would be related to those of the second order by the relation

$$\overline{u_i u_j' u_k'' u_l'''} = \overline{u_i u_j'}\;\overline{u_k'' u_l'''} + \overline{u_i u_k''}\;\overline{u_j' u_l'''} + \overline{u_i u_l'''}\;\overline{u_j' u_k''} \tag{16-1}$$

It is known that triple correlations do not vanish in homogeneous turbulence, but it is still natural to speculate whether Eq. 16-1 may still be true or remains a good approximation without the vanishing of the triple correlations.[17] There is some support of such a step from experimental observations (cf. Fig. C,3a and C,3b).

To give an idea of the application of the hypothesis (Eq. 16-1), let us indicate how the pressure correlation at two points may be derived. One

[17] A hypothesis of this type was first introduced into the theory of turbulence by Millionshchikov [*42*].

first notes that

$$\Delta p = \frac{\partial^2}{\partial x_i \partial x_j}(u_i u_j) \tag{16-2}$$

so that

$$\overline{\Delta p \Delta' p'} = \frac{\partial^4}{\partial r_i \partial r_j \partial r_k \partial r_l} \overline{u_i u_j u_k' u_l'} \tag{16-3}$$

We now break up the quadruple correlation by Eq. 16-1. In this manner, one finds that

$$\overline{pp'} = 2\underline{u}^4 \int_r^\infty \left(\xi - \frac{r^2}{\xi}\right) [f'(\xi)]^2 d\xi \tag{16-4}$$

Eq. 16-4 was given by Batchelor [*12*] while an equivalent relation in the spectral formulation was obtained earlier by Heisenberg [*23*].

An interesting observation may be made here. If the relation (Eq. 16-4) is accepted, it is possible to show that, at high Reynolds numbers of turbulence, the magnitude of the pressure term in the Navier-Stokes equations is much smaller in magnitude than either the local acceleration or the convective acceleration taken individually [*20*].

With the help of Eq. 16-1, one can derive a system of partial differential equations with the same number of equations as unknowns. The equation for the change of double correlation functions involves the triple correlation functions. The equation for the change of the triple correlation function involves the fourth-order correlations, which may be reduced to the double correlations by Eq. 16-1. In this manner, a closed system of equations is obtained. Such a theory was independently developed by Proudman and Reid [*54*] and by Tatsumi [*55*] for decaying isotropic turbulence in the spectral formulation. Without giving a detailed account, a few of the outstanding features are discussed in the following paragraphs.

1. The above reasoning for the establishment of a closed system was obviously only true for multipoint correlations and not for two-point correlations alone. While correlations of the fourth order are represented in terms of two-point correlations by Eq. 16-1, the triple correlations must be kept in the general form of a three-point correlation. In an isotropic case, there are then *three* independent space variables, e.g. the three sides of the triangle with vertices at the points in question. In the spectral formulation, the final equations contain *three* independent wave numbers.
2. According to the experimental results of Stewart (Fig. C,3b) the hypothesis (Eq. 16-1) may become poor for small distances. Thus it would be desirable to examine the behavior of the small eddies according to this theory, and to compare it with the Kolmogoroff-Obukhoff spectrum $\kappa^{-\frac{5}{3}}$ in the case of infinite Reynolds number. Such a comparison has not yet been carried out.

3. On the other hand, the theory gives the definite prediction that there is no permanence of the largest eddies. Thus, there is a definite contradiction between Eq. 16-1 and the hypothesis leading to Loitsiansky's invariant. This led Batchelor and Proudman [*31*] to the extensive investigation mentioned in Art. 12.

Chandrasekhar [*56*] used a different approach. He limited his study to two-point correlations, but considered a difference in time. Thus Eq. 16-1 is replaced by relations of the kind

$$\overline{u_i(\underline{x}', t')u_j(\underline{x}', t')u_k(\underline{x}'', t'')u_l(\underline{x}'', t'')} = Q_{ik}Q_{jl} + Q_{il}Q_{jk} + Q_{ij}(0, 0)Q_{kl}(0, 0) \quad (16\text{-}5)$$

where

$$Q_{ij} = \overline{u_i(\underline{x}', t')u_j(\underline{x}'', t'')} \quad (16\text{-}6)$$

In this approach, the number of space variables is reduced, but another time variable is introduced. Chandrasekhar then introduced the concept of "stationary homogeneous and isotropic turbulence," and assumed that the double correlation (Eq. 16-6) (and similar third order correlations) depend only on the space vector $\underline{x}'' - \underline{x}'$ and the time interval $|t'' - t'|$. In this way, the theory leads to a single partial differential equation in two independent variables, and a number of deductions were made. In particular, a discussion is given to show its compatibility with Kolmogoroff's theory.

**C,17. Hypotheses on Energy Transfer.** Another method for arriving at a theory capable of yielding definite deductions is to assume, on the basis of physical arguments, a relation between the spectrum function $F(\kappa, t)$ and the transfer function $W(\kappa, t)$. Various hypotheses of this type were proposed by Obukhoff [*37*], Heisenberg [*23*], von Kármán [*45*], and Kovásznay [*57*]. It should be recognized that there is no a priori reason that such relations should exist. However, the success of these hypotheses seems to indicate that this type of theory does give a reasonably accurate description of the physical process.

Heisenberg argued that the transfer mechanism is essentially similar to viscous dissipation with the smaller eddies corresponding to molecular motions. This is reasonable provided the smaller eddies are very much smaller than the eddies from which they take energy. If this point of view is accepted, the rate at which energy is lost to the smaller eddies is proportional to

$$-\frac{\partial}{\partial t}\int_0^\kappa F(\kappa)d\kappa = \left[\nu + C\int_\kappa^\infty \sqrt{\frac{F(\kappa'')}{\kappa''^3}}\,d\kappa''\right]\int_0^\kappa 2F(\kappa')\kappa'^2 d\kappa' \quad (17\text{-}1)$$

where $C$ is a constant. The term

$$\epsilon_\kappa = C \int_\kappa^\infty \sqrt{\frac{F(\kappa'')}{\kappa''^3}}\, d\kappa'' \tag{17-2}$$

represents an apparent kinematic viscosity coefficient associated with the motions of wave number above $\kappa$.

Von Kármán proposed the form

$$\int_0^\kappa W d\kappa = C \left\{ \int_\kappa^\infty [F(\kappa')]^\alpha \kappa'^\beta d\kappa' \right\} \cdot \left\{ \int_0^\kappa F(\kappa')^{\frac{3}{2}-\alpha} \kappa'^{\frac{1}{2}-\beta} d\kappa' \right\} \tag{17-3}$$

for the transfer function. It reduces to Heisenberg's form for $\alpha = \frac{1}{2}$, $\beta = -\frac{3}{2}$. It also reduces to a modified Obukhoff form for $\alpha = 1$, $\beta = 0$. In the present discussion, we shall restrict ourselves to the Heisenberg formula and use Eq. 17-1 as the basis for determining the spectrum $F(\kappa, t)$ at any future time from its present knowledge.

For large values of $\kappa$, the rate of loss of energy to still larger wave numbers is expected to be very small. Consequently, the left side of Eq. 17-1 is negligible. It then follows (see Chandrasekhar [*58*]) from Eq. 17-1 that

$$F(\kappa, t) = \text{const} \left(\frac{\kappa_0}{\kappa}\right)^{\frac{5}{3}} \frac{1}{[1 + (\kappa/\kappa_s)^4]^{\frac{4}{3}}} \tag{17-4}$$

where $\kappa_0$ is a constant and $\kappa_s$ is inversely proportional to Kolmogoroff's scale $\eta$. For large values of $\kappa$, $F(\kappa) \sim \kappa^{-7}$. However, theoretical and experimental considerations indicate that $F(\kappa)$ probably decreases faster than $\kappa^{-7}$ at high wave numbers.

If we now introduce the hypothesis of similarity, we can determine the spectrum function completely. In fact, if the hypothesis of complete similarity is used, we have $F(\kappa, t)$ in the form

$$F(\kappa, t) = \frac{1}{C^2 \kappa_0^3 t_0^2} \left(\frac{t}{t_0}\right)^{\frac{1}{2}} f\left(\frac{\kappa}{\kappa_0} \sqrt{\frac{t}{t_0}}\right) \tag{17-5}$$

where $\kappa_0$ and $t_0$ are certain constants. According to Eq. 17-1, $f(x)$ satisfies

$$\int_0^x f(x) dx - \frac{1}{2} x f(x) = \left[\frac{1}{R} + \int_x^\infty \sqrt{\frac{f(x'')}{x''^3}}\, dx''\right] \int_0^x 2 f(x') x'^2 dx' \tag{17-6}$$

where $R = 1/\nu\kappa_0^2 t_0$. This equation has been solved numerically by Chandrasekhar [*58*] for a series of values of $R_\lambda$ (Fig. C,17). Proudman [*59*] computed the correlation function from these spectral functions and found quite good agreement with experiments.

The spectrum defined by Eq. 17-6 has a relatively long range, at low values of $\kappa$, for which $F(\kappa) \sim \kappa$. However, an examination of the stability of the spectrum [*60*] indicates that this part of the spectrum is not stable. At the Reynolds numbers obtained in usual experiments, this unstable range of wave numbers corresponds to about one third of the total energy. However, the contribution to the rate of dissipation from this range is negligible. This agrees with the concept of similarity of the vorticity spectrum $\kappa^2F(\kappa, t)$, and lack of similarity for the energy $F(\kappa, t)$ for low wave numbers (case (c) of the similarity hypothesis spectrum).

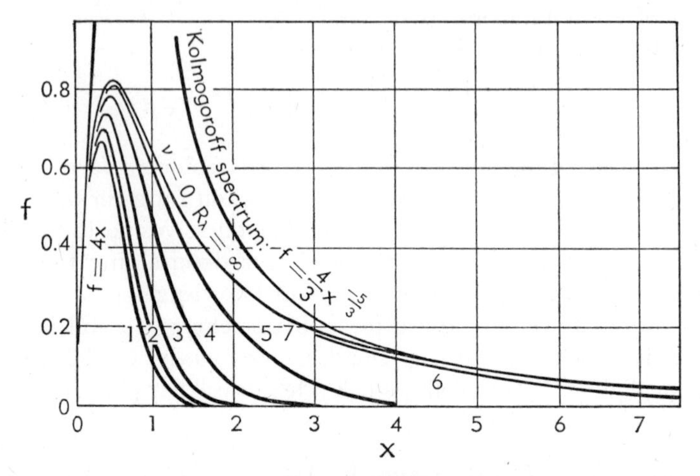


Fig. C,17. The decay spectra for various values of $R$. The curves marked 1, 2, 3, 4, 5, 6, and 7 are for $R^{-1} = 1.65$, 1.34, 0.98, 0.55, 0.22, $10^{-3}$, and 0 respectively. The curve for $R = \infty$ is the decay spectrum for infinite Reynolds number and becomes asymptotic to the Kolmogoroff spectrum $f(x) = \frac{4}{3}x^{-\frac{5}{3}}$ for $x \to \infty$.

It should be pointed out that this case has a special bearing with Heisenberg's formula. If we differentiate Eq. 17-1, we obtain

$$\frac{\partial F}{\partial t} = -2\left[\nu + C\int_\kappa^\infty \sqrt{\frac{F(\kappa'')}{\kappa''^3}}\,d\kappa''\right]\kappa^2F(\kappa) + 2C\sqrt{\frac{F(\kappa)}{\kappa^3}}\int_0^\kappa \kappa'^2F(\kappa')d\kappa' \tag{17-7}$$

Thus, the behavior of the spectrum at frequency $\kappa$ depends on the lower frequencies only to the extent of $\int_0^\kappa \kappa'^2F(\kappa')d\kappa'$. If this integral can be accurately calculated by the similarity spectrum for high values of $\kappa$, Eq. 17-7 is consistent with the hypothesis of similarity. Otherwise, there is some doubt that similarity is possible at all, even at high frequencies, until the last term in Eq. 17-7 becomes negligible.

# CHAPTER 4. TURBULENT DIFFUSION AND TRANSFER

**C,18. Diffusion by Continuous Movements.** One of the most striking properties of turbulent motion is its diffusive property. Observation of smoke from a chimney stack gives a general idea of such a process. Temperature measurements in the wake of a heated wire, such as those made by Schubauer [*61*], and more recently by Uberoi and Corrsin [*62*], give a more quantitative description of the phenomenon. A complete theory of the phenomenon of turbulent diffusion is, however, not available, even in the simplest case of homogeneous isotropic turbulence, because of some inherent difficulties. In the first place, the usual concept of a diffusion coefficient can in general be at best a crude first approximation, because the variation of the statistical properties of interest in turbulent diffusion (or transport) occurs over scales comparable to that of the scale of the turbulent motion itself. The analogy in the molecular case would be variations at scales comparable to the mean free path. Secondly, the mathematical difficulty encountered in trying to develop a detailed theory is extremely heavy. Indeed, a theory of diffusion dealing with the transport of material particles from one point to another suggests the use of the Lagrangian description. This in itself makes the theory difficult. On the other hand, the eventual diffusion of a certain physical property, such as temperature, must be accomplished by the molecular process, which is more conveniently described by the Eulerian method. In the face of these difficulties, most of the existing theories are far from being complete. In the present treatment, we shall therefore limit ourselves to a brief account of some of the elementary concepts developed and some of the issues examined. For a more detailed treatment, the reader is referred to the recent article by Batchelor and Townsend [*63*, pp. 352–399].

A fundamental approach to turbulent diffusion was advanced by Taylor [*64*] in 1921. While the theory deals with an idealized situation, it does reveal some of the essential features of the process, and forms the starting point of many later developments. In the simplest form of this theory of diffusion by continuous movements, we restrict ourselves to the idealized case of a homogeneous isotropic field of turbulence which is not decaying. We consider diffusion from a plane $x$, $z$ where all the diffusing particles are concentrated at time $t = 0$. If $Y$ is the coordinate of a particle at time $T$, then $Y = \int_0^T v dt$, and

$$\frac{1}{2}\frac{d}{dT}\overline{Y^2} = \overline{Y\frac{dY}{dT}} = \overline{Yv_T} = \overline{v_T \int_0^T dvt} \tag{18-1}$$

where the average is taken in the statistical sense or over planes parallel to the $x$, $z$ plane. We may now introduce the correlation coefficient $R(\tau)$ by

$$\overline{v(T)v(t)} = \underline{v}^2 R(\tau), \qquad \tau = T - t \tag{18-2}$$

Then Eq. 18-1 becomes

$$\frac{1}{2}\frac{d}{dT}\overline{Y^2} = \underline{v}^2 \int_0^T R(\tau) d\tau \tag{18-3}$$

and

$$\tfrac{1}{2}\overline{Y^2} = \underline{v}^2 \int_0^t dt' \int_0^{t'} R(\tau)d\tau = \underline{v}^2 \int_0^t (T - t)R(t)dt \qquad (18\text{-}4)$$

In general, we may expect $R(\tau)$ to decrease with increasing $\tau$. Suppose that, for all times $\tau$ greater than $T_1$, $R(\tau)$ is practically zero. Then

$$\int_0^t R(\tau)d\tau = \int_0^\infty R(\tau)d\tau, \qquad \text{for} \quad t > T_1 \qquad (18\text{-}5)$$

and Eq. 18-4 gives

$$\tfrac{1}{2}\overline{Y^2} = \underline{v}^2 T \int_0^\infty R(\tau)d\tau + \text{const} \qquad (18\text{-}6)$$

The integral (Eq. 18-5) is a measure of the time scale of diffusion, and

$$D = \underline{v}^2 \int_0^\infty R(\tau)d\tau \qquad (18\text{-}7)$$

may be regarded as a diffusion coefficient, since for molecular diffusion, $\overline{Y^2} = 2DT$. Thus the concept of a diffusion coefficient is justified for large values of time of diffusion. On the other hand, for small values of time $t$ ($t$ much less than the time scale defined by Eq. 18-5), $R(\tau) \sim 1$, and Eq. 18-4 gives

$$\overline{Y^2} = \underline{v}^2 T^2 \quad \text{or} \quad \sqrt{\overline{Y^2}} = \underline{v}T \qquad (18\text{-}8)$$

It appears that when $T$ is small, $\overline{Y^2}$ is proportional to $T^2$ instead of $T$, as in an ordinary diffusion process. This is clearly so, because over the time interval in which $R(\tau)$ is nearly equal to unity, the velocities of the particles are nearly constant so that for each particle

$$Y = vT \qquad (18\text{-}9)$$

In this case, therefore, not only is Eq. 18-8 valid, but the frequency distribution of $Y$ is the same as the frequency distribution of $v$.

We shall now apply these ideas to the problem of the spread of heat behind a heated wire. If heat is spread from a concentrated plane source, after an interval of time $t$, the distribution of temperature according to the usual process of molecular diffusion is proportional to $t^{-1} \exp[-y^2/4kt]$, where $y$ is the normal distance from the plane source. The temperature distribution behind a heated wire corresponds to such a problem, if there is only molecular diffusion. The distribution is given by the above expression with $t$ replaced by $x/U$, where $x$ is the distance downstream from the wire and $U$ is the speed of the wind. In a turbulent stream, diffusion due to turbulent motion must be superposed on molecular diffusion. In fact, Schubauer has observed the error law for the distribution of temperature, and it would appear that the phenomenon of turbulent diffusion can be described by an adequate diffusion coefficient associated with the turbulent motion. However, the above analysis shows that the use of a diffusion coefficient is valid only for large distances downstream (provided the idealization used is valid). Close to the source, there is no basis for using a diffusion coefficient. Indeed, Taylor [*15*] pointed out that the Gaussian distribution of temperature near the source is not associated with a usual diffusion coefficient but should be accounted for by Gaussian distribution of the velocity of fluctuation (cf. Eq. 18-9). If the frequency distribution of velocities had obeyed some other law, the distribution of temperature near the source would also have deviated from an error curve. On the other hand, the temperature distribution very far from the source must necessarily fit an error curve, whatever the frequency distribution of velocities may be. In reality, however, the analysis at very large distances downstream is complicated by the fact that the turbulence dies away downstream so that the above analysis is not accurate.

For other approaches to the problem of turbulent diffusion, see Frenkiel [*65*], where some semiempirical calculations are given.

**C,19. Analysis Involving More Than One Particle.** In the above analysis, we do not consider the joint configuration of a number of fluid particles. This is of course necessary if we wish to get a more complete description of turbulent diffusion. Indeed, one may consider a large number of particles, and their joint statistical behavior during the course of time would give an almost complete statistical description of the turbulent motion in the Lagrangian scheme.

In practice, one is often limited to the consideration of the separation of two particles. If $s_i$ is the separation between two particles, the rate of variation of the statistical average $\overline{s^2}$ is clearly a measure of the rate of diffusion. We shall now consider a special case where a concrete formula can be obtained for the variation of $\overline{s^2}$ as a function of the time of separation $\tau = t - t_0$ between the initial instant $t_0$ and the present time $t$. If $\tau$ is sufficiently large, then the influence of the initial separation must be negligible. If, furthermore, the separation between the particles lies in the range of scales of turbulence for which the spectral law (Eq. 13-15) holds, there is only one parameter—namely the rate of energy dissipation $\epsilon$—characterizing the properties of the turbulent motion. Thus, dimensional reasoning shows that $\overline{s^2}$ (which depends only on $\tau$ and $\epsilon$) must be of the form

$$\overline{s^2} \sim \epsilon\tau^3 \tag{19-1}$$

or

$$\frac{d\overline{s^2}}{d\tau} \sim \epsilon\tau^2 \sim \epsilon^{\frac{1}{3}}(\overline{s^2})^{\frac{2}{3}} \tag{19-2}$$

This means that the dispersive effect becomes larger and larger as the particles separate further and further from each other, the diffusion coefficient increasing as the $\frac{4}{3}$ power of the separation.[18] The law (Eq. 19-2) was obtained experimentally by Richardson [*66*] and deduced theoretically by Batchelor [*67*] in a somewhat different manner. However, the agreement is partly fortuitous since the length scale involved in Richardson's data does not fulfill the requirements imposed in the theory.

More detailed analyses of the magnitude of separation can be carried out when the distance of separation is small. Such analyses can be used to examine the deformation of a fluid element—material lines, surfaces, and volumes. An interesting question is whether a material volume will eventually be stretched into a needle-shaped line or a disk-shaped surface. For the details of such investigations, the reader is referred to the original articles of Batchelor [*68*] and Reid [*69*] or to the article of Batchelor and Townsend [*63*].

**C,20. Temperature Fluctuations in Homogeneous Turbulence.** The above concepts can be extended to a continuous distribution of sources. The results are particularly instructive when the distribution has a uniform gradient. Following Corrsin [*70*], let us consider a distributed heat source in the plane $x = 0$ with a linear distribution in the $y$ direction:

$$T = T_1 + \alpha y \tag{20-1}$$

Consider the flow of fluid with *nondecaying* isotropic turbulent motion past these sources with a uniform mean speed $U$ which is much higher than the velocities of the turbulent motion. If molecular conduction is omitted, the instantaneous temperature at any point downstream is determined by that of the fluid particle present at that instant. This in turn depends on the location where the particle crossed the plane $x = 0$. Since a point may be reached by a fluid particle from above and from below with equal probability, it is clear that the mean temperature distribution (Eq. 20-1) persists downstream.

Consider now a fixed point $x > 0$ in the plane $y = 0$ (which is in fact a typical plane), and the particle occupying that point at any instant. If the level of turbulence is low, this particle passed by the plane $x = 0$ at the time $\tau = x/U$ earlier. The position of the crossing point is given by $-Y_0$, where

$$Y_0 = \int_{t-\tau}^{t} v(t')dt' \tag{20-2}$$

$t$ being the time under consideration. This introduces a temperature deviation

$$\theta = -\alpha Y_0 \tag{20-3}$$

[18] This result can also be obtained by formally using Heisenberg's formula (Eq. 17-2).

The statistical average rate of temperature transfer is therefore

$$-\overline{v\theta} = \alpha \overline{vY_0} \tag{20-4}$$

The value $\overline{vY_0}$ can be evaluated in a manner very similar to that used in Art. 18. We obtain in this manner

$$\overline{vY_0} = \int_{t-\tau}^{t} \overline{v(t)v(t')}dt' = \overline{v^2} \int_0^{\tau} R(\tau')d\tau' \tag{20-5}$$

It should be noted that although this formula is very similar to Eq. 18-3, the physical interpretation is different. The rate of temperature transfer may now be written in the form

$$-\overline{v\theta} = D' \frac{dT}{dy}, \qquad D' = \overline{v^2} \int_0^{\tau} R(\tau')d\tau' \tag{20-6}$$

where $D'$ is a "diffusion coefficient" in that it gives the rate of increase of the mean square deviation (Art. 18). It is proportional to $x$ at first, and approaches a constant value $D$ after a sufficient distance downstream.

Similarly it can be shown the standard deviation is given by

$$\overline{\theta^2} = \alpha^2 \underline{v}^2 \int_0^{t} (t - \tau)R(\tau)d\tau \tag{20-7}$$

and that it becomes infinite as the first power of $t$ or the distance downstream. In reality, this will be limited by molecular diffusion.

In contrast to the above problem of heat transfer, an analysis of temperature fluctuations in a statistically homogeneous field can be carried out in much the same way as for homogeneous velocity fields. This was done by Corrsin [*71*], who found that in the final stage of the decay process the mean square of the temperature fluctuation decreases as the inverse $\frac{3}{2}$ power. This is different from the case of velocity fluctuations, and the reason for this difference is the absence of the equation of continuity in the present case (cf. Art. 15). Such a law was first obtained by Reissner [*50*] in his asymptotic solution of the heat equation.

**C,21. Statistical Theory of Shear Flow.** Although studies of turbulent flow with shear date back further than studies of isotropic turbulence, a complete statistical theory has not yet been developed. The classical ideas of Reynolds still stand out as the best description of the basic mechanism of turbulent shear. The mixture length theories,[19] while useful for practical purposes, are obviously not adequate statistical theories. Deviations from the classical concepts are especially evident near the edge of the turbulent boundary layer and in turbulent jets and wakes. Intermittency of the turbulent motion appears to be quite predominant in such phenomena. It appears from these intermittent phenomena that

[19] For details, see Sec. B.

a statistical theory of shear flow can be developed only after adequate descriptions are obtained, both for motions on a small scale and for motions on a scale comparable with that of the mean flow. The fact that turbulent transfer is most effectively carried out by such large scale motions is in direct contrast to the phenomenon of molecular transfer. In that case, the mean free path is much smaller than the scale of the mean motion, and a definite coefficient of transfer is established. The difference in scales of the random motion responsible for the transfer mechanism in the two cases makes the analogy imperfect, and is at the root of the difficulties in developing a theory of turbulent transfer.

For steady flow through pipes and channels, the phenomenon is simpler in the sense that intermittency is not apparent. Attempts to develop a statistical theory, based on the use of correlations, have been made by Keller and Friedmann [*72*], von Kármán [*13*], Chou [*73*], and Rotta [*74*]. While the theory predicts the mean velocity and turbulence level in reasonable agreement with experiments, the presence of arbitrary constants shows their weakness. In the following, only an indication of the approach is given; the reader is referred to the original papers for the details.

The equations of motion for the turbulent fluctuations can be obtained by subtracting the Reynolds equations (Eq. 2-3) from the complete equations of motion (Eq. 2-2),

$$\frac{\partial u_i}{\partial t} + U_j \frac{\partial u_i}{\partial x_j} + u_j \frac{\partial u_i}{\partial x_j} + u_j \frac{\partial U_i}{\partial x_j} = -\frac{1}{\rho}\frac{\partial p}{\partial x_i} - \frac{1}{\rho}\frac{\partial \tau_{ij}}{\partial x_j} + \nu \Delta u_i \quad (21\text{-}1)$$

where $p$ is the fluctuation of pressure, and $\tau_{ij}$ are the Reynolds stresses. The velocity fluctuations $u_i$ also satisfy the equation of continuity,

$$\frac{\partial u_k}{\partial x_k} = 0 \quad (21\text{-}2)$$

Instead of dealing with the velocity fluctuations themselves, one may attempt to deal with the statistical correlation of the velocity fluctuations in analogy with the study of homogeneous turbulence. To simplify matters, one may also eliminate the pressure fluctuation by using the Poisson equation obtained by taking the divergence of Eq. 21-1:

$$\frac{1}{\rho}\Delta p = -2\frac{\partial U_m}{\partial x_n}\frac{\partial u_n}{\partial x_m} + \frac{\partial^2}{\partial x_m \partial x_n}(\overline{u_m u_n} - u_m u_n) \quad (21\text{-}3)$$

and solving it under appropriate boundary conditions. However, the fundamental difficulty encountered in the homogeneous case—that higher correlations are invariably brought into the picture when an equation is constructed for dealing with correlations of a given order—also occurs here. Approximations are therefore introduced by the various authors at this stage, and the theory is not entirely free from arbitrariness.

Because of the difficulties encountered in the development of the statistical theory of shear flow, several authors studied the more specialized problem of homogeneous turbulence in a field of uniform velocity gradient. Application of the concepts of Art. 17 was made by Reis [*75*] and later by Burgers and Mitchner [*76*] with almost identical assumptions and results, although the work appears to have been done independently. Application of the concepts of Art. 16 to this case has recently been carried out by Craya [*77*].

An entirely different approach to the problem of turbulent shear flow has been proposed by Malkus [*78*]. The reader is referred to his original paper for the details.

# *CHAPTER 5. OTHER ASPECTS OF THE PROBLEM OF TURBULENCE*

**C,22. Turbulent Motion in a Compressible Fluid.** When a compressible gas is in turbulent motion, there are density and temperature fluctuations as well as velocity fluctuations. At any instant, the velocity fluctuation may be decomposed into two parts,

$$u_i = u_i^{(1)} + u_i^{(2)} \tag{22-1}$$

such that

$$\text{div } \mathbf{u}^{(1)} = 0, \qquad \text{curl } \mathbf{u}^{(2)} = 0 \tag{22-2}$$

The rotation of the fluid is given by the first part $u_i^{(1)}$ and the compression is given by the second part $u_i^{(2)}$.

In general, there is a continuous conversion between the rotation component and the compression component of the velocity fluctuations. This additional degree of freedom in the compressible case naturally makes the theory of turbulence much more difficult. In the case of small disturbances from a homogeneous state these modes are separable from each other.[20] The study of small disturbances superimposed on a shear flow is treated in connection with the instability of the boundary layer at high speeds.

Attempts have been made to extend directly to the compressible case the various approaches to the theory of turbulence in the incompressible case: e.g. the study of isotropic turbulence by Chandrasekhar [*80*], and the consideration of von Kármán's similarity theory by Lin and Shen [*81*] for shear flow. The method discussed in Art. 21 can also be extended to a compressible gas. Obviously, such approaches cannot go beyond the limitations in the incompressible case. It is therefore natural that the more fruitful theoretical results on turbulent motion in a compressible fluid are obtained in connection with the study of the influence of com-

[20] See [*79*] for a detailed discussion of this case.

pressibility on turbulent motion, principally for small Mach numbers of turbulence. It is then plausible that the chief influence of compressibility is that acoustic energy is constantly being radiated, causing the turbulent motion to dissipate faster than in the incompressible case.

Lighthill [*82*] has shown that, in the absence of solid boundaries, turbulent motion acts as *quadrupole* sources of sound. He also showed that the amount of energy radiated per unit volume of turbulence is proportional to $\rho V^8/a^5 l$, where $\rho$ is the density, $V$ is a typical velocity of the turbulent motion, $a$ is the acoustic speed, and $l$ is a typical linear scale. Since the rate of energy conversion in turbulent motion is proportional to $\rho V^3/l$, the acoustic efficiency is proportional to the fifth power of the root mean square Mach number. At low Mach numbers, this would be a very small amount indeed, if it were not for a numerical factor of proportionality of the order of 40, as shown by Proudman [*83*]. In the cases where the theory is applicable, the experimental results bear out the general theoretical conclusions.

If solid boundaries are present, such as in the problem of the noise from the boundary layer of a flat plate, Phillips [*84*] found that *dipole* sources are present if the plate is semi-infinite. Acoustic sources are again of the *quadrupole* type if the plate is infinite and the motion is statistically the same along the plate.

The scattering of energy due to the interaction of turbulence with sound or shock waves has been considered by Lighthill [*85*] and others.

All of the above results are for low Mach numbers of turbulent motion. At the present time, only speculation can be made for the cases of higher Mach numbers where shock waves may appear.

**C,23. Magneto-Hydrodynamic Turbulence.** In astrophysics, one important problem is the turbulent motion of an electrically conducting gas in the presence of magnetic fields. One is then dealing with the conversion of energy from the mechanical form to the electro-magnetic form. There is an extensive and rapidly growing literature on this subject, and it is perhaps inappropriate to try to survey it at the present time in a volume on high speed aerodynamics.

One of the central problems at issue is the partition of energy between the two modes. Batchelor [*86*] noted that the equation for the magnetic field is exactly the same as that for vorticity, and suggested that the energy spectrum of magnetic energy is proportional to $\kappa^2 F(\kappa)$. This would mean that there is little magnetic energy in the large scales. Other authors, however, contended that there should be equipartition of energy of the two modes. Recently, Chandrasekhar [*87*] undertook a systematic development of the theory of turbulent motion for magneto-hydrodynamics along the lines of Art. 16 and 17, and found solutions which are in agreement with the latter opinion. However, since his assumption limited him to moderate and small wavelengths, the former opinion is not yet ruled out. For a more detailed discussion of the arguments for and against the two standpoints, see [*88*, pp. 93–98]. Work decisively distinguishing between them is clearly needed. In this connection, it would perhaps be worthwhile to obtain some special solutions in magneto-hydrodynamics analogous to those obtained by Taylor and Green [*35*] in the ordinary case to get an idea of the validity of the existing arguments.

**C,24. Some Aerodynamic Problems.** There are a number of aerodynamical problems associated with turbulent motion in which its diffusive nature takes on a secondary role. The random nature of turbulent motion still makes it necessary to use statistical treatments. In this category of problems, we briefly discuss (1) the dynamical effects of turbulent motion, (2) the effect of contraction on wind tunnel turbulence, and (3) the effect of damping screens.

*Dynamical effects of turbulent motion.* Dynamical effects caused by turbulent motion are often treated by statistical methods. For example, in the case of a pendulum suspended in a turbulent wind, the spectrum of the motion of the pendulum can be calculated in terms of that of the turbulent motion and the dynamical characteristics of the pendulum [*89*]. Recently, Liepmann [*90*] tried to apply these methods to the buffeting of airplanes moving through a turbulent stream.

*Effect of wind tunnel contraction.* The effect of wind tunnel contraction on the intensity of turbulence has been studied by Prandtl and Taylor [*91*, p. 201]. Recently, Ribner and Tucker [*92*] applied Taylor's ideas to the study of the influence of the contraction on the spectrum. The combined effect of damping screens and stream convergence have also been studied by Tucker [*93*]. The reader is referred to the original papers. An experimental investigation of the detailed behavior of the turbulent fluctuations during contraction has been made by Uberoi [*94*].

*Effect of damping screens on homogeneous turbulence.* Damping screens have long been used for the *reduction* of turbulence level in the wind tunnel. While these screens no doubt act also as a grid in *producing* turbulence, the scale of such turbulent motion is usually so small that it damps out at a comparatively small distance behind the screen. The resistance of the screen to the flow, on the other hand, tends to reduce the large scale turbulent motion already existing in front of it.

The characteristics of a damping screen are usually described in terms of two force coefficients $K_\theta$ and $F_\theta$. If the screen is placed with its normal at an angle $\theta$ relative to a stream of speed $U$, there is a drop of pressure across it, given by

$$p_2 - p_1 = K_\theta \cdot \tfrac{1}{2}\rho U^2 \tag{24-1}$$

where $p_1$ and $p_2$ are the static pressure upstream and downstream of the screen. At the same time, there is a side force in the plane of the screen per unit area, given by

$$S = F_\theta \cdot \tfrac{1}{2}\rho U^2 \tag{24-2}$$

Experiments by Schubauer, Spangenberg, and Klebanoff [*95*] at the National Bureau of Standards (NBS) show that the coefficients $F_\theta$ and $K_\theta$ are related for usual wire gauze screens. Dryden and Schubauer [*96*] proposed the relation

$$\frac{F_\theta}{\theta} = \frac{4K_\theta}{8 + K_\theta} \tag{24-3}$$

which agrees with experiments for $K_\theta < 1.4$. Taylor and Batchelor [*83*] fitted the NBS data with the empirical formula

$$\frac{F_\theta}{\theta} = 2 - \frac{2.2}{\sqrt{1 + K_\theta}} \tag{24-4}$$

which appears to be a reasonable approximation for $0.7 < K_\theta < 4$.

Schubauer, Spangenberg, and Klebanoff also found that $K_\theta/\cos^2\theta$ can be uniquely related to $R\cos\theta$, where $R$ is the Reynolds number. This means that the pressure drop depends essentially on the normal component of the velocity.

Theoretically, it is useful to introduce a "refractive index" $\alpha$. If the departing stream makes an angle $\phi$ with the normal to the screen, then $\alpha = \phi/\theta$. For small angles,

$$\alpha = 1 - \lim_{\theta \to 0}\left(\frac{F_\theta}{2\theta}\right) \tag{24-5}$$

This leads to

$$\begin{aligned} \alpha &= \frac{8 + K}{8 - K} \qquad \text{for} \quad K < 1.4 \\ \alpha &= \frac{1.1}{\sqrt{1 + K}} \qquad \text{for} \quad 0.7 < K < 4 \end{aligned} \tag{24-6}$$

Dryden and Schubauer [*96*] found that the kinetic energy of turbulence is reduced by the factor $(1 + K)^{-1}$ after passing through the screen. This result does not distinguish between the longitudinal and lateral components of the velocity. It has been verified by the more careful measurements of Schubauer, Spangenberg, and Klebanoff for flow Reynolds numbers above a certain critical value. For lower Reynolds numbers, the reduction factor is found to be lower.

A theory developed by Taylor and Batchelor [*97*], however, predicts different reduction factors for the longitudinal and the lateral components. They also predicted a reduction of the turbulence level immediately in front of the screen.

Townsend [*98*] performed experiments to check the theoretical predictions and reached the following conclusions:

1. The reduction of turbulent intensity on the upstream side of the gauze is described by the Taylor-Batchelor theory with adequate accuracy.
2. The reduction of the total turbulent intensity in passing through a gauze is consistent with the theory except for small values of $\kappa$, when the observed reduction is greater than predicted.
3. As predicted by the theory, the turbulence emerging behind the gauze is anisotropic, with the intensities of the lateral components exceeding that of the longitudinal component. The degree of anisotropy is less than the theory predicts.

   The smaller degree of anisotropy is ascribed by Townsend to a possible rapid initial adjustment toward isotropy in the zone of influence of the gauze. Downstream of the gauze, Townsend found that the recovery of isotropy is very slow, but local isotropy is valid within the range of observation in the sense that

$$\overline{\left(\frac{\partial u}{\partial x}\right)^2} = \frac{1}{2}\overline{\left(\frac{\partial v}{\partial x}\right)^2}$$

There is some obvious disagreement between the results of Townsend and the NBS data. Such differences are, however, not unexpected in view of the experimental difficulties attending such measurements. While the effect of damping screens has probably been determined with sufficient accuracy for practical application, further experiments are desirable for checking the theory.

The NBS data show that the scale of turbulence is not changed by the screen. No extensive experimental results are yet available on the change of spectrum. Some of the results obtained by Townsend do not agree with the theoretical predictions. In making such a comparison, it should be borne in mind that the theory is linear and the change of spectrum downstream of the screen is not considered in the theory.

## C,25. Cited References.[21]

1. Batchelor, G. K. *The Theory of Homogeneous Turbulence.* Cambridge Univ. Press, 1953.
2. Lin, C. C. *J. Aeronaut. Sci. 23,* 453–461 (1956).
3. Burgers, J. M. *Adv. Appl. Mech. 1,* 171 (1948).
4. Burgers, J. M. *Proc. Natl. Acad. Amsterdam 53,* 247, 393, 718, 732 (1950).
5. Hopf, E. *J. Rat. Mech. and Anal. 1,* 87 (1952).
6. Hopf, E. *Commun. on Pure and Appl. Math. 1,* 303 (1948).

[21] References [*100*] and [*101*] appeared after the present article was completed. Kraichman's paper [*100*] deals with an approach to the theory of turbulence (both nonmagnetic and magnetic) which differs substantially from those discussed earlier in the text, and is indeed contradictory to the Kolmogoroff theory. Corrsin's paper [*101*] considers the question of local isotropy also discussed in [*99*].

7. Blanco Lapierre, A., and Fortet, R. *Théorie des fonctions aléatoires: application à divers phenomènes de fluctuation*, Chap. 14. Masson, Paris, 1953.
8. Reynolds, O. *Phil. Trans. A186*, 123 (1895).
9. Simmons, L. F. G., and Salter, C. *Proc. Roy. Soc. London A145*, 212 (1934).
10. Townsend, A. A. *Proc. Cambridge Phil. Soc. 43*, 560 (1947).
11. Stewart, R. W. *Proc. Cambridge Phil. Soc. 47*, 146 (1951).
12. Batchelor, G. K. *Proc. Cambridge Phil. Soc. 47*, 359 (1951).
13. von Kármán, Th. *J. Aeronaut. Sci. 4*, 131 (1937).
14. Robertson, H. P. *Proc. Cambridge Phil. Soc. 36*, 209 (1940).
15. Taylor, G. I. *Proc. Roy. Soc. London A151*, 421 (1935).
16. Macphail, D. C. *J. Aeronaut. Sci. 8*, 73 (1940).
17. von Kármán, Th., and Howarth, L. *Proc. Roy. Soc. London A164*, 192 (1938).
18. Kistler, A. L., O'Brien, V., and Corrsin, S. *J. Aeronaut. Sci. 23*, 96 (1956).
19. Taylor, G. I. *Proc. Roy. Soc. London A164*, 476 (1938).
20. Lin, C. C. *Quart. Appl. Math. 10*, 295 (1953).
21. Favre, A. J., Gaviglio, J. J., and Dumas, R. *Compt. rend. 238*, 1561–1563 (1954).
22. Stewart, R. W., and Townsend, A. A. *Phil. Trans. A243*, 359 (1951).
23. Heisenberg, W. *Z. Physik 124*, 628 (1948).
24. Kampé de Fériet, J. *Compt. rend. 227*, 760 (1948).
25. Batchelor, G. K. *Proc. Roy. Soc. London A195*, 513 (1949).
26. Batchelor, G. K. *Proc. Roy. Soc. London A186*, 480 (1946).
27. Chandrasekhar, S. *Proc. Roy. Soc. London A203*, 358 (1950).
28. Lin, C. C. *Proc. First Symposium in Appl. Math., Am. Math. Soc.*, 81 (1947).
29. Loitsiansky, L. G. *NACA Tech. Mem. 1079*, 1945.
30. Birkhoff, G. *Commun. on Pure and Appl. Math. 7*, 19 (1954).
31. Batchelor, G. K., and Proudman, I. *Phil. Trans. 248*, 369 (1956).
32. Taylor, G. I. *Proc. Roy. Soc. London A164*, 15 (1938).
33. Batchelor, G. K., and Townsend, A. A. *Proc. Roy. Soc. London A190*, 534 (1947).
34. Kolmogoroff, A. N. *Compt. rend. Acad. Sci. U.R.S.S. 30*, 301 (1941).
35. Taylor, G. I., and Green, A. E. *Proc. Roy. Soc. London A158*, 499 (1937).
36. Goldstein, S. *Phil. Mag. 30*, (7), 85–102 (1940).
37. Obukhoff, A. M. *Compt. rend. Acad. Sci. U.R.S.S. 32*, 19 (1941).
38. Townsend, A. A. *Proc. Roy. Soc. London A208*, 534 (1951).
39. von Kármán, Th., and Lin, C. C. *Adv. Appl. Mech. 2*, 1 (1951).
40. Dryden, H. L. *Quart. Appl. Math. 1*, 7 (1943).
41. Heisenberg, W. *Proc. Roy. Soc. London A195*, 402 (1948).
42. Millionshchikov, M. *Compt. rend. Acad. Sci. U.R.S.S. 22*, 231, 235 (1939); *32*, 615, 619 (1941).
43. Batchelor, G. K., and Townsend, A. A. *Proc. Roy. Soc. London A194*, 527 (1948).
44. Kolmogoroff, A. N. *Compt. rend. Acad. Sci. U.R.S.S. 31*, 538 (1941); *32*, 16 (1941).
45. von Kármán, Th. *Compt. rend. 226*, 2108 (1948).
46. von Kármán, Th. *Proc. Natl. Acad. Sci. 34*, 530 (1948).
47. Frenkiel, F. N. *J. Appl. Mech. 15*, 311 (1948).
48. Lin, C. C. *Proc. Natl. Acad. Sci. 34*, 540 (1948).
49. Goldstein, S. *Proc. Cambridge Phil. Soc. 47*, 554 (1951).
50. Reissner, E. *Proc. 5th Intern. Congress Appl. Mech.*, 359 (1938).
51. Batchelor, G. K. *Proc. Roy. Soc. London A195*, 513 (1949).
52. Tsuji, H., and Hama, F. R. *J. Aeronaut. Sci. 20*, 848 (1953).
53. Tsuji, H. *J. Phys. Soc. Japan 2*, 1096–1104 (1956).
54. Proudman, I., and Reid, W. H. *Phil. Trans. A247*, 163 (1954).
55. Tatsumi, T. *Proc. Roy. Soc. London A239*, 16–45 (1947).
56. Chandrasekhar, S. *Phys. Rev. 102*, 941 (1956).
57. Kovásznay, L. S. G. *J. Aeronaut. Sci. 15*, 745 (1948).
58. Chandrasekhar, S. *Proc. Roy. Soc. London A200*, 20 (1949).
59. Proudman, I. *Proc. Cambridge Phil. Soc. 47*, 158 (1951).
60. Lin, C. C. *Proc. Fourth Symposium Appl. Math., Am. Math. Soc.*, 19 (1953).
61. Schubauer, G. B. *NACA Rept. 524*, 1935.

62. Uberoi, M. S., and Corrsin, S. *NACA Rept. 1142*, 1953.
63. Batchelor, G. K., and Townsend, A. A. *G. I. Taylor Anniversary Volume*. Cambridge Univ. Press, 1956.
64. Taylor, G. I. *Proc. London Math. Soc. 20*, 196 (1921).
65. Frenkiel, F. N. *Adv. Appl. Mech. 3*, 61 (1953).
66. Richardson, L. F. *Proc. Roy. Soc. London A110*, 709 (1926).
67. Batchelor, G. K. *Quart. J. Roy. Met. Soc. 73*, 133 (1950).
68. Batchelor, G. K. *Proc. Roy. Soc. London A213*, 349 (1952).
69. Reid, W. H. *Proc. Cambridge Phil. Soc. 51*, 350 (1955).
70. Corrsin, S. *J. Appl. Phys. 23*, 113 (1952).
71. Corrsin, S. *J. Aeronaut. Sci. 17*, 417 (1950).
72. Keller, L., and Friedmann, A. *Proc. First Intern. Congress Appl. Mech.*, 395 (1924).
73. Chou, P. Y. *Quart. Appl. Math. 3*, 198 (1945).
74. Rotta, J. *Z. Physik 129*, 547 (1951); *131*, 51 (1951).
75. Reis, F. B. *Ph.D. Dissertation*, Mass. Inst. Technol., 1951.
76. Burgers, J. M., and Mitchner, M. *Proc. Koninkl. Ned. Akad. Wetenschap. 56*, 228, 343 (1953).
77. Craya, A. *Compt. rend. 244*, 560, 847, 1448, 1609 (1957).
78. Malkus, W. V. R. *J. Fluid Mech. 1*, 521–539 (1956).
79. Kovásznay, L. S. G. *J. Aeronaut. Sci. 20*, 657–674 (1953).
80. Chandrasekhar, S. *Proc. Roy. Soc. London A210*, 18 (1951).
81. Lin, C. C., and Shen, S. F. *NACA Tech. Notes 2541 and 2542*, 1951.
82. Lighthill, M. J. *Proc. Roy. Soc. London A211*, 564 (1952).
83. Proudman, I. *Proc. Roy. Soc. London A214*, 119 (1952).
84. Phillips, O. M. *Proc. Roy. Soc. London A234*, 327–335 (1956).
85. Lighthill, M. J. *Proc. Cambridge Phil. Soc. 49*, 531 (1953).
86. Batchelor, G. K. *Proc. Roy. Soc. London A201*, 405 (1950).
87. Chandrasekhar, S. *Proc. Roy. Soc. London A233*, 322, 330 (1955).
88. Cowling, J. G. *Magnetohydrodynamics*. Interscience, 1957.
89. Lin, C. C. *Quart. Appl. Math. 1*, 43 (1943).
90. Liepmann, H. W. *J. Aeronaut. Sci. 19*, 793 (1952).
91. Goldstein, S. *Modern Developments in Fluid Dynamics*, Vol. 1. Clarendon Press, Oxford, 1938.
92. Ribner, H. S., and Tucker, M. *NACA Tech. Note 2606*, 1952.
93. Tucker, M. *NACA Tech. Note 2878*, 1953.
94. Uberoi, M. S. *J. Aeronaut. Sci. 23*, 754–764 (1956).
95. Schubauer, G. B., Spangenberg, W. G., and Klebanoff, P. S. *NACA Tech. Note 2001*, 1950.
96. Dryden, H. L., and Schubauer, G. B. *J. Aeronaut. Sci. 14*, 221 (1947). Also appendix to [*97*].
97. Taylor, G. I., and Batchelor, G. K. *Quart. J. Mech. and Appl. Math. 2*, 1 (1949).
98. Townsend, A. A. *Quart. J. Mech. and Appl. Math. 4*, 308 (1951).
99. Tchen, C. M. *Phys. Rev. 93*, 4 (1954).
100. Kraichnan, R. H. *Phys. Rev. 107*, 1485 (1957); *109*, 1407 (1958).
101. Corrsin, S. *NACA Research Mem.* RM58B 11, 1958.

# SECTION D

# *CONDUCTION OF HEAT*

M. YACHTER
E. MAYER

## *CHAPTER 1. INTRODUCTION*

**D,1. General Remarks.** The mathematical description of temperature distributions, which arise in jet engine walls and other jet engine elements subjected to severe heat transfer rates, is of importance in the development of rational procedures for designing such elements. Owing to uncertainties in numerical data on thermal properties and heat transfer rates, it is usually sufficient in practice to calculate the temperatures for somewhat idealized geometric representations of the jet engine elements and for idealized heat transfer conditions, which nevertheless represent in good approximation the actual physical conditions. Thus the representative geometric models of particular interest are plane parallel slabs, cylinders, and cylindrical shells, in which heat flow is principally one-dimensional. Heat transfer rates across the boundaries are assumed to be of the Newtonian form; i.e. proportional to the difference between the temperature at the boundary and the temperature of the surrounding medium. Insofar as heat transfer through the boundaries occurs primarily by convection, rather than by conduction or radiation, the use of the Newtonian form appears justified. Radiation rates, governed by the Stefan-Boltzmann law, are of some importance in rocket chambers where they may contribute up to one third of the total heat transfer rate, and therefore they are only crudely represented by inclusion in the Newtonian form.

The problems discussed in this section have been selected on the basis of their immediate applicability to heat flow in combustion chambers and nozzles, in skins of high speed aircraft, turbine blades, etc. Emphasis is placed on simple, yet representative, model problems leading to analytic results, which allow an insight into the role played by geometry, heat transfer coefficients, and thermal properties, and which therefore lend themselves to generalizations not readily inferred from the complicated results of more difficult problems. Attention is focused on transient temperature problems which are of importance in uncooled combustion chamber walls. In regard to steady state problems which are important in cooled units, it is merely noted that, on the one hand, their solutions correspond in general to limiting cases of transient heat flow for long times; on the other hand their solutions may be obtained by special, elementary methods abundantly illustrated in the literature [*1,2,3,4,5*].

In the paragraphs below we summarize the general mathematical formulation of the heat conduction problem with emphasis on those features of the solution which have a special bearing on the particular problems presented in this section.

**D,2. Mathematical Formulation.** For our purposes it is sufficient to consider the differential equation of heat conduction in an isotropic two-dimensional domain $G$ without internal heat sources or sinks [*6*]:

$$\frac{\partial}{\partial x}\left(k\,\frac{\partial T}{\partial x}\right) + \frac{\partial}{\partial y}\left(k\,\frac{\partial T}{\partial y}\right) = \rho c\,\frac{\partial T}{\partial t} \tag{2-1}$$

In this equation $T$ is the temperature, $\rho$, $c$, and $k$ are the density, specific heat, and thermal conductivity of the medium in domain $G$, while $x$, $y$, and $t$ are, respectively, the two rectangular coordinates and the time. As stated in Art. 1, we shall consider heat transfer only by conduction and approximate radiation described by the Newtonian form with a heat transfer coefficient $h$ independent of the temperature or time. Thus

$$k\,\frac{\partial T}{\partial n} + h(x, y)[T - T_g] = 0 \quad \text{on the boundary } \Gamma \text{ of the domain } G \tag{2-2}$$

where, under the conditions stated, either $T_g$ = flame or gas temperature when $h \neq 0$ or otherwise $h = 0$. A derivative with respect to the (outer) normal to the boundary is represented by $\partial T/\partial n$.

The initial condition is

$$T(x, y, t_0) = F(x, y)$$

where, without loss of generality, we may write

$$t_0 = 0$$

Actually we are interested primarily in the cases where $F(x, y)$ = const, corresponding to ambient temperature. The conductivity $k$, the density $\rho$, and the specific heat $c$ may be functions of position as well as of the temperature $T$. The boundary condition may be even more general, as in the case of surface melting. In that case a term involving the heat energy absorbed in the change of state will also appear in the boundary condition, while the boundary $\Gamma$ itself will be changing with time (cf. [*7*]).

It is seen that the general differential equation and boundary conditions are *nonlinear* and, except for some special cases, cannot be discussed in any general manner. We shall discuss below at some length only two nonlinear problems: (1) The problem of surface melting as a factor in erosion and (2) the problem of heat conduction in a material with thermal properties ($k$ and $c$) which vary with the temperature. Finally, among the linear problems we shall discuss primarily those which involve only one space coordinate.

In order to reduce the boundary conditions to homogeneous form we make the transformation

$$\Theta = \frac{T}{T_g} - 1$$

Then the linear problems to be discussed are included in the following formulation:

$$\left.\begin{aligned} \frac{\partial}{\partial x}\left(k\,\frac{\partial \Theta}{\partial x}\right) + \frac{\partial}{\partial y}\left(k\,\frac{\partial \Theta}{\partial y}\right) &= \rho c\,\frac{\partial \Theta}{\partial t} \quad &&\text{in } G \\ \frac{\partial \Theta}{\partial n} + \frac{h(s)}{k}\,\Theta &= 0 &&\text{on } \Gamma \\ \Theta &= H(x, y) &&\text{at } t = 0 \end{aligned}\right\} \tag{2-1a}$$

where $s$ is the arc length on $\Gamma$ measured from a reference position and $k$, $\rho$, and $c$ are functions only of position. Detailed discussion of the mathematical system represented by Eq. 2-1a is given in texts dealing generally with the theory of partial differential equations. Here we merely summarize what may be considered as the most important characteristics of the system, particularly so in relation to analysis of heat conduction in solid mediums.

1. It is always possible to eliminate the time either by separation of variables or by the Laplace transform [6]. Thus by the method of separation of variables, if we write

$$\Theta = \varphi(x)\psi(t)$$

then

$$\frac{1}{\rho c \varphi}\left[\frac{\partial}{\partial x}\left(k\,\frac{\partial \varphi}{\partial x}\right) + \frac{\partial}{\partial y}\left(k\,\frac{\partial \varphi}{\partial y}\right)\right] = \frac{1}{\psi}\frac{d\psi}{dt} = -\lambda^2$$

$\lambda$ must be independent of $x$, $y$, and $t$, i.e. a constant, since the left-hand side is independent of $t$ while the right-hand side is independent of $x$ and $y$. Moreover, it can be shown that $\lambda^2$ is positive [8, Vol. 1, p. 252]. We obtain firstly

$$\psi = e^{-\lambda^2 t}$$

and secondly the eigenvalue problem

$$\left.\begin{aligned} \frac{\partial}{\partial x}\left(k\,\frac{\partial \varphi}{\partial x}\right) + \frac{\partial}{\partial y}\left(k\,\frac{\partial \varphi}{\partial y}\right) + \lambda^2 \rho c \varphi &= 0 \quad \text{in } G \\ k\,\frac{\partial \varphi}{\partial n} + h\varphi &= 0 \quad \text{on } \Gamma \end{aligned}\right\} \tag{2-2}$$

In general, the eigenvalue problem leads to an infinite set of eigenfunctions $\varphi_n$ with a corresponding infinite set of eigenvalues $\lambda_n$ which are obtained by satisfying the boundary conditions.

2. The eigenfunctions $\varphi_n$, when multiplied by $\sqrt{\rho c}$, form an orthogonal set. Since this is perhaps the most important property of the eigenfunctions we shall indicate briefly the proof of this important result: If $k$, $\rho$, and $c$ are continuous with continuous derivatives in the domain $G$, we have by a generalized Green's formula [8, Vol. 1, p. 239]:

$$\iint_G [\varphi_n L(\varphi_m) - \varphi_m L(\varphi_n)] dx dy = \int_\Gamma k\left(\varphi_n \frac{\partial \varphi_m}{\partial n} - \varphi_m \frac{\partial \varphi_n}{\partial n}\right) ds \qquad (2\text{-}3)$$

where $ds$ is an element of arc on $\Gamma$, and

$$L(\varphi) \equiv \frac{\partial}{\partial x}\left(k \frac{\partial \varphi}{\partial x}\right) + \frac{\partial}{\partial y}\left(k \frac{\partial \varphi}{\partial y}\right)$$

Substituting the differential equation and boundary condition (Eq. 2-2) into Eq. 2-3, we get

$$(\lambda_n^2 - \lambda_m^2) \iint_G \rho c \varphi_m \varphi_n dx dy = \int_\Gamma h(\varphi_m \varphi_n - \varphi_n \varphi_m) ds \equiv 0 \qquad (2\text{-}4)$$

Hence

$$\iint_G \rho c \varphi_m \varphi_n dx dy = 0 \quad \text{for} \quad m \neq n, \quad \lambda_m \neq \lambda_n$$

so that the functions

$$\Phi_n = \sqrt{\rho c}\, \varphi_n \qquad (n = 1, 2, \ldots)$$

form an orthogonal set.

It often happens that the thermal properties $k$, $\rho$, and $c$ are continuous in different subdomains $G_1$, $G_2$, etc., but are discontinuous across the boundaries $\Gamma_1$, $\Gamma_2$, . . . separating the domains, as is the case in composite rocket walls. In this case the general Green's formula must be applied to the subdomains $G_1$, $G_2$, etc., separately and the results added. Suppose for the sake of simplicity that the total domain $G$ is thus divided into only two subdomains, $G_1$ and $G_2$, separated by the boundary $\Gamma_1$ (see Fig. D,2). Let the $m$th and $n$th eigenfunction in $G$ be

$$\varphi = \begin{cases} \varphi_{1m}, \varphi_{1n} & \text{in} \quad G_1 \\ \varphi_{2m}, \varphi_{2n} & \text{in} \quad G_2 \end{cases}$$

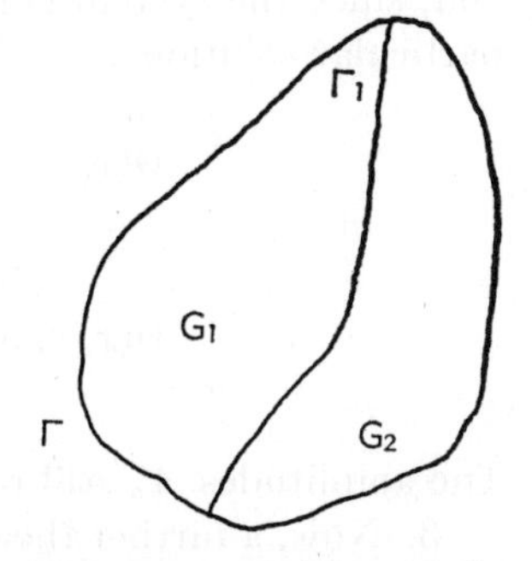

Fig. D,2. Division of the domain $G$ into the subdomains $G_1$ and $G_2$ by the boundary $\Gamma_1$.

Then, applying Green's formula in both domains separately and adding, we have

$$(\lambda_n^2 - \lambda_m^2)\left(\iint_{G_1} \rho_1 c_1 \varphi_{1m}\varphi_{1n} dxdy + \iint_{G_2} \rho_2 c_2 \varphi_{2m}\varphi_{2n} dxdy\right)$$

$$= \int_{\Gamma_1} \left[ k_1 \left( \varphi_{1n} \frac{\varphi_{1m}}{\partial n} - \varphi_{1m} \frac{\partial \varphi_{1n}}{\partial n} \right) - k_2 \left( \varphi_{2n} \frac{\partial \varphi_{2m}}{\partial n} - \varphi_{2m} \frac{\partial \varphi_{2n}}{\partial n} \right) \right] ds$$

$$= \int_{\Gamma_1} \left\{ \left[ \varphi_{1n} \left( k_1 \frac{\partial \varphi_{1m}}{\partial n} \right) - \varphi_{2n} \left( k_2 \frac{\partial \varphi_{2m}}{\partial n} \right) \right] - \left[ \varphi_{1m} \left( k_1 \frac{\partial \varphi_{1n}}{\partial n} \right) - \varphi_{2m} \left( k_2 \frac{\partial \varphi_{2n}}{\partial n} \right) \right] \right\} ds$$

the integrands on the exterior boundary vanishing identically as in Eq. 2-3, $n$ being a normal to the boundary.

Hence the function set

$$\Phi_n = \sqrt{\rho c}\, \varphi_n \qquad (n = 1, 2, \ldots)$$

will be orthogonal if

$$\varphi_{1n} = \varphi_{2n} \qquad k_1 \frac{\partial \varphi_{1n}}{\partial n} = k_2 \frac{\partial \varphi_{2n}}{\partial n} \quad \text{on} \quad \Gamma_1 \tag{2-5}$$

Now, the above conditions represent the physical requirements of continuity of temperature and heat flux through any internal boundary, and therefore the above relations represent the boundary conditions which must be used in internal boundaries separating domains of different mediums. It is seen, therefore, that by the imposition of the physical requirements, the orthogonality property of the function set $\sqrt{\rho c}\, \varphi_n$ is always automatically assured.

A particular solution is then

$$\Theta_n(x, y, t) = \varphi_n(x, y) e^{-\lambda_n^2 t}$$

and, since the system is linear, the complete solution is a linear sum of particular solutions:

$$\Theta(x, y, t) = \sum_{n=1}^{\infty} A_n \Theta_n = \sum_{n=1}^{\infty} A_n \varphi_n e^{-\lambda_n^2 t} \tag{2-6}$$

$$\Theta(x, y, 0) = \sum_{n=1}^{\infty} A_n \varphi_n(x, y) = F(x, y)$$

The amplitudes $A_n$ still remain to be determined.

3. Now, a further theorem [8, Vol. 1, p. 319] states that if $F(x, y)$ is a continuous function in the domain $G$ with continuous first and second derivatives and in addition *satisfies the boundary conditions of the problem*, then $F(x, y)$ can be expanded in an absolutely and uniformly convergent

series in terms of the eigenfunctions

$$F(x, y) = \sum_{n=1}^{\infty} A_n\varphi_n(x, y)$$

where, in view of the orthogonality property,

$$A_n = \frac{\iint\limits_G \rho c F \varphi_n dxdy}{\iint\limits_G \rho c \varphi_n^2 dxdy} \tag{2-7}$$

Actually, the function $F(x, y)$, representing the initial temperature distribution in the domain, seldom satisfies the boundary conditions, the usual form being $F(x, y) = \text{const}$. However, this is not a serious difficulty, for there always exists a function $\bar{F}(x, y)$ which satisfies all conditions of the theorem and is, nevertheless, arbitrarily close to $F(x, y)$. This can be seen immediately if $z = F(x, y)$ is regarded as the equation of a surface. The only consequence is that, in general, there will not be uniform convergence but rather convergence "in the mean," that is:

$$\lim_{n\to\infty} \iint\limits_G \Big[ \sum_{m=1}^{n} A_m\varphi_m(x, y) - F(x, y) \Big]^2 dxdy = 0$$

which is sufficient for all practical purposes (cf. [*8*, Vol. 1, p. 43]).

The practical use of the Fourier series solution (Eq. 2-6) for transient temperature calculations is contingent on rapid convergence of the series, which is assured for sufficiently large times $t$ by virtue of the decreasing exponential factors $e^{-\lambda_n^2 t}$. At small times, however, the convergence may become slow and calculations with Eq. 2-6 may become cumbersome. In this case, special approximate procedures, based on Laplace transform, source and image methods, etc. [*6*], prove to be more convenient. We shall have occasion to employ such procedures in the limit of small times when use of the Fourier series is not practical (cf. Art. 5).

It is seen then that the general problem reduces to the solution of the eigenvalue problem, or what is usually known as the third boundary-value problem in mathematical physics. It may be worthwhile to mention that the boundary-value problem can always be formulated as an equivalent isoperimetric problem in the calculus of variations, designated by Riemann as Dirichlet's principle (cf. [*8*, Vol. 2, Chap. 7]). In problems of vibration of beams, membranes, and plates, in aeroelastic problems, etc., this principle, also known as the Rayleigh-Ritz method, is a very powerful tool of analysis. However, in the case of heat conduction this method does not prove to be so useful.

**D,3. Thermal Property Data and Range of Heat Transfer Coefficients.** For purposes of orientation, Table D,3a below lists some thermal properties of typical materials employed in the construction of experimental and practical rocket engine walls. The listed data represent averaged properties between temperatures at ambient and 2000°F, as obtained from various sources.

*Table D,3a*

| Material | Metals | | | | Refractories | | |
|---|---|---|---|---|---|---|---|
| | Low carbon steel | Stainless steel | Copper | Molybdenum | Graphite | Alumina | Zirconia |
| $\rho$, lb/ft³ | 485 | 485 | 550 | 563 | 140 | 250 | 360 |
| $k$, $\frac{\text{BTU/hr}}{\text{ft}^2\ ^\circ\text{F/ft}}$ | 20 | 15 | 210 | 80 | 60 | 2.5 | 1.2 |
| $c$, BTU/lb °F | 0.15 | 0.15 | 0.10 | 0.08 | 0.17 | 0.30 | 0.16 |
| Melting temperature $T_m$, °F | 2700 | 2700 | 1980 | 4750 | .... | 3110* | 3850* |

* Failure temperature under 40 lb/in.²

Table D,3b below shows the range of gas heat transfer coefficients $h$(BTU/hr/ft² °F) occurring in various phases of jet propulsion engineering.

*Table D,3b*

| | Chamber | Nozzle throat | Ramjet and turbopump elements | Supersonic and hypersonic missile skin friction |
|---|---|---|---|---|
| $h$ | 100–400 | 700–4000 | 100–1000 | 100–2000 |

These ranges of $h$ are based on both experimental data and theoretical calculations.

# CHAPTER 2. ONE-DIMENSIONAL HEAT CONDUCTION IN A HOMOGENEOUS MEDIUM

**D,4. Slab of Thickness *d*.** The differential equation governing heat flow in the solid is

$$k\frac{\partial^2 T}{\partial x^2} = \rho c \frac{\partial T}{\partial t} \tag{4-1}$$

In accordance with the remarks in Art. 2 the boundary conditions (see Fig. D,4) are:

$$\left. \begin{aligned} k\frac{\partial T}{\partial x} &= h(T_g - T) \\ &= 0 \end{aligned} \right\} \quad \begin{aligned} &\text{at} \quad x = 0 \\ &\text{at} \quad x = d \end{aligned}$$

The initial condition is $T = 0$ at $t = 0$.

Introducing a transformation to nondimensional variables:

$$\Theta = \frac{T}{T_g} - 1 \quad \xi = \frac{x}{d} \quad \tau = \frac{kt}{\rho c d^2} \equiv \frac{\kappa t}{d^2} \tag{4-2}$$

where $\kappa$ is the thermal diffusivity of the material, $\kappa = k/\rho c$, we obtain the differential equation and boundary conditions in nondimensional form:

$$\frac{\partial^2 \Theta}{\partial \xi^2} = \frac{\partial \Theta}{\partial \tau} \tag{4-3}$$

$$\left. \begin{aligned} \frac{\partial \Theta}{\partial \xi} &= \frac{hd}{k} \\ &= 0 \end{aligned} \right\} \quad \begin{aligned} &\text{at} \quad \xi = 0 \\ &\text{at} \quad \xi = 1 \end{aligned} \tag{4-4}$$

with the initial condition

$$\Theta = -1 \quad \text{at} \quad \tau = 0 \tag{4-5}$$



Fig. D,4.

When the system is solved by separation of variables as discussed in Art. 2, we obtain the following results: The eigenfunctions are

$$\varphi_n(\xi) = \cos \mu_n(1 - \xi) \qquad (n = 1, 2, \ldots)$$

where the eigenvalues $\mu_n$ are the roots[1] of the eigenvalue equation

$$\mu \tan \mu = \frac{hd}{k} \tag{4-6}$$

The complete solution is

$$\theta(\xi, \tau) = \frac{T}{T_g} = 1 + \Theta(\xi, \tau) = 1 + \sum_{n=1}^{\infty} A_n \cos \mu_n(1 - \xi)e^{-\mu_n^2\tau} \tag{4-7}$$

where the amplitudes, determined from the initial condition $\Theta(\xi, 0) = -1$, are

$$A_n = \frac{-\int_0^1 \cos \mu_n(1 - \xi)d\xi}{\int_0^1 \cos^2 \mu_n(1 - \xi)d\xi} = -\frac{4 \sin \mu_n}{2\mu_n + \sin 2\mu_n} \tag{4-8}$$

It is seen from the nondimensional formulation (Eq. 4-3, 4-4, and 4-5)

[1] The first six roots of this transcendental equation, for $0 \leqq hd/k \leqq \infty$, are given in [6 (Appendix IV, Table 1)].

that the problem involves only one essential parameter, namely, the Biot number

$$N = \frac{hd}{k} \tag{4-9}$$

In the solution (Eq. 4-7) the Biot number enters via the eigenvalues which depend on $N$, according to Eq. 4-6.

Except for small values of $\tau$, corresponding to $\theta \ll 1$, the series in Eq. 4-7 converges rather rapidly and one or at the most two terms (in case of large $N$) are sufficient for practical purposes. When the convergence of the series is slow, good approximations of the temperature distribution in the slab can be obtained by application of results for the semi-infinite solid discussed in the next article.

**D,5. The Semi-Infinite Solid.** The heat flow problem for this case is formulated by the differential equation (Eq. 4-1) with its initial and boundary conditions for $d \to \infty$. Its solution [6, Chap. 2] can be put in the form,

$$\theta(N_x, \tau^*) = \operatorname{erfc} \frac{N_x}{\sqrt{\tau^*}} - e^{(N_x + \tau^*)} \operatorname{erfc} \left( \frac{N_x}{\sqrt{\tau^*}} + \sqrt{\tau^*} \right) \tag{5-1}$$

where erfc $z$ is the complementary error function,

$$\operatorname{erfc} z = 1 - \frac{2}{\sqrt{\pi}} \int_0^z e^{-z^2} dz$$

while the dimensionless variables are

$$\theta = \frac{T}{T_g} \qquad N_x = \frac{hx}{k} \qquad \tau^* = \frac{h^2 t}{k\rho c} \tag{5-2}$$

Curves of $\theta(N_x, \tau^*)$ vs. $\sqrt{\tau^*}$ with $N_x$ as parameter are shown in Fig. D,5.

In application to slabs of thickness $d$, the significant feature of these curves is that $\theta$ at $x = d$ in the semi-infinite solid is close to zero, until some time $\tau_d^*$ when the temperature at the position represented by $N_{x=d}$ begins to rise rapidly. For shorter times $\tau^* < \tau_d^*$, the temperature distribution in the slab is approximately represented by that in the semi-infinite solid with increasing accuracy as $x = \xi d$ approaches the flame side ($\xi \to 0$).

However, as $\xi \to 1$ the slab temperature given by Eq. 4-7 rises above that for the semi-infinite solid at $N_{x=\xi d}$, given by Eq. 5-1, owing to the influence of the boundary at $x = d$ where heat flow is blocked in accordance with the boundary condition $\partial T/\partial x = 0$ for the slab. The effect of this thermal barrier can be represented by supposing that, in addition to the *heat source* of strength $h(T_g - T)$ at $x = 0$, the region defined by $0 \leqq x \leqq d$ in the semi-infinite solid receives heat from an *image* source of this strength located at $x = 2d$, i.e. a distance $x = (2 - \xi)d$ from the plane at $x = \xi d$. It can be shown that, with two such sources located symmetrically about $x = d$, the conduction of heat in the region $0 \leqq x \leqq d$ is governed by the same differential equation and initial and boundary conditions as in the slab during a time $\tau^* < \tau^*_{2d}$, when the temperature rise

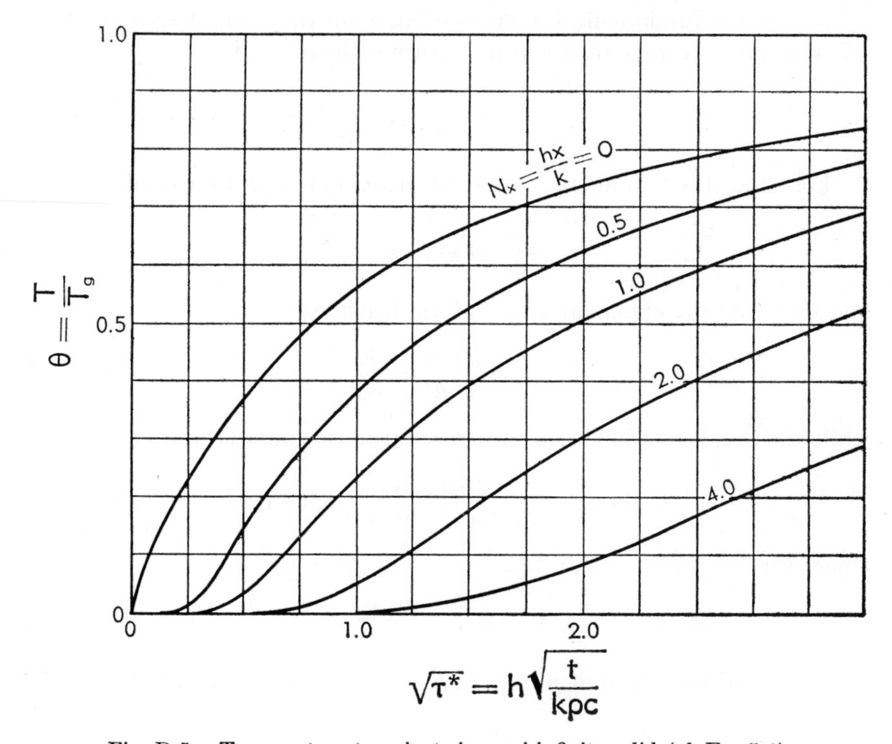


Fig. D,5. Temperature transients in semi-infinite solid (cf. Eq. 5-1).

at $x = 0$ is not yet influenced by the image source at $x = 2d$. The temperature in the slab given by Eq. 4-7 is therefore accurately represented at short times $\tau^* < \tau^*_{2d}$ by the superposed effect of the two sources:

$$\theta(\xi, \tau) = \theta(N_{x=\xi d}, \tau^*) + \theta(N_{x=(2-\xi)d}, \tau^*) \tag{5-3}$$

where the conversion from $\tau^*$ to $\tau$ for the slab is $\tau = \tau^*/N^2_{x=d}$.

In practice, Eq. 5-3 is accurate within 1 per cent of $\theta$ up to times when the Fourier representation (Eq. 4-7) requires only one term for 1 per cent accuracy. Computations of $\theta(N_x, \tau^*)$ in Eq. 5-1 and 5-3 are facilitated by tables of $e^{z^2}$ erfc $z$ and appropriate asymptotic expansions given in [*6*].

**D,6. Applications.** The temperature distribution in the slab given by Eq. 4-7 may be regarded as a superposition of damped spatial modes, $\cos \mu_n(1 - \xi)$, with decreasing amplitudes $A_n$ and increasing exponential damping due to the factor $e^{-\mu_n^2\tau}$ as the mode number increases. Insofar as the fundamental mode $n = 1$ is the dominant term in the Fourier series, the physical role of the material and heating parameters $(h, T_g)$ in the development of temperatures in the slab can be deduced from the expression for this mode.

If only the fundamental mode is retained in the Fourier series of Eq. 4-7, the space average of the temperature ratio $\theta(\xi, \tau)$ is

$$\bar{\theta}(\tau) = \int_0^1 \theta(\xi, \tau) d\xi = 1 + A_1 \frac{\sin \mu_1}{\mu_1} e^{-\mu_1^2\tau} + \cdots \tag{6-1}$$

For small Biot numbers $N \ll 1$ the eigenvalue equation yields

$$N = \mu_1 \tan \mu_1 \cong \mu_1^2 \cong \frac{hd}{k}$$

and therefore the exponential time term becomes

$$\mu_1^2\tau = \frac{hd}{k}\frac{\kappa t}{d^2} = \frac{ht}{\rho c d}$$

while the amplitude in the mean temperature formula (Eq. 6-1) is

$$A_1 = -\frac{4 \sin^2 \mu_1}{\mu_1(2\mu_1 + \sin 2\mu_1)} \cong -1 \tag{6-2}$$

Hence for $N \ll 1$, the mean temperature is given by

$$\bar{\theta}(\tau) \cong 1 - e^{-\frac{ht}{\rho c d}} \tag{6-3}$$

showing that, for low Biot numbers, the slab has a time constant

$$t_c = \frac{\rho c d}{h} \qquad N \ll 1 \tag{6-4}$$

which, in contrast with time constants of vibratory mechanical or electrical systems, depends not only upon the system structure (thermal properties and thickness) but also upon an external factor, namely the heat transfer coefficient.

For larger $N$ the amplitude given by Eq. 6-2 is still approximately $-1$, and a more general expression, analogous to Eq. 6-4, is obtained for the time constant:

$$t_c = \frac{d^2}{\kappa\mu_1^2} \tag{6-5}$$

where the heat transfer coefficient enters $t_c$ via the Biot number implicit in $\mu_1$. The dependence on $N$ becomes weak for $N > 2$ as $\mu_1$ approaches its asymptotic value of $\pi/2$ for large $N$.

In application to rocket wall design, Eq. 4-7 is useful in determining the thicknesses of relatively thin cylindrical elements in which heat flow is principally in the radial direction (cf. Art. 7). The design problem usually consists of the determination of $d$ for given material constants and heat transfer parameters $h$ and $T_g$, subject to the condition that, at the end of a specified duration time $t_d$, a given critical temperature $T_{cr}$ shall be attained at a position $x_{cr}$. Thus $T_{cr}$ might be the melting temperature and the position might be at the flame boundary $x_{cr} = 0$.

In thin-walled rocket chambers, $T_{cr}$ usually corresponds to a space average temperature at which the strength of the material begins to decrease appreciably. From Eq. 6-1 and 6-2 we obtain for this case the following expression for $t_d$ in terms of $t_c$ and $\theta_{cr} = T_{cr}/T_g$:

$$t_d = t_c \ln \frac{1}{1 - \theta_{cr}} \tag{6-6}$$

For small Biot numbers the above criterion yields from Eq. 6-4

$$d = \frac{ht_d}{\rho c \ln \dfrac{1}{1 - \theta_{cr}}} \tag{6-7}$$

and for greater Biot numbers we have from Eq. 6-5

$$d \cong \mu_1 \sqrt{\frac{\kappa t_d}{\ln \dfrac{1}{1 - \theta_{cr}}}} \tag{6-8}$$

The latter is applicable in the approximation that the temperature drop across the slab at the time $t_d$ as computed from Eq. 4-7 is small compared with $T_{cr}$:

$$T(0, t_d) - T(d, t_d) \ll T_{cr} \tag{6-9}$$

Under many conditions the inequality (Eq. 6-9) cannot be well satisfied by use of the criteria, represented by Eq. 6-7 and 6-8, based on the mean temperature formula (Eq. 6-1). Thus when $h$ and $T_g$ are sufficiently large, there may be large temperature drops across the wall at the time $t_d$; then $T_{cr}$ is usually specified at (or near) the flame side. Here either one or two terms in the Fourier series of Eq. 4-7 or the use of Eq. 5-3 may suffice to determine $d$. It may happen, however, that the desired duration time $t_d$ is so large with given large heat transfer parameters $(h, T_g)$ that $\theta_{cr}$ will be exceeded regardless of the thickness $d$, i.e. Eq. 4-7 or Eq. 5-3 cannot be solved for $d$. This can be ascertained by noting that the flame side temperature transient for the semi-infinite solid $\theta(0, \tau^*)$ in Eq. 5-1 rises slower than that of any finite slab with the same $h$, $T_g$, and material constants. In other words, when the following condition,

$$\theta(0, \tau_d^*) = 1 - e^{\tau_d^*} \operatorname{erfc} \sqrt{\tau_d^*} > \theta_{cr}$$

with

$$\tau_d^* = \frac{h^2 t_d}{k\rho c}$$

holds, then the desired duration time $t_d$ cannot be attained for any slab thickness whatever.

# CHAPTER 3. TRANSIENT RADIAL HEAT CONDUCTION IN A HOMOGENEOUS HOLLOW CYLINDER

**D,7. Classical Results for Newtonian Heat Transfer.** Let the inner and outer radii of the hollow cylinder be $a$ and $b$, respectively, as

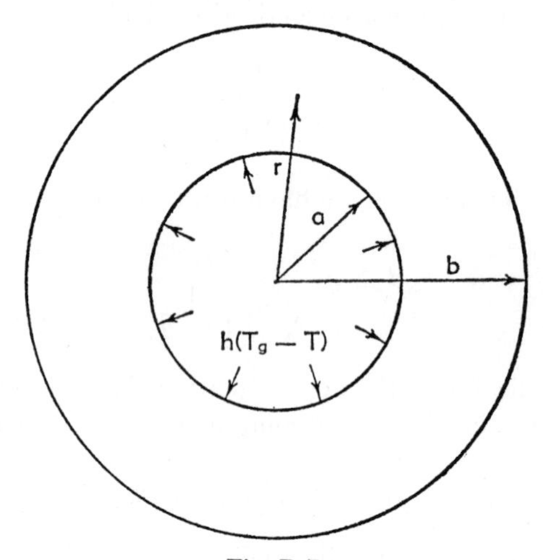


Fig. D,7.

shown on Fig. D,7. The temperature distribution $T(r, t)$ satisfies the differential equation in polar coordinates,

$$k\left(\frac{\partial^2 T}{\partial r^2} + \frac{1}{r}\frac{\partial T}{\partial r}\right) = \rho c \frac{\partial T}{\partial t} \tag{7-1}$$

We consider a Newtonian heat input at $r = a$ from a flame at temperature $T_g$

$$k \frac{\partial T}{\partial r}\bigg|_{r=a} = h(T(a, t) - T_g)$$

and no heat transfer through the boundary at $r = b$

$$\frac{\partial T}{\partial r}\bigg|_{r=b} = 0$$

The initial condition is, as usual, $T(r, 0) = 0$. The dimensionless variables appropriate to the cylinder problem are

$$\Theta = \frac{T}{T_g} - 1, \qquad \omega = \frac{r}{a}, \qquad \tau_a = \frac{\kappa t}{a^2} \tag{7-2}$$

by which Eq. 7-1 and its initial and boundary conditions become

$$\frac{\partial^2 \Theta}{\partial \omega^2} + \frac{1}{\omega}\frac{\partial \Theta}{\partial \omega} = \frac{\partial \Theta}{\partial \tau_a} \tag{7-3}$$

$$\left.\begin{aligned} \frac{\partial \Theta}{\partial \omega} &= \left(\frac{ha}{k}\right)\Theta \quad \text{at} \quad \omega = 1 \\ \frac{\partial \Theta}{\partial \omega} &= 0 \qquad\quad \text{at} \quad \omega = \frac{b}{a} \end{aligned}\right\} \tag{7-4}$$

$$\Theta = -1 \qquad \text{at} \quad \tau_a = 0 \tag{7-5}$$

From this nondimensional form it is seen that the solution depends essentially on only two dimensionless parameters, namely a type of Biot number, $N_a = ha/k$ and the ratio $b/a$, which we shall designate as $\Omega$, the thickness number. When the system is solved by separation of variables as discussed in Art. 2, the results are expressed in terms of the following combinations of Bessel functions $J$ and Neumann functions $Y$:

$$R_0(\mu\omega) = \frac{J_0(\mu\omega)}{J_1(\mu\Omega)} - \frac{Y_0(\mu\omega)}{Y_1(\mu\Omega)}$$

$$R_1(\mu\omega) = \frac{J_1(\mu\omega)}{J_1(\mu\Omega)} - \frac{Y_1(\mu\omega)}{Y_1(\mu\Omega)}$$

where the general eigenvalue $\mu$ satisfies the characteristic equation [9],

$$-\mu\frac{R_1(\mu)}{R_0(\mu)} = N_a \tag{7-6}$$

the eigenfunction corresponding to the $n$th root $\mu_n$ of Eq. 7-6 is:

$$\varphi_n(\omega) = R_0(\mu_n\omega)$$

with the orthogonality condition in this case (i.e. polar coordinates)

$$\int_1^\Omega \varphi_n(\omega)\varphi_m(\omega)\omega d\omega = 0 \qquad (m \neq n) \tag{7-7}$$

The complete solution in nondimensional variables is:

$$\theta(\omega, \tau_a) = \frac{T}{T_g} = 1 + \Theta(\omega, \tau_a) = 1 + \sum_{n=1}^{\infty} A_n R_0(\mu_n\omega)e^{-\mu_n^2\tau_a} \tag{7-8}$$

where the amplitudes [9] determined from the initial condition $\Theta(\omega, 0) = -1$ are

$$A_n = -\frac{\int_1^\Omega R_0(\mu_n\omega)\omega d\omega}{\int_1^\Omega R_0^2(\mu_n\omega)\omega d\omega} = -\frac{2N_a R_0(\mu_n)}{(\mu_n\Omega)^2 R_0^2(\mu_n\Omega) - (\mu_n^2 + N_a^2)R_0^2(\mu_n)} \tag{7-9}$$

Analogous expressions for temperature transients due to Newtonian heat input at the outer radius of the shell, $r = b$, are given in [10]. All of the above results can be readily deduced from the somewhat more general result, i.e. the heat transfer through both boundaries, obtained in [6, p. 278].

It is seen that the formal expressions for the hollow cylinder are considerably more cumbersome than those for the slab. It is therefore of practical importance to ascertain the range of wall thickness to radius ratio, so that the problem can still be treated in a good approximation by expressions for an equivalent slab. This point will be discussed in more detail in the next article.

**D,8. Applications. Thermal Stresses.** For a hollow cylinder of rather large thickness number $\Omega = 2$ and a slab of thickness $d = b - a = (\Omega - 1)a = a$, the flame side temperature transients are shown in Fig. D,8 for $hd/k = h(b - a)/k = 1$. Initially, the temperatures rise at the same rate in both structures; subsequently, as the larger heat capacity of the cylinder is utilized by the heat flow, the temperature falls below that in the slab. Thus, in relatively thick (refractory) cylinders, use of the slab formula may lead to considerable error in the calculation of temperatures. However, for relatively thin cylinders (metallic walls), the heat capacities of the cylinder and slab of same thickness are approximately equal, in the ratio

$$\rho c \frac{\pi(b^2 - a^2)}{2\pi a} : \rho c(b - a) = \frac{1}{2}(\Omega + 1) \tag{8-1}$$

It is to be noted further that the effect of the larger heat capacity on the temperature is to some extent counteracted by the Newtonian type of heat input, which is greater at lower wall temperature. By detailed studies of temperature distributions based on Eq. 7-8, it is found [9,11] that the equivalent slab solution is applicable within the approximation with which $h$ and the material data can be specified in practice, provided the thickness number $\Omega$ does not exceed 1.2. This result justifies the use of slab formulas in application to thin-walled cylindrical structures, such as rocket chambers, metallic nozzle walls, etc.

Larger thickness numbers $\Omega$ occur for refractory shells used as inserts in rocket chambers and nozzles. With such refractory liners the problem of thermal stresses becomes important in design considerations. In the approximation that the material behaves elastically in the temperature range of interest, the transient thermal stresses in the cylinder can be calculated by use of Eq. 7-6 in the thermoelastic equations [*12*], relating the stresses to instantaneous temperature distributions. This has been done in [*11*] with the following principal results for the long hollow cylinder heated by Newtonian heat transfer through the inner boundary.

At any instant $t > 0$ the transient hoop stresses $\sigma(r, t)$ have extreme values at the boundaries, there being maximum compressive stress $\sigma_a(t) = \sigma(a, t)$ at the inner boundary and maximum tensile stress $\sigma_b(t) = \sigma(b, t)$ at the outer boundary. Similarly, axial stresses also have extreme values

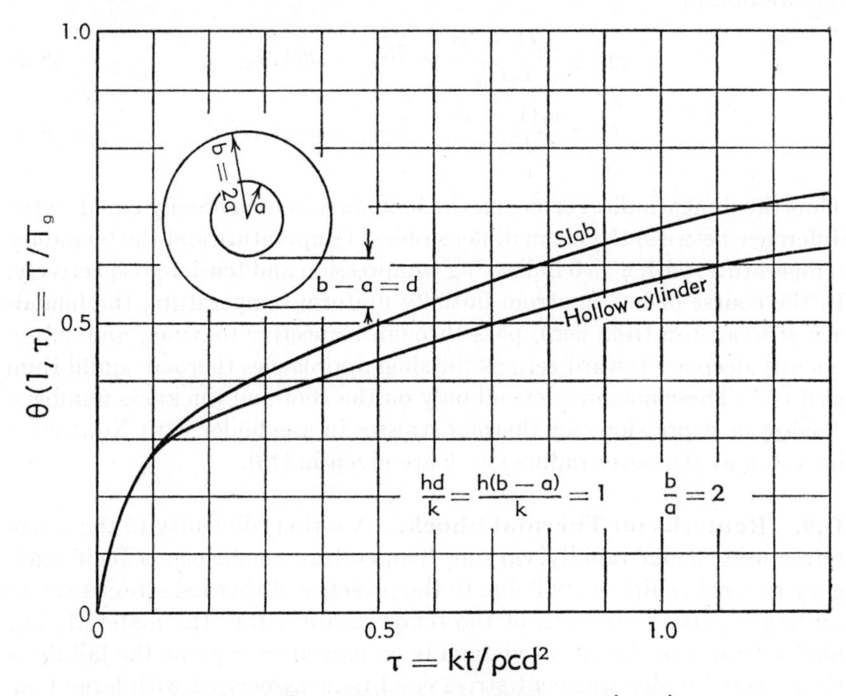


Fig. D,8. Comparison of temperature transients in plane parallel slab and hollow cylinder.

at any instant at the boundaries, $r = a, b$, where these extremes are equal numerically to the local hoop stresses $\sigma_a(t)$, $\sigma_b(t)$ respectively. Radial stresses are zero at the boundaries and rise to a maximum within the shell, but this maximum is small compared with boundary stresses at any instant. The thermoelastic equations [*11*] lead to rather simple expressions, as given below, for the boundary stresses $\sigma_a(t)$ and $\sigma_b(t)$. These boundary stresses in turn possess absolute maxima attained at some time during the heating process.

We define the dimensionless stress $\eta$ by

$$\eta = \frac{\sigma(1 - \nu)}{E\beta T_g} \tag{8-1}$$

where $\nu$, $E$, and $\beta$ represent Poisson's ratio, Young's modulus, and the coefficient of thermal expansion, respectively.

By the use of Eq. 7-8, the mean dimensionless temperature in the cylinder is

$$\bar{\theta}(\tau_a) = \frac{1}{\pi(b^2 - a^2)} \int_a^b \frac{T(r, t)}{T_g} 2\pi r dr = \frac{2}{\Omega^2 - 1} \int_1^\Omega \theta(\omega, \tau_a)\omega d\omega$$

Accordingly, solving the thermoelastic equations for the heated cylinder [*11*] we obtain:

$$\eta_a = \frac{\sigma_a(1 - \nu)}{E\beta T_g} = \bar{\theta}(\tau_a) - \theta(1, \tau_a) \tag{8-2}$$

$$\eta_b = \frac{\sigma_b(1 - \nu)}{E\beta T_g} = \bar{\theta}(\tau_a) - \theta(\Omega, \tau_a) \tag{8-3}$$

Thus the dimensionless stress on the boundary is numerically equal to the difference between the mean dimensionless temperature and the boundary temperature, with $\eta \lessgtr 0$ indicating compression and tension, respectively. In the course of heating from initially uniform temperature, the boundary stresses rise from zero, pass through respective maxima, and subsequently decrease toward zero as the shell approaches thermal equilibrium at $\theta = 1$. These maxima depend only on the Biot and thickness numbers. Analogous expressions for thermal stresses in a cylinder with Newtonian heat flux at the outer radius $r = b$ are given in [*13*].

**D,9. Remarks on Thermal Shock.** A serious difficulty in the use of refractories under rapidly varying temperature conditions is their tendency to crack, chip, or spall due to the presence of thermal stresses set up by large spatial variations of the temperature within the material. The phrase "thermal shock" is commonly employed to describe the failure of the material under transient stress conditions associated with large temperature gradients. In the literature on the subject, various criteria have been proposed to express the resistance to thermal shock in terms of material properties and size factors. Recently [*14*] an attempt has been made to include the effect of heating parameters in the criterion for resistance to thermal shock. On this basis it can be shown that previously proposed criteria are special cases corresponding to various regimes of the heat transfer coefficient $h$.

The physical role of material and heating parameters in the occurrence of thermal shock can be described, assuming that the material behaves elastically, by comparison of transient thermal stresses with maximum stresses such as, say, the yield stress of the material.

This has been done in [*14*] on the model of a slab of thickness $2d$ heated (or cooled) symmetrically by Newtonian heat transfer through its boundaries. The results given below from [*14*] can also be deduced from Eq. 8-2 and 8-3 for the hollow cylinder,[2] in the limit $\Omega \to 1$.

At any instant $t > 0$ the thermal stresses have maximum values at the boundaries (compression on heating) and the midplane (tension on heating). Let the dimensionless stresses at the boundaries and midplane be denoted by $\eta_0(\tau)$ and $\eta_m(\tau)$ respectively. As functions of $\tau$ these have absolute maxima, $|\eta_0|_{max}$ and $|\eta_m|_{max}$, the magnitude of which depend only on the Biot number $N = hd/k$ as shown in Fig. D,9. If $S_c$ and $S_t$ denote,

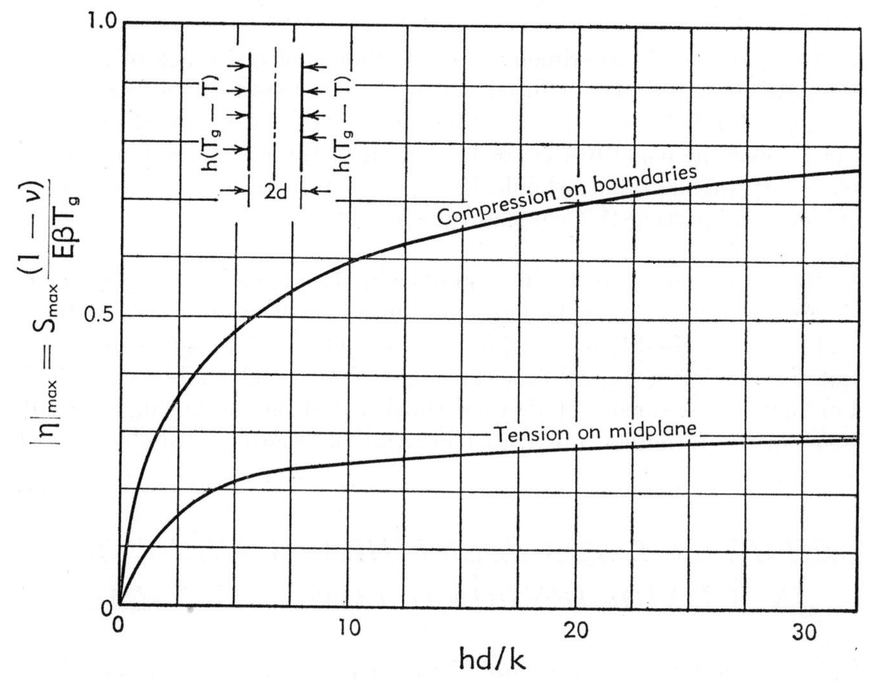


Fig. D,9. Maximum dimensionless stresses $|\eta|_{max}$ in symmetrically heated plane parallel slab vs. Biot number.

respectively, the yield stress in compression and tension, the corresponding allowed dimensionless stresses are

$$\eta_c = \frac{S_c(1 - \nu)}{E\beta T_g}$$

$$\eta_t = \frac{S_t(1 - \nu)}{E\beta T_g}$$

Thus, in heating the slab, the resistance to thermal shock is measured by

[2] The midplane divides the slab into two regions, in each of which the thermal stress distributions correspond to limiting cases of the thin hollow cylinder with $d = b - a$, $\Omega \to 1$.

the ratios

$$R_{\text{compression}} = \frac{\eta_c}{|\eta_0|_{\max}} \qquad R_{\text{tension}} = \frac{\eta_t}{|\eta_m|_{\max}} \tag{9-1}$$

which involve, in addition to material properties, the heat transfer parameters $h$ and $T_g$. On symmetric cooling of the slab, analogous relations are [*14*]

$$R_{\text{tension}} = \frac{\eta_t}{|\eta_0|_{\max}} \qquad R_{\text{compression}} = \frac{\eta_c}{|\eta_m|_{\max}} \tag{9-2}$$

Comparisons of experimentally rated values of resistance to thermal shock with analytically deduced values show a one-to-one correlation of $R_{\text{tension}}$ in Eq. 9-2 with experimental data [*14*]. It is conjectured therefore that, under the usual test conditions of alternate heating and cooling of refractory bricks, failure should be expected primarily in tension. Some evidence supporting this conjecture is provided by experimental data in [*15*, p. 16].

The appearance of the Biot number in the above thermal shock resistance formulas shows the varying importance of thermal conductivity and size factor in different regimes of the heat transfer coefficient $h$. Detailed discussion of the resistance formulas (Eq. 9-1 and 9-2) is given in [*14*]. For further treatments of thermal shock based on the use of transient temperature formulas substituted in available thermal stress equations see [*16,17*].

## *CHAPTER 4. TRANSIENT HEAT CONDUCTION IN A UNIDIMENSIONAL COMPOSITE SLAB*

**D,10. General Results for Newtonian Heat Transfer.** The problem of heat flow in a composite rocket wall may be treated approximately on the basis of heat conduction in a composite slab (Fig. D,10) consisting of an *inner* layer between $x = -d_1$ and $x = 0$, possessing uniform thermal properties (distinguished by subscript 1) and an *outer* layer between $x = 0$ and $x = d_2$ with uniform thermal properties (distinguished by subscript 2). The inner material usually serves as a thermal shield of low inherent strength (refractories) preventing excessive temperature rises in the outer material (metals, Fiberglas at low temperatures) which must withstand the combustion pressures developed during the operation of the rocket engine.

In accordance with the results in Art. 2, we formulate the problem for the dimensionless temperature defect $\Theta = (T/T_g) - 1$ as

$$\Theta = \varphi(x)\psi(t) \quad \psi(t) = e^{-\lambda^2 t} \qquad \Theta = -1 \quad \text{at} \quad t = 0$$

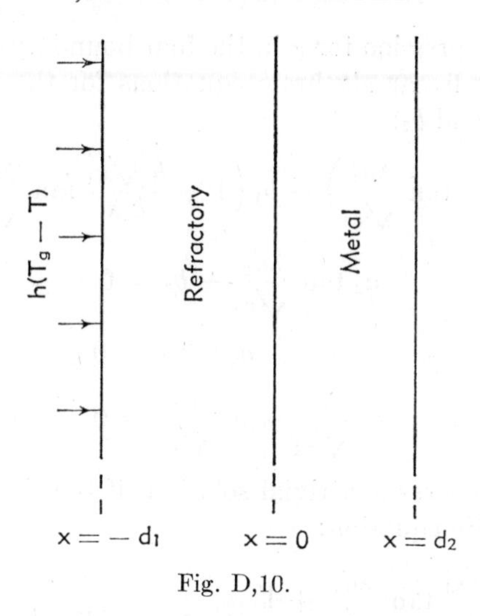


Fig. D,10.

where the eigenvalue differential equation for $\varphi(x)$ is

$$k \frac{d^2\varphi}{dx^2} + \rho c \lambda^2 \varphi = 0 \tag{10-1}$$

$$\left.\begin{array}{llll} k = k_1 & \rho c = \rho_1 c_1 & \kappa = \kappa_1 = \dfrac{k_1}{\rho_1 c_1} & \varphi = \varphi_1(x) \\ k = k_2 & \rho c = \rho_2 c_2 & \kappa = \kappa_2 = \dfrac{k_2}{\rho_2 c_2} & \varphi = \varphi_2(x) \end{array}\right\} \begin{array}{l} -d_1 \leqq x \leqq 0 \\ 0 \leqq x \leqq d_2 \end{array}$$

with exterior boundary conditions

$$k_1 \frac{d\varphi_1}{dx} = h\varphi_1 \qquad x = -d_1 \tag{10-2}$$

$$\frac{d\varphi_2}{dx} = 0 \qquad x = d_2 \tag{10-3}$$

and interior boundary conditions

$$\varphi_1 = \varphi_2 \qquad x = 0 \tag{10-4}$$

$$k_1 \frac{d\varphi_1}{dx} = k_2 \frac{d\varphi_2}{dx} \qquad x = 0 \tag{10-5}$$

The eigenfunction obtained from Eq. 10-1 is

$$\varphi(x) = \begin{cases} \varphi_1(x) = a_1 \cos \dfrac{\lambda x}{\sqrt{\kappa_1}} + b_1 \sin \dfrac{\lambda x}{\sqrt{\kappa_1}} & -d_1 \leqq x \leqq 0 \\ \varphi_2(x) = a_2 \cos \dfrac{\lambda x}{\sqrt{\kappa_2}} + b_2 \sin \dfrac{\lambda x}{\sqrt{\kappa_2}} & 0 \leqq x \leqq d_2 \end{cases} \tag{10-6}$$

Substituting the expression for $\varphi$ in the four boundary conditions, we get four homogeneous linear algebraic equations for the constants of integration $a_1$, $a_2$, $b_1$, and $b_2$:

$$a_1\left(\frac{h\sqrt{\kappa_1}}{k_1\lambda} - \tan\frac{\lambda d_1}{\sqrt{\kappa_1}}\right) - b_1\left(1 + \frac{h\sqrt{\kappa_1}}{k_1\lambda}\tan\frac{\lambda d_1}{\sqrt{\kappa_1}}\right) = 0 \quad (10\text{-}2a)$$

$$a_2 \tan\frac{\lambda d_2}{\sqrt{\kappa_2}} - b_2 = 0 \quad (10\text{-}3a)$$

$$a_1 - a_2 = 0 \quad (10\text{-}4a)$$

$$b_1\frac{k_1}{\sqrt{\kappa_1}} - b_2\frac{k_2}{\sqrt{\kappa_2}} = 0 \quad (10\text{-}5a)$$

These equations possess nontrivial solutions if the eigenvalue $\lambda$ is a root of the characteristic equation:

$$\frac{\dfrac{h\sqrt{\kappa_1}}{k_1\lambda}\tan\dfrac{\lambda d_1}{\sqrt{\kappa_1}} + 1}{\dfrac{h\sqrt{\kappa_1}}{k_1\lambda} - \tan\dfrac{\lambda d_1}{\sqrt{\kappa_1}}}\tan\frac{\lambda d_2}{\sqrt{\kappa_2}} - \frac{k_1}{k_2}\sqrt{\frac{\kappa_2}{\kappa_1}} = 0 \quad (10\text{-}7)$$

This characteristic equation yields, of course, an infinite set of eigenvalues

$$\lambda = \lambda_n \qquad (n = 1, 2, \ldots)$$

For each eigenvalue $\lambda_n$ there exists a set of integration constants ($a_{1n}$, $a_{2n}$, $b_{1n}$, $b_{2n}$) and the ratios of any three to the fourth one can be determined from the boundary conditions, Eq. 10-2a through 10-5a. Thus

$$\frac{a_{2n}}{a_{1n}} = 1, \quad \frac{b_{1n}}{a_{1n}} = \frac{k_2}{k_1}\sqrt{\frac{\kappa_1}{\kappa_2}}\tan\frac{\lambda_n d_2}{\sqrt{\kappa_2}}, \quad \frac{b_{2n}}{a_{1n}} = \tan\frac{\lambda_n d_2}{\sqrt{\kappa_2}} \quad (10\text{-}8)$$

The particular solution corresponding to $\lambda_n$ is

$$\Theta_n = \varphi_n(x)\psi_n(t) = \begin{cases} \Theta_{1n} = \varphi_{1n}(x)\psi_n(t) = \left(\cos\dfrac{\lambda_n x}{\sqrt{\kappa_1}} + b_1 \sin\dfrac{\lambda_n x}{\sqrt{\kappa_1}}\right)e^{-\lambda_n^2 t} \\[2ex] \Theta_{2n} = \varphi_{2n}(x)\psi_n(t) = \left(\cos\dfrac{\lambda_n x}{\sqrt{\kappa_2}} + b_1 \sin\dfrac{\lambda_n x}{\sqrt{\kappa_2}}\right)e^{-\lambda_n^2 t} \end{cases} \quad (10\text{-}9)$$

where, without loss of generality we have set $a_{1n} = 1$, since this constant can always be included in the amplitudes $A_n$ which appear in the general solution (cf. Eq. 2-6),

$$\Theta(x, t) = \sum A_n\Theta_n = \sum A_n\varphi_n(x)e^{-\lambda_n^2 t}$$

$$\frac{T(x, t)}{T_g} = \theta(x, t) = 1 + \Theta(x, t)$$

By the results of Art. 2 we determine the amplitudes $A_n$ upon expansion of $\Theta(x, 0) = -1$ in terms of the eigenfunctions $\varphi_n(x)$. Thus we obtain from Eq. 2-7

$$A_n = -\frac{\int \rho c \varphi_n dx}{\int \rho c \varphi_n^2 dx} = -\frac{\int_{-d_1}^{0} \rho_1 c_1 \varphi_{1n} dx + \int_0^{d_2} \rho_2 c_2 \varphi_{2n} dx}{\int_{-d_1}^{0} \rho_1 c_1 \varphi_{1n}^2 dx + \int_0^{d_2} \rho_2 c_2 \varphi_{2n}^2 dx}$$

At this point it is convenient to introduce the following nondimensional quantities:

$$\xi_1 = \frac{x}{d_1}, \quad \xi_2 = \frac{x}{d_2}, \quad \tau_1 = \frac{\kappa_1 t}{d_1^2}, \quad \tau_2 = \frac{\kappa_2 t}{d_2^2}$$

$$\mu_{1n}^2 \tau_1 = \mu_{2n}^2 \tau_2 = \lambda_n^2 \tau, \quad \left(\frac{\mu_{2n}}{\mu_{1n}} = \frac{d_2}{d_1} \sqrt{\frac{\kappa_1}{\kappa_2}}\right)$$

Then the characteristic equation for $\mu_1$ (or $\mu_2$) is

$$\frac{N_1 \tan \mu_1 + \mu_1}{N_1 - \mu_1 \tan \mu_1} \tan \mu_2 = \frac{k_1}{k_2} \sqrt{\frac{\kappa_2}{\kappa_1}}, \quad N_1 = \frac{h d_1}{k_1} \tag{10-7a}$$

and the expression for the amplitude in Eq. 10-6 becomes

$$A_n = -\frac{\rho_1 c_1 G_{1n} + \rho_2 c_2 G_{2n}}{\rho_1 c_1 H_{1n} + \rho_2 c_2 H_{2n}} \tag{10-10}$$

where

$$G_{1n} = \frac{d_1}{\mu_{1n}} [\sin \mu_{1n} + b_{1n} (\cos \mu_{1n} - 1)]$$

$$G_{2n} = \frac{d_2}{\mu_{2n}} [\sin \mu_{2n} - b_{2n} (\cos \mu_{2n} - 1)]$$

$$H_{1n} = \frac{d_1}{2\mu_{1n}} [(1 + b_{1n}^2)\mu_{1n} + (1 - b_{1n}^2) \sin \mu_{1n} \cos \mu_{1n} - 2b_{1n} \sin^2 \mu_{1n}]$$

$$H_{2n} = \frac{d_2}{2\mu_{2n}} [(1 + b_{2n}^2)\mu_{2n} + (1 - b_{2n}^2) \sin \mu_{2n} \cos \mu_{2n} + 2b_{2n} \sin^2 \mu_{2n}]$$

Thus we obtain for the temperature distribution:

$$\frac{T(x, t)}{T_g} = \theta(\xi, \tau)$$

$$= \begin{bmatrix} 1 + \sum A_n (\cos \mu_{1n}\xi_1 + b_{1n} \sin \mu_{1n}\xi_1) e^{-\mu_{1n}^2 \tau_1} & -1 \leqq \xi_1 \leqq 0 \\ 1 + \sum A_n (\cos \mu_{2n}\xi_2 + b_{2n} \sin \mu_{2n}\xi_2) e^{-\mu_{2n}^2 \tau_2} & 0 \leqq \xi_2 \leqq 1 \end{bmatrix} \tag{10-11}$$

where the $\mu_{1n}$'s ($\mu_{2n}$'s) are computed from the eigenvalue equation (Eq. 10-7a), the amplitudes $A_n$ are determined by Eq. 10-10, and the $b_n$'s are computed from Eq. 10-8 for $a_{1n} = 1$. The first two eigenvalues satisfying Eq. 10-7a are obtainable from curves in [*18*].

Computation of temperatures from Eq. 10-11 are generally rather cumbersome. However, for two limiting cases of importance in rocket engineering, i.e. thin and thick shielding layers, computations based on Eq. 10-11 can be considerably simplified, as shown in the next two articles.

**D,11. The "Thin" Shield.** In practice, some thermal shielding of rocket walls is effected by very thin refractories or protective paints on the inner boundary under conditions when, while $N_1 > 1$, the thickness $d_1$ is sufficiently small to give rise to the following relations in Eq. 10-7a:

$$\mu_{1n} < \mu_{2n}, \quad \mu_{11} \cong \tan \mu_{11}, \quad \mu_{11}^2 \ll N_1 = \frac{hd_1}{k_1} \tag{11-1}$$

When these relations are satisfied, Eq. 10-7a leads to an approximate equation for $\mu_{21}$

$$\mu_{21} \tan \mu_{21} \cong \frac{hd_2/k_2}{1 + hd_1/k_1} \tag{11-2}$$

Furthermore, upon substitution of these approximations into the formula for $A_1$ in Eq. 10-10, it is found that the expression

$$A_1(\cos \mu_{21}\xi_2 + b_{21} \sin \mu_{21}\xi_2)$$

reduces to

$$-\frac{4 \sin \mu_{21}}{2\mu_{21} + \sin 2\mu_{21}} \cos \mu_{21}(1 - \xi_2)$$

Hence, when the higher Fourier terms in Eq. 10-11 are negligible, the temperature of the shielded material given by this equation reduces to the simple slab formula (cf. Eq. 4-7 and 4-8):

$$\theta(\xi_2, \tau_2) \cong 1 - \frac{4 \sin \mu_{21}}{2\mu_{21} + \sin 2\mu_{21}} \cos \mu_{21}(1 - \xi_2)e^{-\mu_{21}^2\tau_2} \tag{11-3}$$

where, in view of the eigenvalue equation (Eq. 11-2), the effective "Biot" number is

$$N_{\text{eff}} = \frac{N_2}{1 + N_1}, \qquad N_2 = \frac{hd_2}{k_2}$$

i.e. the shielding reduces the heat transfer coefficient to the shielded material to an effective value

$$h_{\text{eff}} = \frac{h}{1 + N_1} \tag{11-4}$$

It is thus seen that the problem of the composite slab reduces, in this limit, to the case of the simple slab with a reduced effective heat transfer coefficient. Furthermore, Eq. 11-4 shows that even a thin thermal shield can cause a large reduction in the heat input rates if $h$ is large, which is indeed the case for rocket nozzles. For example let the allowable temperature be $\theta_{cr} = T_{cr}/T_g = 0.5$ at the flame side boundary of a low carbon steel[3] wall of thickness $d_2 = 0.25$ in. $= 0.0208$ ft with heat transfer coefficient at the nozzle throat $h = 1500$ (BTU/hr)/ft²°F. The Biot number is $N = N_2 = hd_2/k_2 = 1.56$, and the duration time $t_d = d_2^2\tau_d/\kappa_2$, computed with two terms in the Fourier series for the simple slab equation (Eq. 4-7) in this case

$$\theta(0, \tau_d) = \theta_{cr} = 1 - 0.625e^{-1.00\tau_d} - 0.095e^{-12.6\tau_d} = 0.5$$

is $t_d = 1.25$ sec. If a zirconia layer of thickness $d_1 = 0.02$ in. $= 0.0017$ ft shields the steel, the effective Biot number is $N_2/[1 + (hd_1/k_1)] = 0.50$. Eq. 4-7, in this case,

$$\theta(0, \tau_d') = \theta_{cr} = 1 - 0.850e^{-0.427\tau_d'} - 0.086e^{-10.8\tau_d'} = 0.5$$

gives for the duration time $t_d' = 7.1$ sec.

The expression for $h_{eff}$ in Eq. 11-4 can be deduced from steady state considerations given in [*6*, p. 15] in a discussion of thin layers of oxide, grease, or scale. The application to transient states is justified in the approximations of Eq. 11-1.

**D,12. "Thick" Thermal Shields.** Another important limiting case arises when the temperature in the shielded material has no appreciable gradients either because of large conductivity in the latter, $k_2 \gg k_1$, or because of large insulation thickness $d_1 \gg d_2$. By a limiting procedure for $k_2 \to \infty$ (i.e. $\mu_2 \to 0$, $b_{1n} \to \mu_{1n}(\rho_2 c_2 d_2/\rho_1 c_1 d_1)$, etc.) Eq. 10-7a can be reduced to an eigenvalue equation for $\mu_{1n}$:

$$\mu_1 \tan \mu_1 = \frac{N_1 - \gamma\mu_1^2}{1 + \gamma N_1} \tag{12-1}$$

where $\gamma$ is the ratio of heat capacities

$$\gamma = \frac{\rho_2 c_2 d_2}{\rho_1 c_1 d_1}$$

The temperature distribution (Eq. 10-10a) becomes

$$\frac{T(x, t)}{T_g} = \theta(\xi, \tau)$$

$$= \begin{cases} 1 + \sum A_n(\cos \mu_{1n}\xi_1 + b_{1n} \sin \mu_{1n}\xi_1)e^{-\mu_{1n}^2\tau_1} & -1 \leqq \xi_1 \leqq 0 \\ 1 + \sum A_n e^{-\mu_{2n}^2\tau_2} = 1 + \sum A_n e^{-\mu_{1n}^2\tau_1} & 0 \leqq \xi_2 \leqq 1 \end{cases} \tag{12-2}$$

[3] Material data and units are given in Table D,3a.

where $A_n$, in this limiting case, is

$$A_n = -\frac{2(\sin \mu_{1n} + \gamma\mu_{1n} \cos \mu_{1n})}{[1 + (\gamma\mu_{1n})^2]\mu_{1n} + [1 - (\gamma\mu_{1n})^2] \sin \mu_{1n} \cos \mu_{1n} + 2\gamma\mu_{1n} \cos^2 \mu_{1n}} \tag{12-3}$$

Eq. 12-2 shows that the shielded material is at a uniform temperature equal to the interface temperature $\theta(0, \tau)$ at any instant. It is to be noted that the result (Eq. 12-2) represents, for $-d_1 \leqq \xi_1 \leqq 0$, the solution of the simple slab problem with Newtonian heat input through one boundary

$$k_1 \frac{\partial T}{\partial x} = h(T - T_g) \quad \text{at} \quad x = -d_1$$

and heat transfer through the other boundary governed by

$$k_1 \frac{\partial T}{\partial x} = \rho_2 c_2 d_2 \frac{\partial T}{\partial t} \quad \text{at} \quad x = 0$$

In view of the latter boundary condition the shielded material behaves essentially as a thermal capacity of magnitude $\rho_2 c_2 d_2$ per unit area of the slab.

**D,13. Design Criterion for Minimum Weight.** The considerations of the preceding article can be applied to the design of uncooled composite rocket chamber walls in which the outer material (envelope) provides structural strength, while the inner material acts as a thermal shield to prevent the attainment of excessive temperatures in the envelope during the firing period $t_d$, which may be of the order of a minute in duration. In the approximation that the composite thickness $d_1 + d_2$ is small compared with the chamber radius, and $k_2 d_1 \gg k_1 d_2$, the envelope temperature $T_2$ is given by the interface temperature in Eq. 12-2

$$\frac{T(0, t)}{T_g} = \frac{T_2}{T_g} = \theta(0, \tau) \tag{13-1}$$

Because of strength requirements, the hoop stresses in the envelope must not exceed a critical stress $S_2$, say the yield stress of the material, which is specified as a function of $T_2$, i.e. $S_2 = S_2(T_2)$. This requirement is expressed by

$$pR \leqq S_2(T_2)d_2 \tag{13-2}$$

where $p$ is the combustion pressure in the rocket chamber and $R$ is the chamber radius. A second requirement is that the composite weight per unit area of the wall,

$$w = \rho_1 d_1 + \rho_2 d_2 \tag{13-3}$$

shall be a minimum. Now, $S_2(T_2)$ generally diminishes as $T_2$ increases and therefore it diminishes also as $t$ increases during the firing period.

For any desired duration time $t_d$, however, it is possible to select an infinite set of thicknesses ($d_1$, $d_2$) large enough to assure that the inequality in Eq. 13-2 holds up to $t_d$. In the set ($d_1$, $d_2$) there is, in general, a particular pair of dimensions which makes the weight $w$ a minimum. The prob-

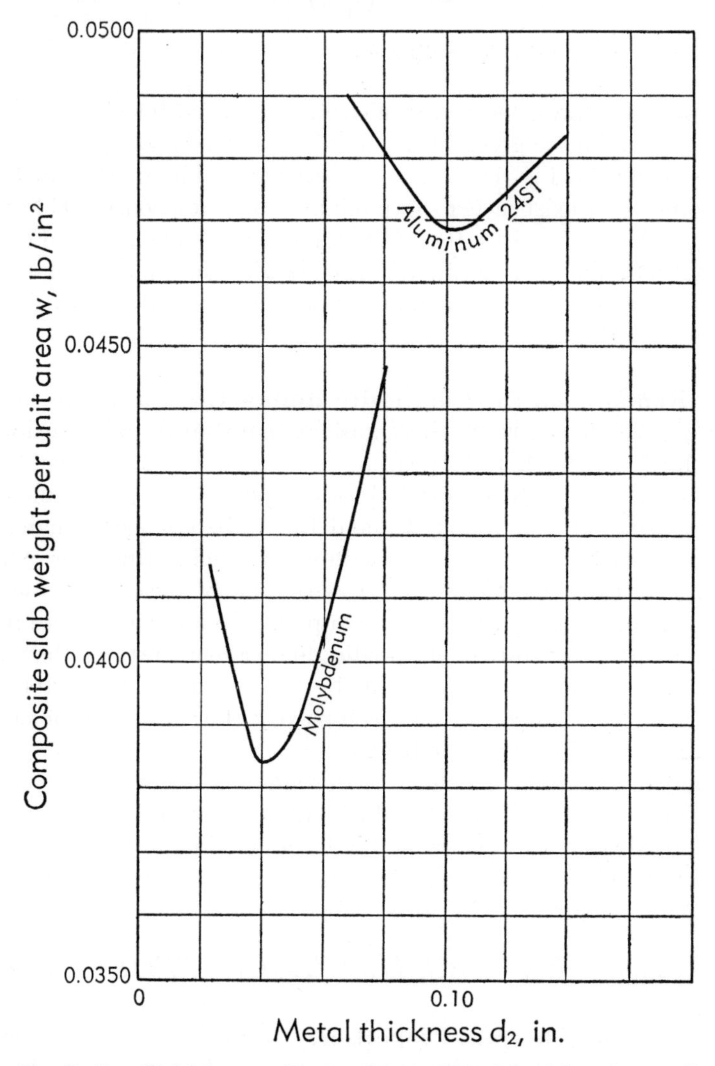


Fig. D,13. Weight per unit area of composite slabs (zirconia-metal) vs. metal thickness [*19*]. (Cf. Art. 13.)

lem of optimum design is to determine, for specified materials and heating parameters, the pair of dimensions ($d_1$, $d_2$) which minimize $w$ and lead to equality in Eq. 13-2 at the time $t_d$.

Fig. D,13 shows curves of $w$ vs. $d_2$ for combinations of zirconia shielding aluminum and molybdenum envelopes with the following data:

$$h = 300 \text{ (BTU/hr)/ft}^2\text{°F}$$
$$T_g = 4500\text{°F}$$
$$\rho R = 1400 \left(\frac{\text{lb}}{\text{in.}^2}\right) \text{in.}$$
$$t_d = 60 \text{ sec}$$

The critical stress vs. temperature curves employed for aluminum 24ST and molybdenum are given in [*20*] and [*21*] respectively.

It is seen from Fig. D,13 that for certain combinations of metal and refractories there exist rather sharp minima, so that a considerable weight saving can be achieved by the optimum choice of thicknesses. For other combinations, however, as in the case of zirconia and aluminum, the choice of thicknesses from the point of view of minimum weight is not so critical.

**D,14. Remarks on the Composite Hollow Cylinder.** On the basis of the discussion in Art. 8, the transient temperature distribution in a relatively thin shell ($\Omega \leqq 1.2$) can be computed from an equivalent slab formula. This rule appears justified for composite media also, and therefore the results of Art. 10, 11, 12, and 13 can be applied in many composite cylinder problems which arise in rocket engineering. For cylinders of greater thickness number ($\Omega > 1.2$) the use of these results leads to conservative estimates from the design point of view, since these results, based upon the composite slab, predict higher temperatures than would actually occur in cylinders. Accordingly the solution for the latter case is not discussed here because of its complexity. For related problems the interested reader is referred to [*22,23*].

It may be noted further that, for the combination of a thin refractory with a thick metal shell, a reduced effective heat transfer coefficient can be computed from Eq. 11-4 and this $h_{\text{eff}}$ applied in the formula for the temperature transients in a simple cylinder as given by Eq. 7-8.

# *CHAPTER 5. SOME SPECIAL PROBLEMS*

**D,15. Variable Thermal Properties.** In metals, $c$ increases while $k$ may decrease or increase with temperature. In the latter case the effect of the variation of the thermal properties is at least partially neutralized, as can be seen from the expression for the time scale (i.e. the conversion factor from the dimensionless to the physical time $t = t_s\tau$),

$$t_s = \frac{\rho c d^2}{k} = \frac{d^2}{\kappa}$$

In the former case, however, the effect on temperature transients may be considerable. Accordingly we shall discuss only the former case.

To a first approximation, $c$ and $k$ may be considered to vary linearly with the temperature,

$$k = k_0 - k_1 \frac{T}{T_g} \quad \rho c = c_0 + c_1 \frac{T}{T_g} \qquad (0 < k_1 < k_0),\ (0 < C_1) \qquad (15\text{-}1)$$

The differential equation and initial and boundary conditions for a homogeneous slab (unidimensional) are

$$\begin{aligned} \frac{\partial}{\partial x}\left(k \frac{\partial T}{\partial x}\right) &= \rho c \frac{\partial T}{\partial t} \\ \frac{\partial T}{\partial x} &= \frac{h}{k}(T - T_g) \quad \text{at} \quad x = 0 \\ \frac{\partial T}{\partial x} &= 0 \qquad \text{at} \quad x = d \\ T &= 0 \qquad \text{at} \quad t = 0 \end{aligned} \qquad (15\text{-}2)$$

Let

$$\xi = \frac{x}{d}, \quad \tau = \frac{t}{\bar{t}_s}, \quad \bar{t}_s = \frac{c_0 + c_1}{k_0 - k_1} d^2, \quad \Theta = \frac{T}{T_g} - 1 \qquad (15\text{-}3)$$

Substituting Eq. 15-1 and 15-3 into Eq. 15-2 we obtain after some algebraic manipulation

$$\begin{aligned} \frac{\partial^2 f_1(\Theta)}{\partial \xi^2} &= \frac{\partial f_2(\Theta)}{\partial \tau} \\ \frac{\partial \Theta}{\partial \xi} &= \frac{hd}{k_0 - k_1} f_3(\Theta) \quad \text{at} \quad \xi = 0 \\ \frac{\partial \Theta}{\partial \xi} &= 0 \qquad \text{at} \quad \xi = 1 \\ \Theta &= -1 \quad \text{at} \quad \tau = 0 \quad (-1 \leqq \Theta \leqq 0) \end{aligned} \qquad (15\text{-}4)$$

where

$$f_1(\Theta) = \Theta(1 - p_k\Theta), \quad f_2(\Theta) = \Theta(1 + p_c\Theta), \quad f_3(\Theta) = \frac{\Theta}{1 - 2p_k\Theta};$$

$$0 \leqq p_k = \frac{1}{2}\frac{k_1}{k_0 - k_1}; \quad 0 \leqq p_c = \frac{1}{2}\frac{c_1}{c_1 + c_0} \leqq \frac{1}{2} \qquad (15\text{-}5)$$

In the purely mathematical range, $-\infty \leqq \Theta \leqq \infty$, the functions $f_1$, $f_2$, and $f_3$ are, of course, nonlinear, so that in principle the differential equation and boundary conditions are nonlinear. However, the actual entire physical range of $\Theta$ is $-1 \leqq \Theta \leqq 0$, and in this range it develops that in the practical ranges of $p_k$ and $p_c$ the three functions are rather close to straight lines.

In Fig. D,15a the graphs of $f_1$, $f_2$, and $f_3$ vs. $\Theta$ are shown in the entire range $-1 \leqq \Theta \leqq 0$. These graphs are drawn for $p_k = \frac{1}{2}$ and $p_c = \frac{1}{4}$. These values correspond to $66\frac{2}{3}$-per cent increase in $c$ and $33\frac{1}{3}$-per cent decrease in $k$ from their initial values up to the melting point, on the basis that the melting temperature $T_m$ is $\frac{2}{3}$ of the flame temperature $T_g$. These values represent a rather wide range of variation in thermal properties.

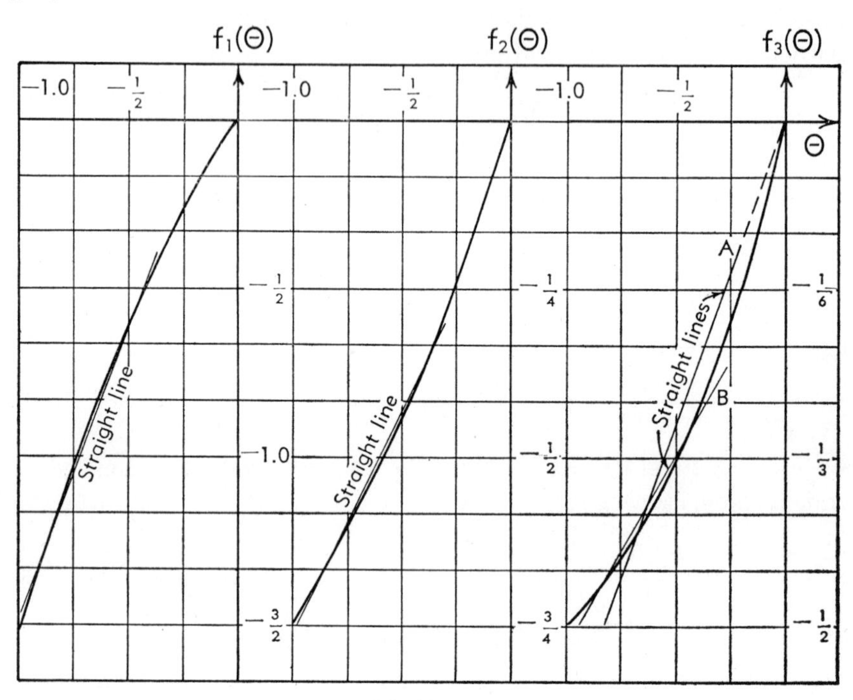


Fig. D,15a.

It is neither necessary nor useful to calculate temperature transients beyond the time at which the fire side wall reaches the melting temperature. Beyond this time the phenomenon of heat conduction changes in character, and the results which are based upon the boundary condition in Eq. 15-2 are no longer valid. This point will be discussed in more detail in the next article. Hence one needs to consider only the range

$$-1 \leqq \Theta \leqq \Theta_m$$

where

$$\Theta_m = \frac{T_m}{T_g} - 1$$

Thus if, say $T_m = \frac{2}{3}T_g$, then the range of interest is

$$-1 \leqq \Theta \leqq -\tfrac{1}{3}$$

It will now be observed from Fig. D,15a that in this range the curves can be approximated rather closely with straight lines. If this is done, then the differential equation and boundary conditions become *linear* and the solution can be written immediately on the basis of the simple slab solution with constant thermal properties. The essential feature of this method of linearization is the fact that now there exists at least a qualitative criterion whereby one may judge the accuracy of the solution; in general, the closer the fit between the straight lines and the curves in the range $-1 \leqq \Theta \leqq \Theta_m$ the more accurate the solution. However, it is not necessary to carry out the solution by this linearization method because of the following result.

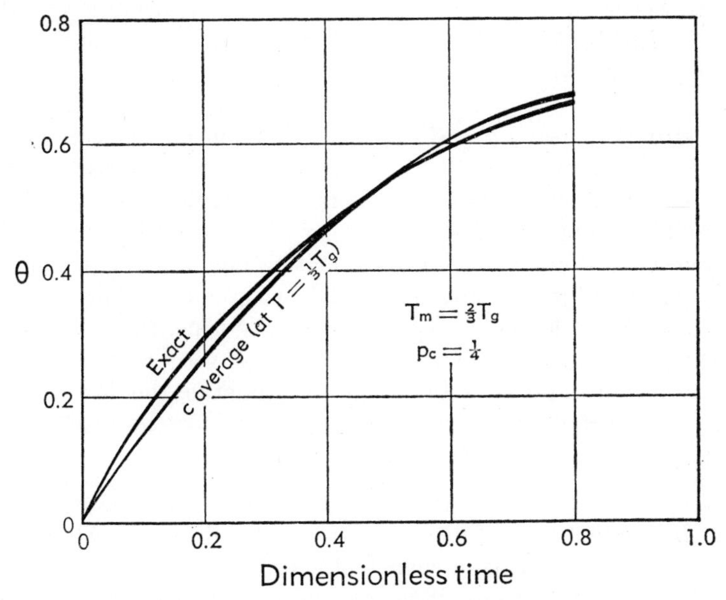


Fig. D,15b. Comparison between exact results and results based on average $c$ for small $N$.

Suppose that two straight lines are drawn so as to *minimize the mean square error* between these lines and the curves representing $f_1(\Theta)$ and $f_2(\Theta)$ in a range $-1 < \Theta \leqq \bar{\Theta} \leqq 0$. Suppose further that a third straight line, line $A$ in the figure, is drawn, passing through the origin $(\Theta = 0)$ and intersecting the curve $f_3(\Theta)$ at $\Theta = -\frac{1}{2}(1 - \bar{\Theta})$ (i.e. at $\Theta$ corresponding to the midpoint of the range). Then it is found that the results based upon this linearization are *exactly* the same as the results which would be obtained if *average* thermal properties were assumed at a temperature corresponding precisely to the mid-interval. This then is the geometric meaning of the use of average thermal properties.

Observing then that the generally used method of average thermal properties corresponds to the fitting of certain straight lines to the graphs representing $f_1$, $f_2$, and $f_3(\Theta)$ and observing further from Fig. D,15a that these fits appear to be quite reasonable, it follows that the method of average thermal properties cannot lead to excessive errors.

Indeed this conclusion can be verified *exactly* in the case of small Biot numbers, for in the latter case it is easy to obtain an exact solution. In Fig. D,15b a comparison is shown between the exact solution, in a range $0 \leqq T \leqq T_m = \frac{2}{3}T_g$, and the solution based upon an average value of $c$ at $T = \frac{1}{3}T_g$ with $p_c = \frac{1}{4}$. The variation of conductivity does not matter in this limiting case.

As seen from Fig. D,15a, somewhat better results might be obtained by the use of line $B$ instead of line $A$ in relation to the curve representing $f_3(\Theta)$. However, on the basis of the above results and in view of the inaccuracies involved in the given data it is concluded that the method of average properties is adequate.

**D,16. Surface Melting and Erosion.** The phenomenon of erosion in rocket nozzles, occurring usually in the immediate neighborhood of the throat, is of much importance but is rather complex and does not lend itself readily to analysis. There are many causes at the root of this phenomenon but it appears that surface melting may be a major one. With respect to the latter, the problem of interest is the rate of melting. Thus, in the case of nozzle inserts, say of the plastic type, the latter begin to disintegrate at a rather low temperature and the problem of rate of destruction is of importance in design, in estimating the duration time.

The following is an approximate expression for the rate of surface melting, as given in [*7,24,25*]:

Let $V$ = rate of melting (velocity of surface recession)
$L$ = latent heat of fusion or, more generally, the heat energy absorbed during a change of state.
$H$ = a constant heat input rate at the flame side wall or the surface which just begins to melt.

At the surface just defined, the boundary condition representing the heat energy balance is

$$H = -k\frac{\partial T}{\partial t} \qquad \text{before melting}$$

$$= -k\frac{\partial T}{\partial t} + \rho L\frac{ds}{dt} \qquad \text{after melting}$$

where $ds/dt = V(t)$ is the rate of melting. Then the *steady state* rate of melting is given by

$$V = \frac{H}{\rho[L + c(T_m - T_0)]}$$

where $T_m$ and $T_0$ are the melting and initial temperatures respectively. The above expression is approximate in several respects. Firstly, this is a limiting expression corresponding to the final, or steady state, rate of melting. The actual rate of melting is less, so that the above formula yields conservative results. Graphs for more exact values of the melting rate are given in [*7*]. Secondly, the result is based upon heat propagation in a semi-infinite solid. Finally, the boundary condition, up to melting, is not of the convective type and corresponds approximately to the latter only in the case where the melting temperature is small as compared to the flame temperature. Thus the whole nature of the boundary condition is such that, up to melting, the temperature gradient at the flame side wall is constant. With the exception of the limiting case just referred to, this type of boundary condition does not appear to correspond very well to the usual boundary conditions (convection and radiation) resulting from actual types of heat inputs.

Another drawback in the use of the above expression for the melting rate is the fact that data for values of $L$ for plastic materials, such as bakelites, are not readily available at present. Nevertheless the result is of importance in that it yields an insight into the role of the physical parameters affecting the rate of surface melting. For more detailed results the reader is referred to the references cited above.

Finally it may be added that the same type of boundary conditions may be used in the study of heat conduction phenomena with general changes of state, not necessarily surface melting (cf. [*26*]).

**D,17. Axial Heat Conduction in Nozzle Walls.** Along a nozzle wall, the heat transfer coefficient varies with axial position, as shown in Fig. D,17a. It is known, both experimentally and on the basis of approximate theoretical results [*2,27,28,29*], that the variation in $h$ in the neighborhood of the throat is rather large.

Now, to within a good approximation the problem of heat conduction in the nozzle wall reduces to the problem of heat flow in a slab with a variable coefficient $h$. The differential equation is now

$$k\left(\frac{\partial^2 T}{\partial x^2} + \frac{\partial^2 T}{\partial y^2}\right) = \rho c \frac{\partial T}{\partial t}$$

while the boundary conditions are (see Fig. D,17b)

$$\begin{aligned} k\frac{\partial T}{\partial y} &= h(x)(T - T_g) \quad & y = 0 \\ &= 0 & y = d \end{aligned}$$

with the initial condition $T = 0$ at $t = 0$. The principal difficulty arises from the boundary condition, a problem discussed at length in [*30*]. It appears that it is difficult to obtain an explicit *continuous* solution in the

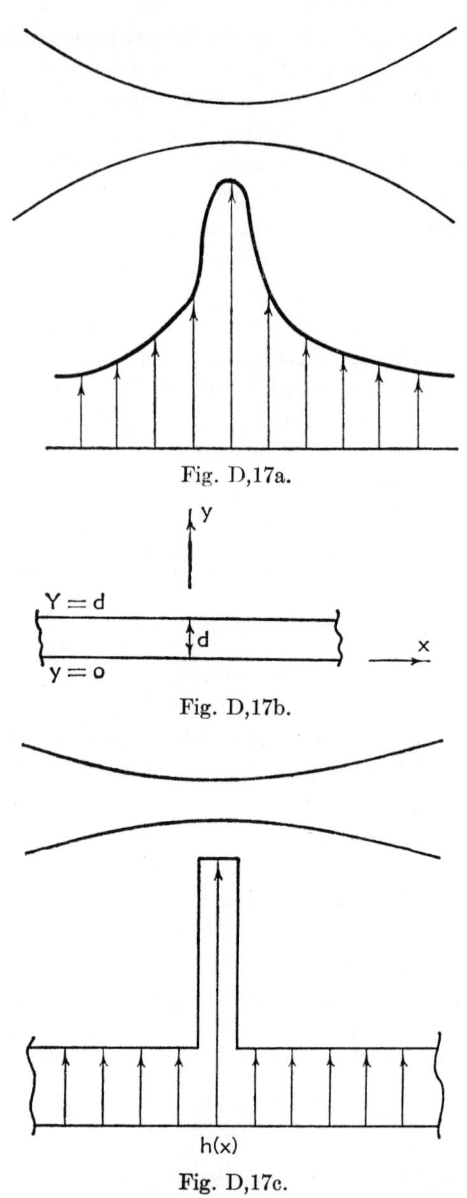


Fig. D,17a.

Fig. D,17b.

Fig. D,17c.

case when $h$ is a rapidly varying function of $x$, and this is indeed the case in practice.

On the other hand, a reasonable approximate solution can be obtained on the basis of the following simplified, yet representative, model: The actual $h$-distribution is approximated by a rectangular symmetric distribution as shown in Fig. D,17c, while the slab is assumed to extend to $\pm\infty$. It is shown in [30] that this idealization is a reasonable one. Finally, in the approximate solution, continuity of temperature and temperature gradient at the $h$ discontinuity is satisfied only in the mean. The solution thus obtained is not valid in the immediate neighborhood of the $h$ discontinuity (say within one thickness) but is reasonable outside such a neighborhood. This is analogous to, say, the Saint Venant principle in elasticity. The results are rather lengthy and cannot be given here in full detail. The interested reader is referred to [*30*] where the detailed results are given.

## D,18. Cited References.


1. *Jet Propulsion.* Prepared by Staffs of Jet Propul. Lab. and Guggenheim Lab., Calif. Inst. Technol. for Air Tech. Service Command, 1946.
2. McAdams, W. H. *Heat Transmission.* McGraw-Hill, 1942.
3. Boelter, L. M. K., et al. *Heat Transfer Notes.* Univ. Calif. Press, 1946.
4. Jakob, M. *Heat Transfer,* Vol. 1. Wiley, 1949.
5. Sutton, G. P. *Rocket Propulsion Elements.* Wiley, 1949.
6. Carslaw, H. S., and Jaeger, J. C. *Conduction of Heat in Solids.* Oxford Univ. Press, 1948.
7. Landau, H. G. *Quart. Appl. Math. 8,* 8 (1950).
8. Courant, R., and Hilbert, D. *Methoden der Mathematischen Physik,* Vol. 1, 2. Springer, Berlin, 1931–1937. 1st English edition, Interscience, 1953.
9. Mayer, E. Analysis of temperature transients in rocket walls. *M. W. Kellogg Rept. SPD 169,* 1948.
10. Geckler, R. D. *Jet Propulsion 25,* 31 (1955).
11. Mayer, E. Transient thermal stresses in concentric cylindrical shells. *M. W. Kellogg Rept. SPD 269,* 1950.
12. Timoshenko, S. *Strength of Materials,* Vol. 2. Van Nostrand, 1945.
13. Geckler, R. D. *Jet Propulsion 26,* 93 (1956).
14. Mayer, E. Analysis of thermal shocks in refractories. *M. W. Kellogg Rept. SPD 267,* 1950.
15. Westbrook, J. H., and Wulff, J. Thermal shock failure of hollow ceramic cylinders. *Mass. Inst. Technol. Meteor Rept. 43,* 1949.
16. Cheng, C. M. *J. Am. Rocket Soc. 21,* 147 (1951).
17. Heisler, M. P. *J. Appl. Mech. 20,* 261 (1953).
18. Mayer, E. *J. Am. Rocket Soc. 22,* 150 (1952).
19. Doane, V., et al. Development of thrust chamber assemblies for ATO rocket power plants. *M. W. Kellogg Rept. SPD 301,* 1950.
20. *Alcoa Aluminum and its Alloys.* Aluminum Corp. of America, 1947.
21. Parke, R. M. Molybdenum as a heat resistant metal. *Battelle Memorial Inst. Tech. Rept. G132-1,* 1950.
22. Lowan, A. N. *Duke Math. J. 1,* 94 (1935).
23. Jaeger, J. C. *Phil. Mag. 7,* 324 (1941).
24. Landau, H. G., and Hicks, B. L. Transient heat flow in composite or melting solids. *Ballist. Research Lab. Rept. 663,* 1948.
25. Nordheim, L. W., Soodak, H., and Nordheim, G. Thermal effects of propellant gases in erosion vents and guns. *Natl. Defense Research Council,* 1944.
26. Evans, G. W., Isaacson, E., and McDonald, J. K. L. *Quart. Appl. Math. 8,* 312 (1950).
27. Reinhardt, I. F., et al. *Bell Aircraft Corp. Meteor Rept. BAC-26,* 1950.
28. Yachter, M. Theoretical investigation of the steady state laminar boundary layer and heat transfer in supersonic nozzles. *M. W. Kellogg Rept. SPD 220,* 1949.
29. Yachter, M. Effect of nozzle geometry on heat transfer in supersonic nozzles. *M. W. Kellogg Rept. SPD 221,* 1949.
30. Yachter, M. Two problems in heat propagation in solids. *M. W. Kellogg Rept. SPD 290,* 1950.

# SECTION E

# CONVECTIVE HEAT TRANSFER AND FRICTION IN FLOW OF LIQUIDS

## CHAPTER 1. TURBULENT HEAT TRANSFER AND FRICTION IN SMOOTH PASSAGES

ROBERT G. DEISSLER

**E,1. Introduction.** When turbulent flow occurs in a passage, macroscopic portions of fluid move about in an apparently random fashion. Inasmuch as the mean velocity varies with distance from the wall, some of the portions of fluid move into regions of different mean velocities. Momentum is then transferred from one portion to another, and a shear stress in addition to that caused by molecular action is produced.

If heat transfer takes place between the passage wall and the fluid, a temperature (or enthalpy) gradient occurs across the passage, and some of the portions of fluid move into regions of different mean temperature. This motion produces heat transfer in addition to that caused by molecular conduction.

**E,2. Basic Equations.** Using the method of Reynolds, the instantaneous velocities, temperatures (or enthalpies), and fluid properties in the equations of momentum, energy, and continuity [*1*, pp. 49, 50, 55] can be divided into mean and fluctuating components. If time averages are taken, the following equations for shear stress $\tau$ and heat transfer $q$, applicable to flow in a passage or boundary layer, are obtained:

$$\tau = \mu \frac{du}{dy} - \rho \overline{u'v'} \tag{2-1}$$

$$q = -k \frac{dT}{dy} + \rho \overline{h'v'} \tag{2-2}$$

In these equations $u$ is the mean velocity in the $x$ direction, $u'$ and $v'$ the fluctuation in velocity in the $x$ and $y$ directions respectively, while $\rho$, $\mu$, and $k$ are the density, the viscosity, and the thermal conductivity of the fluid. The enthalpy fluctuation $h'$ rather than the temperature fluctuation appears in Eq. 2-2 when variable specific heat is considered. Frictional heating is small except at very high velocities and is neglected.[1]

Eq. 2-1 and 2-2 indicate that the molecular and turbulent contributions to the shear stress and heat transfer are additive, and that the turbulent components are both proportional to the density $\rho$. However, they contain the unknown quantities $\overline{u'v'}$ and $\overline{h'v'}$, so that it appears that additional assumptions must be made before solutions can be obtained. For making these assumptions, it is convenient to introduce Boussinesq-type relations as follows [2]:

$$\overline{u'v'} \equiv -\epsilon_u \frac{du}{dy} \qquad \overline{h'v'} \equiv -\epsilon_h \frac{dh}{dy}$$

where $\epsilon_u$ and $\epsilon_h$ are known as the eddy diffusivities for momentum and heat transfer, the values for which are dependent upon the amount and kind of turbulent mixing at a point. Inasmuch as the pressure is essentially constant across the passage $dh/dy = c_p dT/dy$. Eq. 2-1 and 2-2 become, when these relations are introduced,

$$\tau = (\mu + \rho\epsilon_u) \frac{du}{dy} \tag{2-3}$$

$$q = -(k + \rho c_p \epsilon_h) \frac{dT}{dy} \tag{2-4}$$

The physical significance of $\epsilon_u$ and $\epsilon_h$ lies in the fact that $\epsilon_u/(\mu/\rho)$ is the ratio of turbulent to molecular shear stress [3], and $\epsilon_h/(k/\rho c_p)$ is the ratio of turbulent to molecular heat transfer. The use of Eq. 2-3 and 2-4 may be preferable to that of Eq. 2-1 and 2-2, inasmuch as the former imply the physical requirement that $\tau$ and $q$ should be zero when the velocity and temperature gradients are zero. Eq. 2-3 and 2-4 can be written in dimensionless form as follows:

$$\frac{\tau}{\tau_w} = \left(\frac{\mu}{\mu_w} + \frac{\rho}{\rho_w}\frac{\epsilon_u}{\mu_w/\rho_w}\right)\frac{du^*}{dy^*} \tag{2-5}$$

$$\frac{q}{q_w} = \left(\frac{k}{k_w}\frac{1}{Pr_w} + \frac{\rho}{\rho_w}\frac{c_p}{c_{p_w}}\alpha\frac{\epsilon_u}{\mu_w/\rho_w}\right)\frac{dT^*}{dy^*} \tag{2-6}$$

where

$$u^* \equiv \frac{u}{\sqrt{\tau_w/\rho_w}} \qquad y^* \equiv \frac{\sqrt{\tau_w/\rho_w}\, y}{(\mu_w/\rho_w)}$$

$$T^* \equiv \frac{(T_w - T)c_p\tau_w}{q_w\sqrt{\tau_w/\rho_w}}, \quad \text{and} \quad \alpha \equiv \frac{\epsilon_h}{\epsilon_u}$$

The subscript $_w$ refers to values at $y = 0$, i.e. at the wall.

[1] Terms involving $\overline{\rho'v'}$ are sometimes included in Eq. 2-1 and 2-2. These terms can, however, be combined with $\bar{\rho}\bar{v}$ in the equations of momentum, energy, and continuity to give $\overline{\rho v}$. The variable $\overline{\rho v}$, rather than $\bar{v}$, then appears in the conservation equations. Consideration of $\overline{\rho'v'}$ would be necessary only if it were desired to calculate $\bar{v}$.

Probably the first attempt to predict heat transfer from Eq. 2-5 and 2-6, or Eq. 2-3 and 2-4, was made by Reynolds [*4*, pp. 81–85]. He assumed constant properties, that $\tau/\tau_w = q/q_w$, that the molecular shear stress and heat transfer terms in the equations are negligible compared with the turbulent terms, and $\alpha = 1$. With these assumptions, Eq. 2-5 can be divided by Eq. 2-6 and integrated to give $T^* = u^*$. If the temperatures and velocities are weighted in the same way to calculate bulk temperatures and velocities, $T_b^* = u_b^*$, or

$$q_w = \frac{c_p(T_w - T_b)\tau_w}{u_b} \tag{2-7}$$

Eq. 2-7, which relates the heat transfer to the shear stress, is usually called Reynolds analogy. It applies reasonably well to gases, which have Prandtl numbers close to one, but fails for liquids. In fact, Eq. 2-7 follows from Eq. 2-5 and 2-6 if $Pr = 1$, even if the molecular terms are not neglected.

A number of refinements of Reynolds' original analysis to make it more general are given by various authors. Prandtl and Taylor [*5*, pp. 110–113] introduced a laminar layer near the wall and obtained better agreement with the data for fluids with Prandtl numbers close to 1. Von Kármán [*6*] added a buffer layer between the laminar layer and the turbulent core and thus extended the analysis to somewhat higher Prandtl numbers, i.e. to liquids. Further improvements in the theory are given in [*3,7,8,9,10,11,12,13,14,15*].

It is desirable to obtain relations for the heat transfer which do not contain the shear stress or friction factor, as does Eq. 2-7. This is especially true in the case of variable fluid properties, where the friction factors may be no better known that the heat transfer coefficients. In order to obtain such relations it is necessary to make an assumption for the eddy diffusivity $\epsilon_u$, in Eq. 2-5 and 2-6.

**E,3. Expressions for Eddy Diffusivity.** Several assumptions to relate the eddy diffusivity in Eq. 2-5 and 2-6 to the mean flow have been made by various investigators [*7,11,13,15,16,17,18*]. Reasonable assumptions for the variation of $\epsilon_u$ follow. For purposes of analysis, the flow is divided into two portions termed the "region away from the wall" and the "region close to the wall."

*Region away from wall.* In the region away from the passage wall, it is assumed that the turbulence at a point is a function mainly of local conditions, that is, of the relative velocities in the vicinity of the point [*19*, p. 351]. This is probably not a good assumption near the passage center where considerable diffusion of the turbulence occurs [*20*]. However, in that region the velocity or temperature gradients are so small that the error in calculated velocities or temperatures should not be large. A Taylor's series expansion for $u$ as a function of transverse distance (changes in the axial direction neglected) then indicates that $\epsilon_u$ is a function of $du/dy$, $d^2u/dy^2$, $d^3u/dy^3$, etc. If, as a first approximation, we consider $\epsilon_u$ to be a function only of the first and second derivatives, and apply dimensional analysis, there results

$$\epsilon_u = \epsilon_u\left(\frac{du}{dy}, \frac{d^2u}{dy^2}\right) = \kappa^2 \frac{(du/dy)^3}{(d^2u/dy^2)^2} \tag{3-1}$$

where $\kappa$ is an experimental constant. This expression was obtained by von Kármán in a somewhat different manner and is generally known as the Kármán similarity hypothesis [*18*]. A critical examination of the Kármán hypothesis from the point of view of statistical turbulence theories is given by Lin and Shen [*21*]. Eq. 3-1 can be written in dimensionless form, as

$$\frac{\epsilon_u}{\mu_w/\rho_w} = \kappa^2 \frac{(du^*/dy^*)^3}{(d^2u^*/dy^{*2})^2} \tag{3-1$'$}$$

*Region close to wall.* In the region close to the wall it is assumed that $\epsilon_u$ is a function only of quantities measured relative to the wall $u$ and $y$, and of the kinematic viscosity. This assumption includes, to a first approximation, an effect of the derivatives of $u$ with respect to $y$. Since the flow becomes very nearly laminar as the wall is approached, the first derivative approaches the value $u/y$, and hence may be omitted since $u$ and $y$ already appear in the functional relation. The second derivative approaches the constant value zero as the wall is approached. The kinematic viscosity is included, inasmuch as the ratio of viscous to inertia effects is high near the wall where the turbulence level is low. The eddies in that region are small, so that the shear stresses between the eddies and the viscous dissipation of the energy in the eddies are large. With these assumptions, and dimensional analysis,

$$\epsilon_u = \epsilon_u\left(u, y, \frac{\mu}{\rho}\right) = n^2uyF\left(\frac{n^2uy}{\mu/\rho}\right)$$

The form of the function $F$ cannot be determined by dimensional analysis. On the basis of simplicity, and the fact that $F$ should approach zero at the wall (effect of $\mu/\rho$ large) and should approach one asymptotically as $uy/(\mu/\rho)$ becomes large (effect of $\mu/\rho$ small), it is assumed in reference [*15*] that

$$F = 1 - e^{-\frac{n^2uy}{\mu/\rho}}$$

or

$$\epsilon_u = n^2uy(1 - e^{-\frac{n^2uy}{\mu/\rho}}) \tag{3-2}$$

where $n$ is an experimental constant.[2]

Eq. 3-2 becomes, in dimensionless form,

$$\frac{\epsilon_u}{\mu_w/\rho_w} = n^2u^*y^*(1 - e^{-n^2\frac{\rho}{\rho_w}\frac{\mu_w}{\mu}u^*y^*}) \tag{3-2'}$$

Eq. 3-1 and 3-2 for $\epsilon_u$ can be considered as reasonable first approximations. Whether or not these approximations are adequate can, at present, be determined only by experiment.

**E,4. Analysis for Constant Fluid Properties.** Velocity distribution data for flow without heat transfer have been used to evaluate the constants $\kappa$ and $n$ in Eq. 3-1 and 3-2.

*Velocity distributions.* Eq. 2-3, with Eq. 3-1 or 3-2, was integrated numerically or analytically for constant properties for the regions close to and at a distance from the wall in [*15*] and [*22*]. The integration was carried out for both a constant and a linearly varying shear stress ($\tau = 0$ at passage center) with similar results for Reynolds numbers >10,000, so that the effect of variation of shear stress is neglected in most of the following calculations.[3] In the region at a distance from the wall the molecular shear stress is neglected because it is small compared with the turbulent shear stress [*14*, Fig. 12]. The familiar Kármán-Prandtl logarithmic equation is obtained in the region away from the wall:

$$u^* = \frac{1}{\kappa}\ln\frac{y^*}{y_1^*} + u_1^*$$

where $y_1^*$ is the lowest value of $y^*$ for which the equation applies and $u_1^*$ is the value of $u^*$ at $y_1^*$. In obtaining this equation, one integration constant was set equal to 0 by using the usual condition that $du^*/dy^* = \infty$ for $y^* = 0$ [*18*]. This assumption can be avoided by including the molecular shear stress and heat transfer in the region away from the wall and evaluating the constant by assuming a continuous velocity derivative at $y_1^*$ [*14*, Fig. 12]. This assumption gives essentially the same numerical results as that made above.

[2] The quantity in parenthesis in Eq. 3-2, which represents the effect of kinematic viscosity on $\epsilon_u$, becomes important only for heat or mass transfer at Prandtl or Schmidt numbers appreciably greater than one. For Prandtl or Schmidt numbers on the order of one or less, or for velocity profiles, $\epsilon_u = n^2uy$ (the value of $n$ differs from that in Eq. 3-2) is a good approximation for the region close to the wall [*13*].

[3] The variation of shear stress is neglected only for the purpose of simplifying the calculations, and as shown in [*14*, Fig. 11], this neglect has little or no effect on the results, even for variable properties.

Fig. E,4a shows, on semilogarithmic coordinates, velocity profile data from [20,22], together with the analytical curves obtained. The data are for fully developed adiabatic flow in tubes. The constants $\kappa$ and $n$ in Eq. 3-1 and 3-2 were found, from the data, to have values of 0.36 and 0.124 respectively. The relation for $\epsilon_u$ from Eq. 3-2 applies for $y^* < 26$, and that from Eq. 3-1, for $y^* > 26$. In matching the two solutions it was assumed that the velocity is continuous at the junction of the two regions.

The velocity distribution is often divided into three regions rather than two: the laminar layer, where turbulence is supposed to be absent, the buffer layer, and the turbulent core [6]. The use of Eq. 3-2′ for $\epsilon_u$ close

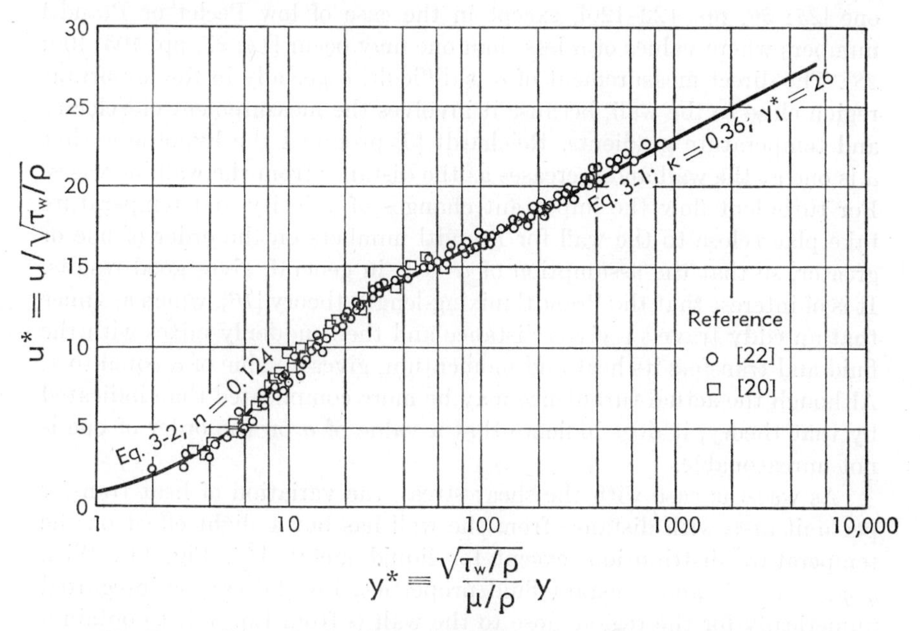


Fig. E,4a. Generalized velocity distribution for adiabatic turbulent flow (vertical line is dividing line between equations at $y_1^* = 26$).

to the wall eliminates the need for a laminar layer and reduces the number of regions to two. For values of $y^* < 5$, Eq. 3-2 indicates that $\epsilon_u/(\mu/\rho) \ll 1$, so that the flow is nearly laminar in that region. This can be seen from the plot of $u^*$ against $y^*$ in Fig. E,4a, where, for small values of $y^*$, $u^* \cong y^*$.

Several other analyses were made recently and might be mentioned at this point. Van Driest [23] used a modified form of Prandtl's mixing-length theory which assumed that the presence of the wall reduces the universal constant $\kappa$ or the mixing length. By introducing a damping factor into the expression for shear stress, he was able to obtain a velocity profile which agreed with the data for the regions both close to and away from the wall.

An analysis by Einstein and Li [*24*] assumed that the laminar sublayer is basically unsteady; that is, the sublayer grows until it becomes unstable and then collapses, the cycle repeating itself. This model gave a velocity profile agreement with data for the region close to the wall.

*Temperature distributions.* For extending the analysis to heat transfer an assumption must be made for $\alpha$, the ratio of eddy diffusivities for heat transfer to momentum transfer, in Eq. 2-6. The relation for $\alpha$ has not been clearly established. It is a fact that analyses based on an $\alpha$ of one agree closely with experiment [*6*,*14*]. However, some attempts to measure $\alpha$ directly indicate values which, in general, are somewhat greater than one [*25*; *26*, pp. 122–126], except in the case of low Peclet or Prandtl numbers where values of $\alpha$ less than one may occur [*14*; *27*, pp. 405–409; *28*]. The direct measurement of $\alpha$ is difficult, especially in the important region close to the wall, because it involves the measurement of velocity and temperature gradients. Reichardt [*3*] proposed the hypothesis that $\alpha$ is one at the wall and increases as the distance from the wall increases. For turbulent flow the important changes of velocity and temperature take place close to the wall for Prandtl numbers on the order of one or greater, so that the assumption of $\alpha = 1$, in general, gives good results. It is of interest that the Prandtl mixing-length theory [*16*], which assumes that an eddy travels a given distance and then suddenly mixes with the fluid and transfers its heat and momentum, gives a value of $\alpha$ equal to 1. Although the actual turbulence may be more complicated than indicated by that theory, it does indicate that a value of $\alpha$ on the order of one is not unreasonable.

As was the case with the shear stress, the variation of heat transfer per unit area with distance from the wall has but a slight effect on the temperature distribution, except for liquid metals [*14*, Fig. 11]. With $q/q_w = \alpha = 1$, and constant fluid properties, Eq. 2-6 can be integrated numerically for the region close to the wall ($\epsilon$ from Eq. 3-2) to obtain a relation between $T^*$ and $y^*$ [*15*]. For the region away from the wall ($y^* > 26$), where the molecular shear stress and heat transfer are neglected, it is easily shown from Eq. 2-5 and 2-6 that

$$T^* - T_1^* = u^* - u_1^* \tag{3-3}$$

where $T_1^*$ and $u_1^*$ are the values of $T^*$ and $u^*$ at $y_1^* = 26$ (Fig. E,4a).

Calculated temperature distributions are shown in Fig. E,4b on log-log coordinates. The temperature parameter $T^*$ is plotted against $y^*$ for various Prandtl numbers. The curves indicate that the temperature distributions become flatter over most of the passage cross section as the Prandtl number increases. From Eq. 2-6, $dT^*/dy^* = Pr$ at or very near the wall, so that the slopes of the curves at the wall increase with Prandtl number. The slopes of the curves in Fig. E,4b near the wall appear equal, because the curves are plotted on log-log coordinates ($d(\log T^*)/d(\log y^*) = 1$ at the wall).

Included for comparison is the temperature distribution for a Prandtl number of 300, calculated by assuming $\epsilon_u = n^2uy$ ($n = 0.109$) close to the wall rather than Eq. 3-2. This expression is a good approximation for velocity profile but, as indicated in the figure, is not accurate at high Prandtl numbers. Somewhat better results were obtained in [*11*], where it was assumed that $\epsilon_u = \text{const}\ u^2/(du/dy)$, but the analysis is again inaccurate at very high Prandtl numbers. The sensitivity of the temperature profile at high Prandtl numbers to various assumptions for the

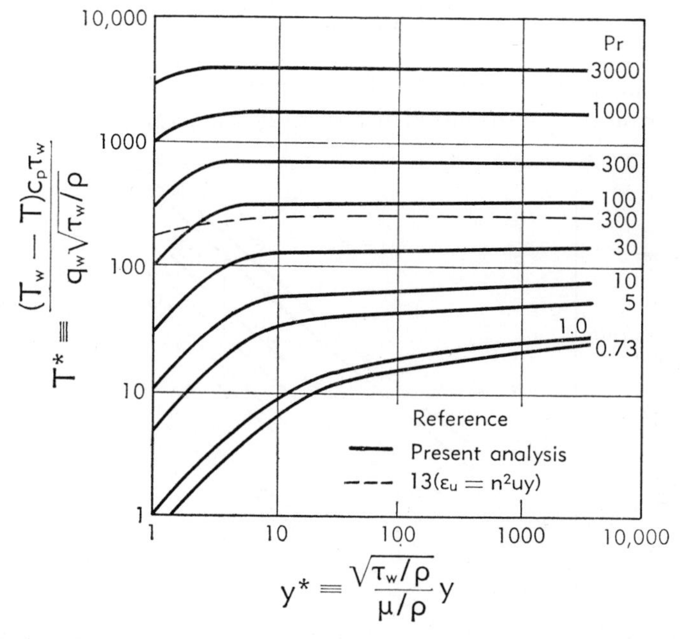


Fig. E,4b. Generalized temperature distributions for various Prandtl numbers.

turbulent transfer in the region close to the wall, compared with that of the velocity distribution, indicates that the region very close to the wall could be studied advantageously by measuring temperatures at high Prandtl numbers, rather than by measuring velocities in that region. Some work along these lines has been reported in [*12*]. In that case, concentration profiles, rather than temperature profiles, were measured for mass transfer at high Schmidt numbers. No evidence of a purely laminar layer (linear concentration profile) was found for values of $y^*$ as low as one. This result is in agreement with Eq. 3-2, which indicates that $\epsilon_u = 0$ only at the wall.

*Relations among Nusselt, Reynolds, and Prandtl numbers.* It can readily be shown from the definitions of the various quantities involved that the Nusselt and Reynolds numbers for a tube are given by

$$Nu = \frac{2r_w^* Pr}{T_b^*} \tag{3-4}$$

$$Re = 2u_b^* r_w^* \tag{3-5}$$

where $r_w^* = r_w \sqrt{\tau_w/\rho_w}/(\mu_w/\rho_w)$, $r_w$ being the tube radius,

$$T_b^* = \frac{\int_0^{r_w^*} T^* u^*(r_w^* - y^*)dy^*}{\int_0^{r_w^*} u^*(r_w^* - y^*)dy^*} \tag{3-6}$$

and

$$u_b^* = \frac{2}{(r_w^*)^2} \int_0^{r_w^*} u^*(r_w^* - y^*)dy^* \tag{3-7}$$

The Nusselt number in Eq. 3-4 is based on the difference between the wall temperature and the mixed mean or bulk temperature $T_b^*$. The relation

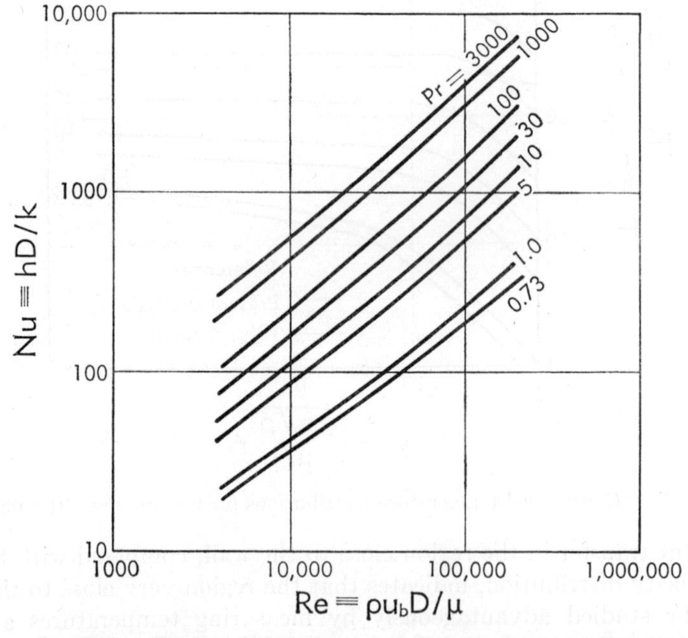


Fig. E,4c. Predicted fully developed Nusselt numbers plotted against Reynolds number for various Prandtl numbers.

among Nusselt, Reynolds, and Prandtl numbers can be obtained from these equations and the generalized distributions given in Fig. E,4a and E,4b. The parameter $r_w^*$ appears in all the equations and is assigned arbitrary values for plotting the curves.

Predicted Nusselt numbers for fully developed heat transfer are plotted against Reynolds number for various values of Prandtl number in Fig. E,4c. Examination of the curves indicates that the slopes of the various curves are approximately equal on a log-log plot. This result justifies the usual practice in heat transfer investigations of writing $Nu = f(Re, Pr)$ as $f(Re) \times f(Pr)$ (usually as $Re^a Pr^b$). The same result does not hold for very low Prandtl numbers where the slopes change considerably.

A comparison between predicted and experimental results is given in Fig. E,4d. Fully developed mass transfer as well as heat transfer data are included, inasmuch as an analogy exists between heat and mass transfer when the concentration of the diffusing substance is small. The Stanton number is plotted against the Prandtl or Schmidt number for a Reynolds number of 10,000. Similar results were obtained for Reynolds number, of 25,000 and 50,000 [*15*]. The predicted Stanton numbers were

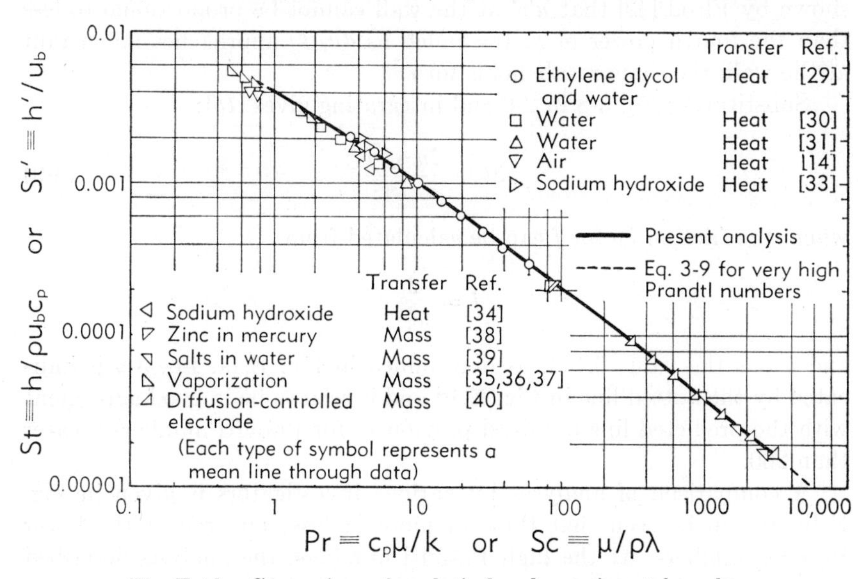


Fig. E,4d. Comparison of analytical and experimental results for fully developed heat and mass transfer.

obtained from Fig. E,4c and the relation $St = Nu/(RePr)$. The symbols represent mean lines through data for heat transfer in gases [*14*] and in liquids [*29,30,31,32,33,34*] and mass transfer by evaporation from wetted walls [*35,36,37*] by solution of the wall material in a liquid [*38,39*] and by diffusion-controlled electrodes [*40*]. The predicted and measured values are in good agreement over the entire range of Prandtl and Schmidt numbers shown (0.5 to 3000).

A simplified equation can be obtained for the case of very high Prandtl numbers. For that case the essential temperature changes take place in the region very close to the wall where $u^*$ is very nearly equal to $y^*$. Converting Eq. 3-2 to dimensionless form, setting $u^* = y^*$, expanding the exponential function in a series, and retaining only the first two terms of the series result in

$$\frac{\epsilon_u}{\mu/\rho} = n^4 y^{*4} \tag{3-8}$$

In connection with this equation it is of interest that Reichardt [3] assumed $\epsilon_u$ proportional to $y^3$ for moderate Prandtl numbers and to $y^5$ for higher Prandtl numbers. Also, an analysis by Hama [41] assumed an expression for $\epsilon_u/(\mu/\rho)$ similar to Eq. 3-8, except that the right-hand side was multiplied by $du^*/dy^*$. For small values of $y^*$, where $du^*/dy^* \cong 1$, his expression therefore reduces to Eq. 3-8. Eq. 3-8 is also consistent with exact information obtainable from the continuity relation and the condition that the fluctuating velocity components are zero at the wall. It is shown by Elrod [42] that $\overline{u'v'}$ at the wall cannot be proportional to less than the fourth power of $y$. Inasmuch as $du/dy$ approaches a constant at the wall, the same result holds for $\epsilon$.

Substituting Eq. 3-8 in 2-6 and integrating gives [15]:

$$St = \frac{2n}{\pi} \frac{\sqrt{f}}{Pr^{\frac{3}{4}}} \tag{3-9}$$

where the friction factor $f$ can be calculated from

$$f = \frac{2}{u_b^{*2}}$$

and $n$ has the value 0.124, as determined in Fig. E,4a. Eq. 3-9 is indicated by the dotted line in Fig. E,4d and is seen to be in good agreement with the predicted line obtained previously for Prandtl numbers greater than 200.

A comparison of analyses by various investigators is given in Fig. E,4e. It can be seen that they all more or less converge at the lower Prandtl numbers. At the high Prandtl numbers, the analysis described herein [15] and the analyses from [7,12] are in fair agreement, whereas those from [6,11] diverge considerably. The present analysis and that from [12] represent the experimental data about equally well. The analysis in [12] modifies that of von Kármán, which utilized a laminar layer, a buffer layer, and a turbulent core. A small amount of turbulence was introduced into the laminar layer in order to give better agreement with experiment at high Prandtl and Schmidt numbers.

*The entrance region.* Most of the results given so far are for fully developed flow or heat transfer, that is, for the region at a large distance from an entrance, or from the point where heat transfer begins. In the region close to an entrance, the heat transfer coefficients and shear stresses are higher than those for fully developed flow, because of the thin boundary layers and consequently severe temperature and velocity gradients at the wall near the entrance. One of the first studies of turbulent heat transfer in an entrance region was made by Latzko [*43*]. His analysis was for a Prandtl number of one and was based on an assumed $\frac{1}{7}$-power velocity profile and the Blasius resistance formula. More recent developments are given in [*15,44,45,46,47*].

For analyzing heat transfer and flow in an entrance region, integral methods will be utilized here. The usual boundary layer assumptions used with integral methods are made; that is, it is assumed that the effects of heat transfer and friction are confined to fluid layers close to the surface (thermal and flow boundary layers, respectively). The temperature and velocity distributions outside the boundary layers are assumed uniform, and the temperature and total pressure are constant along the length of

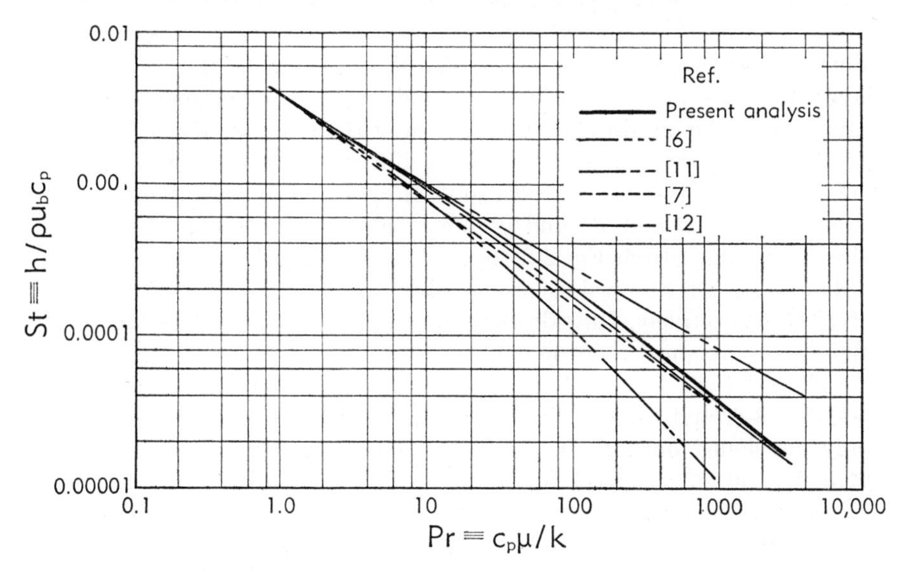


**Fig. E,4e.** Comparison of various analyses. Reynolds number = 10,000.

the passage for the region outside the boundary layers. More exact analyses [*48*] indicate that these assumptions are valid, even for laminar flow, except in the region at a distance from the entrance where the boundary layer fills a large portion of the tube. In that region, however, the Nusselt number and friction factors have values very close to the values for fully developed flow.[4]

In order to obtain a relation between distance along the passage $x$ and thermal boundary layer thickness $\delta_h$, we can write an energy balance

[4] A recent analysis by E. M. Sparrow, T. M. Hallman, and R. Siegel [*85*] indicates, however, that the entrance lengths computed by this method may be too short, although the entrance length is still on the order of 10 diameters. The difference is apparently due to the assumption that the temperature is constant along the length of the passage for the region outside the boundary layer. That should still be a good assumption when the boundary layer is very thin.

on an annulus of fluid of differential length of $dx$ [47]. This gives, for a tube, the equation shown:

$$q_w r_w dx = d\left[\int_0^{\delta_h} c_p T \rho u (r_w - y) dy\right] - c_p T_e d\left[\int_0^{\delta_h} \rho u (r_w - y) dy\right] \quad (3\text{-}10)$$

where the differentials of the integrals indicate changes in the $x$ direction. The temperature outside the thermal boundary layer $T_e$ does not vary with $x$ inasmuch as it is assumed that no heat penetrates the region outside the boundary layer. For uniform heat flux at the wall, and constant properties, Eq. 3-10 can then be integrated to give, in dimensionless form,

$$\frac{x}{D} = \frac{1}{2r_w^{*2}} \int_0^{\delta_h^*} (T_e^* - T^*) u^* (r_w^* - y^*) dy^* \quad (3\text{-}11)$$

This equation gives $x/D$ as a function of $\delta_h^*$, or dimensionless boundary layer thickness, and of $r_w^*$, which is a kind of Reynolds number. A similar equation can be obtained for the growth of the flow, or velocity, boundary layer, whose thickness in general differs from that of the thermal boundary layer [47]. In order to solve these equations, the relations between $u^*$ and $y^*$ and $T^*$ and $y^*$ must be known. These relations were already obtained from Eq. 2-5, 2-6, 3-1, and 3-2, and are plotted in Fig. E,4a and E,4b. Those values of $u^*$ and $T^*$ are to be used for $y^* \leqq \delta_u^*$ and $y^* \leqq \delta_h^*$ respectively. Outside the flow and thermal boundary layers, $u^*$ and $T^*$ are assumed uniform.

The relations for the Nusselt and Reynolds numbers given by Eq. 3-4, 3-5, 3-6, and 3-7 can be used in the entrance region as well as for fully developed flow. It is necessary, of course, that $T^* = T^*(\delta_h)$ for $y^* \geqq \delta_h^*$ and $u^* = u^*(\delta_u)$ for $y^* \geqq \delta_u^*$. If the velocity profile is fully developed, $\delta^* = r_w^*$.

Fig. E,4f shows predicted values of local Nusselt number over the fully developed value plotted against $x/D$ for Prandtl numbers of 1, 10, and 100, and for various Reynolds numbers. The curves are for a uniform wall heat flux and a fully developed velocity distribution ($\delta_u = r_w$). A fully developed velocity distribution at the thermal entrance could be obtained experimentally by placing a long unheated length of tubing ahead of the heated section.

In general the Nusselt numbers, or heat transfer coefficients, very nearly reach their fully developed values in an entrance length less than 10 diameters. These entrance lengths for turbulent heat transfer are much shorter than those for the laminar case, apparently because of the rapid radial diffusion of heat by turbulence. The entrance effect also decreases as Prandtl number increases. This trend is opposite to that for laminar flow [49]. The heat diffuses through the fluid more slowly at the higher Prandtl numbers in the case of laminar flow, so that the thermal boundary layer develops more slowly. The same phenomenon also tends to increase the effect of $x/D$ for turbulent heat transfer. In that case, however, the shape of the temperature profile within the boundary layer changes and becomes considerably flatter at high Prandtl numbers. This effect apparently more than offsets the effect previously mentioned, so that the entrance region becomes less important at the higher Prandtl numbers.

Fig. E,4g gives a comparison between predicted results and experimental results from [*50*] for water and for oil flowing in the entrance region of a tube. The velocity profile is again fully developed and the

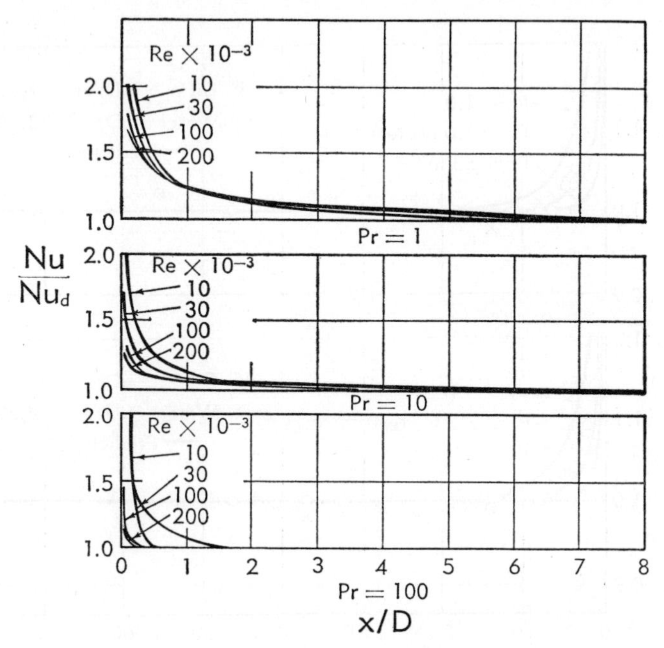


Fig. E,4f. Effect of Reynolds and Prandtl numbers on heat transfer in thermal entrance region of tube. Uniform wall heat flux, uniform initial temperature distribution, and fully developed velocity distribution.

wall heat flux uniform. In general the agreement between theory and experiment is satisfactory.

Various other cases, including that in which the initial velocity profile is uniform, and in which the wall temperature, rather than the heat flux, is uniform, are calculated in [*47*]. It was found that the heat transfer coefficients in the entrance region are higher for a uniform than for a fully developed initial velocity profile. Very little difference was, however, obtained between the results for the cases of uniform wall heat flux and uniform wall temperature. That result would not be expected to apply to liquid metals.

*Liquid metal heat transfer*. Liquid metals are characterized, from the point of view of heat transfer, by their very low Prandtl numbers ($Pr \cong 0.01$). Eq. 2-6 indicates that, at sufficiently low Prandtl numbers, the molecular heat transfer term will be important in comparison with the turbulent term, even in the region away from the wall. Martinelli was the first to extend the analysis to low Prandtl numbers by retaining the molecular term in Eq. 2-6, in the region away from the wall [9]. Also, $q/q_w$ cannot be set equal to one for low Prandtl number fluids, because the important temperature changes with respect to distance from the wall do not all take place near the wall, as they do at higher Prandtl numbers. Martinelli approximated $q/q_w$ by using a linear variation in

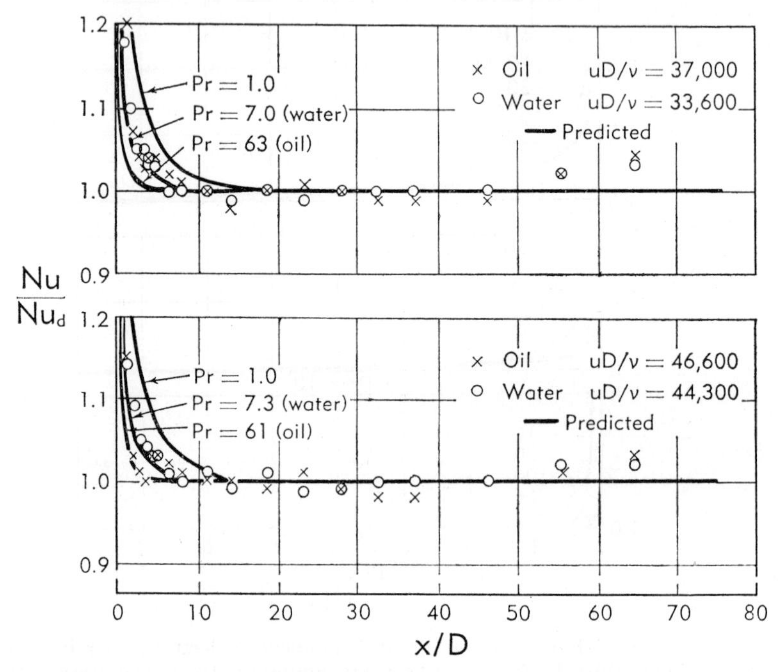


Fig. E,4g. Comparison between predicted and experimental Nusselt numbers in thermal entrance region for liquids. Data from [50].

which $q/q_w = 0$ at the tube center. More accurate variations of $q/q_w$ were later used in [28,51].

Most of the data for liquid metal heat transfer fall somewhat below the original Martinelli analysis (about 30 per cent) although considerable scatter exists in the data. Several attempts have been made to bring the analysis into better agreement with the data by making various modifications of the turbulence mechanism [28,52]. However, the reason for the discrepancy between analysis and experiment has not been established. It is possible that the low experimental heat transfer coefficients are due to a thermal resistance at the interface between the wall and the liquid metal. It appears that more experimental information will be needed before any of the existing theories can be verified or an adequate theory formulated. A review of the present status of research on liquid metal heat transfer is given in [*53*].

*Noncircular passages.* Although most of the preceding calculations were for turbulent flow in circular tubes, it is shown in [*46*] that, except for liquid metals, the Nusselt numbers and friction factors for round tubes apply with small error to flow between parallel plates. It is only necessary to use the hydraulic diameter in the definitions of Nusselt number, Reynolds number, and friction factor. The hydraulic diameter is defined as 4 times the cross-sectional area divided by the wetted perimeter.

In an analysis in [*54*] it is found that the results for a tube can be used with small error for a concentric annulus with a diameter ratio of $3\frac{1}{2}$. As the annulus became eccentric, however, the Nusselt numbers and friction factors decreased appreciably.

Flow and heat transfer in the vicinity of corners have been analyzed in [*55,56*]. It was found that, for uniform heat generation in the passage wall, the temperature at the corner may be considerably higher than the average, because the convective heat transfer is zero at the corner. Although average Nusselt numbers and friction factors for passage cross sections were not predicted in [*55,56*], experimental results [*57*] indicated that the results for tubes apply reasonably well to rectangular and triangular passages when the equivalent diameter is used. That result, again, would not be expected to apply to liquid metals. Further discussion of flow and heat transfer in noncircular passages is given in [*58,59*].[5]

**E,5. Analysis for Variable Fluid Properties.** The analysis for constant fluid properties in the preceding section applies, strictly speaking, only to the limiting case of heat transfer, with infinitesimal temperature difference, inasmuch as the fluid properties of a real fluid are temperature-dependent. This does not imply that the results of a constant-property analysis are not useful. In many instances, substantial temperature differences are required before the effect of variable properties becomes important. Also, in the case of variable properties, it is often possible to use the results of a constant-property analysis by evaluating the fluid properties in the various dimensionless groups at a suitable reference temperature. In order to calculate the required reference temperature, however, an analysis for variable properties is necessary.

Eq. 2-5, 2-6, 3-1′, and 3-2′ are already in a form suitable for a variable-property analysis. For a given wall temperature and pressure, the various property ratios in those equations are functions of $T/T_w$. From the definitions of $\beta$ and $T^*$

$$\frac{T}{T_w} = 1 - \beta T^* \tag{5-1}$$

[5] See also [*86,87*].

where

$$\beta \equiv \frac{q_w \sqrt{\tau_w/\rho_w}}{c_p \tau_w T_w}$$

The property ratios are therefore functions of $1 - \beta T^*$, and Eq. 2-5 and 2-6 can be solved simultaneously to obtain velocity and temperature distributions for various values of $\beta$. As in the case of constant properties, the variations of heat transfer and shear stress across the passage have but a slight effect on the velocity and temperature distributions for Reynolds numbers above 10,000 [*14*, Fig. 11] so that in most cases $\tau/\tau_w$ and $q/q_w$ are set equal to one in Eq. 2-5 and 2-6. The quantity $\beta$ is a heat flux parameter and is a measure of the effect of variable fluid properties. For constant properties, $\beta = 0$.

Most of the experimental and analytical work on variable properties has been carried out for air as a fluid. Some of the work for air will therefore be considered at this point, even though the present section is mainly concerned with liquids. The analyses for various fluids differ significantly only in the assumptions made for the variation of their properties with temperature.

*Analysis for air.* In this case the viscosity, thermal conductivity, and density are considered variable with temperature. The Prandtl number and specific heat are considered constant, inasmuch as their variations with temperature are of a lower order of magnitude than those of the other properties. The viscosity of air and many common gases varies approximately as the 0.68 power of the absolute temperature for temperatures between 0 and 2000°F. From the assumptions of constant Prandtl number and specific heat, the thermal conductivity must vary with temperature in the same way as the viscosity, or

$$\frac{\mu}{\mu_w} = \frac{k}{k_w} = \left(\frac{T}{T_w}\right)^{0.68} = (1 - \beta T^*)^{0.68} \tag{5-2}$$

From the perfect gas law and the assumption of constant static pressure across the passage,

$$\frac{\rho}{\rho_w} = \frac{T_w}{T} = \frac{1}{1 - \beta T^*} \tag{5-3}$$

By substituting Eq. 5-2 and 5-3 into Eq. 2-5, 2-6, 3-1′, and 3-2′, and letting $\tau/\tau_w = q/q_w = 1$, Eq. 2-5 and 2-6 can be integrated numerically or analytically for the regions close to and away from the wall [*14,15*]. The molecular shear stress and heat transfer terms are neglected in the region away from the wall. The values of the constants $n$ and $\kappa$ are 0.124 and 0.36 as determined from the data in Fig. E,4a. The constants $\kappa$ and $n$ and the function $F$ in Eq. 3-1 and 3-2 have the same values for variable properties as for constant properties if the assumptions for $\epsilon_u$ in Art. 3

apply to variable properties; that is, if $\epsilon_u = \epsilon_u(du/dy, d^2u/dy^2)$ away from the wall and $\epsilon_u = \epsilon_u(u, y, \mu/\rho)$ close to the wall.

The relations between $u^*$ and $y^*$ and $T^*$ and $y^*$ are thus obtained for various values of $\beta$. The result for $u^*$ against $y^*$ for a Prandtl number of 0.73 is shown in Fig. E,5a. The positive value of $\beta$ corresponds to heat addition to the gas, the negative value to heat extraction. Similar curves were obtained for $T^*$ against $y^*$ [*14*].

For calculating the curves for various values of $\beta$ in Fig. E,5a it was assumed, somewhat arbitrarily, that the value of $y_1^*$, which is the point of intersection of the curves for the regions close to and away from the

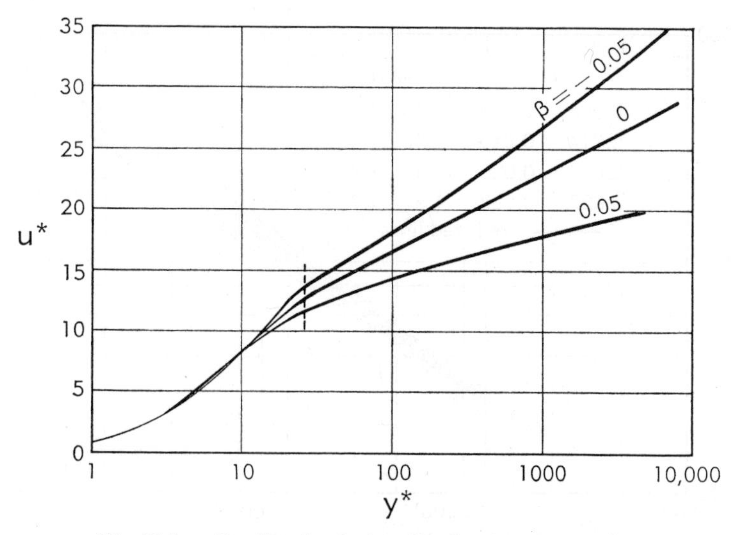


Fig. E,5a. Predicted velocity distributions for air with variable properties (Prandtl number = 0.73).

wall, remains constant at $y_1^* = 26$. A somewhat more reasonable assumption for $y_1^*$ might be made by including the molecular shear stress and heat transfer terms in the region away from the wall, and using the condition that $y_1^*$ occurs at a constant ratio of turbulent to molecular shear stress $\epsilon_u/(\mu/\rho)$. That is, the turbulence changes over from that described by Eq. 3-2 to that described by Eq. 3-1 when the ratio of turbulent to molecular shear stress reaches a certain value. This assumption was made in [*14*, Fig. 13], where it was shown to give essentially the same results as the assumption of constant $y_1^*$.

With the relations among $u^*$, $T^*$, and $y^*$ known, the relations between Nusselt number and Reynolds number can be calculated from Eq. 3-4, 3-5, 3-6, and 3-7. For variable properties, Eq. 3-4 and 3-5 give Nusselt and Reynolds numbers with properties evaluated at the wall temperature. The integrands in the numerator and denominator of Eq. 3-6 must be multiplied by $\rho/\rho_w$ when the density is variable. Nusselt and

Reynolds numbers with the properties evaluated at the bulk temperature, or at some temperature between the wall and bulk temperatures, can be calculated by using the relation

$$\frac{T_b}{T_w} = 1 - \beta T_b^* \tag{5-4}$$

Fig. E,5b and E,5c show fully developed experimental and predicted Nusselt numbers for air ($Pr = 0.73$) plotted against Reynolds number for various values of $\beta$. In Fig. E,5b the physical properties including density, in the Reynolds and Nusselt number, are evaluated at the fluid

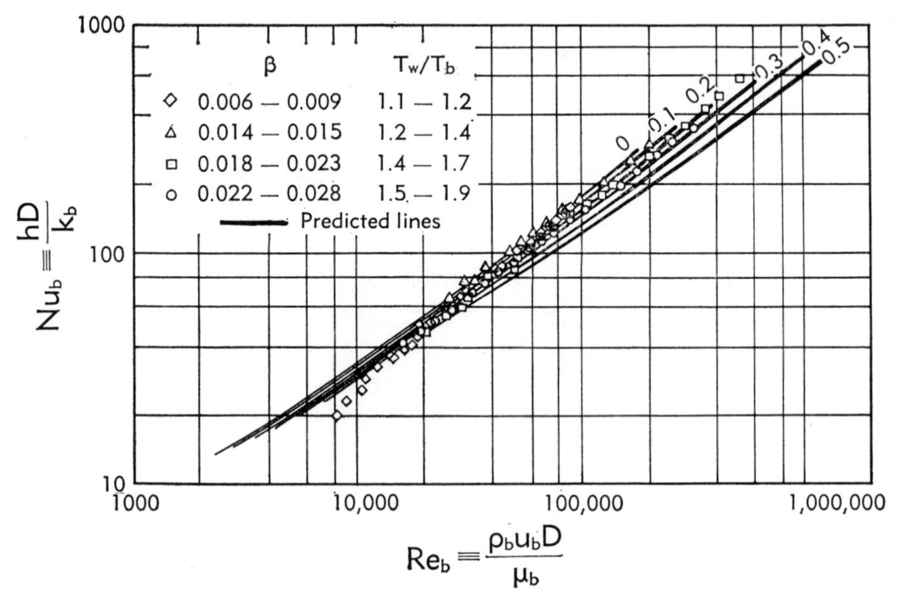


Fig. E,5b. Variation of Nusselt number with Reynolds number for flow of air with heat addition and properties evaluated at bulk temperature. Prandtl number = 0.73.

bulk temperature. Both the experimental and predicted Nusselt numbers at a given Reynolds number show a decrease with increasing values of $\beta$ or of ratio of wall to bulk temperature. If the properties are evaluated at the wall, rather than the bulk temperature, the Nusselt numbers increase as $\beta$ increases [*14*]. The same trends with $\beta$ were obtained in the data for average heat transfer coefficients given in [*60*].

In Fig. E,5c the properties in the Nusselt and Reynolds numbers are evaluated at a reference temperature $T_{0.4}$, which is slightly closer to the bulk temperature than the average of the wall and bulk temperatures. It is observed that the effect of $\beta$ or of ratio of wall to bulk temperature on both the experimental and predicted Nusselt numbers is practically eliminated when the properties are evaluated at this temperature. The data follow the predicted line very closely for Reynolds numbers above 15,000. For low Reynolds numbers the separation of the data from the predicted line is probably caused by a partial transition from turbulent to laminar heat transfer, which was not considered in the analysis. It should perhaps be mentioned that, in using the foregoing correlation for calculating heat transfer coefficients, the same assumptions for the variation of physical properties with temperature must be made as were made in the analysis: constant specific heat and both thermal conductivity and viscosity proportional to $T^{0.68}$.

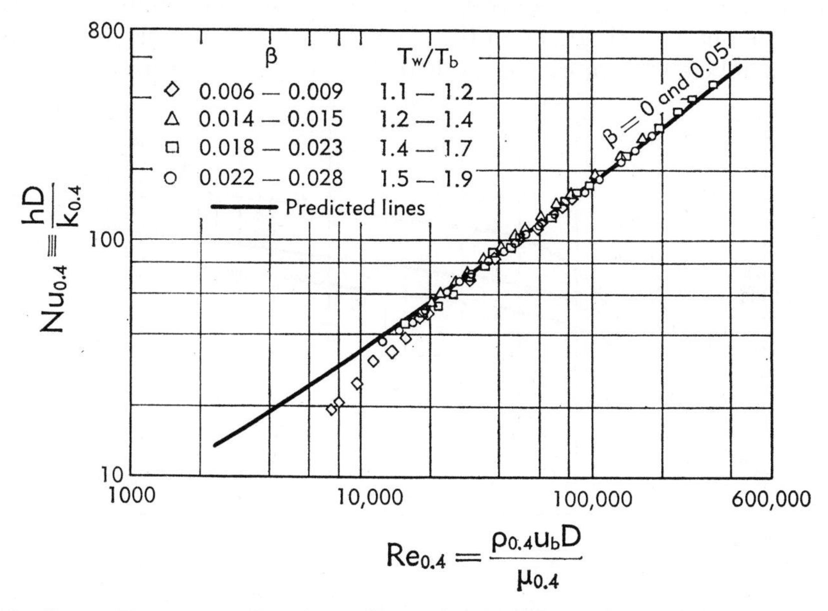


Fig. E,5c. Variation of Nusselt number with Reynolds number for flow of air with heat addition and properties evaluated at $T_{0.4} = 0.4(T_w - T_b) + T_b$. Prandtl number = 0.73.

Similar trends with $\beta$, or heat flux, were obtained for friction factors [*14*]. The effects of heat flux were again eliminated by evaluating the properties at a temperature close to the average of the wall and fluid bulk temperatures.

*Analysis for liquids.* In the case of heat transfer to liquids, the variation of the viscosity with temperature is considerably greater than the variation of the other properties. A good approximation to the actual heat transfer in liquids can therefore be obtained by considering only the viscosity to vary with temperature. For some liquids, including water, oil, ethylene glycol, and sodium hydroxide, $\mu/\mu_w$ can be represented approximately by $(T/T_w)^d$ if the liquid is not too near the freezing point. The exponent $d$ varies from $-1$ to $-4$ and the temperatures are measured in

°F. This differs from the case for gases where the temperatures were measured in °R. From the definitions of $T^*$ and $\beta$,

$$\frac{\mu}{\mu_w} = (1 - \beta T^*)^d$$

The analysis proceeds similarly to that for air, with the exception that $\rho/\rho_w = k/k_w = 1$ in Eq. 2-5, 2-6, and 3-2′ [15].

Generalized temperature distributions for a Prandtl number at the wall of 10 and a $d$ of $-4$ are shown for various values of the heat flux parameter in Fig. E,5d. Corresponding curves can be obtained for the variation of $u^*$ with $y^*$. From these curves, Nusselt numbers and Reynolds numbers with properties evaluated at the wall temperature can be

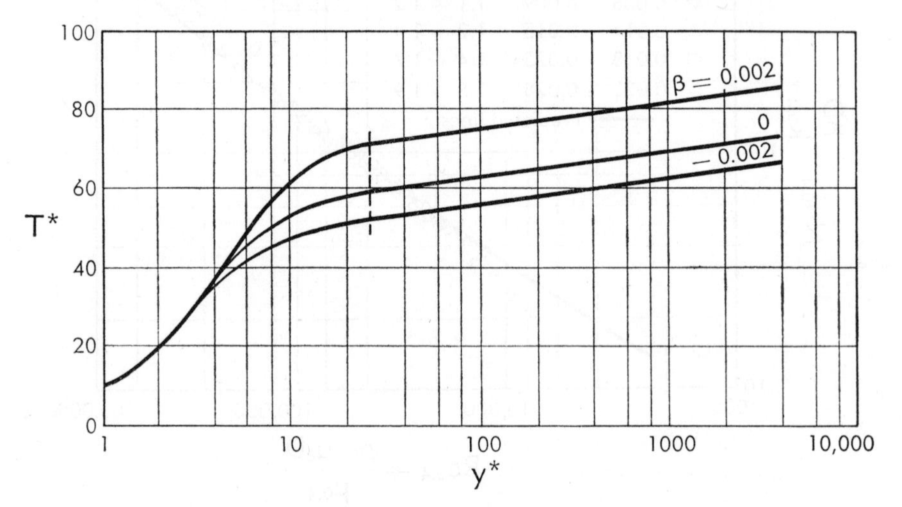


Fig. E,5d. Generalized temperature distribution for liquid with variable viscosity, $\mu/\mu_w = (T/T_w)^{-4}$. Prandtl number = 10.

calculated by using Eq. 3-4, 3-5, 3-6, and 3-7. Reference temperatures for evaluating the viscosity in the Reynolds and Prandtl numbers in order to eliminate the effects of heat flux, or variable viscosity, can then be calculated.

Fig. E,5e summarizes the results of the calculations. Curves are shown for both Nusselt numbers and friction factors. If we define the reference temperature $T_r$ by

$$T_r \equiv r(T_w - T_b) + T_b \tag{5-5}$$

then $r$ is given by Fig. E,5e. Nusselt numbers can be obtained from Fig. E,4c if the viscosity in the Reynolds and Prandtl numbers is evaluated at $T_r$. The values of $r$ in Fig. E,5e were computed for values of $d$ ($\mu/\mu_w = (T/T_w)^d$) of $-1$ and $-4$ and for values of $\mu_b/\mu_w$ of about 0.5 and 2. The value of $d$ had little effect on the curves, but different curves are obtained for heating and cooling of the liquid. In the case of heat transfer, the reference temperature does not depart greatly from that in the experimental Colburn equation [*59*, p. 168], wherein the viscosity is evaluated at $T_{0.5}$, except at the lower Prandtl numbers. Deviations from the curves in Fig. E,5e might occur for very high viscosity ratios or for cases in which the viscosity variation with temperature could not be represented by a simple power function.

An analysis for liquids with variable viscosity by Rannie [*11*] utilized somewhat different assumptions than those in the analysis given here. It

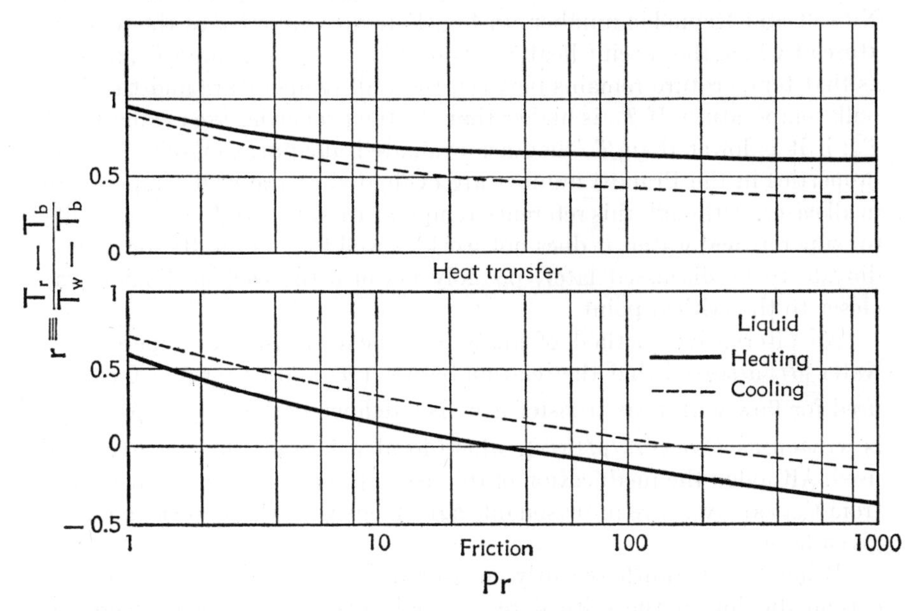


Fig. E,5e. Values of $r \equiv (T_r - T_b)/(T_w - T_b)$ against Prandtl number for evaluating viscosity in Prandtl and Reynolds numbers in Fig. E,4c or a similar curve for friction factors. $\mu/\mu_w = (T/T_w)^{-1}$ or $(T/T_w)^{-4}$; $\mu_b/\mu_w \cong 0.5$ or 2.

assumed that the oscillations in the wall layer are produced by the disturbances or turbulence outside the wall layer. An attempt was then made to determine the effect of a viscosity gradient on these impressed oscillations. It appears that the available experimental data are not sufficient to decide whether that theory or the one presented here is to be preferred.

*Fluids near the critical point.* The last subject to be discussed is that of heat transfer to supercritical fluids. A supercritical fluid is defined as one in which the pressure is above critical and the temperature is in the vicinity of the critical temperature. In that region all the fluid properties vary rapidly with temperature and also with pressure. The viscosity, thermal conductivity, and density decrease rapidly as the temperature increases above the critical point. The specific heat peaks at a temperature near the critical point and then decreases. With such unusual property variations, it is evident that the property ratios in Eq. 2-5, 2-6, and 3-2′ will be functions of wall temperature $T_w$ and pressure, as well as of $T/T_w$. A separate calculation must therefore be made for each wall temperature (or wall Prandtl number) and for each pressure and each value of $\beta$. Calculations with all the properties variable were carried out for supercritical water at a pressure of 5000 lb/in.$^2$ (critical pressure $\approx$ 3200 lb/in.$^2$) [*14*].

The results of the calculations for heating the water can be summarized as follows [*14*, discussion by Eckert]: The properties in the Nusselt and Reynolds numbers in Fig. E,4c are evaluated at the temperature at which the specific heat $c_p$ assumes its maximum value $T_m$, as long as that temperature remains between the wall temperature and the fluid bulk temperature. If $T_m$ is higher than $T_w$ the properties are evaluated at $T_w$; if it is lower than $T_b$ they are evaluated at approximately $T_b$. The properties in the Prandtl number are evaluated at the wall temperature in all cases. Although this reference temperature rule correlates the results for supercritical water, it does not work as well for the results for carbon dioxide to be discussed later, possibly because the carbon dioxide was closer to the critical point.

An alternative method of analysis of heat transfer to supercritical water [*61*] assumed that the relation between $u^*$ and $y^*$ for $\beta = 0$ can be used for flow with heat transfer if $u^*$ is redefined as $\int_0^u du/\sqrt{\tau_w/\rho}$ and $y^*$ is written as $\int_0^y dy\sqrt{\tau_w/\rho}/(\mu/\rho)$, where local values of the properties are used. Although the justification of this assumption is not clear, the results from that analysis are in reasonable agreement with those in the analysis given here.

Bringer and Smith recently measured heat transfer coefficients for carbon dioxide in the critical region [*62*]. The measurements were for turbulent flow in a tube at a pressure of 1200 lb/in.$^2$ abs (critical pressure = 1070) and fluid temperatures between 70 and 120°F (critical temperature = 88°F). They also calculated heat transfer coefficients by the analytical method given here, that is, by using Eq. 2-5, 2-6, 3-1′, and 3-2′.

Fig. E,5f, E,5g, E,5h, and E,5i give a comparison between analytical and experimental results. The Nusselt number is plotted against the Reynolds number (fluid properties evaluated at the wall) for various values of $\beta$, the heat flux parameter. The effects of $\beta$ are large, and in some cases the trends reverse as $\beta$ increases. The agreement between theory and experiment is very good. Inasmuch as these tests represent extreme variations of fluid properties, they lend considerable support to the theory given here. When it was attempted to correlate the data by conventional methods, deviations on the order of 50 to 120 per cent were obtained.

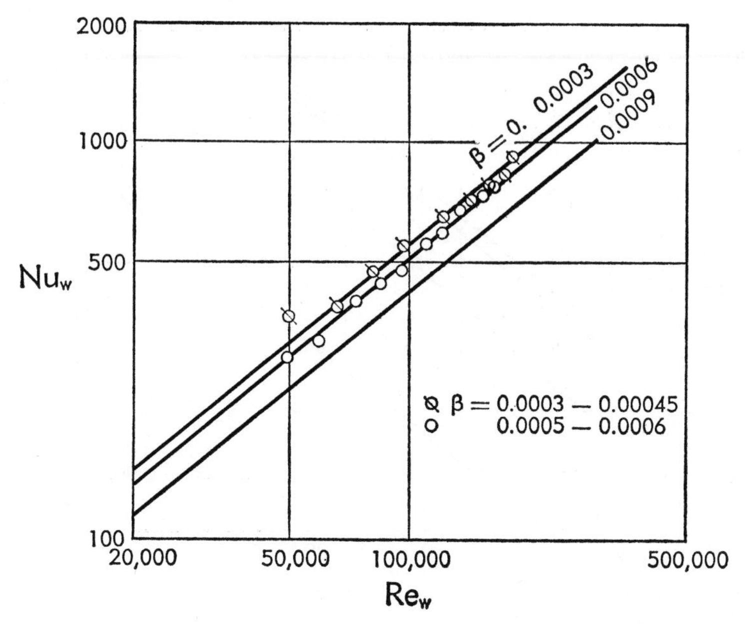


Fig. E,5f. $-T_w = 100°F$. Experimental and theoretical results for heat transfer to carbon dioxide in the critical region. Pressure = 1200 lb/in.² abs. From [*62*].

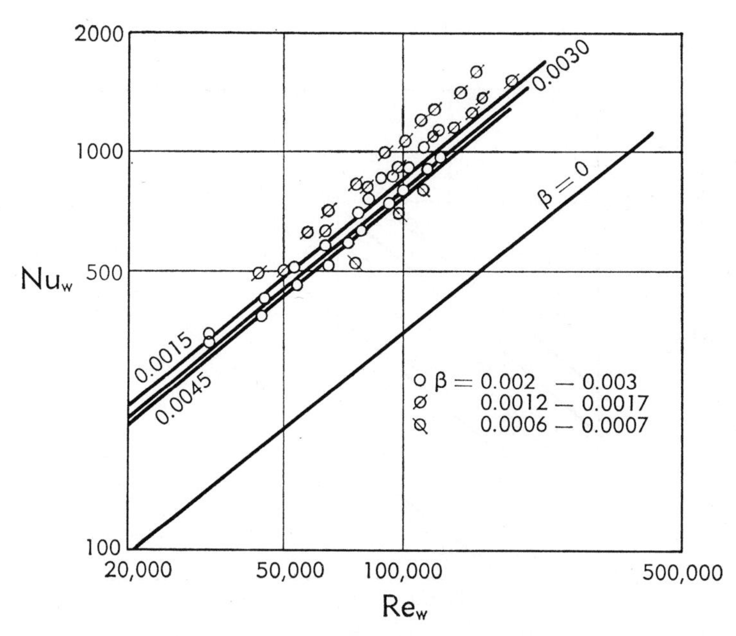


Fig. E,5g. $-T_w = 110°F$. Experimental and theoretical results for heat transfer to carbon dioxide in the critical region. Pressure = 1200 lb/in.² abs. From [*62*].

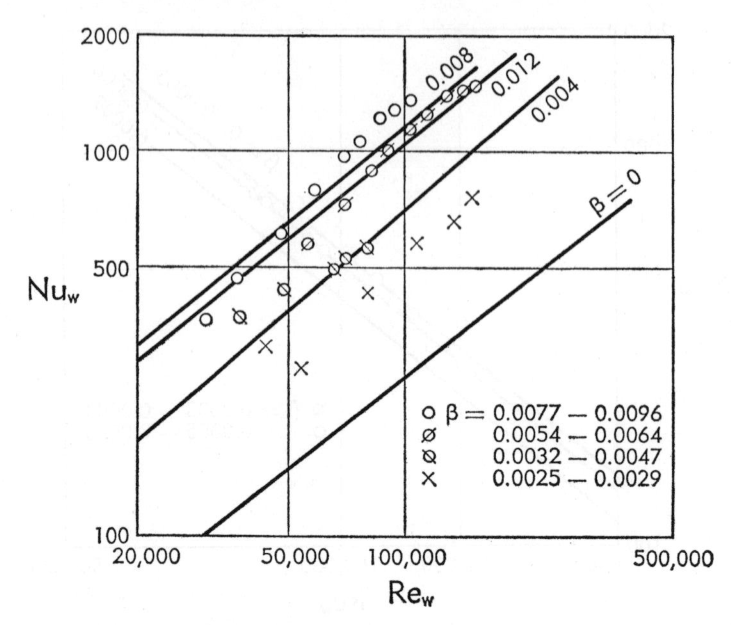


Fig. E,5h. —$T_w$ = 130°F. Experimental and theoretical results for heat transfer to carbon dioxide in the critical region. Pressure = 1200 lb/in.² abs. From [*62*].

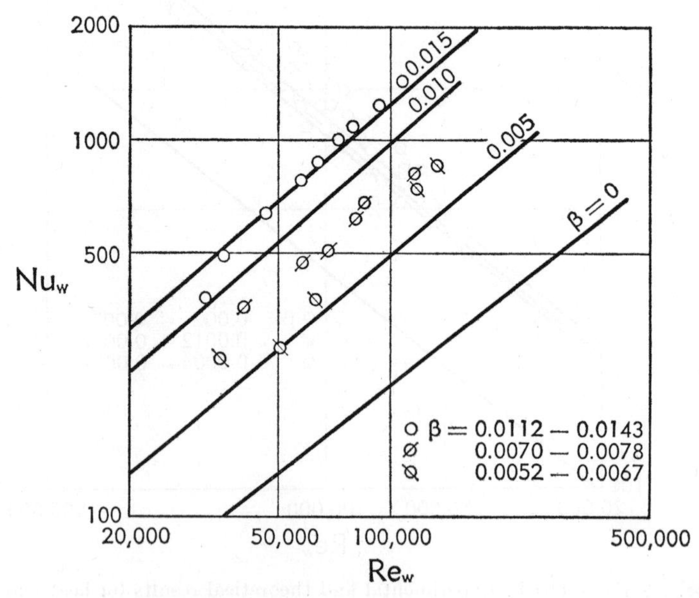


Fig. E,5i. —$T_w$ = 150°F. Experimental and theoretical results for heat transfer to carbon dioxide in the critical region. Pressure = 1200 lb/in.² abs. From [*62*].

**E,6. Concluding Remarks.** The calculation of turbulent flow and heat transfer in passages from the conservation equations of momentum, energy, and continuity alone has not yet been found practicable. By introducing physical assumptions to relate the eddy diffusivity to the mean flow, however, and determining several dimensionless constants by measuring a velocity profile, heat transfer and friction in a number of circumstances can be calculated. These cases include heat transfer and friction for various Prandtl numbers for fully developed flow, for the entrance region, for constant and variable properties, and for noncircular passages. In most cases where an experimental check is available the agreement between theory and experiment is good. A particularly good check for the case where the fluid properties are variable was obtained for heat transfer to carbon dioxide in the critical region.

Although considerable progress has been made in turbulent forced convection heat transfer, much work, both analytical and experimental, remains to be done. The relation between eddy diffusivities of heat and momentum should be more clearly established. Experimental work on heat transfer for liquids with variable properties is desirable. Knowledge of local heat transfer in noncircular passages is still limited and more definitive research on liquid metals is needed.

## *CHAPTER 2. SURVEY OF PROBLEMS IN BOILING HEAT TRANSFER*

R. H. SABERSKY

**E,7. Introduction.** Boiling heat transfer is defined as the heat transfer from a surface to a liquid under such conditions that the temperature at and near the surfaces is sufficient to create the vapor phase. The temperature of the bulk of the fluid is equal to or below the saturation temperature, and the difference between the saturation temperature and the actual bulk temperature is usually called the subcooling. The existence of this type of heat transfer has of course been recognized for a long time. The first technical discussion of the problem is probably that contained in a paper by Mosciki and Broder [*63*] in 1926. The interest in boiling heat transfer has increased, particularly in the last ten years, during which the problem has become of great technical importance in connection with the cooling of rocket engines, the construction of rapid response boilers, and the operation of nuclear power producers.

Boiling heat transfer may be subdivided into problems occurring under conditions of free convection or forced convection. A typical experimental apparatus for studying free convection boiling may consist of a vessel filled with the test fluid into which an electrically heated metal strip is submerged [*64*]. Instead of a strip a wire may also be used [*65*], although the curvature of the heating surface must then be counted as one of the variables. Boiling heat transfer with forced convection may be studied by pumping the test fluid through an electrically heated section of metal tubing [*66*]. If visual observations are to be made, the fluid can, for example, be made to flow in an annulus formed by an inner heating tube and an outer Lucite tube [*64*], or an axial heating strip may be enclosed in a Lucite duct [*67*]. Instead of electrical heating, other heating methods can be used, and some experiments have been performed using a condensing vapor as a heat source. Most workers in the field have preferred electrical heating because of its ease of control and its flexibility. Many investigators have also found it necessary to study the vapor formation near the heating surface in detail, making use of high speed photographs for this purpose. Frame speeds up to 20,000 frames per second were needed in some of these investigations [*67*].

**E,8. General Results.** Typical results obtained from boiling heat transfer experiments are shown in a graph of heat transfer rate per unit

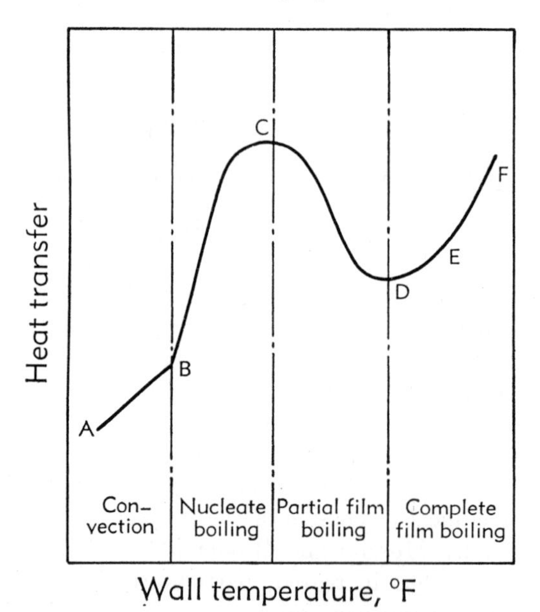


Fig. E,8a. Typical curve for boiling heat transfer.

area vs. wall temperature (Fig. E,8a). The same type of curve is obtained for forced or free convection conditions, with or without subcooling. The first part of the curve ($A$ to $B$) corresponds to the usual convection conditions without boiling. When the wall temperature reaches a certain value (somewhat above the boiling point of the liquid) the heat transfer increases sharply with the wall temperature until a maximum is reached at point $C$. A decrease in heat transfer occurs with further increase in wall temperature and only at very high wall temperatures does this trend reverse. If electrical heating is used, the part from $C$ to $D$ is unstable and special care has to be taken to obtain measurements in this region [*64*]. If the heat transfer rate is increased beyond the value at $C$, the wall temperature has to jump to a value indicated by point $F$. Since, in many cases, this temperature is higher than the melting point of the heating surface, failure of the heater may occur if the heat transfer at $C$ is exceeded.

Point $C$ is therefore generally called the "burnout" point. This name is somewhat misleading since, depending on the fluid and the material of the heater, physical destruction does not necessarily occur. The existence of a maximum in the heat transfer curve, however, is a significant engineering characteristic of boiling heat transfer, since an abrupt temperature increase occurs if an attempt is made to transfer an amount of heat greater than that indicated by this point. The determination of the burnout point is therefore important for the design of heat transfer equipment which is to operate in the boiling range. An exact knowledge of the shape of the curve from $B$ to $C$ is often not required because of the relatively small change in wall temperature which corresponds to this range.

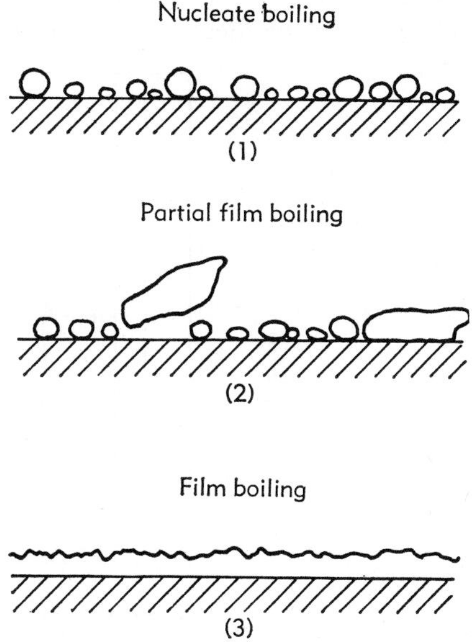


Fig. E,8b. Schematic representation of typical bubble formations.

Visual examination [*65,67,64*] of the processes at the heating surface shows that, at point $B$, small bubbles appear at the surface (see Fig. E,8b (1)). These bubbles may grow and collapse without ever leaving the surface or they may leave the surface, depending on the conditions of the bulk fluid. As the temperature of the surface is increased, more and more bubbles appear. When it is increased beyond $C$, the bubbles become so numerous that several of them will merge into a larger vapor mass which may adhere to the surface for some time. Eventually it will detach and float into the bulk fluid (see Fig. E,8b (2)). Progressively more of the larger vapor masses are formed as the temperature is increased, until at point $D$ a rather stable continuous vapor film is formed, which covers the entire heating surface (see Fig. E,8b (3)). The heat transfer mechanism corresponding to section $BC$ of the curve in Fig. E,8a is called "nucleate boiling," that corresponding to section $DF$ (and beyond) is called "film boiling," and that corresponding to section $CD$ is called "partial film boiling," in reference to the observed surface phenomena.

In Fig. E,8c, E,8d, and E,8e some actual test results of the type described in the foregoing are shown. The test fluid in these cases is distilled degassed[6] water and the pertinent test conditions are noted in the figures. In Fig. E,8c data for two different temperatures of the bulk fluid are given and it is seen that the burnout point has increased with decreasing fluid temperature. The behavior in the pure convection region follows the usual heat transfer laws. It is interesting to note that nucleate

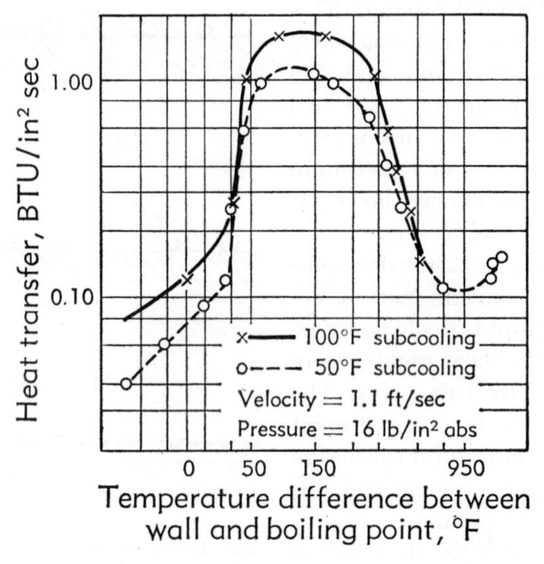


Fig. E,8c. Effect of subcooling on boiling heat transfer. Distilled degassed water [*64*].

boiling begins only at a wall temperature of approximately 30°F above the ordinary boiling temperature.

Fig. E,8d shows the effect of velocity, which again is to increase the burnout point. As before, the behavior of the curves at the lower temperatures is explained by the usual theory of forced convection. Fig. E,8e illustrates the effect of fluid pressure. For better comparison, these measurements have been made at constant liquid subcooling (normal boiling point − liquid temperature) rather than at constant fluid temperature. The resulting data can be plotted on practically the same curve if the temperature difference between the wall and the liquid is taken as the abscissa. As a consequence it has frequently been assumed that the degree of subcooling rather than the absolute pressure itself was the important

[6] The word "degassed liquid" is used to designate liquids in which the gas content has been reduced to a value of less than approximately 15 per cent of saturation.

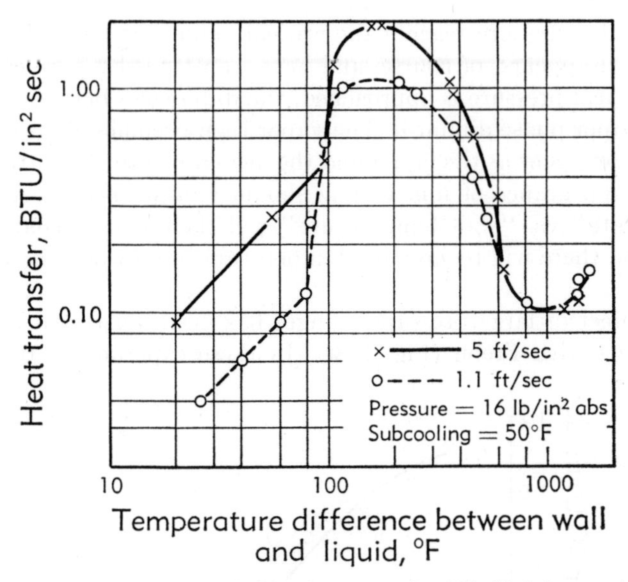


Fig. E,8d. Effect of velocity on boiling heat transfer. Distilled degassed water [*64*].

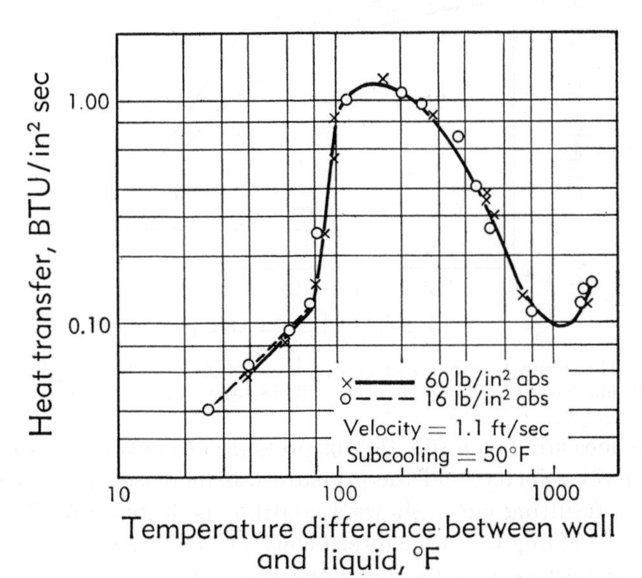


Fig. E,8e. Effect of pressure on boiling heat transfer. Distilled degassed water [*64*].

characteristic in boiling heat transfer. On the basis of this assumption it has often been attempted to simplify the presentation of experimental data (see, for example, Fig. E,9f). This simplification, however, should be used with some caution, since it applies only when the pressure changes are relatively small.

When the pressure reaches the critical value, the entire boiling phenomenon disappears, of course, and heat transfer is by pure convection. As the critical pressure is approached, the differences between the liquid and the vapor phase diminish. The vapor then becomes almost as good a heat transfer agent as the liquid and the decrease in the heat transfer rate with the appearance of film boiling should vanish. The curve of "heat transfer rate" vs. "wall temperature" will then show a continuous increase, and there will be no more temperature jump when the vapor film forms.

The effect of large pressure changes has been illustrated by a set of experiments with Freon (Fig. E,8f). In these experiments the burnout

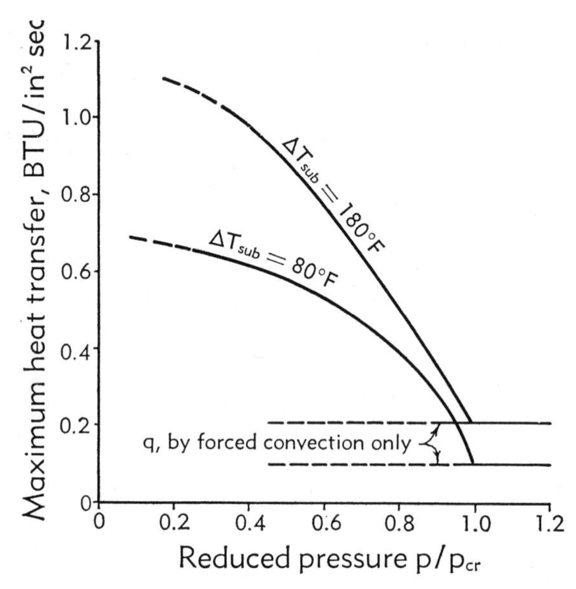


Fig. E,8f. Maximum heat transfer to Freon as a function of reduced pressure. The fluid is Freon No. 114. Mass velocity 5.2 lb/in.²-sec. Annular cooling passage [*68*].

point was measured as a function of pressure at constant subcooling and constant fluid velocity, and the pressure was increased above the critical value. The resulting curve shows a continuous decrease until finally the value corresponding to simple forced convection is reached, a result which should be expected from the foregoing discussion. The disappearance of the temperature jump in the graphs of the heat transfer rate vs. temperature is well illustrated by a set of curves in Fig. E,8g. The data in Fig. E,8g were obtained for a "jet fuel" consisting of a mixture of hydrocarbons. The critical pressure in this case was approximately 600 lb/in.² abs. An extensive set of experiments showing the effect of pressure on the maximum heat transfer rates of hydrocarbons is reported in [*70*].

In the following pages the information presently available on nucleate

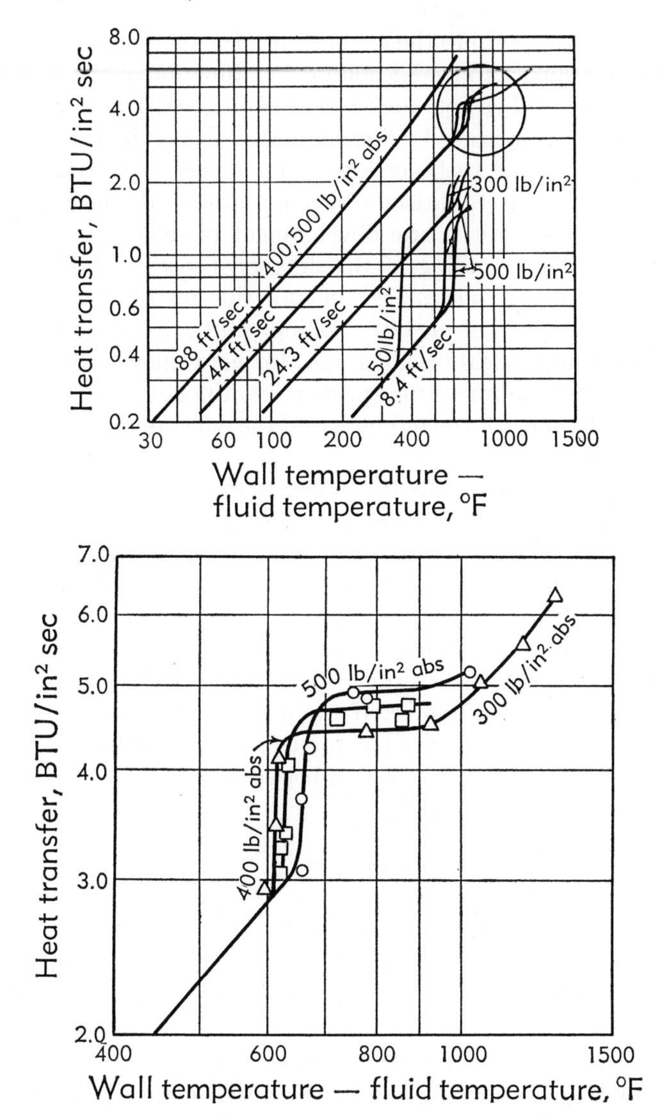


Fig. E,8g. Heat transfer to jet fuel [*69*].

boiling will be discussed in some detail. Only a short review of the problem of film boiling will be given, because experimental results for this type of heat transfer are still scarce.

## E,9. Nucleate Boiling.

Description of the Problem. In the previous section an over-all description of the problem of boiling heat transfer was given, and the effect of some of the variables was indicated. The information which may eventually be most useful to the engineer is a correlation of the maximum allowable heat transfer (burnout points) as a function of the fluid properties. For some special cases a correlation of the heat transfer rate in the complete region of nucleate boiling may also be required, although this information is believed to be of lesser importance (see Art. 8). To the knowledge of the writer, satisfactory correlations of this kind are not available at present. For future development of such relations it is believed that an understanding of the detailed processes taking place in nucleate boiling will be necessary, and for this reason the present concepts of the mechanism of nucleate boiling will be discussed below.

The process of nucleate boiling can, for convenience, be subdivided into three phases: the nucleation proper (i.e. the generation of the bubbles), the growth cycle of the bubbles, and the effect of the bubble motion on heat transfer.

NUCLEATION PROCESS. As the name "nucleate boiling" indicates, it is believed that the vapor bubbles in question originate from nuclei. These nuclei are imagined as consisting of small gas or vapor pockets stabilized on submicroscopic solid particles of low wettability. Upon heating, part of the vapor (or gas) is forced away from the stabilizing particle. If the resulting gas or vapor mass is sufficiently large, the inside pressure overcomes the surface tension forces as well as the outside pressure, and the nucleus grows into a bubble. If the detached gas mass is too small, it collapses by the surface tension forces and no bubble forms. If the initial cavity is spherical, the relation between the surface tension forces and the pressure becomes simply

$$p_i - p_o = \frac{2\sigma}{r} \tag{9-1}$$

where $p_i$ is the pressure inside the initial cavity, $p_o$ is the pressure of the surroundings, $r$ is the radius of the cavity, and $\sigma$ is the surface tension. If gas is present in the cavity in addition to the vapor, $p_i$ would be the sum of the vapor pressure and the partial pressure of the gas. In order to create a bubble, the temperature surrounding the nucleus has to be sufficiently high to create a pressure in the initial cavity larger than that indicated in Eq. 9-1. By measuring the temperature at which a bubble is observed and assuming the pressure $p_i$ to be approximately equal to the vapor pressure corresponding to this temperature, an estimate of the size of the initial cavity in terms of "equivalent spherical size" can be made.

Nuclei of the kind described are believed to be present throughout the test fluids as well as on the heating surface. The existing nuclei cover a certain range of sizes, and a certain distribution curve of number vs. size can be imagined in each case. Nucleate boiling first becomes noticeable when the temperature near the heating surface becomes high enough to cause the growth of a significant number of the largest nuclei. As the temperature is increased, smaller nuclei become capable of forming bubbles, and the number of bubbles per unit area per unit time increases. The temperature may be raised until the bubble population becomes so high that the burnout point is reached. The number of bubbles per unit area per unit time at the burnout point depends on several conditions, such as the fluid temperature and velocity. As an example, for water at a velocity of 10 ft/sec, at a pressure of 25 lb/in.$^2$ abs, and at 155°F subcooling, a bubble frequency of $16 \times 10^6$ bubbles/in.$^2$ sec was measured near the burnout point [*67*]. According to the concept of nucleation, the wall temperature at the burnout point should depend on these same conditions. This dependence has also been observed experimentally [*66*].

The observed bubbles always occur at or in the immediate vicinity of the heating surface. One should be somewhat hesitant, however, to conclude from this that the heating surface is solely responsible for the supply of nuclei. Nuclei existing in the fluid would also begin to grow near the surface, because the temperature in this region is the highest. It is of interest here to cite an experiment in which distilled degassed water was heated by radiation, in such a way that the walls of the vessel would be below the bulk fluid temperature [*71*]. In this case bubbles were created inside the water at a temperature quite similar to that of the heating surface in nucleate boiling. It is believed, therefore, that the nuclei responsible for boiling may come from either source. Whether the sources are of equal importance, or whether more nuclei come from the fluid itself than from the surface probably depends on the particular fluid and the particular surface. It may also be possible that the relative importance depends on the rate of heat transfer. The surface, for example, may be able to supply the nuclei for the rather low bubble frequencies required at low rates of heat transfer but, for the high nucleation rates occurring at high heat flow rates, the fluid might act as the main nucleation source. The fact that the surface can influence the results has been demonstrated by a set of experiments by Farber and Scorah [*65*]. In these experiments the heat transfer rates to boiling water were measured for a set of wires of different materials with results shown in Fig. E,9a.

As mentioned previously, by measuring the wall temperature and using Eq. 9-1 an estimate of the size of the original nucleus in terms of "equivalent spherical diameter" can be made. From experiments with distilled degassed water at 1 atm [*64*], this size was found to be of the order of $10^{-4}$ inch. Measurements for distilled degassed carbon tetrachloride at 1 atm [*64*] indicate approximately the same size. The heating surface in both cases was a strip of stainless steel, type 347. Estimates of equivalent nucleus size made from cavitation experiments [*72*] lead again to the same order of magnitude. There is not, however, sufficient information available to draw any general conclusions.

As seen again from Eq. 9-1, for a given nucleus size, lower surface tension should lead to boiling at a smaller temperature excess above the normal saturation temperature. Experiments with distilled degassed water and a degassed water-aerosol solution [*64*] tended to verify this result. In the first case a wall temperature of approximately 30°F above the normal boiling point was required to initiate nucleate boiling, whereas only about 15°F was required for the aerosol water solution, the surface tension of which was considerably below that of pure water. The presence of gas in the initial nucleus according to Eq. 9-1, should have the same effect as decreasing the surface tension. This fact has also been shown experimentally [*64*].

The concept that nuclei are responsible for the boiling as discussed in this section is the most widely accepted theory at present. The precise

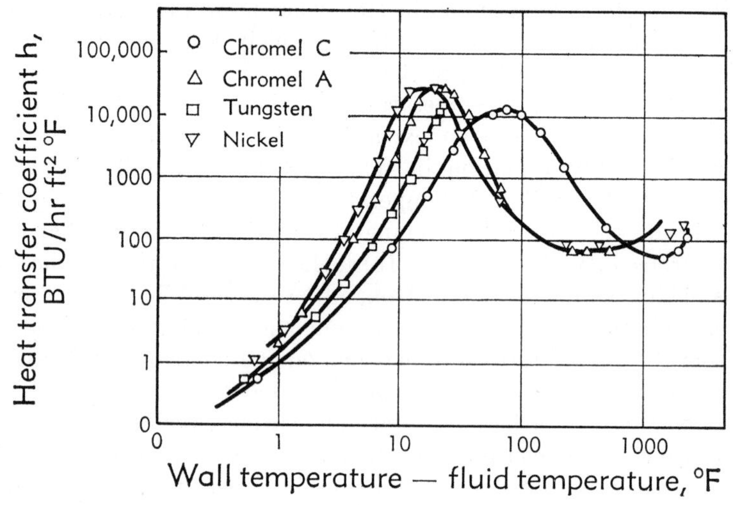


Fig. E,9a. Heat transfer coefficient for four different surface materials. Bulk boiling, 1 atm pressure; wire diameter 0.040 inches; wire length 6 inches. Distilled water, free convection, horizontal wire [*65*].

role of surface and liquid in supplying nuclei, as well as the size distribution of nuclei in each case, is still not known.

There is one other mechanism of bubble generation which has been considered. In any liquid, cavities are continuously formed due to the random fluctuations of the molecules. These cavities, if large enough, could grow into bubbles. The probability that cavities of sufficient size would form [*73*] to cause boiling at the observed temperatures, however, is practically zero. It has further been suggested that these cavities might form at the surface of "nonwettable" solids [*74*], in which case the required size would be much smaller. The probability that the necessary fluctuations would occur at such specific points is, however, again expected to be very small.

Experimental evidence, which would clearly indicate which of the two mechanisms is the essential one, is difficult to obtain, but the results of the following set of experiments may be pertinent. In these experiments [*75*] a vessel containing water and a submerged heating wire was subject to pressures of the order of 15,000 lb/in.$^2$ for approximately 10 minutes. The pressure was then lowered to the atmospheric value and the wire was heated electrically. It was found under these circumstances that the first bubbles would form only when the wire temperature was raised considerably above the usual nucleation temperature. Very similar results had been obtained previously by several investigators [*76*] who observed that a body of water, after being subjected to a pressure treatment as described above, could be heated to temperatures much higher than the normal boiling point before any bubbles would form. This observation was explained in terms of the theory of pre-existing nuclei. In accordance with this theory, the pressure treatment causes a decrease in the number and size of the initial nuclei and the smaller nuclei require a higher temperature before becoming capable of growing. The observed increase in nucleation temperature on the other hand would be difficult to explain in terms of thermal fluctuations. Since the same type of phenomenon was observed in the experiments with the heated wire, it is reasonable to assume that the presence of the wire did not change the nucleation mechanism and that pre-existing nuclei were again responsible for the bubble formation. In general, therefore, thermal fluctuations are not believed to play a major role in boiling heat transfer. The thermal fluctuations, on the other hand, are probably of essential importance in determining the maximum tensile strength of a perfectly pure liquid [*73*].

Growth and Collapse Process. Bubble motion has been discussed in detail in [*66,67,64*] and the concepts given in these references will be used in this section, since they appear to be the most plausible ones at this time. In Fig. E,9b the typical stages of the growth and collapse of a bubble are shown schematically. In Fig. E,9b (1), a nucleus is shown surrounded by superheated liquid. The dotted line indicates the isotherm which is at the temperature of the normal boiling point. The pressure in the nucleus is essentially equal to the vapor pressure of the surrounding liquid plus the pressure exerted by any gas present. If the nucleus is of sufficient size, it begins to grow (Fig. E,9b (2), (3)). As the size increases, the surface tension forces decrease rapidly and further motion depends principally on the pressure inside the bubble. This pressure is a function of the rate at which vapor can be supplied to the growing bubble, assuming the fluid to be sufficiently degassed so that gas diffusion can be neglected. The rate of this vapor flow is determined by two processes: the heat transfer from the liquid to the surface of the cavity, and the evaporation from the surface. The temperatures influencing these processes are the temperature of the superheated liquid and the temperature of the vapor inside the bubble. The temperature of the bulk liquid should have little influence at this stage of the growth. In Fig. E,9b (2) the bubble is shown after some growth has taken place. The isotherm of the normal boiling point has approached the bubble surface partly because of the stretching of the hot film of liquid over the bubble and partly because of the heat transfer from the film. The part of the film which is stretched over the top of the bubble is further cooled by heat transfer to the surrounding cold liquid. The superheat of the liquid surrounding the upper part of the bubble is finally removed completely (Fig. E,9b (3)) and vapor is condensed over this portion of the bubble. The rate of vapor removal depends on the rate of the condensation mechanism itself, as well as on the rate of heat transfer to the cold bulk liquid. The significant temperatures in this case are the temperature of the bulk liquid and the

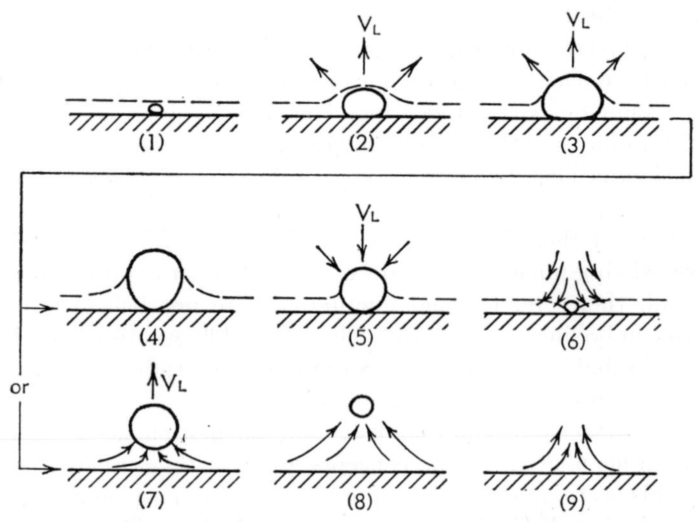


Fig. E,9b. Schematic representation of bubble growth.

temperature of the vapor in the bubble. As the bubble grows, the evaporation rate over the lower portion of the bubble also changes, because of changes in the surrounding temperature and configuration. Eventually the heat transfer from the upper part of the bubble may become sufficiently large so that the condensation overcomes the evaporation. The pressure inside the bubble then decreases rapidly and falls below the pressure of the fluid, the resulting force reducing the momentum of the surrounding fluid. If large enough, it reverses the fluid motion and brings about the collapse of the bubble at the surface (Fig. E,9b (4 through 6)). If the heat transfer from the bubble is low, the resulting pressure decrease in the bubble may not be sufficient to cause a reversal of the momentum in the fluid. In this case the bubble will be carried with the fluid, away from the surface. It will then collapse in the bulk of the fluid, provided the fluid is subcooled. Fig. E,9b (7 through 9) illustrates this latter process. For a particular combination of properties and temperature, bubbles may also become stationary on the heating surface. The tendency of the bubble to leave the surface, as well as its shape during the growth cycle, probably also depends on the contact angle between the fluid, the vapor, and the surface [*77*].

In the following, effects of some of the more important variables on bubble motion will be discussed in the light of the foregoing description. Comparisons with experimental data will be made whenever possible.

EFFECT OF VARIABLES ON BUBBLE MOTION.

*Nucleus size and surface tension.* As mentioned previously, the nucleus size determines the temperature at which boiling begins. Since this temperature also influences the initial growth rate (see Fig. E,9b), nucleus

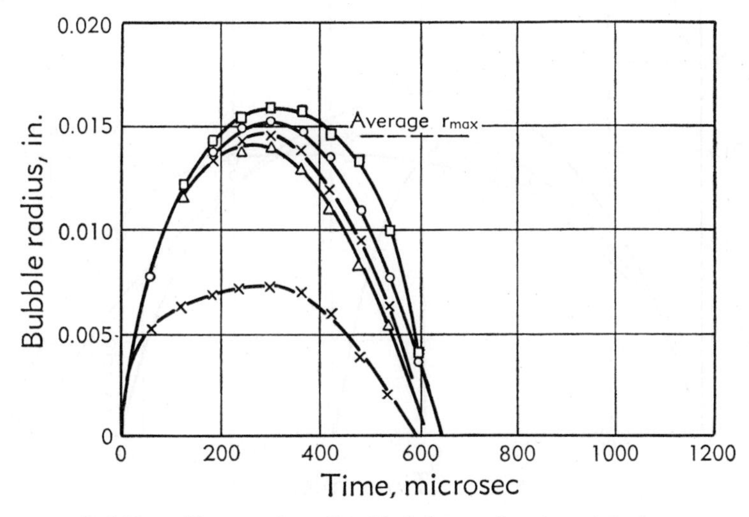


Fig. E,9c. Bubble radius vs. time. Distilled degassed water at 1 atm pressure and 78°F. Heat flux 50 per cent of burnout value. Free convection [*64*].

size and initial growth should be interdependent. Smaller nuclei should correspond to higher initial growth rates. In a very similar way, a reduction in surface tension should lead to a decrease in the initial growth rate. This latter effect is believed to be principally responsible for the difference in initial bubble growth rates in water with and without dissolved aerosol (see Fig. E,9c and E,9d).

*Shape of vapor pressure curve.* The size of the nucleus and the surface tension actually determine the pressure which is required to initiate boiling; they only indirectly control the required temperature of the surrounding liquid. The temperature, however, is an important factor in the growth of the bubble, and the relation between vapor pressure and temperature of the liquid therefore becomes a property affecting this growth. If the amount of superheat required to produce the necessary pressure in the nucleus is large, the bubble is surrounded by a wide region of greatly superheated fluid. The temperature differential for the initial heat transfer is then large and the bubble is expected to grow rapidly. A steep vapor pressure-temperature curve, on the other hand, should lead to slow bubble growth. The rate of change of vapor pressure with temperature for each liquid is a function of the absolute pressure.

Growth rate measurements over a sufficiently wide pressure range, to indicate the effect of the slope of the vapor pressure-temperature curve directly, have not been made. The fact, however, that the superheat required for boiling decreases with increasing pressure has been checked experimentally [*78*] and the results are shown in Fig. E,9e. The curve is

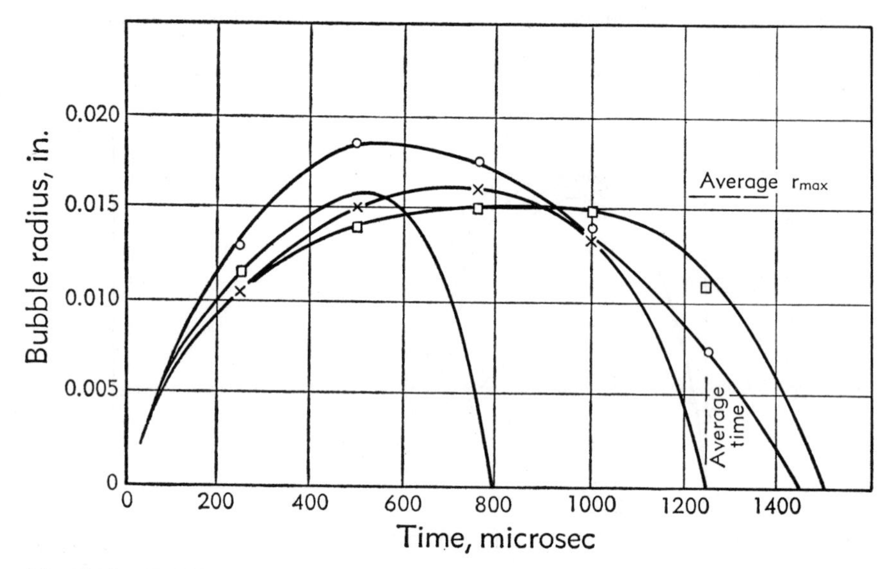


Fig. E,9d. Bubble radius vs. time. Distilled degassed water-aerosol solution at 1 atm pressure and 90°F. Heat flux 80 per cent of burnout value. Free convection [*64*].

partly influenced, of course, by changes in surface tension and possible changes in nucleus size, but these changes cannot fully explain the large variation in superheat. The change in slope of the vapor pressure curve is believed to be the principal factor [*64*]. Explosive boiling at very low pressure, a phenomenon well known to the chemical worker, is another instance which may be explained by the slope of the vapor pressure curve. For water at 0.1 atm pressure, e.g., the superheat necessary to produce a 15-lb/in.$^2$ over-pressure would be 100°F. A nucleus, growing in such a highly superheated liquid, would of course grow very rapidly, which could explain the observed results. In vacuum work it is often necessary to make a special effort to introduce large nuclei in order to avoid explosive processes.

*Thermal diffusivity.* In the brief description of bubble motion given above it was seen that the heat transfer from the liquid to the bubble played a role in determining the bubble motion. The thermal diffusivity of the liquid therefore should be an important property affecting this motion. A low diffusivity should favor slow bubble growth and collapse. It is difficult to isolate this effect because changes in other properties are usually involved when using fluids of different thermal diffusivity, but a comparison of experimental data obtained for carbon tetrachloride with those obtained with a water-aerosol solution is probably pertinent. The surface tensions of the two liquids are quite similar and the thermal diffusivity for carbon tetrachloride is only about $\frac{1}{2}$ that of the water solution. Measurements under comparable conditions at a pressure of

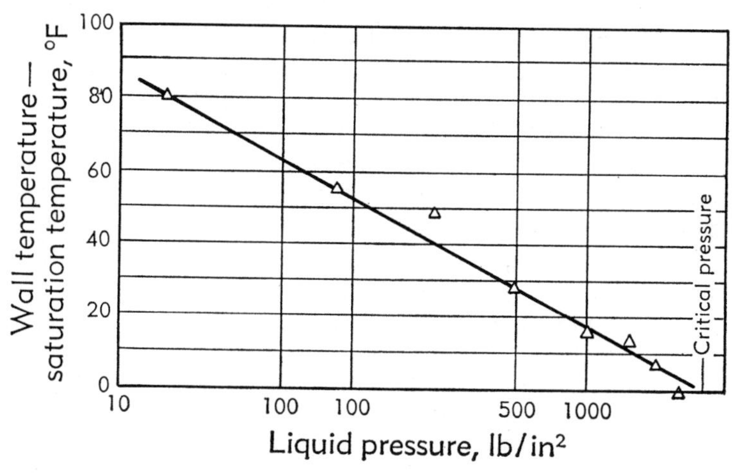


Fig. E,9e. Excess of wall temperature over saturation temperature as a function of pressure for fully established boiling. Distilled degassed water. Heat transfer surface is SS347 except for the point at the lowest pressure, in which case the surface is SS304 [*78*].

1 atm show considerably slower growth and collapse rates for the carbon tetrachloride than for the water solution [*64*].

*Temperature of bulk liquid.* The temperature of the bulk liquid influences the heat transfer from the bubble to the bulk fluid, which in turn limits the growth of the bubble and is responsible for its collapse. If the temperature of the bulk fluid is low, the growth of the bubble stops early and the collapse is rapid. For free convection boiling of distilled water at 1 atm, e.g., the maximum bubble radius decreases from 0.022 to 0.014 inches as the fluid temperature is changed from 170 to 60°F [*64*]. If the fluid temperature is high, the bubble may grow to a rather large size. The under-pressure eventually created in the bubble may not be sufficient to reverse the momentum stored in the fluid during the growth and the bubble may detach itself from the surface. If, in the limit, the temperature of the bulk fluid is itself at the boiling point, there is no heat transfer from the bubble to the fluid at all. The bubbles will then always detach themselves from the surface.

*Velocity.* The effect of the velocity of the bulk fluid on bubble motion is similar to that of the temperatures of the fluid. Higher velocities, like lower temperatures, improve the heat transfer from the bubble to the fluid and lead to smaller bubble sizes and faster collapse. It should also be mentioned that a moving bulk fluid exerts a drag on the bubbles, so that they have been observed to slide along the heating surface at velocities approximately equal to 80 per cent of that of the fluid itself [*67*].

HEAT TRANSFER IN NUCLEATE BOILING.

*Effect of bubble motion on heat transfer.* The last phase of nucleate boiling to be discussed is the effect of bubble motion on the heat transfer. In early analyses it was suggested that the increased heat transfer could possibly be explained by the fact that the vapor created near the heating surface absorbed a large amount of heat and that this vapor was then carried away with the rising bubbles. For the case in which the bubbles did not detach from the surface, the increased heat transfer was explained by the vapor flow from the lower to the upper regions of the bubble. Numerical estimates of the amount of heat that could possibly be removed in this way [*77*, Chap. 29; *79*; *80*], however, showed that this mechanism could not account for the observed heat transfer.

There are at present two mechanisms which have been suggested as explanations for the heat transfer improvement. According to the first concept, which is held by many investigators [*64,66,67,80*], the improved heat transfer is caused by the agitation of the bubbles. The transfer process is essentially one of forced convection and accordingly it should depend on a characteristic Reynolds number and Prandtl number. The typical velocity in this case should be the average fluid velocity induced by the bubbles, and the maximum bubble diameter might be chosen as the typical dimension. Attempts at verifying this concept have been made with some success [*64*], although the available data do not cover a sufficient range of variables to allow any definite conclusions.

The second concept [*81*] is based on the following idea: After the collapse of each bubble, relatively cold fluid is suddenly brought into direct contact with the hot heating surface at the point of collapse. The resulting large temperature gradients, momentarily and locally, cause extreme rates of heat transfer. Initial estimates [*81*] indicate that these rates could increase the average heat transfer sufficiently to yield the values observed experimentally.

So far it has not been possible to determine which of the two mechanisms is predominant. From experiments, the heat transfer—and in particular the burnout point—seems to improve with increased bubble activity. Both concepts could serve as an explanation for this observation; therefore this fact alone is not sufficient to determine the actual process.

Because of the observed effect of activity on heat transfer, however, it is possible to make qualitative predictions for the effect of some of the variables on boiling heat transfer. The factors discussed below, which lead to increased bubble activity, should also lead to improved heat transfer. This view may be kept in mind when examining the experimental data that follow.

EXPERIMENTAL RESULTS.

*Heat transfer.* Having considered a number of the factors which may influence nucleate boiling, some experimental results as well as references for additional data will be given. A considerable amount of information

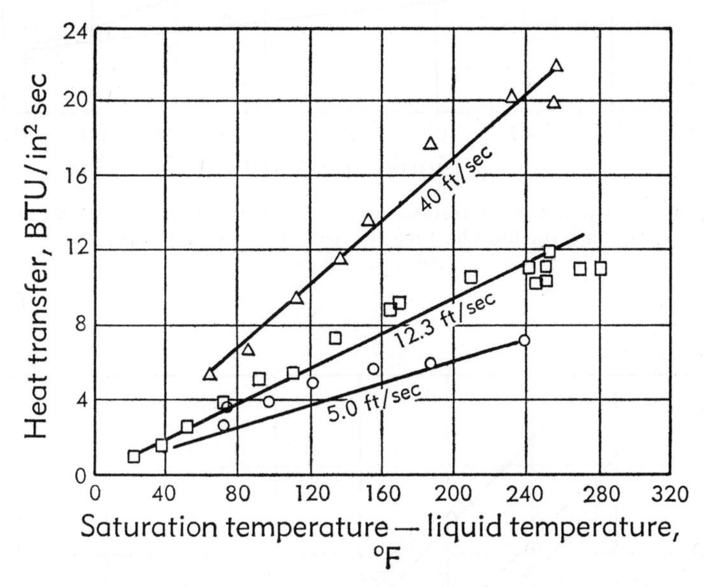


Fig. E9f. Heat transfer vs. subcooling. Distilled degassed water. Pressure range from 15 lb/in.² abs to 164 lb/in.² abs [*67*].

on water can be found in [*66,67,78*]. Some results from [*67*] on the burnout points for distilled degassed water at various velocities are reproduced in Fig. E,9f.

The extremely high heat transfer rates observed in some of these tests are certainly noteworthy. Data on burnout points with free convection for distilled water, distilled carbon tetrachloride, a water-aerosol solution, as well as aerated water, are shown in Fig. E,9g and E,9h [*64*]. An attempt may be made to give some explanation for the shape and relative position of these curves.

The increase in heat transfer with decreasing temperature is probably caused principally by the increase in the temperature differential itself. The reason that the water-aerosol data is below that for distilled water may be traced to the difference in surface tension. Lower surface tension

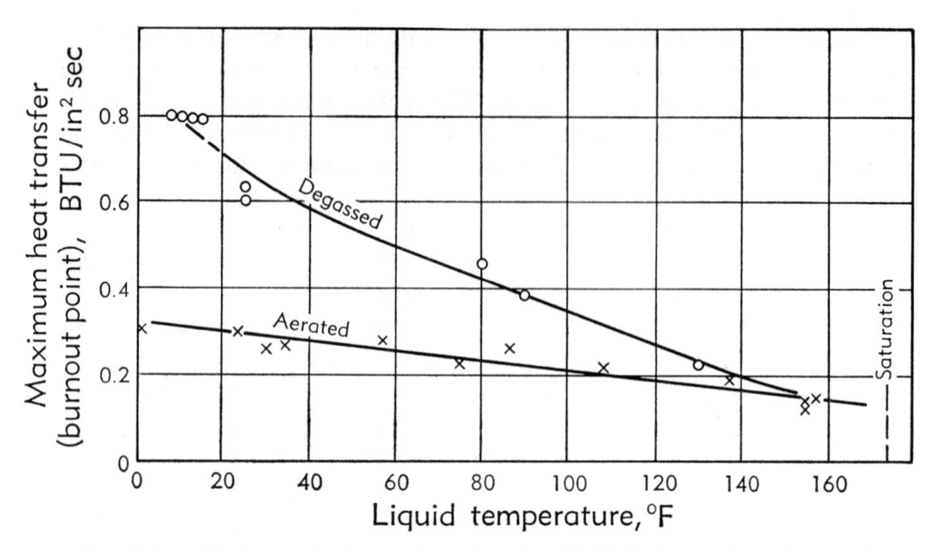


Fig. E,9g. Maximum heat transfer values for distilled, degassed, and aerated carbon tetrachloride. Free convection, pressure 1 atm [*64*].

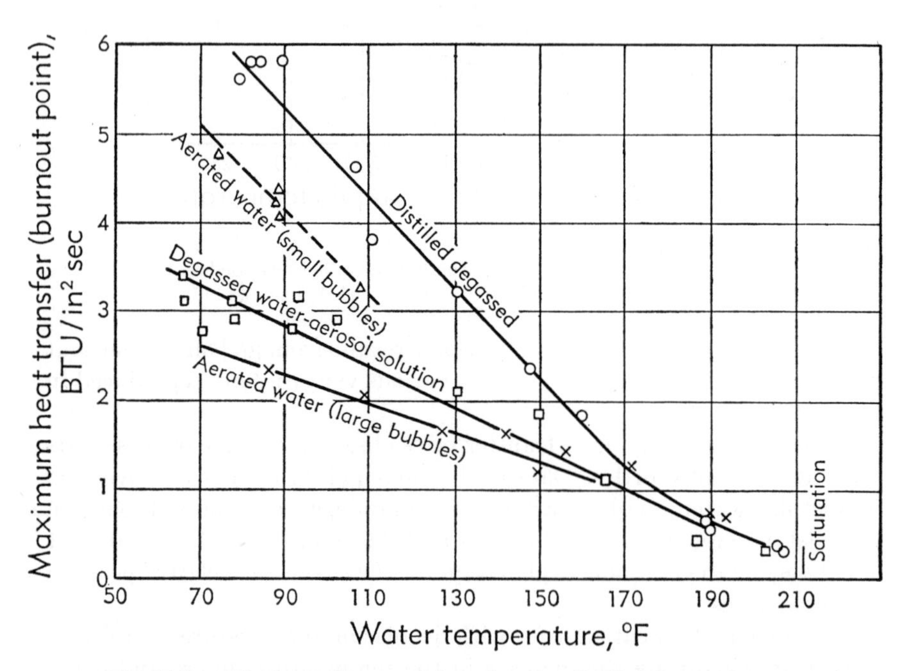


Fig. E,9h. Maximum heat transfer values for distilled degassed water, aerated water, and a water-aerosol solution. Free convection, pressure 1 atm [*64*].

allows boiling at less superheat, the bubble velocity and agitation is less, and lower heat transfer results. The values for carbon tetrachloride are still lower because of its low thermal diffusivity which influences the heat transfer directly and also leads to lower bubble velocity (see above). As already stated, the effect of increasing gas content is similar to that of decreasing the surface tension. In addition, gas diffusion influences bubble motion to some extent and gas bubbles can rather easily become stable and adhere to the heating surface [*64*]. For both of these reasons the

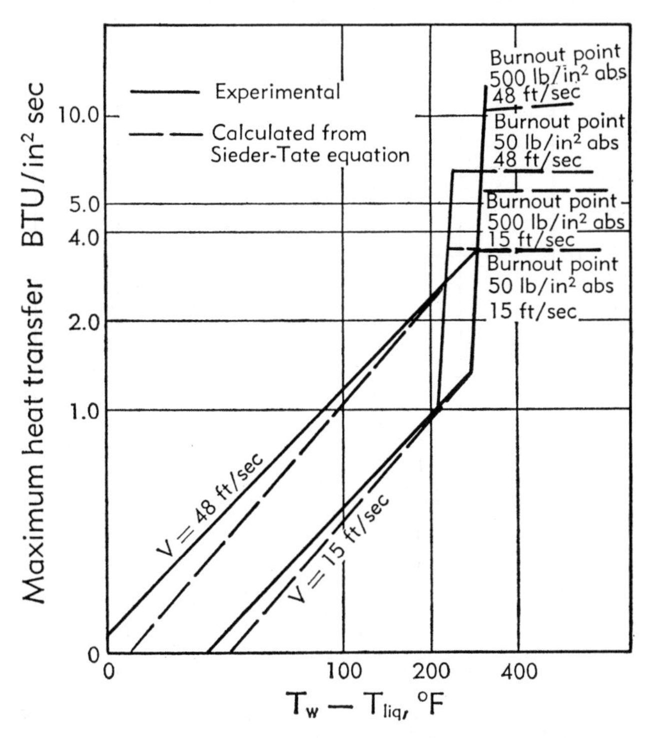


Fig. E,9i. Heat transfer to red fuming nitric acid. Forced convection-nucleate boiling. Burnout points are indicated. Liquid temperature 80°F. Heat transfer surface SS347. $NO_2$ content of acid $6\frac{1}{2}$ per cent, water content $\frac{1}{2}$ to 2 per cent [*82*].

burnout points of the two liquids, when containing gas, are below the values which are obtained when they are degassed. Fig. E,9h also contains some burnout points for aerated water which were not caused by the adherence of bubbles, a random process which generally cannot be controlled. For design purposes the lower curve would have to be taken.

Further experimental results on boiling heat transfer are given in Fig. E,9i, which contains information on nitric acid [*82*]. Burnout points for Freon have already been given in Fig. E,8f and for "jet fuel" in Fig. E,8g. For information on the heat transfer to a number of hydrocarbons under bulk boiling conditions, the reader is referred to [*70*].

*Friction.* There is one other phenomenon applying to boiling heat transfer with forced convection which should be pointed out. As the heat transfer improves, the frictional pressure drop increases. Typical results are shown in Fig. E,9j. The increase in friction is certainly an important consideration in the design of heat transfer equipment.

With the purpose of studying the inter-relation between friction and heat transfer, some experiments have been performed [*83*] in which water

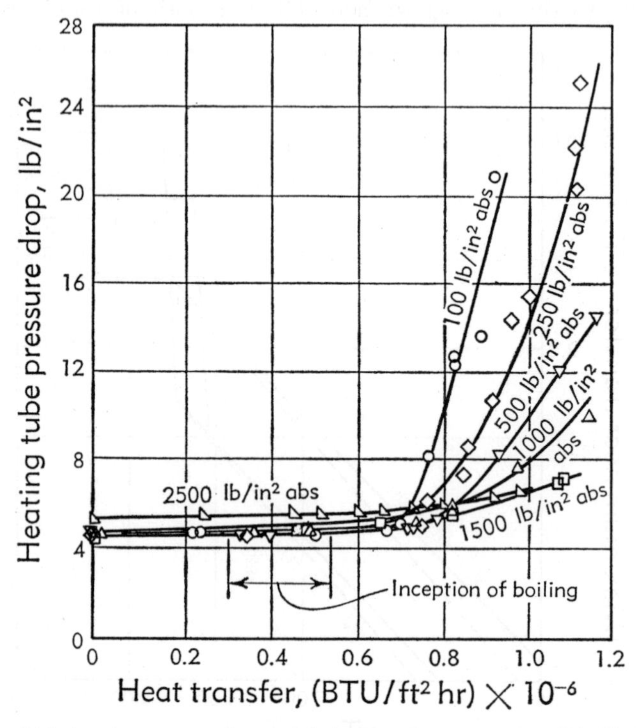


Fig. E,9j. Frictional pressure drop with boiling heat transfer. Distilled degassed water. SS347 tube, 0.226 I.D., 25 inches long. Data taken at constant subcooling of 100°F and constant mass flow of 3.81 × $10^6$ lb/hr-ft² [*78*].

was forced through an electrically heated tube of about $\frac{3}{8}$-in. diameter. Sufficient measurements were taken so that the local Stanton number *St*, as well as the local friction coefficient $c_f$, could be computed. The two coefficients are defined by the equations

$$St = \frac{q}{\rho \bar{V} c_p (T_w - T_b)}$$

and

$$c_f = -\frac{\frac{dp}{dx} d}{2\rho \bar{V}^2}$$

where

$q$ = heat transfer rate per unit area

$\frac{dp}{dx}$ = local pressure gradient

$\rho$ = fluid density

$\overline{V}$ = average fluid velocity (adjusted for bubble obstruction)

$c_p$ = specific heat of fluid

$d$ = effective diameter of unobstructed flow passage

$T_w$ = wall temperature

$T_b$ = bulk temperature of fluid.

It may be pointed out that the average velocity $\overline{V}$ required in the above equations is not equal to the ratio of the volume flow rate to the unobstructed cross-sectional area of the pipe. The vapor bubbles on the wall may represent a significant reduction of the available flow area and the velocity $\overline{V}$ may differ substantially from the above-mentioned ratio, particularly where the diameter of the tube is small.

The results of the experiments [*83*] indicated that the relation between the two coefficients was approximately given by the simple equation

$$\frac{c_f}{2} = St$$

This, however, is the relationship obtained from Reynolds' analogy, either for the case where a laminar boundary layer at the heating surface is nonexisting or for the case where the Prandtl number of the fluid is equal to unity. For the temperatures of the water in the above experiments, the Prandtl number of the water was relatively close to unity, and any conclusion will have to be limited to that case. For this limited case, however, the experimental results indicate that the postulate which forms the basis of Reynolds' analogy for forced convection still applies in the nucleate boiling region. This would mean that the mechanisms of heat transfer and momentum transfer are "similar," within the meaning of Reynolds' analogy. These results, if verified over a wider range of variables, would incidentally tend to confirm the point of view that the improved heat transfer in nucleate boiling is obtained by increased agitation rather than by the creation of periodic steep temperature gradients.

**E,10. Film Boiling.** In addition to the nucleate boiling region, the film boiling region is of engineering importance, although considerably less experimental work has been published concerning results in this region than in the nucleate region. In film boiling, the heating surface is separated from the fluid by a continuous, stable vapor film. The film is in motion due to free or forced convection, and the flow of the film may be either laminar or turbulent. The heat from the surface is largely transmitted through the film to the liquid. Some of the heat serves to evaporate liquid and to provide vapor for the film, and some may be transmitted to the bulk fluid. No detailed investigations on the distribution of the heat or on the stability of the film have been carried out, but some calculations, based on the assumptions that the film is laminar and all of the heat is used to evaporate fluid, have been performed. For this case the problem becomes very similar to the familiar one of the condensation on a surface [77, Chap. 30]. For the heat transfer coefficient $h$ from a horizontal wire, with some additional simplification, the expression

$$h = 0.6 \left[ \frac{k^3 \rho (\rho_l - \rho) g L}{\mu D \Delta t} \right]^{\frac{1}{4}} \tag{10-1}$$

can be obtained [84]. In Eq. 10-1, $\rho$ is the density of the vapor, $\rho_l$ the density of the liquid, $\Delta t$ the temperature difference between the wall and the liquid, $D$ the diameter of the wire; $k$, $\mu$, and $L$ are the thermal conductivity, the viscosity, and the latent heat of vaporization of the liquid respectively, and $g$ the acceleration due to gravity. Heat transfer rates predicted from Eq. 10-1 and adjusted for radiation have been compared with experimental data on film boiling to both nitrogen and water. The agreement between the measured and predicted values was rather satisfactory.

**E,11. Closing Remarks.** In the foregoing an attempt has been made to acquaint the reader with some of the problems concerning boiling heat transfer. The attention of investigators has so far been directed mostly towards nucleate boiling rather than toward film boiling. The principal aim of studies in nucleate boiling is to arrive at a method of predicting heat transfer rates—in particular at the "burnout point"—as a function of fluid properties. This aim has not as yet been reached.

In order to eventually arrive at a satisfactory method of prediction, it will first be necessary to determine which of the two proposed heat transfer mechanisms is essential. Then, it would seem possible, on the basis of the discussion on bubble motion, to select the significant fluid properties and to form the dimensionless groups on which boiling heat transfer should depend. The success of this approach, however, is somewhat in question because the nucleation process plays a key role in boiling and for any predictions, therefore, some information on the nuclei distribution will be essential. Information of this kind is not available at present.

It is known that the number and size of nuclei in a fluid depend on the previous history of this fluid and to some extent on the type and treatment of the heating surface. If the nuclei distribution should be very sensitive to outside influences, and if in addition various liquids should react in a markedly different manner to a given treatment, it may be practically impossible to predict this distribution. In that case it seems doubtful that general rules for the prediction of boiling heat transfer can be formulated. If, on the other hand, the nuclei distribution is found to be predictable, a correlation for boiling heat transfer can probably be developed. Some encouragement for this latter view may be taken from the fact that results obtained with distilled water by different investigators and at different times have yielded essentially identical results. Further hope may be derived from the result that the effective nucleus size found in distilled carbon tetrachloride was about the same as that found in distilled water under similar conditions. In any case, further investigations on the problem of nucleation are believed to be necessary for a satisfactory solution of the problem.[7]

## E,12. Cited References and Bibliography.

*Cited References*


1. Howarth, L. *Modern Developments in Fluid Dynamics. High Speed Flow,* Vol. 1. Oxford Univ. Press, 1953.
2. Boussinesq, J. Essai sur la théorie des eaux courantes. *Mémoires présentés par divers savants a l'académie des sciences 23,* Paris, 1877.
3. Reichardt, H. The principles of turbulent heat transfer. *Archiv. Ges. Wärmetech. 617,* 129–142 (1951).
4. Reynolds, O. *On the Extent and Action of the Heating Surface of Steam Boilers. Scientific Papers,* Vol. 1. Cambridge Univ. Press, 1901.
5. Eckert, E. R. G. *Introduction to the Transfer of Heat and Mass,* 1st ed. McGraw-Hill, 1950.
6. von Kármán, Th. The analogy between fluid friction and heat transfer. *Trans. Am. Soc. Mech. Engrs. 61,* 705–710 (1939).
7. Murphree, E. V. Relation between heat transfer and fluid friction. *Ind. Eng. Chem. 24,* 726–736 (1932).
8. Boelter, L. M. K., Martinelli, R. C., and Jonassen, F. *Trans. Am. Soc. Mech. Engrs. 63,* 447–455 (1941).
9. Martinelli, R. C. Heat transfer to molten metals. *Trans. Am. Soc. Mech. Engrs. 69,* 947–959 (1947).
10. Seban, R. A., and Shemazaki, T. T. Heat transfer to a fluid flowing turbulently in a smooth pipe with walls at constant temperature. *Am. Soc. Mech. Engrs. Paper 50-A-128,* 1950.
11. Rannie, W. D. *Heat Transfer in Turbulent Stream Flow. Ph.D. Thesis,* Calif. Inst. Technol., 1951.
    See also: Summerfield, M. Recent developments in convective heat transfer. *Heat Transfer Symposium, Univ. Mich. Eng. Research Inst.,* 164–169 (1953).
12. Lin, C. S., Moulton, R. W., and Putnam, G. L. Mass transfer between solid walls and fluid streams. *Ind. Eng. Chem. 45,* 636–640 (1953).
13. Deissler, R. G. Investigation of turbulent flow and heat transfer in smooth tubes, including the effects of variable fluid properties. *Trans. Am. Soc. Mech. Engrs. 73,* 101–107 (1951).
14. Deissler, R. G. Heat transfer and fluid friction for fully developed turbulent flow of air and supercritical water with variable fluid properties. *Trans. Am. Soc. Mech. Engrs. 76,* 73–86 (1954).
15. Deissler, R. G. Analysis of turbulent heat transfer, mass transfer and friction


[7] The preceding chapter was revised in June, 1955. Several important advances have been made since that time. A very few references are mentioned in the bibliography, which will serve to introduce the reader to more recent work. The list of references is not meant to be complete. For additional publications attention is directed to the bibliographies at the end of the cited references.

in smooth tubes at high Prandtl and Schmidt numbers. *NACA Tech. Rept. 1210,* 1955. (Supersedes NACA Tech. Note 3145, 1954.)

16. Prandtl, L. Bericht über Untersuchungen zur ausgebildeten Turbudenz. *Z. angew. Math. u. Mech. 5,* 136 (1925).
17. Taylor, G. I. The transport of vorticity and heat through fluids in turbulent motion. *Proc. Roy. Soc. London A135,* 1932.
18. von Kármán, Th. Turbulence and skin friction. *J. Aeronaut. Sci. 1,* 1–20 (1934).
19. Goldstein, S. *Modern Developments in Fluid Dynamics,* Vol. II. Clarendon Press, Oxford, 1938.
20. Laufer, J. The structure of turbulence in fully developed pipe flow. *NACA Tech. Note 2954,* 1953.
21. Lin, C. C., and Shen, S. F. Studies of von Kármán's similarity theory and its extension to compressible flows. A critical examination of similarity theory for incompressible flows. *NACA Tech. Note 2541,* 1951.
22. Deissler, R. G. Analytical and experimental investigation of adiabatic turbulent flow in smooth tubes. *NACA Tech. Note 2138,* 1950.
23. van Driest, E. R. On turbulent flow near a wall. *Preprints of Papers for 1955 Heat Transfer and Fluid Mech. Inst.,* Stanford Press, 1955.
24. Einstein, H. A., and Li, H. Shear transmission from a turbulent flow to its viscous boundary sub-layer. *Reprints of Papers for 1955 Heat Transfer and Fluid Mech. Inst.,* Stanford Press, 1955.
25. Cavers, S. D., Hsu, N. Y., Schlinger, W. G., and Sage, B. H. Temperature gradients in turbulent gas streams. Behavior near boundary in two-dimensional flow. *Ind. Eng. Chem. 45,* 2139–2145 (1953).
26. Seban, R. A., and Shimazki, T. T. Temperature distributions for air flowing turbulently in a smooth heated pipe. *Proc. General Discussion on Heat Transfer, Inst. Mech. Engrs., London,* Sept. 1951.
27. Isakoff, S. E., and Drew, T. B. Heat and momentum transfer in turbulent flow of mercury. *Proc. General Discussion on Heat Transfer, Inst. Mech. Engrs., London,* 1951.
28. Deissler, R. G. Analysis of fully developed turbulent heat transfer at low Peclet numbers in smooth tubes with application to liquid metals. *NACA Research Mem. E52F05,* 1952.
29. Bernardo, E., and Eian, C. S. Heat transfer tests of aqueous ethylene glycol solutions in an electrically heated tube. *NACA Wartime Rept. E136,* 1945.
30. Kaufman, S. J., and Isely, F. D. Preliminary investigation of heat transfer to water flowing in an electrically heated inconel tube. *NACA Research Mem. E50G31,* 1950.
31. Eagle, A. E., and Ferguson, R. M. On the coefficient of heat transfer from the internal surface of tube walls. *Proc. Roy. Soc. London A127,* 540–566 (1930).
32. Kreith, F., and Summerfield, M. Pressure drop and convective heat transfer with surface boiling at high heat flux; Data for aniline and n-butyl alcohol. *Trans. Am. Soc. Mech. Engrs. 72,* 869–879 (1950).
33. Grele, M. D., and Gedeon, L. Forced convection heat transfer characteristics of molten sodium hydroxide. *NACA Research Mem. E52L09,* 1953.
34. Hoffman, H. W. Turbulent forced convection heat transfer in circular tubes containing molten sodium hydroxide. *Oak Ridge Natl. Lab. Rept. 1370,* 1952.
35. Barnet, W. I., and Kobe, K. A. Heat and vapor transfer in a wetted-wall tower. *Ind. Eng. Chem. 33,* 436–442 (1941).
36. Chilton, T. H., and Colburn, A. P. Mass transfer (absorption) coefficients. *Ind. Eng. Chem. 26,* 1183–1187 (1934).
37. Jackson, M. L., and Ceaglske, N. H. Distillation, vaporization, and gas absorption in a wetted-wall column. *Ind. Eng. Chem. 42,* 1188–1198 (1950).
38. Bonilla, C. F. Mass transfer in liquid metal and fused salt systems. *U.S. Atomic Energy Comm. Tech. Information Service, First Quarterly Progress Rept. NYO-3086,* Oak Ridge, Sept. 1951.
39. Linton, W. H., Jr., and Sherwood, T. K. Mass transfer from solid shapes to water in streamline and turbulent flow. *Chem. Eng. Progr. 46,* 258–264 (1950).

40. Lin, C. S., Denton, E. B., Gaskill, H. S., and Putnam, G. L. Diffusion controlled electrode reactions. *Ind. Eng. Chem. 43,* 2136–2143 (1951).
41. Hama, F. R. On the velocity distribution in the laminar sub-layer and transition region in turbulent shear flows. *J. Aeronaut. Sci. 20,* 648 (1953).
42. Elrod, H. G., Jr. Note on the turbulent shear stress near a wall. *J. Aeronaut. Sci. 24,* 468 (1957).
43. Latzko, H. Heat transfer in a turbulent liquid or gas stream. *NACA Tech. Mem. 1068,* 1944.
44. Elser, K. Der Warmeubergang in Rohreinlauf. *Allgemeine Wärmetechnik 3,* 1952.
45. Poppendick, H. F., and Palmer, L. D. Forced convection heat transfer in thermal entrance regions, Part II. *Oak Ridge Natl. Lab. Rept. 914,* May 1952.
46. Deissler, R. G. Analysis of turbulent heat transfer and flow in the entrance regions of smooth passages. *NACA Tech. Note 3016,* 1953.
47. Deissler, R. G. Turbulent heat transfer and friction in the entrance regions of smooth passages. *Trans. Am. Soc. Mech. Engrs. 77,* 1221–1233 (1955).
48. Langhaar, H. L. Steady flow in the transition length of a straight tube. *J. Appl. Mech. 9,* A55–A58 (1942).
49. Sparrow, E. M. Analysis of laminar forced-convection heat transfer in entrance region of flat rectangular ducts. *NACA Tech. Note 3331,* 1955.
50. Hartnett, J. P. Experimental determination of the thermal entrance length for the flow of water and of oil in circular pipes. *Trans. Am. Soc. Mech. Engrs. 77,* 1211–1220 (1955).
51. Lyon, R. N. Forced convection heat transfer theory and experiment with liquid metals. *Oak Ridge Natl. Lab. Rept. 361,* 1949.
52. Jenkins, R. Variation of the eddy conductivity with Prandtl modulus and its use in prediction of turbulent heat transfer coefficients. *Preprints of Papers for 1951 Heat Transfer and Fluid Mech. Inst., Stanford,* 147–158 (1951).
53. Lubarsky, B., and Kaufman, S. J. Review of experimental investigations of liquid-metal heat transfer. *NACA Tech. Note 3336,* 1955.
54. Deissler, R. G., and Taylor, M. F. Analysis of fully developed turbulent heat transfer and flow in an annulus with various eccentricities. *NACA Tech. Note 3451,* 1955.
55. Eckert, E. R. G., and Low, G. M. Temperature distribution in walls of heat exchangers composed of noncircular flow passages. *NACA Rept. 1022,* 1951.
56. Elrod, H. G., Jr. Turbulent heat transfer in polygonal flow sections. *Nuclear Develop. Associates NDA-10-7,* New York, 1952.
57. Lowdermilk, W. H., Weiland, W. F., Jr., and Livingood, J. N. B. Measurement of heat-transfer and friction coefficients for flow of air in noncircular ducts at high surface temperatures. *NACA Research Mem. L53J07,* 1954.
58. Knudson, J. G., and Katz, D. L. *Fluid Dynamics and Heat Transfer,* 1st ed. Univ. Mich. Eng. Research Inst., 1953.
59. McAdams, W. H. *Heat Transmission,* 2nd ed. McGraw-Hill, 1942.
60. Humble, L. V., Lowdermilk, W. H., and Desmon, L. G. Measurements of average heat transfer and friction coefficient for subsonic flow of air in smooth tubes at high surface and fluid temperatures. *NACA Rept. 1020,* 1951.
61. Goldman, K. Heat transfer to supercritical water and other fluids with temperature-dependent properties. Nuclear engineering, Part I. *Amer. Inst. Chem. Engrs., Chem. Eng. Progr. Symposium Series 50,* 1954.
62. Bringer, R. P., and Smith, J. M. Heat transfer in the critical region. *Am. Inst. Chem. Engrs. J. 3,* 49–55 (1957).
63. Mosciki, I., and Broder, J. Heat transfer from a platinum wire. *Roczniki Chem. 6,* 319–354 (1926). Complete English translation on file at *Eng. Research Lab. Exptl. Sta., E. I. duPont de Nemours and Co.,* Wilmington, Delaware.
64. Ellion, M. E. A study of the mechanism of boiling heat transfer. *Calif. Inst. Technol. Jet Propul. Lab. Mem. 20-88,* Mar. 1954.
65. Farber, E. A., and Scorah, R. L. Heat transfer to water boiling under pressure. *Trans. Am. Soc. Mech. Engrs. 70,* 369–384 (1948).
66. McAdams, W. H., Addoms, J. N., and Kennel, W. E. Heat transfer at high

rates to water with surface boiling. *Mass. Inst. Technol. Rept. ANL-4268,* Dec. 1948.
67. Gunther, F. C. Photographic study of surface-boiling heat transfer to water with forced convection. *Trans. Am. Soc. Mech. Engrs. 73,* 115–123 (1951).
68. Gunther, F. C. Private communication.
69. Hatcher, J. B. *Calif. Inst. Technol. Jet Propul. Lab. Progress Rept. 20-157,* 1952.
70. Cichelli, M. T., and Bonilla, C. F. Heat transfer to liquids boiling under pressure. *Trans. Am. Inst. Chem. Engrs. 42,* 411 (1946).
71. Dergarabedian, P. The rate of growth of vapor bubbles in superheated water. *J. Appl. Mech. 75,* 537–545 (1953).
72. Parkin, B. R. Scale effects in cavitating flow. *Calif. Inst. Technol. Hydrodynam. Lab. Rept. 21-8,* July 1952.
73. Volmer, M. *Kinetik der Phasen Bildung.* Steinkopff, Dresden, 1939.
74. Larson, R. F. Factors that influence heat transfer in boiling. *Fluid Mech. Inst.,* Los Angeles, 1953.
75. Sabersky, R. H., and Gates, C. W. On the start of nucleation in boiling heat transfer. *Jet Propulsion 2,* 67–70 (1955).
76. Harvey, E. N. On the cavity formation in water. *J. Appl. Phys. 18,* 162 (1947).
77. Jakob, M. *Heat Transfer.* Wiley, 1949.
78. Buchberg, H., Romie, F., Lipkis, R., and Greenfield, M. Heat transfer, pressure drop, and burnout studies with and without surface boiling for de-aerated and gassed water at elevated pressures in a forced flow system. *Heat Transfer and Fluid Mech. Inst.,* Stanford, 1951.
79. Plesset, M. S. Note on the flow of vapors between liquid surfaces. *Calif. Inst. Technol. Hydrodynam. Lab. Rept. 26-5 to Office of Nav. Research,* 1951.
80. Rohsenow, W. M., and Clark, J. A. A study of the mechanism of boiling heat transfer. *Trans. Am. Soc. Mech. Engrs. 73,* 609–620 (1951).
81. Rannie, W. D. Private communication.
82. Hatcher, J. B., and Bartz, D. R. High flux heat transfer to JP-3 and RFNA. Coke deposition of JP-3. *Calif. Inst. Technol. Jet Propul. Lab. Publ. EP119,* 1951.
83. Sabersky, R. H., and Mulligan, H. E. On the relationship between fluid friction and heat transfer in nucleate boiling. *Jet Propulsion 1,* 9–12 (1955).
84. Bromley, L. R. Heat transfer in stable film boiling. *Chem. Eng. Progr. 46,* 221–227 (1950).
85. Sparrow, E. M., Hallman, T. M., and Siegel, R. Turbulent heat transfer in the thermal entrance region of a pipe with uniform heat flux. *Appl. Sci. Research 7, Sec. A,* 37–52 (1957).
86. Deissler, R. G., and Taylor, M. F. Analysis of axial turbulent flow and heat transfer through banks of rods or tubes. *TID–7529, Reactor Heat Transfer Conf. of 1956, Pt. 1, Book 1,* 416–461 (1957).
87. Deissler, R. G., and Taylor, M. F. Analysis of turbulent heat transfer in noncircular passages. *NACA Tech. Note 4384,* 1958.

*Bibliography*

Camack, W. G., and Forster, H. K. Test of heat transfer correlation for boiling metals. *Jet Propul. 10,* 1104–1106 (1957).

Forster, H. K., and Greif, R. Heat transfer to a boiling liquid; Mechanism and correlations. *Dept. of Eng., Univ. Calif., Papers Rept. 7,* 1958.

Griffith, P. The correlation of nucleate boiling burnout data. *Am. Soc. Mech. Eng. Paper 57 HT-21,* 1957.

Zuber, N., and Tribus, M. Further remarks on the stability of boiling heat transfer. *Dept. of Eng., Univ. Calif., Rept. 58–5,* 1958.

# SECTION F

# *CONVECTIVE HEAT TRANSFER IN GASES*

E. R. VAN DRIEST

**F,1. Introduction.** Any discussion of convective heat transfer in gases is essentially a discussion of the characteristics of the boundary layer in a compressible real fluid subjected to arbitrary wall temperature. Since the density, viscosity, thermal capacity, and thermal conductivity of gases vary considerably with the temperature in the boundary layer, they thereby affect the rate at which heat may be transferred to or from the adjacent surface. The state of the boundary layer is important; it may be laminar, turbulent, or mixed, depending upon the Reynolds number, the Mach number, and the wall-to-free stream temperature ratio. At high temperatures the gas may dissociate, or even ionize, the result of which would be a change in the physical properties of the gas. Owing to the variety of problems brought about by high temperature, a careful analysis of heat transfer is paramount in the successful design of high speed aircraft. Performance-wise, a knowledge of the temperature of the skin of a high speed vehicle is necessary for accurate calculation of skin friction.

**F,2. The Mechanism of Convective Heat Transfer.** Convective heat transfer is heat transfer to or from a flowing fluid. The region of the flowing fluid which absorbs or gives up the heat is the boundary layer. Strictly speaking, the heat transfer to or from the boundary layer takes place by molecular conduction at the wall, whether the flow is laminar or turbulent; thus the transfer of heat from a wall to a flowing fluid, or vice versa, is the product of the thermal conductivity and temperature gradient in the fluid at the surface of contact of fluid and wall. Since, with fixed wall temperature, the heat transfer at the wall is proportional to the temperature gradient in the fluid at the wall, any means of increasing that gradient will increase the rate of heat transfer; and, of course, decreasing the temperature gradient will decrease the heat transfer.

Now the temperature gradient at the wall may be steepened by either increasing the mass flow external to a given boundary layer or inducing transition from laminar to turbulent flow. At low speeds, the effect of increasing the external flow is to thin the boundary layer by inertial force, thereby steepening the temperature gradient. However, as the external speed continues to increase, direct compression as at a stagnation point, or dissipation of energy by internal friction, rapidly increases the temperature of the fluid within the boundary layer, thereby also steepening the wall temperature gradient; thus the effect of high speed is literally to cover the wall with a layer of hot fluid, between which and the wall the heat transfer then takes place. As a practical consequence, for example,

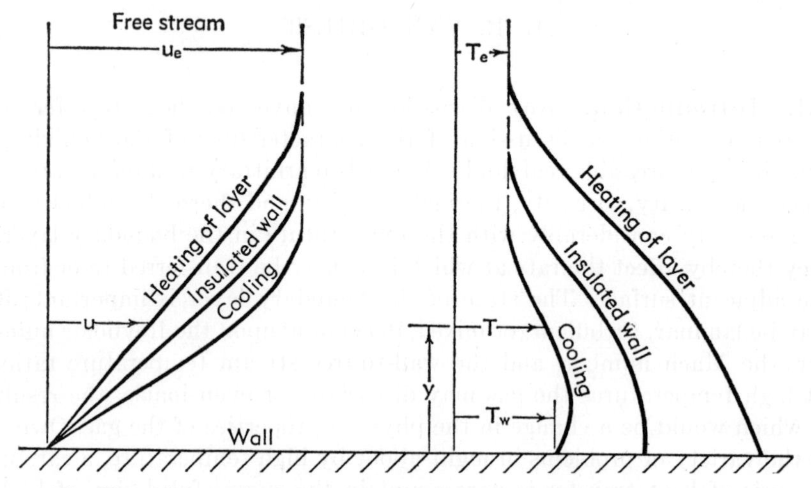


Fig. F,2. Schematic of boundary layer in a compressible viscous fluid.

increasing the external flow speed will first cool, and later heat, a surface whose temperature is initially higher than the free stream temperature. Transition from laminar to turbulent flow effectively thins out the inner regions of the boundary layer by scouring action, thus greatly increasing the temperature gradient and consequent heat transfer for low as well as high speeds.

Since, in high speed flow, the temperature of the boundary layer rises because of compression or energy dissipation, it follows that for a given speed there will be a certain wall temperature, above the free stream temperature, at which no heat transfer will take place. It is proper to consider the zero heat transfer temperature as the reference temperature. Thus, at low speeds, the free stream temperature becomes the reference temperature. When the wall is hotter than the reference temperature, heat flows from the wall into the boundary layer, whereas, when the wall is cooler than the reference temperature, the reverse is true (Fig. F,2).

# CHAPTER 1. SURVEY OF THEORETICAL RESULTS APPLICABLE TO AERODYNAMIC HEAT TRANSFER. STATUS OF EXPERIMENTAL KNOWLEDGE

## LAMINAR FLOW

**F,3. Flat Plate Solution.** The investigation of the thin laminar boundary layer (cf. IV,B) in steady state on a smooth flat plate is of fundamental importance in aerodynamic-heating problems, because of its practical possibilities and relative simplicity of solution. Typical velocity and temperature curves across a thin compressible laminar boundary layer with heat transfer are shown in Fig. F,2. The heat transfer to or from such a layer in the steady state is obtained upon solution of the continuity, momentum, and energy equations, viz.

$$\frac{\partial}{\partial x}(\rho u) + \frac{\partial}{\partial y}(\rho v) = 0 \tag{3-1}$$

$$\rho u \frac{\partial u}{\partial x} + \rho v \frac{\partial u}{\partial y} = \frac{\partial}{\partial y}\left(\mu \frac{\partial u}{\partial y}\right) - \frac{dp}{dx} \tag{3-2a}$$

$$\frac{\partial p}{\partial y} = 0 \tag{3-2b}$$

$$\rho u \frac{\partial h}{\partial x} + \rho v \frac{\partial h}{\partial y} = \mu \left(\frac{\partial u}{\partial y}\right)^2 + \frac{\partial}{\partial y}\left(k \frac{\partial T}{\partial y}\right) + u \frac{dp}{dx} \tag{3-3}$$

respectively.

In these equations, $u$ and $v$ are the $x$ and $y$ components of the velocity at any point, the $x$ axis being taken along the plate in the direction of the free stream and the $y$ axis perpendicular to the plate. The symbols $\rho$, $\mu$, $k$, $c_p$, $T$, $h$, and $p$ represent the density, absolute viscosity, thermal conductivity, specific heat at constant pressure, absolute temperature, enthalpy per unit mass, and pressure, respectively. Since $c_p = \partial h/\partial T$, Eq. 3-3 can be written in terms of the Prandtl number $Pr = c_p\mu/k$ as follows:

$$\rho u \frac{\partial h}{\partial x} + \rho v \frac{\partial h}{\partial y} = \mu \left(\frac{\partial u}{\partial y}\right)^2 + \frac{\partial}{\partial y}\left(\frac{\mu}{Pr} \frac{\partial h}{\partial y}\right) + u \frac{dp}{dx} \tag{3-4}$$

in which the Prandtl number is variable and a function of temperature. The equations include the variation of free stream velocity and surface temperature in the direction of flow.

While the above equations have been studied by many investigators after Prandtl first announced the concept of the boundary layer in 1904, a complete solution of the equations is not readily available. However, under certain restricted conditions, such as constant free stream velocity and constant wall temperature, exact solutions can be obtained, and these have practical application for supersonic flow over cones and slender ogives, and over wedges and thin airfoils, especially when covered with thin skins.

The analytical and numerical results of Crocco [1] for the case of constant free stream velocity, wall temperature, and Prandtl number are singular because of their extensiveness and applicability. Crocco not only developed an accurate method of numerical solution of the momentum equation (Eq. 3-2a), but also gave a practical solution of the energy equation (Eq. 3-4) for Prandtl number near unity. (For a review of the Crocco analysis and detailed calculations, the reader is referred to [2].) van Driest [3] in turn has extended the Crocco analysis to include variable Prandtl number in the solution of the energy equation.

Owing to the importance of the numerical results derivable therefrom, the extension of the Crocco analysis to include variable Prandtl number will be outlined here with pertinent formulas. Following the procedure of Crocco, the independent variables $x$ and $y$ are first transformed to $x$ and $u$ by $u = u(x, y)$ and $x = x$. Eq. 3-1, 3-2a, and 3-4 then become, upon elimination of $v$,

$$\frac{\partial}{\partial x}\left(\frac{\rho u \mu}{\tau}\right) + \frac{\partial^2 \tau}{\partial u^2} - \frac{dp}{dx}\frac{\partial}{\partial u}\left(\frac{\mu}{\tau}\right) = 0 \tag{3-5}$$

$$\tau^2\left[\frac{\partial}{\partial u}\left(\frac{1}{Pr}\frac{\partial h}{\partial u}\right) + 1\right] + (1 - Pr)\left(\frac{1}{Pr}\frac{\partial h}{\partial u}\right)\frac{\partial \tau}{\partial u}\tau - \rho u \mu \frac{\partial h}{\partial x} + \mu\left(\frac{\partial h}{\partial u} + u\right)\frac{dp}{dx} = 0 \tag{3-6}$$

where shear stress $\tau = \mu(\partial u/\partial y)$. These equations are still in general form. However, when $\partial h/\partial x = 0$ and $dp/dx = 0$, they simplify considerably. The enthalpy $h$ is accordingly a function of $u$ only, and for a perfect gas the density varies inversely with the temperature. Since $\mu = \mu_1(T) = \mu_2(u)$, Crocco next showed, upon satisfaction of the boundary condition $\tau \rightarrow \infty$ as $x \rightarrow 0$, that Eq. 3-5 becomes

$$g\frac{d^2 g}{du^2} + \rho \mu u = 0 \tag{3-7}$$

where $g(u) = \tau\ (x, y)\sqrt{2x}$. In dimensionless form, Eq. 3-5 and 3-6 are then, for $\partial h/\partial x = 0$ and $dp/dx = 0$,

$$g_* g_*'' + 2u_* \rho_* \mu_* = 0 \tag{3-8}$$

$$\left(\frac{h_*'}{Pr}\right)' + (1 - Pr)\frac{g_*'}{g_*}\left(\frac{h_*'}{Pr}\right) = -\frac{u_e^2}{i_e} \tag{3-9}$$

with boundary conditions

$$g'_* = 0, \quad h_* = h_*(0) \quad \text{at} \quad u_* = 0 \tag{3-10a}$$

$$g_* = 0, \quad h_* = 1 \quad \text{at} \quad u_* = 1 \tag{3-10b}$$

and in which $u_* = u/u_e$, $\rho_* = \rho/\rho_e$, $h_* = h/h_e$, and $g_* = 2\sqrt{x/\rho_e\mu_e u_e^3} \cdot \tau$. Subscript $_e$ indicates conditions at the outer edge of the boundary layer, and the primes denote differentiation with respect to $u_*$.

Inspection of Eq. 3-8 and 3-9 shows that the momentum equation (Eq. 3-8) is nonlinear, and besides, according to Eq. 3-10a and 3-10b, the boundary conditions are on opposite sides of the boundary layer. Hence the solution of Eq. 3-8 is expected to be somewhat troublesome. On the other hand, the energy equation (Eq. 3-9) is linear and first order in $h'_*/Pr$ as a function of $u_*$, so that the solution of Eq. 3-9 is readily

$$\frac{h'_*}{Pr} = \exp\left[-\int_{g_*(0)}^{g_*} (1 - Pr)\frac{dg_*}{g_*}\right]\left\{\frac{h'_*(0)}{Pr(0)} - \frac{u_e^2}{h_e}\int_0^{u_*} \exp\left[\int_{g_*(0)}^{g_*} (1 - Pr)\frac{dg_*}{g_*}\right] du_*\right\} \tag{3-11}$$

assuming that the shear distribution is known from the momentum equation. Further integration gives

$$\begin{aligned} h_*(u_*) = h_*(0) &+ \frac{h'_*(0)}{Pr(0)}\int_0^{u_*} Pr \cdot \exp\left[-\int_{g_*(0)}^{g_*} (1 - Pr)\frac{dg_*}{g_*}\right] du_* \\ &- \frac{u_e^2}{h_e}\int_0^{u_*} Pr \cdot \exp\left[-\int_{g_*(0)}^{g_*} (1 - Pr)\frac{dg_*}{g_*}\right] \\ &\quad \left\{\int_0^{u_*} \exp\left[\int_{g_*(0)}^{g_*} (1 - Pr)\frac{dg_*}{g_*}\right] du_*\right\} du_* \end{aligned} \tag{3-12}$$

or

$$h_*(u_*) = h_*(0) + \frac{h'_*(0)}{Pr(0)} S(u_*) - \frac{u_e^2}{h_e} R(u_*) \tag{3-13}$$

where

$$S(u_*) = \int_0^{u_*} Pr \cdot \exp\left[-\int_{g_*(0)}^{g_*} (1 - Pr)\frac{dg_*}{g_*}\right] du_* \tag{3-14}$$

and

$$\begin{aligned} R(u_*) = \int_0^{u_*} Pr \cdot \exp&\left[-\int_{g_*(0)}^{g_*} (1 - Pr)\frac{dg_*}{g_*}\right] \\ &\left\{\int_0^{u_*} \exp\left[\int_{g_*(0)}^{g_*} (1 - Pr)\frac{dg_*}{g_*}\right] du_*\right\} du_* \end{aligned} \tag{3-15}$$

Now, $h_*(1) = 1$. Hence from Eq. 3-13,

$$h'_*(0) = \frac{Pr(0)}{S(1)}\left[1 - h_*(0) + \frac{u_e^2}{h_e} R(1)\right] \tag{3-16}$$

which, when substituted back into Eq. 3-13, gives

$$h_*(u_*) = h_*(0) - [h_*(0) - 1]\frac{S(u_*)}{S(1)} + \frac{u_e^2}{h_e}\left[\frac{S(u_*)}{S(1)} R(1) - R(u_*)\right] \tag{3-17}$$

$S$ and $R$ will be found to depend upon the free stream Mach number, the free stream temperature, and the plate temperature (i.e. heat transfer).

When the Prandtl number is constant, $S = PrI$ and $R = PrJ$, where

$$I(u_*) = \int_0^{u_*}\left[\frac{g_*}{g_*(0)}\right]^{Pr-1} du_* \tag{3-18}$$

and

$$J(u_*) = \int_0^{u_*}\left[\frac{g_*}{g_*(0)}\right]^{Pr-1}\int_0^{u_*}\left[\frac{g_*}{g_*(0)}\right]^{1-Pr} du_* du_* \tag{3-19}$$

Hence there results Crocco's original formula:

$$h_*(u_*) = h_*(0) - [h_*(0) - 1]\frac{I(u_*)}{I(1)} + Pr\frac{u_e^2}{h_e}\left[\frac{I(u_*)}{I(1)} J(1) - J(u_*)\right] \tag{3-20}$$

Crocco tabulated $I$ and $J$ for various fixed $Pr$ and the Blasius shear distribution. Extensive calculations by Crocco had shown that $I$ and $J$ were approximately independent of Mach number and heat transfer for moderate supersonic speeds, regardless of viscosity-temperature law (i.e. $\rho_*\mu_*$ variation) when the Prandtl number was not too far from unity. (Indeed, this is exactly true for $Pr = 1$.) Hence it was concluded that the Blasius (incompressible flow) shear profile, which resulted from the assumption that $\rho_*\mu_*$ equaled unity, was appropriate for the calculation of $I$ and $J$ and consequently the approximate enthalpy distribution from Eq. 3-19, given an average constant Prandtl number. The Blasius shear distribution is tabulated in Table F,3a. The $I$'s and $J$'s, calculated by Crocco, are tabulated in Table F,3b. For moderate Mach numbers, the specific

*Table F,3a.* Shear function $g_*$, when $\rho_*\mu_* = 1$.

| $u_*$ | $g_*$ | $u_*$ | $g_*$ | $u_*$ | $g_*$ |
|---|---|---|---|---|---|
| 0 | 0.66411 | 0.45 | 0.61772 | 0.875 | 0.27994 |
| 0.05 | 0.66405 | 0.50 | 0.60013 | 0.900 | 0.23881 |
| 0.10 | 0.66361 | 0.55 | 0.57836 | 0.925 | 0.19293 |
| 0.15 | 0.66242 | 0.60 | 0.55183 | 0.95 | 0.14097 |
| 0.20 | 0.66009 | 0.65 | 0.51985 | 0.96 | 0.11797 |
| 0.25 | 0.65625 | 0.70 | 0.48161 | 0.97 | 0.09334 |
| 0.30 | 0.65050 | 0.75 | 0.43607 | 0.98 | 0.06659 |
| 0.35 | 0.64245 | 0.80 | 0.38189 | 0.99 | 0.03681 |
| 0.40 | 0.63167 | 0.85 | 0.31715 | 1.00 | 0 |

*Table F,3b.* Values of $I$ and $J$ based upon the Blasius solution for $g_*$.

| $u^*$ | $Pr = 0.5$ | | $Pr = 0.725$ | | $Pr = 0.75$ | | $Pr = 1.00$ | | $Pr = 1.25$ | | $Pr = 1.50$ | | $Pr = 2.00$ | |
|---|---|---|---|---|---|---|---|---|---|---|---|---|---|---|
| | $I$ | $J$ | $I$ | $J$ | $I$ | $J$ | $I$ | $J$ | $I$ | $J$ | $I$ | $J$ | $I$ | $J$ |
| 0 | 0 | 0 | 0 | 0 | 0 | 0 | 0 | 0 | 0 | 0 | 0 | 0 | 0 | 0 |
| 0.1 | 0.1000 | 0.0050 | 0.1000 | 0.0050 | 0.1000 | 0.0050 | 0.1000 | 0.0050 | 0.1000 | 0.0050 | 0.1000 | 0.0050 | 0.1000 | 0.0050 |
| 0.2 | 0.2002 | 0.0200 | 0.2001 | 0.0200 | 0.2001 | 0.0200 | 0.2000 | 0.0200 | 0.1999 | 0.0200 | 0.1998 | 0.0200 | 0.1997 | 0.0200 |
| 0.3 | 0.3008 | 0.0452 | 0.3004 | 0.0451 | 0.3004 | 0.0451 | 0.3000 | 0.0450 | 0.2996 | 0.0449 | 0.2992 | 0.0448 | 0.2985 | 0.0447 |
| 0.4 | 0.4025 | 0.0806 | 0.4014 | 0.0803 | 0.4012 | 0.0803 | 0.4000 | 0.0800 | 0.3988 | 0.0797 | 0.3975 | 0.0794 | 0.3951 | 0.0788 |
| 0.5 | 0.5062 | 0.1269 | 0.5034 | 0.1260 | 0.5031 | 0.1260 | 0.5000 | 0.1250 | 0.4969 | 0.1240 | 0.4939 | 0.1232 | 0.4881 | 0.1213 |
| 0.6 | 0.6135 | 0.1849 | 0.6073 | 0.1827 | 0.6066 | 0.1824 | 0.6000 | 0.1800 | 0.5935 | 0.1776 | 0.5872 | 0.1753 | 0.5750 | 0.1708 |
| 0.7 | 0.7267 | 0.2567 | 0.7144 | 0.2512 | 0.7130 | 0.2507 | 0.7000 | 0.2450 | 0.6875 | 0.2396 | 0.6756 | 0.2342 | 0.6531 | 0.2246 |
| 0.8 | 0.8505 | 0.3454 | 0.8268 | 0.3337 | 0.8243 | 0.3324 | 0.8000 | 0.3200 | 0.7776 | 0.3086 | 0.7564 | 0.2980 | 0.7186 | 0.2787 |
| 0.9 | 0.9967 | 0.4612 | 0.9500 | 0.4343 | 0.9451 | 0.4315 | 0.9000 | 0.4050 | 0.8605 | 0.3817 | 0.8251 | 0.3613 | 0.7660 | 0.3276 |
| 0.92 | 1.0390 | 0.4899 | 0.9770 | 0.4579 | 0.9715 | 0.4542 | 0.9200 | 0.4232 | 0.8757 | 0.3965 | 0.8367 | 0.3731 | 0.7727 | 0.3353 |
| 0.94 | 1.0696 | ...... | 1.0056 | ...... | 0.9991 | ...... | 0.9400 | ...... | 0.8901 | ...... | 0.8472 | ...... | 0.7780 | ...... |
| 0.96 | 1.1131 | 0.5591 | 1.0363 | 0.5103 | 1.0286 | 0.5050 | 0.9600 | 0.4608 | 0.9037 | 0.4245 | 0.8564 | 0.3941 | 0.7824 | 0.3475 |
| 0.98 | 1.1671 | ...... | 1.0708 | ...... | 1.0614 | ...... | 0.9800 | ...... | 0.8159 | ...... | 0.8638 | ...... | 0.7852 | ...... |
| 0.99 | ...... | 0.6369 | ...... | 0.5602 | ...... | 0.5523 | 0.9900 | 0.4901 | ...... | 0.4429 | ...... | 0.4060 | ...... | 0.3527 |
| 1.00 | 1.2806 | 0.7039 | 1.1210 | 0.5871 | 1.1070 | 0.5768 | 1.0000 | 0.5000 | 0.9252 | 0.4473 | 0.8682 | 0.4080 | 0.7863 | 0.3532 |

heat can be considered constant, whence $u_e^2/h_e$ may be expressed by $(\gamma - 1)M_e^2$, where $\gamma$ is the ratio of the specific heat at constant pressure to that at constant volume and $M_e$ is the free stream Mach number.

It is seen above that the energy equation can be written as an integral, dependent, however, upon the momentum equation. On the other hand, the momentum equation can be written as an integral equation, dependent upon the energy equation. Thus

$$g_*(u_*) = \int_{u_*}^{1} du_{*2} \int_0^{u_{*2}} \frac{2u_* \rho_* \mu_*}{g_*} du_{*1} \tag{3-21}$$

which can be integrated by the method of successive approximations, starting with the Blasius solution (Table F,3a), if none better can be assumed as a first approximation. However, as Crocco pointed out, the iterative process does not converge upon a single solution in general but rather yields values of $g_*$, which oscillate about the exact value. For, if an initial value of the shear function $g_{*1}$, equal to $Ag_{*\text{ex}}$ in which $A$ is a constant and $g_{*\text{ex}}$ is the exact value, is substituted into the right-hand side of Eq. 3-21, the new $g_{*2}$, obtained upon integration, will be equal to $g_{*\text{ex}}/A$. Resubstitution of $g_{*2}$ yields $g_{*3} = Ag_{*\text{ex}} = g_{*1}$. Therefore it is seen that the next substitution should be $\sqrt{g_{*1}g_{*2}} = g_{*\text{ex}}$. In the iterative process of solving Eq. 3-8 (Eq. 3-21), it follows that successive values of $g_*$ for resubstitution into Eq. 3-21 should be the geometric mean of the two previous substitutions.

It is next observed that a singularity exists at $u_* = 1$, owing to the boundary condition $g_* = 0$ at the outer edge of the boundary layer. Therefore, in the case of Eq. 3-21, numerical integration cannot be carried all the way across the layer but must stop at some point $u_* = 1 - i$ just short of $u_* = 1$, where $i$ is arbitrarily small. Hence Eq. 3-21 becomes

$$g_*(u_*) = g_*(1 - i) + \int_{u_*}^{1-i} du_{*2} \int_0^{u_{*2}} \frac{2u_* \rho_* \mu_*}{g_*(u_*)} du_{*1} \tag{3-22}$$

or, in order to avoid double integration,

$$g_*(u_*) = g_*(1 - i) + (1 - u_*) \int_0^{u_*} \frac{f(u_*)}{g_*(u_*)} du_* - i \int_0^{1-i} \frac{f(u_*)}{g_*(u_*)} du_* + \int_{u_*}^{1-i} (1 - u_*) \frac{f(u_*)}{g_*(u_*)} du_* \tag{3-23}$$

where $f(u_*) = 2u_* \rho_* \mu_*$.

Since the first term, $g_*(1 - i)$, on the right-hand side of Eq. 3-23 is unchanged by successive iteration, a method to adjust $g_*(1 - i)$ in each iteration is necessary so that the boundary condition $g_*(1) = 0$ is more nearly approached. Following Crocco, one notes that for $u_* \to 1$, Eq. 3-8

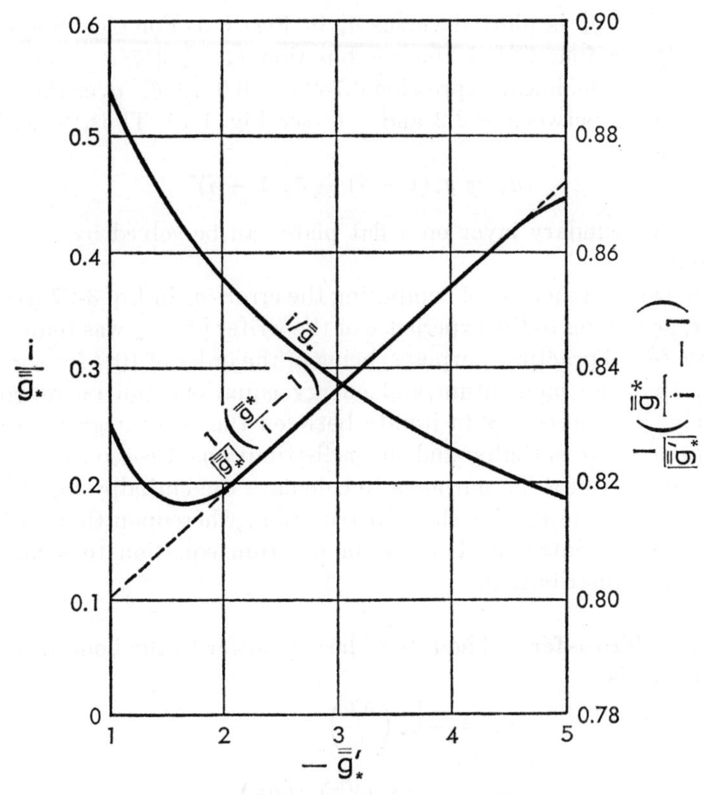


**Fig. F,3.** $\bar{\bar{g}}_*$ as a function of $\bar{\bar{g}}'_*$.

is approximated by

$$\bar{\bar{g}}_*\bar{\bar{g}}''_* + 2 = 0 \tag{3-24}$$

which can be integrated in closed form. The double bar is used to designate the solution of this approximate equation. In terms of $\bar{\bar{g}}'_*$, the solution of Eq. 3-24 which satisfies the condition $g_*(1) = 0$ is

$$\frac{i}{\bar{\bar{g}}_*} = \frac{1}{2}\sqrt{\pi}\, e^{(\bar{\bar{g}}'_*/2)^2}\left[1 - \phi\left(\frac{-\bar{\bar{g}}'_*}{2}\right)\right] \tag{3-25}$$

where $\phi$ is the error function, viz.

$$\phi(x) = \frac{2}{\sqrt{\pi}}\int_0^x e^{-t^2}\, dt$$

Now $\bar{\bar{g}}'_*$ can be obtained from the requirement that the slopes of $g_*$ and $\bar{\bar{g}}_*$ must match at $u_* = 1 - i$. Hence it follows from the first integral of Eq. 3-8 that

$$\bar{\bar{g}}'_*(1 - i) = g'_*(1 - i) = -\int_0^{1-i} \frac{f(u_*)}{g_*(u_*)}\, du_* \tag{3-26}$$

The ratio $i/\bar{g}_*$ is plotted versus $\bar{g}'_*$ in Fig. F,3. For algebraic calculations, Crocco found that the combination $(1/|\bar{g}'_*|)[(\bar{g}/i) - 1]$ can be represented by the linear expression $0.7828 + 0.0178\,|\bar{g}'_*|$ over the practical range of $\bar{g}'_*$ between $-2.2$ and $-4$ (see Fig. F,3). Thus, to within a slight error, viz.

$$\delta g_* = g_*(1 - i) - \bar{g}_*(1 - i) \tag{3-27}$$

the laminar boundary layer on a flat plate can be solved by successive approximation.

Crocco gives a method of computing the error $\delta g_*$ in Eq. 3-27 (see [1]); however, according to the experience of the writer [2], $\delta g_*$ was found to be negligible for all practical purposes, being of the order of $10^{-4}$ for $i = 0.02$.

Now that the momentum and energy equations can be integrated separately, it is necessary to iterate between the two integrals in order to obtain accurate enthalpy and shear distributions. Crocco found it sufficiently accurate for his purposes to calculate the enthalpy distribution only once using the Blasius shear distribution, whereupon that enthalpy distribution was introduced in the momentum equation to compute a new and final distribution.

**F,4. Heat Transfer.** The rate of heat transfer to the boundary layer per unit area is

$$q_w = -k_w\left(\frac{\partial T}{\partial y}\right)_w \tag{4-1}$$

$$= -\frac{k_w}{c_{p_w}}\left(\frac{dh}{du}\right)_w\left(\frac{\partial u}{\partial y}\right)_w$$

$$= -\frac{k_w}{c_{p_w}\mu_w}\frac{h_e}{u_e}h'_*(0)\tau_w$$

$$= -\frac{1}{Pr_w}\frac{h_e}{u_e}h'_*(0)\tau_w \tag{4-2}$$

where subscript $_w$ refers to the wall.

Substitution of Eq. 3-16 into Eq. 4-2 gives

$$q_w = -\frac{1}{S(1)}\frac{h_e}{u_e}\tau_w\left[1 + \frac{u_e^2}{h_e}R(1) - h_*(0)\right] \tag{4-3}$$

$$= -\frac{1}{S(1)}\frac{\tau_w}{u_\delta}\left[h_e + 2R(1)\frac{u_e^2}{2} - h_w\right]$$

$$= -\frac{1}{S(1)}\frac{g_*(0)}{2\sqrt{Re}}\rho_e u_e\left[h_e + 2R(1)\frac{u_e^2}{2} - h_w\right] \tag{4-4}$$

since

$$g_*(0) = 2\sqrt{\frac{x}{\rho_e\mu_e u_e^3}}\,\tau_w \quad \text{and} \quad Re = \frac{\rho_e u_e x}{\mu_e}$$

Defining

$$St = \frac{1}{S(1)} \frac{g_*(0)}{2\sqrt{Re}} \tag{4-5}$$

and

$$h_r = h_e + 2R(1)\frac{u_e^2}{2} \tag{4-6}$$

Eq. 4-4 becomes

$$q_w = -St\rho_e u_e(h_r - h_w) \tag{4-7}$$

The symbol $Re$ is the Reynolds number.

The dimensionless heat transfer coefficient $St$ is called the Stanton number. Since heat transfer is proportional to skin friction by Eq. 4-2, it is sometimes desirable to write the heat transfer coefficient $St$ in terms of the local skin friction coefficient defined by $c_f = 2\tau_w/\rho_e u_e^2$, thus

$$St = \frac{1}{S(1)} \frac{c_f}{2} \tag{4-8}$$

The factor $S(1)$ is called the *Reynolds analogy factor* and is denoted by the symbol $s$. Hence [3]

$$s = S(1) = \int_0^1 Pr \cdot \exp\left[-\int_{g_*(0)}^{g_*} (1 - Pr)\frac{dg_*}{g_*}\right] du_* \tag{4-9}$$

Now the quantity $[h_e + 2R(1)u_e^2/2]$ in Eq. 4-4 is equal to the total enthalpy of the free stream, except for the factor $2R(1)$. Furthermore, when the plate is insulated, i.e. when $q_w = 0$, it follows from Eq. 4-7 that $h_w = h_e + 2R(1)u_e^2/2$. For these reasons, the quantity $[h_e + 2R(1)u_e^2/2]$ will be called the boundary layer enthalpy (or simply) recovery enthalpy, $h_r$, and the factor $2R(1)$ the *enthalpy recovery factor* $r$. Therefore [3]

$$r = 2R(1) = 2\int_0^1 Pr \cdot \exp\left[-\int_{g_*(0)}^{g_*} (1 - Pr)\frac{dg}{g}\right] \left\{\int_0^{u_*} \exp\left[\int_{g_*(0)}^{g_*} (1 - Pr)\frac{dg_*}{g_*}\right] du_*\right\} du_* \tag{4-10}$$

Eq. 4-9 and 4-10 reduce to Crocco's results, viz.

$$s = Pr\int_0^1 \left[\frac{g_*}{g_*(0)}\right]^{Pr-1} du_* \tag{4-11}$$

and

$$r = 2Pr\int_0^1 \left[\frac{g_*}{g_*(0)}\right]^{Pr-1} \int_0^{u_*} \left[\frac{g_*}{g_*(0)}\right] du_* du_* \tag{4-12}$$

when $Pr$ is constant.

It will be found that in general both $s$ and $r$ are functions of speed and heat transfer. However, for moderate speeds and heat transfer rates,

Crocco has shown that $s = Pr^{\frac{2}{3}}$, approximately, and $r = Pr^{\frac{1}{2}}$, closely, where $Pr$ is constant. Since the variation of the Prandtl number with temperature is ordinarily not great for common gases such as air [*4*], the approximate formulas $s = Pr^{\frac{2}{3}}$ and $r = Pr^{\frac{1}{2}}$ can be used for practical purposes for moderate flight conditions when an average $Pr$ is assumed. At very high speeds where skin temperatures become great, and for accurate experimentation, the more exact solutions are necessary.

**F,5. Numerical Results for Zero Pressure and Temperature Gradients along the Flow.** Results of calculations of friction and heat transfer coefficients, as well as of recovery and Reynolds analogy factors

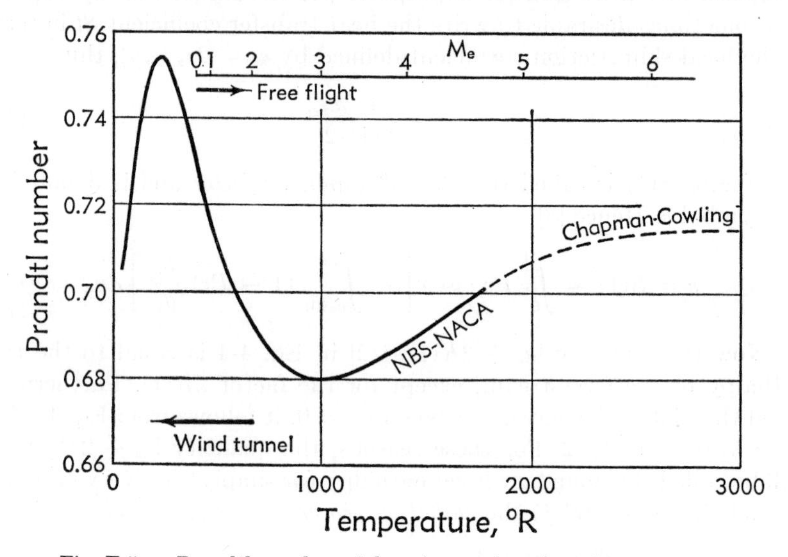


Fig. F,5a. Prandtl number of dry air as a function of temperature.

for laminar flow of air on flat plates in free flight and in heated wind tunnels are presented in [*3*] and reproduced to a large extent here. These represent exact calculations with variable specific heat, viscosity, and Prandtl number, based on the NBS-NACA Tables of Thermal Properties of Gases [*5*].

The variation of Prandtl number with temperature for dry air, upon which the calculations of [*3*] were based, is shown in Fig. F,5a. The NBS-NACA Table 2.44 on Prandtl number could not be used below about 400°R, because the table was based on 1-atmosphere pressure, whereas the pressures in the test sections of supersonic wind tunnels are usually very low under ordinary atmospheric supply conditions. Therefore, in order to carry out boundary layer calculations for low pressure, low temperature conditions in supersonic wind tunnels, new Prandtl numbers were calculated below 400°R using the following information:

(1) specific heat of air as an ideal gas as given in NBS-NACA Table 2.10, (2) a viscosity variation made up of Hirschfelder's formula (treating air as a single-component substance) below 216°R, and (3) the thermal conductivity of air in NBS-NACA Table 2.42. Above 400°R, the Prandtl

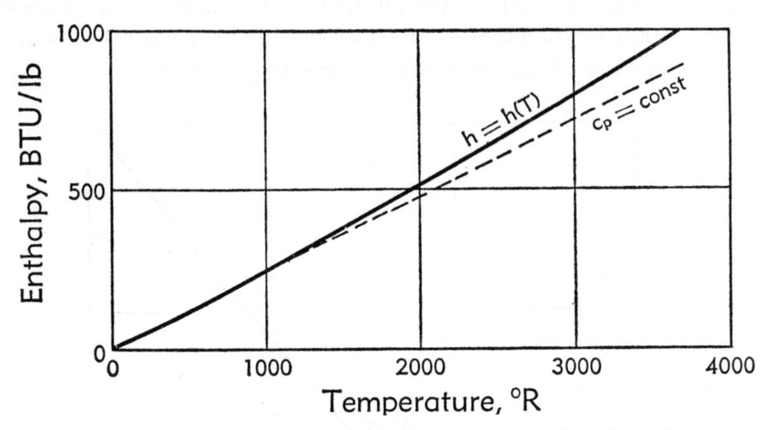


Fig. F,5b. Enthalpy of dry air in the ideal-gas state as a function of temperature.

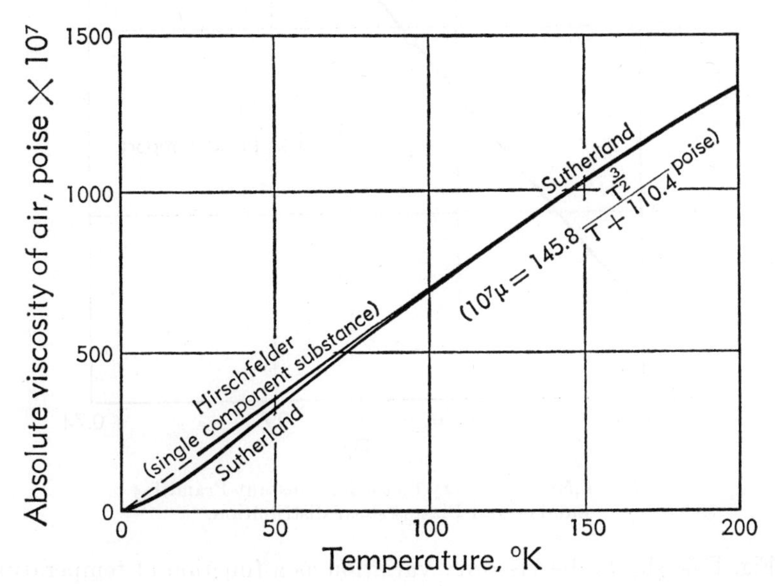


Fig. F,5c. Absolute viscosity of dry air as a function of temperature.

numbers were obtained from NBS-NACA Table 2.44, which is in accord with the recent measurements of Keyes [4]. Although the uncertainty in the Prandtl number is less than 2 per cent at temperatures below about 1200°R and greater at higher temperatures, the curve in Fig. F,5a was taken as definitive for calculation purposes.

The enthalpy-temperature data for air as an ideal gas (see Fig. F,5b), necessary for the calculation of density and viscosity in the solution of the momentum equation (Eq. 3-8), were obtained from NBS-NACA Table 2.10 which provides data up to 5400°R. The data were extrapolated to higher temperatures. Since the specific heat is appreciably constant up to about 1000°R, the greatest effect of specific heat variation is in the free flight condition where the temperatures are greatest.

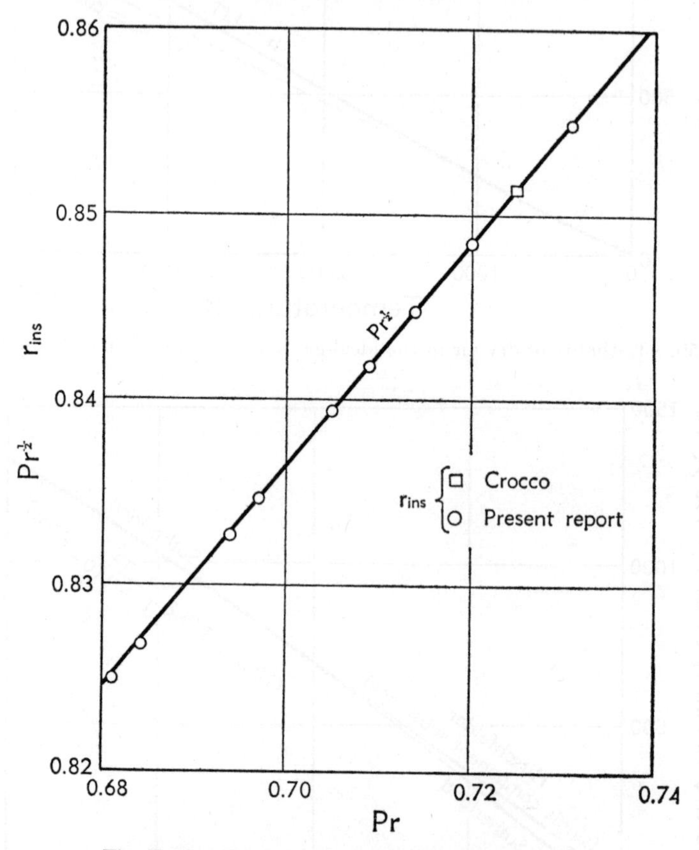


Fig. F,5d. Recovery factor for constant Prandtl number and Blasius shear distribution.

Fig. F,5c shows the viscosity variation as a function of temperature. Except for the Hirschfelder portion below 216°R, the Sutherland law of NBS-NACA Table 2.39 was used.

Eq. 3-8 and 3-9 were solved numerically by hand using the trapezoidal rule, the interval $\Delta u_*$ being taken extremely small over the outer half of the boundary layer. Consequently, the calculations were accurate to approximately one part in ten thousand. The accuracy is indicated in Fig. F,5d and F,5e where some recovery and Reynolds analogy factors assuming the Blasius shear distributions and constant Prandtl number are compared with results of Crocco, who used the Blasius shear distribution with constant Prandtl number in his calculations.

The numerical method of solution utilized in [3] was as follows: a mean constant Prandtl number was first estimated, whereupon an enthalpy distribution was computed using Eq. 3-19 with the Blasius shear distribution. A new Prandtl number distribution was then obtained from Fig. F,5a

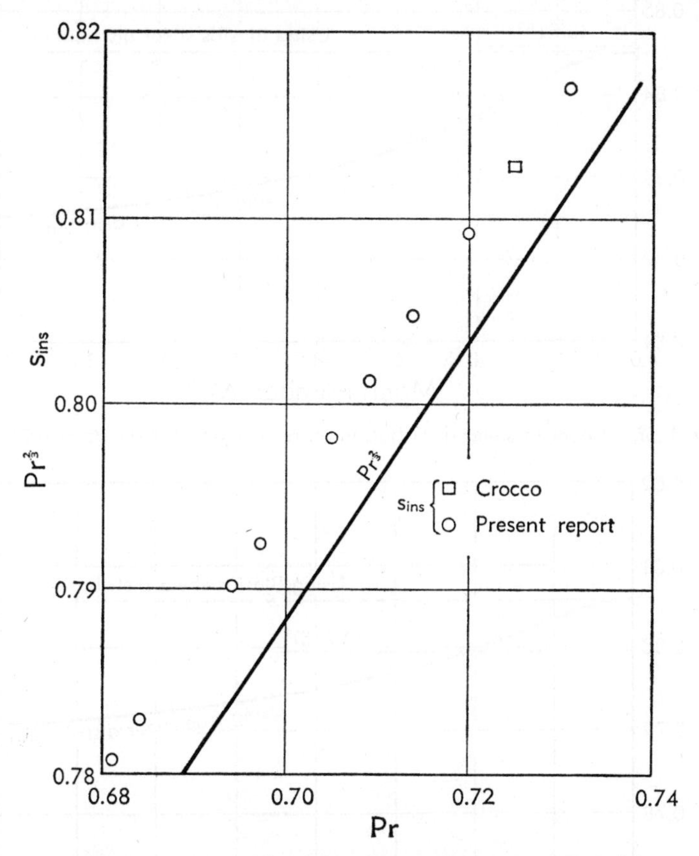


Fig. F,5e. Reynolds-analogy factor for constant Prandtl number and Blasius shear distribution.

after converting the enthalpy to temperature by means of NBS-NACA Table 2.10. A new shear distribution was also computed with enthalpy distribution using the Crocco method for solving numerically the momentum equation. The new Prandtl number and shear distributions were then substituted in Eq. 3-14 and 3-15 to obtain the final recovery and Reynolds analogy factors. It was not necessary to iterate any further for both shear or enthalpy distribution, because of the rapid convergence of the iteration process. It is seen, however, that it was necessary to make one more iteration beyond Crocco for enthalpy, even for constant Prandtl number, in order to attain the accuracy desired; this is illustrated in Fig. F,5f and F,5g where the exact recovery and Reynolds analogy factor are plotted as functions of Mach number for both a true shear distribution, corre-

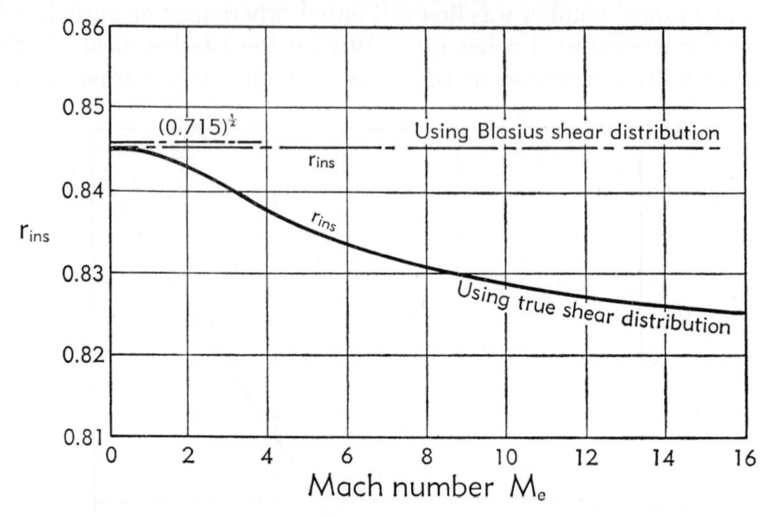


Fig. F,5f. Effect of shear distribution on recovery factor for Pr = 0.715.

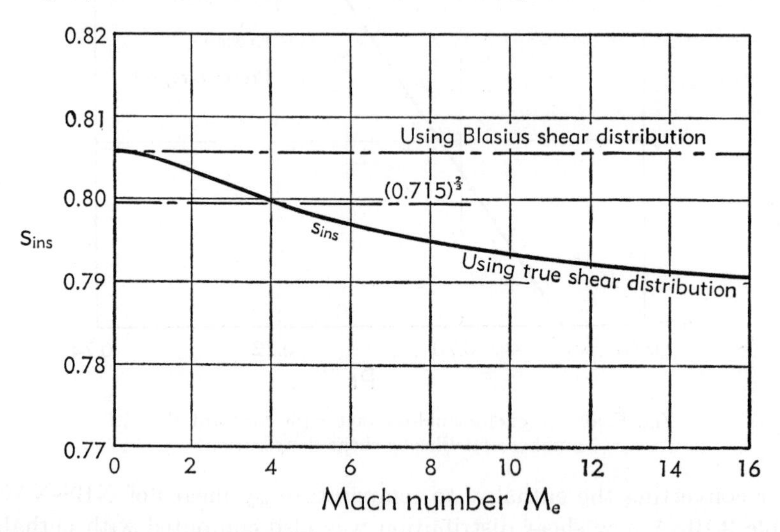


Fig. F,5g. Effect of shear distribution on Reynolds analogy factor for Pr = 0.715.

sponding to a constant Prandtl number of 0.715 and $T_e$ = 400°R, and the Blasius shear distribution. Fig. F,5h shows typical shear and Prandtl number distributions for a complete calculation.

Fig. F,5i shows the local heat transfer coefficient (multiplied by $\sqrt{Re}$) for a laminar boundary layer on a flat plate at zero angle of attack in free flight with a free stream temperature of 400°R and various wall-to-free stream enthalpy ratios. The recovery factor when the plate is insulated is plotted in Fig. F,5j. It is seen that the recovery factor follows $Pr_w^{\frac{1}{2}}$ up to about Mach number 3 after which $r$ overshoots and remains consistently below $Pr_w^{\frac{1}{2}}$. Fig. F,5k gives the recovery factor for different wall-to-free stream enthalpy ratios. Fig. F,5l is a cross plot of Fig. F,5k.

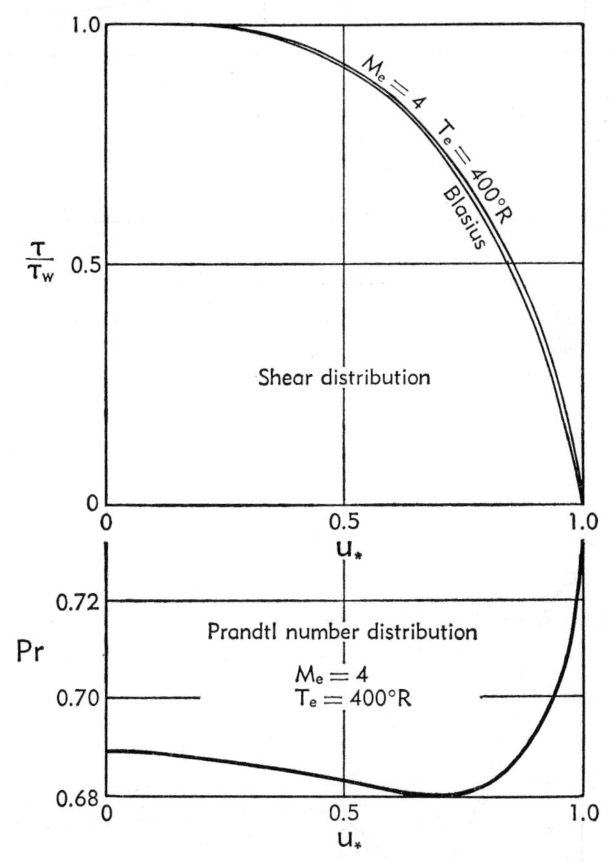


Fig. F,5h. Typical shear and Prandtl number distributions across a laminar boundary layer.

Fig. F,5m gives the Reynolds analogy factor for the limiting case of the insulated plate. $s$ has the same characteristics as $r$, overshooting $Pr_w^{\frac{2}{3}}$ in the neighborhood of $M_e = 4$. Fig. F,5n and F,5o gives the Reynolds analogy factor for various wall-to-free stream enthalpy ratios.

Local heat transfer coefficients, recovery factors, and Reynolds analogy factors for insulated flat plates in heated wind tunnels are presented in Fig. F,5p, F,5q, F,5r, F,5s, F,5t, F,5u, and F,5v. In particular, Fig. F,5q and F,5r show the relation of $r_{ins}$ to $Pr_e^{\frac{1}{2}}$ and $Pr_w^{\frac{1}{2}}$, and of $s_{ins}$ to $Pr_e^{\frac{2}{3}}$ and

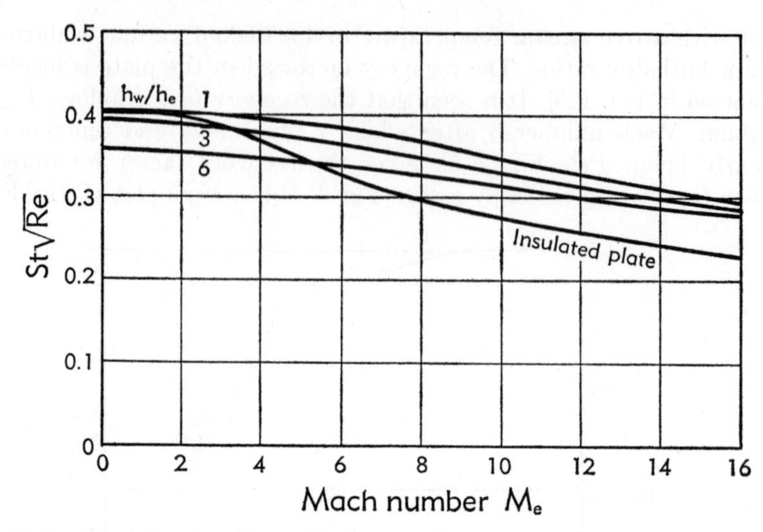


Fig. F,5i. Local heat transfer coefficient for a laminar boundary layer on a flat plate in free flight for various wall-to-free stream enthalpy ratios. $T_e = 400°R$.

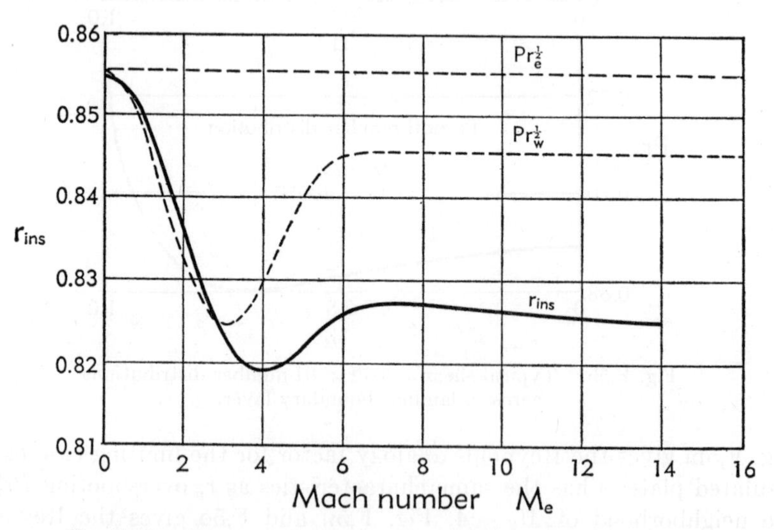


Fig. F, 5j. Recovery factor for a laminar boundary layer on an insulated flat plate in free flight. $T_e = 400°R$.

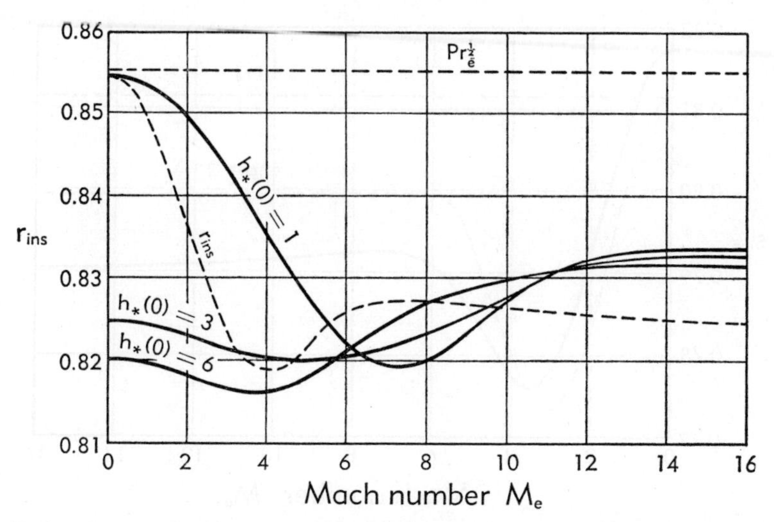


Fig. F,5k. Recovery factor for a laminar boundary layer on a flat plate in free flight for various wall-to-free stream enthalpy ratios. $T_e = 400°R$.

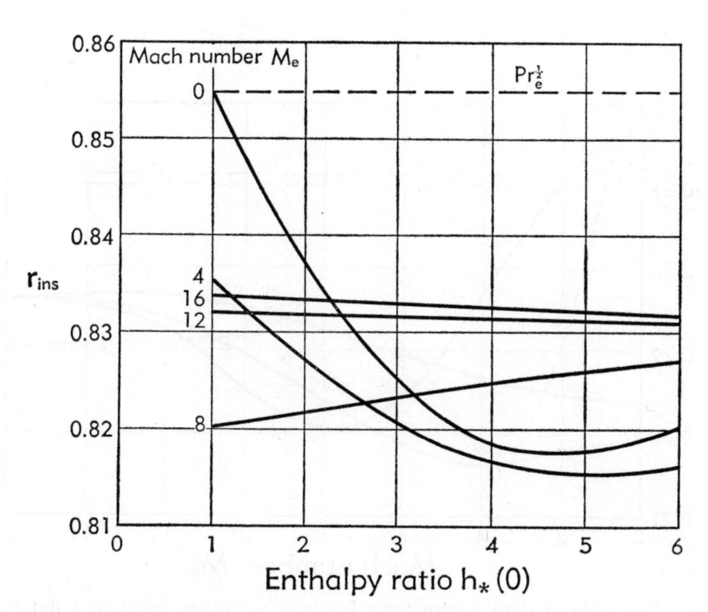


Fig. F,5l. Recovery factor for a laminar boundary layer on a flat plate in free flight for various Mach numbers. $T_e = 400°R$.

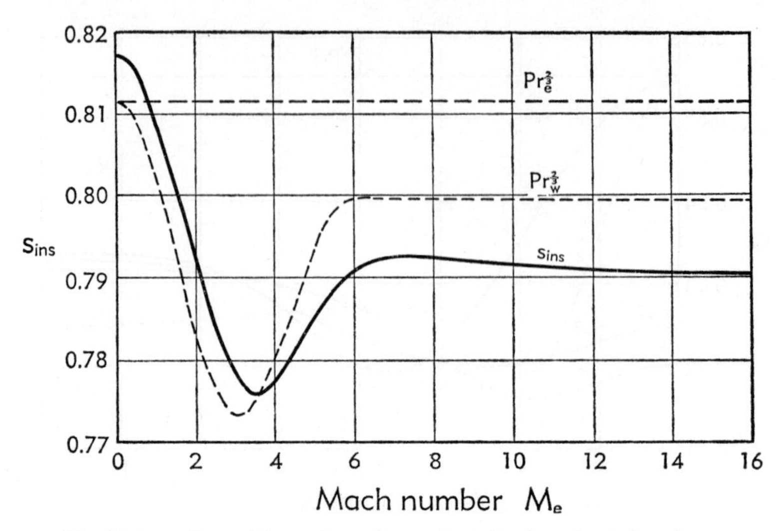


Fig. F,5m. Reynolds analogy factor for a laminar boundary layer on an insulated flat plate in free flight. $T_e = 400°R$.

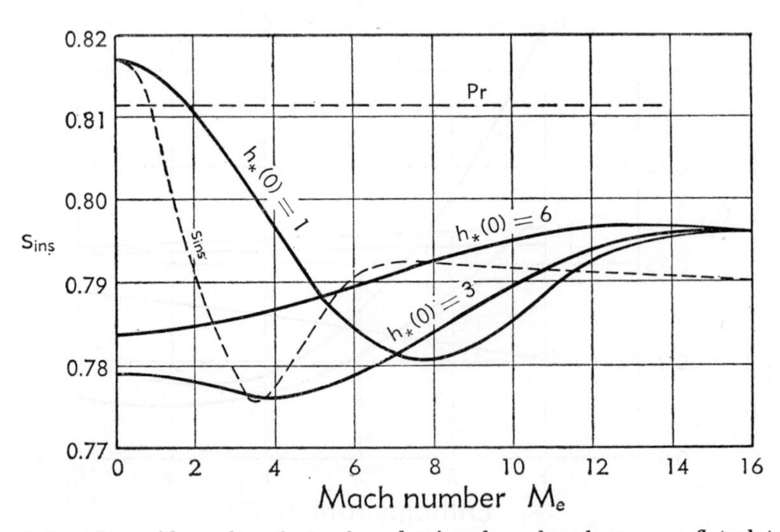


Fig. F,5n. Reynolds analogy factor for a laminar boundary layer on a flat plate in free flight for various wall-to-free stream enthalpy ratios. $T_e = 400°R$.

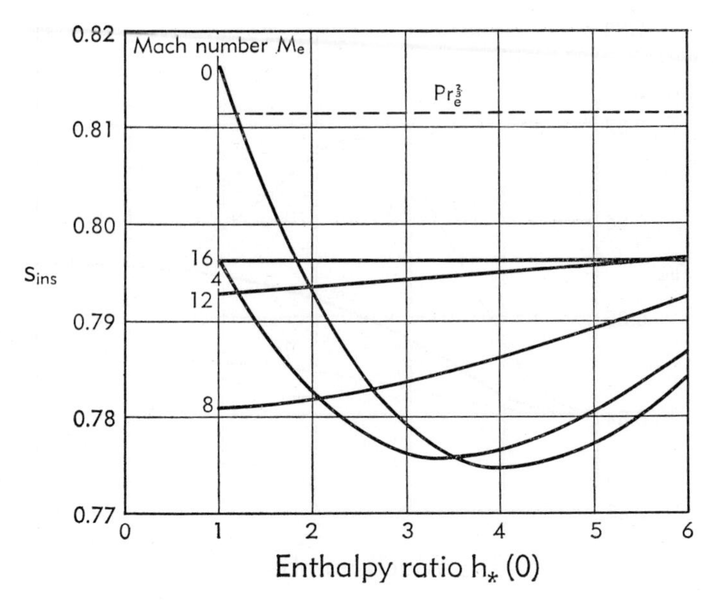


Fig. F,5o. Reynolds analogy factor for a laminar boundary layer on a flat plate in free flight for various Mach numbers. $T_e$ = 400°R.

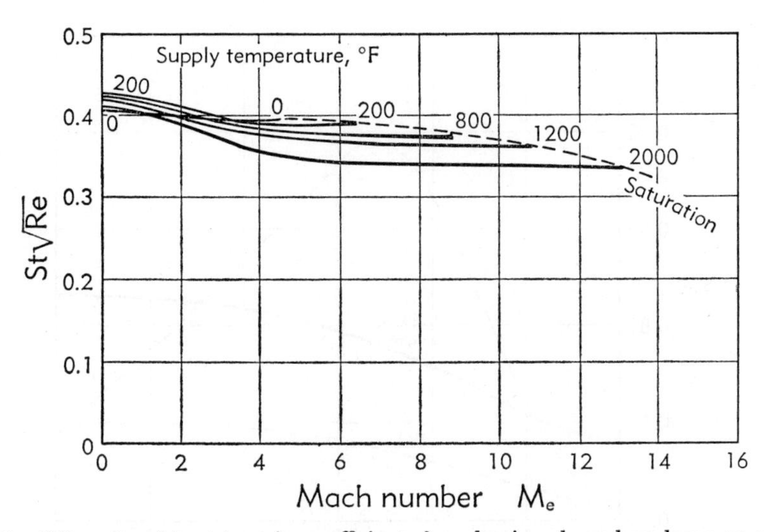


Fig. F,5p. Local heat transfer coefficients for a laminar boundary layer on an insulated flat plate in a wind tunnel at various supply temperatures.

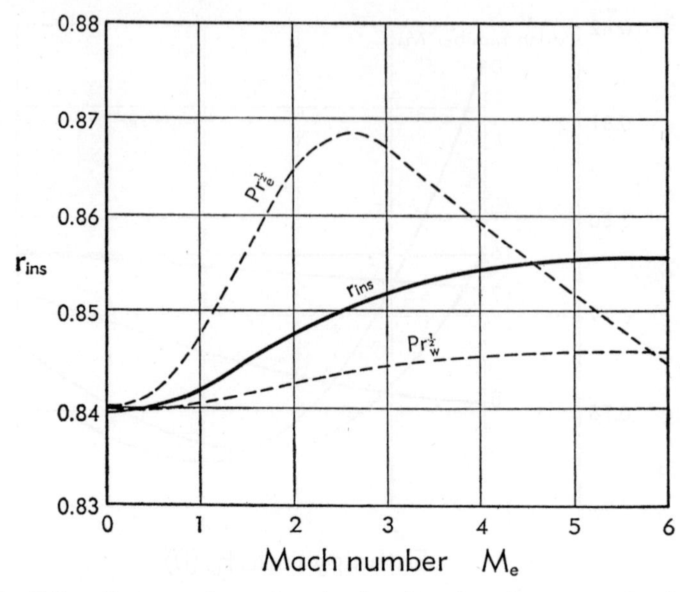


Fig. F,5q. Recovery factor for a laminar boundary layer on an insulated flat plate in a wind tunnel at a supply temperature of 100°F.

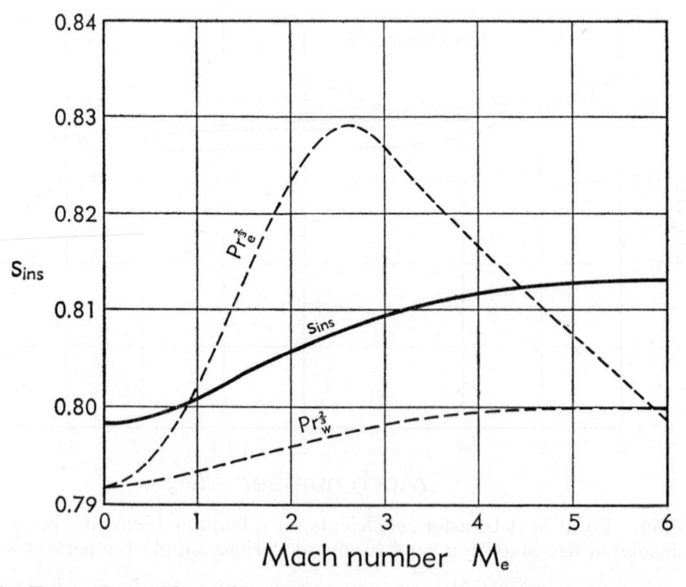


Fig. F,5r. Reynolds analogy factor for a laminar boundary layer on an insulated flat plate in a wind tunnel at a supply temperature of 100°F.

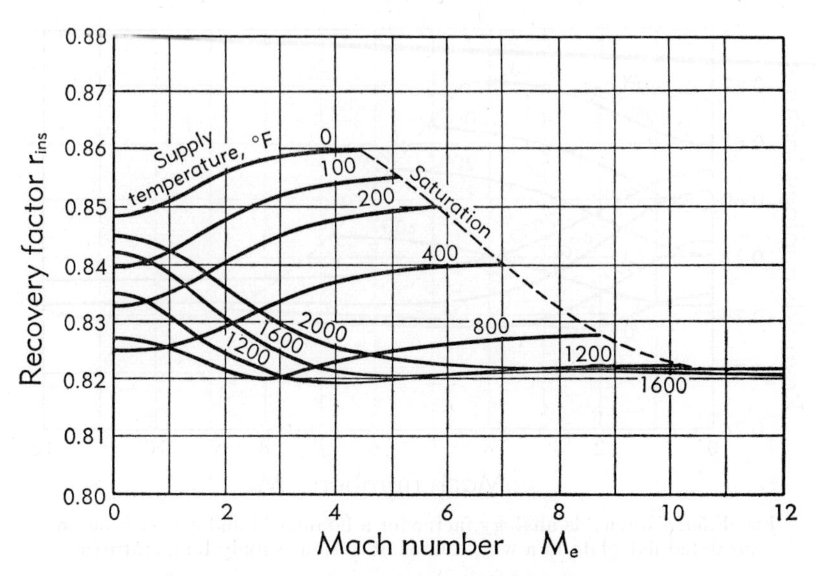


Fig. F,5s. Recovery factor for a laminar boundary layer on an insulated flat plate in a wind tunnel at various supply temperatures.

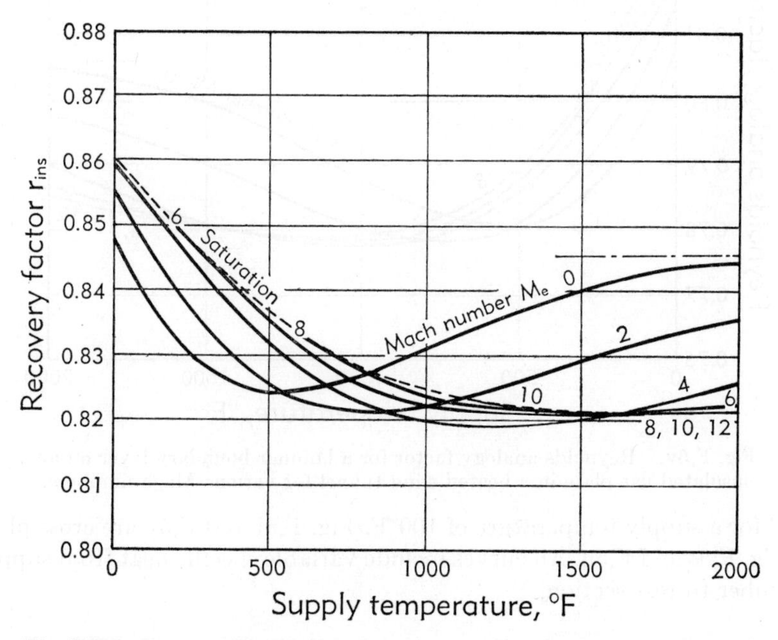


Fig. F,5t. Recovery factor for a laminar boundary layer on an insulated flat plate in a heated wind tunnel for various Mach numbers.

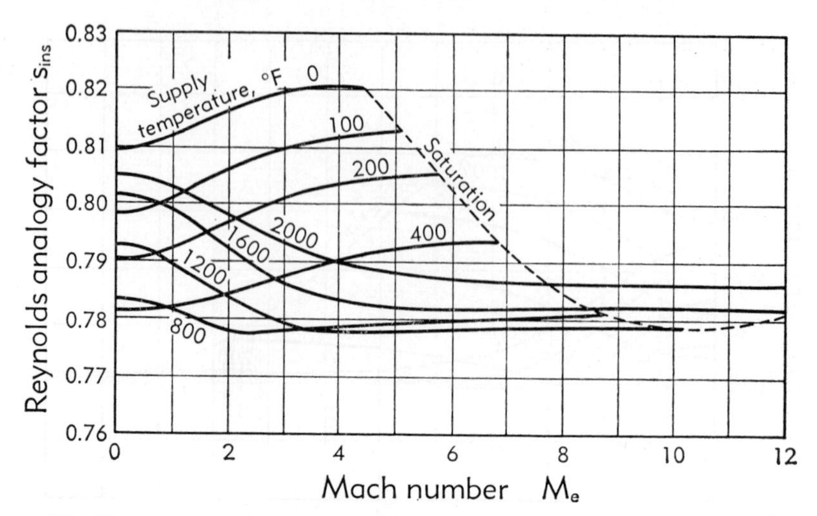


Fig. F,5u. Reynolds analogy factor for a laminar boundary layer on an insulated flat plate in a wind tunnel at various supply temperatures.

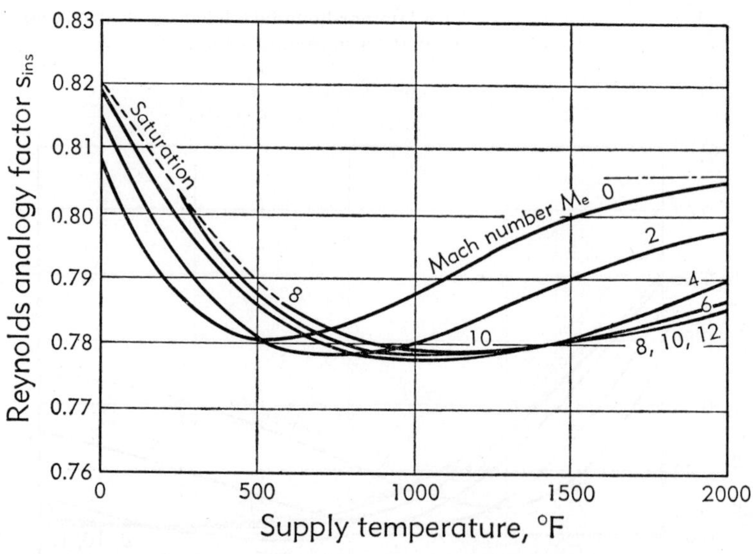


Fig. F,5v. Reynolds analogy factor for a laminar boundary layer on an insulated flat plate in a heated wind tunnel for various Mach numbers.

$Pr_w^{\frac{2}{3}}$, for a supply temperature of 100°F. Fig. F,5t and F,5v are cross plots in Fig. F,5s and F,5u. All curves include variable specific heat from supply chamber to test section.

**F,6. Cone Solution.** Hantzsche and Wendt [6] have shown that the equations for a thin laminar boundary layer on a circular cone at zero angle of attack in a supersonic stream with attached shock wave can be reduced by means of a simple transformation to equations of the same form as those for a flat plate. As a consequence, the local coefficient of heat transfer for the cone is $\sqrt{3}$ times the corresponding coefficient for the flat plate. In other words, since the local heat transfer coefficient

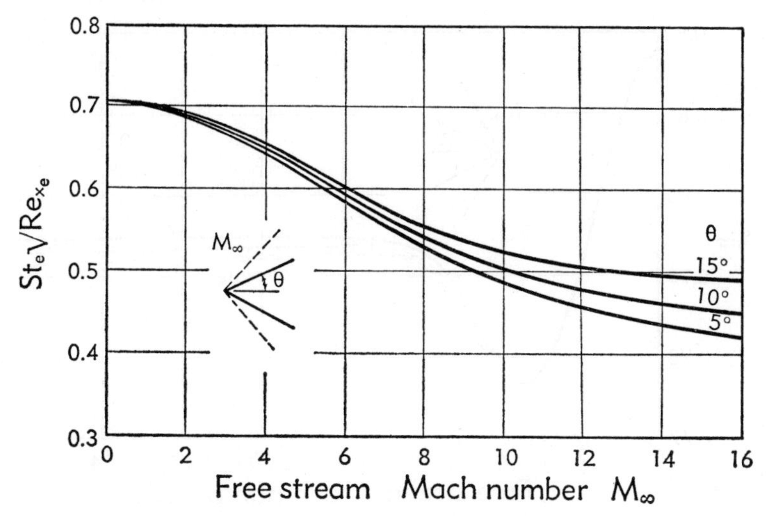


Fig. F,6a. Local heat transfer coefficient for laminar boundary layers on insulated cones in free flight. $T_\infty = 400°R$.

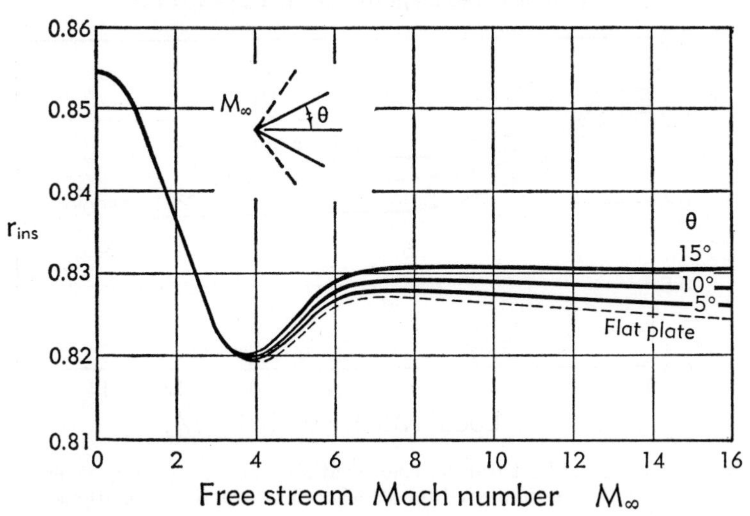


Fig. F,6b. Recovery factor for laminar boundary layers on insulated cones in free flight. $T_\infty = 400°R$.

varies inversely with the square root of the Reynolds number, the coefficient for the cone can be obtained by dividing the cone Reynolds number by 3 and using flat plate results. Furthermore, there follows, as a result of the geometry, that the mean coefficient of heat transfer for the cone is $\frac{2}{3}\sqrt{3}$ times the mean coefficient for the plate based on the same slant area. It must be mentioned also that the coefficients for the cone are based upon the flow condition just outside the boundary layer of the cone and not in front of the attached shock wave.

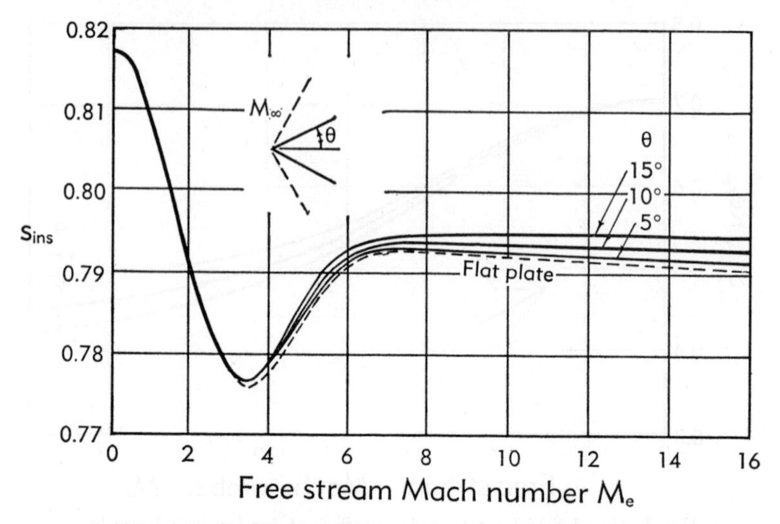


Fig. F,6c. Reynolds analogy factor for laminar boundary layers on insulated cones in free flight. $T_\infty = 400°R$.

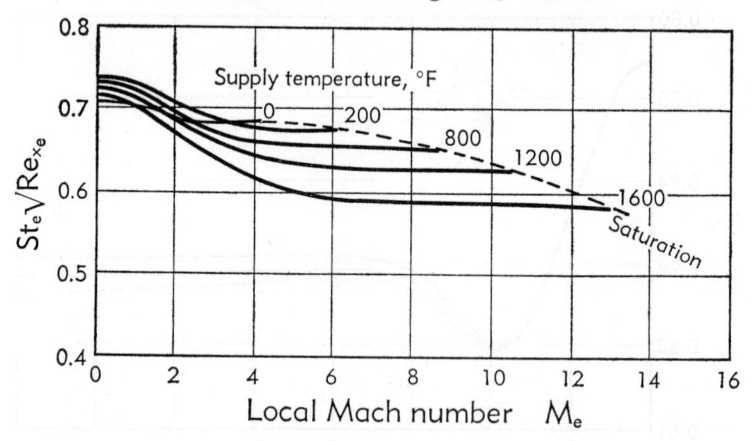


Fig. F,6d. Local heat transfer coefficient for laminar boundary layers on insulated cones in a wind tunnel at various supply temperatures.

Because of engineering interest in cones, the local heat transfer coefficient, recovery factor, and Reynolds analogy factor are plotted in Fig. F,6a, F,6b, and F,6c, respectively, for insulated cones at zero angle of attack in free flight.

With experimental work in wind tunnels, Fig. F,5s, F,5t, F,5u, and F,5v can be used directly for recovery factor and Reynolds analogy factor on cones, provided that the Mach number is the local value just outside the boundary layer. In the case of the local heat transfer coefficient, Fig. F,5p can be used also for cones except that the ordinate must be multiplied by $\sqrt{3}$ in accordance with the above discussion. Fig. F,6d represents a corrected (by $\sqrt{3}$) plot for moderate heat transfer to or from cones in heated wind tunnels.

**F,7. Stagnation Point Solution.** Because of its importance in general missile design, heat transfer at stagnation points of cylindrical and spherical surfaces should be given a few words at this time. It may be desirable to round the leading edges of airfoils and the noses of bodies of revolution at high speeds in order to diminish the local heat transfer rates at those locations and to allow easier internal cooling, if necessary.

The heat transfer problem for incompressible flow lends itself readily to analysis. For the cylindrical surface, Squire [*7*, p. 631] used Homann's solution [*8*] of the momentum equation near the stagnation point and found, upon simultaneous solution with the energy equation, that the local heat transfer coefficient *St*, defined by

$$q_w = -St c_p \rho U (T_\infty - T_w) \tag{7-1}$$

may be expressed by the relation

$$St = 0.570 \left(\frac{c_p \mu}{k}\right)^{-0.6} \left(\frac{\beta D}{U}\right)^{0.5} \left(\frac{\rho U D}{\mu}\right)^{-0.5} \tag{7-2}$$

where $D$ is the diameter of curvature of the cylindrical surface and $\beta = (\partial u_e/\partial x)_{x=0}$ where $x$ is measured along the body from the stagnation point. Subscript $_\infty$ refers to the undisturbed flow. From incompressible perfect fluid theory, it is found that $\beta D/u_\infty = 4$. This relationship has been verified experimentally [*7*, p. 631].

For the spherical surface, Sibulkin [*9*] also used Homann's results, and following the method of Squire [*7*, p. 631], obtained the formula

$$St = 0.763 \left(\frac{c_p \mu}{k}\right)^{-0.6} \left(\frac{\beta D}{U}\right)^{0.5} \left(\frac{\rho U D}{\mu}\right)^{-0.5} \tag{7-3}$$

in which $D$ is the diameter of curvature of the spherical surface. Also from incompressible perfect fluid theory, $\beta D/U = 3$.

Eq. 7-1, 7-2, and 7-3 can be used for approximate heat transfer calculation with supersonic flow about a body when it is remembered that the problem is strictly a local one and therefore the fluid properties $c_p$, $k$, $\mu$, and $\rho$ in all three equations must now be taken at the stagnation temperature $T^0$ at the outer edge of the boundary layer. Thus, Eq. 7-1 becomes for gases

$$q_w = St^0 \rho^0 U (h^0 - h_w) \tag{7-1a}$$

with

$$St = 0.570 \left(\frac{c_p^0 \mu^0}{k^0}\right)^{-0.6} \left(\frac{\beta D}{U}\right)^{0.5} \left(\frac{\rho^0 U D}{\mu^0}\right)^{-0.5} \tag{7-2a}$$

for the cylindrical face, and

$$St = 0.763 \left(\frac{c_p^0 \mu^0}{k^0}\right)^{-0.6} \left(\frac{\beta D}{U}\right)^{0.5} \left(\frac{\rho^0 U D}{\mu^0}\right)^{-0.5} \tag{7-3a}$$

for the spherical nose, where the superscript $^0$ indicates stagnation conditions. (Note that $U$ in the equations is arbitrary, because the effect of speed is already accounted for in $c_p$, $k$, $\mu$, $\rho$, and $\beta$.) However, in terms of undisturbed conditions, Eq. 7-1a, 7-2a, and 7-3a become

$$q_w = -St_\infty \rho_\infty U(h^0 - h_w) \tag{7-1b}$$

$$St_\infty = - \quad = 0.570 \left(\frac{\beta D}{U}\right)^{0.5} \left(\frac{\rho_\infty U D}{\mu_\infty}\right)^{-0.5} \left(\frac{c_p^0 \mu^0}{k^0}\right)^{-0.6} \left(\frac{\rho^0}{\rho_\infty}\right)^{0.5} \left(\frac{\mu^0}{\mu_\infty}\right)^{0.5} \tag{7-2b}$$

for cylinders, and

$$St_\infty = 0.763 \left(\frac{\beta D}{U}\right)^{0.5} \left(\frac{\rho_\infty U D}{\mu_\infty}\right)^{-0.5} \left(\frac{c_p^0 \mu^0}{k^0}\right)^{-0.6} \left(\frac{\rho^0}{\rho_\infty}\right)^{0.5} \left(\frac{\mu^0}{\mu_\infty}\right)^{0.5} \tag{7-3b}$$

for spheres.

With supersonic flow, $\beta$ can be approximated upon the assumption that Newtonian flow prevails between the bow wave and the body. The derivation goes as follows: In Newtonian flow [*10*], the pressure $p$ over the surface of a circular arc of diameter $D$ is given by

$$\frac{p - p_\infty}{\frac{1}{2}\rho_\infty U^2} = 2 \cos^2 \frac{2x}{D} \tag{7-4}$$

But, at the stagnation point,

$$\beta^2 x = -\frac{1}{\rho}\frac{\partial p}{\partial x} \tag{7-5}$$

Hence, from Eq. 7-4

$$\beta = \sqrt{8 \frac{\rho_\infty}{\rho^0}} \frac{U}{D} \tag{7-6}$$

in which $\rho^0$ is the density at the stagnation (local ambient) point.

Across a normal shock,

$$\frac{\rho^0}{\rho_\infty} = \frac{(\gamma + 1)M_\infty^2}{(\gamma - 1)M_\infty^2 + 2}\left[1 + \frac{\gamma - 1}{2}\frac{(\gamma - 1)M_\infty^2 + 2}{2\gamma M_\infty^2 - (\gamma - 1)}\right]^{\frac{1}{\gamma - 1}} \tag{7-7}$$

so that, from Eq. 7-6, the nondimensional quantity $\beta D/U$ is

$$\frac{\beta D}{U} = \left\{\frac{8[(\gamma - 1)M_\infty^2 + 2]}{(\gamma + 1)M_\infty^2}\left[1 + \frac{\gamma - 1}{2}\frac{(\gamma - 1)M_\infty^2 + 2}{2\gamma M_\infty^2 - (\gamma - 1)}\right]^{-\frac{1}{\gamma - 1}}\right\}^{\frac{1}{2}} \tag{7-8}$$

Eq. 7-8 is plotted in Fig. F,7a. Also plotted in the figure are experimental values of $\beta$ at the stagnation point of a hemispherical nose on the end of a cylinder in a wind tunnel. The values were obtained by Korobkin [*11*] from surface-pressure measurements. The theory seems to follow the data quite well over the whole supersonic range.

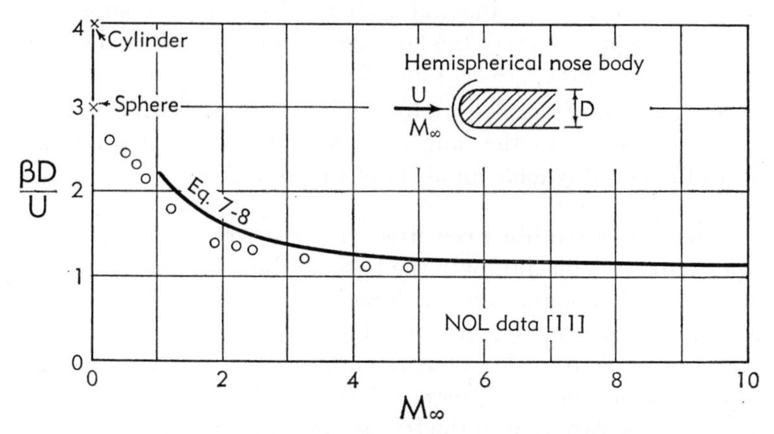


Fig. F,7a. Local velocity gradient at the stagnation point of a hemisphere-cylinder combination.

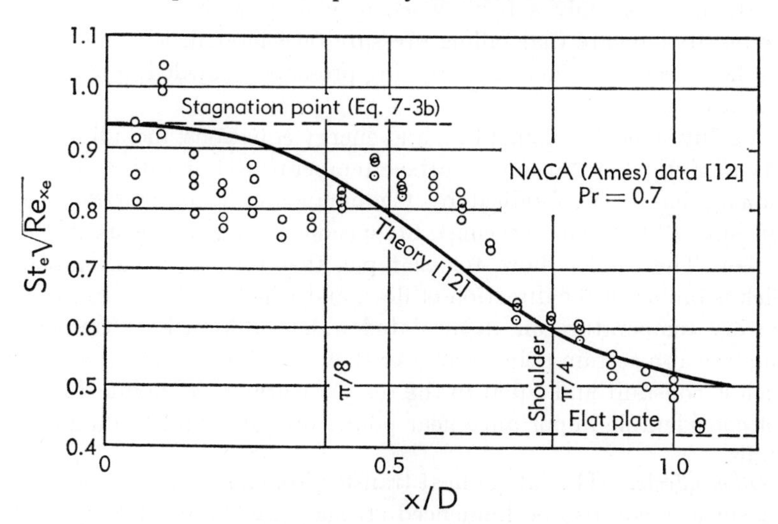


Fig. F,7b. Local heat transfer data for a hemispherical nose at Mach number 1.97.

Eq. 7-1b, 7-2b, and 7-3b can also be used to yield approximate results when the speed is so great that the air dissociates behind the shock and in the boundary layer. However, this topic will be discussed later in Art. 22.

When the flow over the nose of a blunt body is completely laminar, the maximum heat transfer rate occurs at the stagnation point. This follows immediately from the fact that the terms $\rho^0/\rho_\infty$ and $\mu^0/\mu_\infty$ in Eq. 7-2b and 7-3b decrease as the ambient temperature decreases with expansion of the gas about the body. The way in which $St_\infty$ varies over the face of the body was worked out by Stine and Wanlass [*12*]. The theoretical variation as well as experimental data for $Pr = 0.7$ are shown in Fig. F,7b, when the properties of the flow are put in terms of local conditions, i.e. $St_e = -q_w/c_{p_e}\rho_e u_e(T_e - T_w)$ and $Re_{x_e} = \rho_e u_e x/\mu_e$.

All of the above formulas are for laminar flow. It is expected that the flow will be laminar in the immediate vicinity of the stagnation point owing to the low Reynolds numbers of the local flow.

**F,8. Effect of Variable Free Stream Pressure and Variable Wall Temperature.** Thus far, only the basic problem of the heat transfer to a compressible boundary layer with constant wall temperature and constant free stream velocity, but variable properties, has been discussed. It is now desirable to make a few remarks about the effects of wall temperature gradient and free stream velocity gradient.

The effect of variation in the free stream pressure (velocity) has been studied by many authors (e.g. Goland [*13*], Levy [*14*], Morris and Smith [*15*], to mention only a few), working mainly with integral equations. The results indicate that falling pressure (accelerated flow) increases the local heat transfer, whereas increasing pressure (retarded flow) decreases local heat transfer.

A solution of the momentum and energy equations, including an arbitrary analytic distribution of surface temperature but with zero pressure gradient, has been obtained by Chapman and Rubesin [*16*] (see also Lighthill [*17*]), assuming constant specific heat and constant Prandtl number. The results show, for example, that for a surface temperature which is falling in the direction of flow, and which is always less than the recovery temperature on an insulated wall, the local heat transfer rate to a plate at a certain point is greater than that for a surface temperature which is constant and equal to the temperature at the point. This result is of considerable importance near points of ogives and leading edges of airfoils.

*Other effects.* The rate of heat transfer from a laminar boundary layer to a surface can also be influenced strongly by the insulating action of fluid injection (cf. Sec. G). The diffusion of a foreign gas into the boundary layer from the wall is discussed by Smith [*18*], who finds that helium produces considerable decrease in the rate of heat transfer to a plate.

**F,9. Status of Experimental Knowledge.** At the outset, it is very difficult to obtain accurate laminar flow data, because the magnitudes to be measured are small. Although a number of experimental investigations concerned with heat transfer with laminar boundary layers have been attempted, the results of Eber [*19*] at the Naval Ordnance Laboratory and Shoulberg, Hill, and Rivas [*20*] at the Massachusetts Institute of Technology are of particular interest. These experiments were conducted in supersonic wind tunnels, the NOL facility being intermittent and the MIT tunnel continuous. Because of the symmetry of flow, and because the theory for cones is as well developed as for flat plates, Eber used cones for the experimental determination of recovery factors and heat transfer coefficients. The cones were constructed as follows: (1) thin-walled cones for recovery factor measurement because thin walls immediately assume the insulated-wall temperature, (2) thick-walled cones for

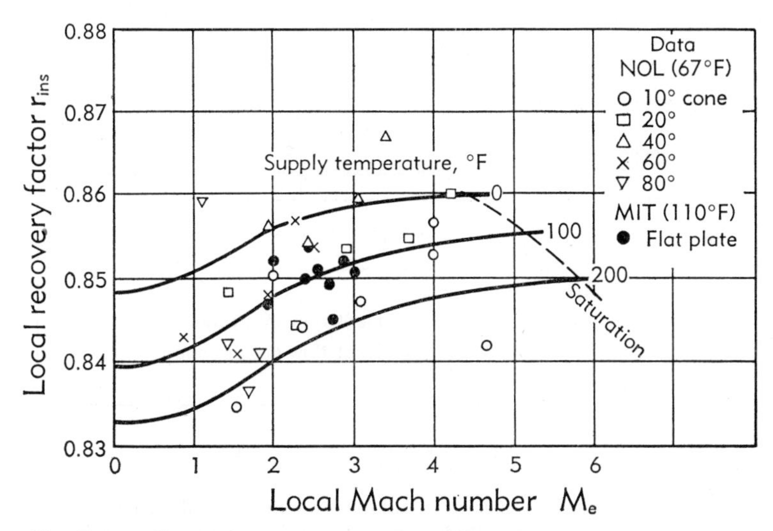


Fig. F,9a. Comparison of theory and experiment on recovery factor for laminar boundary layers on flat plates and cones in a wind tunnel.

heat transfer measurement because of their high heat capacity, (3) solid cones for average heat transfer measurement, and (4) subdivided cones for local heat transfer measurement. Inviscid conical flow theory determined conditions just outside the boundary layer. Shoulberg, Hill, and Rivas measured recovery factors by means of a flat plate containing heat-insulated material covered with a sheet of stainless steel.

Experimental data on recovery factors are plotted in Fig. F,9a, which contains the 0°F, 100°F, and 200°F supply-temperature curves of Fig. F,5s. It is seen that the NOL data, obtained at an average supply temperature of 67°F, appears to have some correlation with the theory with respect to Mach number. The MIT data, obtained at an average supply temperature of 110°F, clusters well about the theoretical 100°F supply-temperature curve.

The data of Eber for local heat transfer coefficients for cones are plotted in Fig. F,9b, where the 0°F and 200°F supply-temperature curves are taken from Fig. F,6d. The local Reynolds number varied from $2 \times 10^5$ to $1.5 \times 10^6$. Now in the case of flat plates in wind tunnels, the theory predicts hardly any effect of Mach number as compared to free flight conditions. Thus, according to Fig. F,9b, the theory seems to be corroborated. The fact of the matter is that, in the wind tunnel, the density effect is offset by the nearly linear viscosity variation at the lower wind tunnel temperatures. Indeed, for linear viscosity-temperature variation, there is no effect of Mach number or heat transfer. It should be pointed out that according to Fig. F,6a, free flight data with moderate heating or cooling (nearly insulated cone) would show more clearly the compressibility effect, although the effect compared to the drag of the entire test vehicle

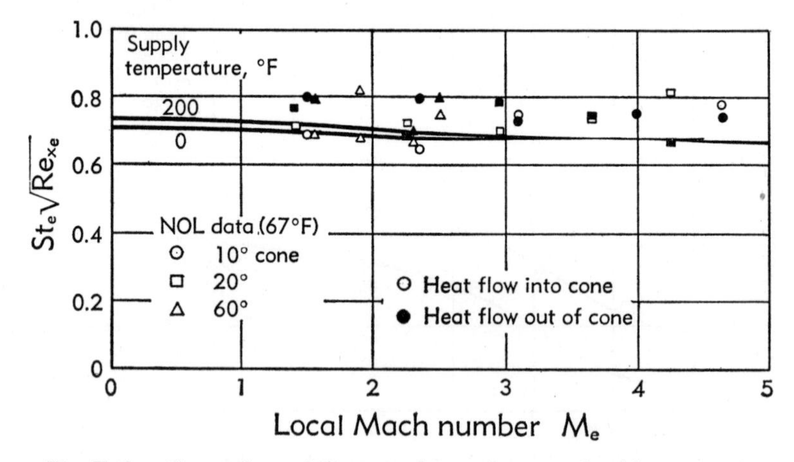


Fig. F,9b. Comparison of theory and experiment on local heat transfer coefficient for laminar boundary layers on cones in a wind tunnel.

would be difficult to detect, owing to the small proportion of the laminar flow drag compared to the drag of the whole vehicle. The Reynolds number effect is certainly verified in Fig. F,9b, since the error in the data is small compared to the range of the square root of the Reynolds number.

### *TURBULENT FLOW*

**F,10. Flat Plate Solution.** When the boundary layer is turbulent, the energy equation can be solved in the same way as for laminar flow. However, the momentum equation is not amenable to solution, even after certain assumptions are made concerning the turbulent mechanism. The integral method will therefore be used in the following paragraphs to obtain surface friction, based on a velocity profile derived from mixing-length theory.

It can be shown [*21*] that the continuity, momentum, and energy equations for a thin turbulent boundary layer in the mean steady state are, respectively,

$$\frac{\partial}{\partial x}(\overline{\rho u}) + \frac{\partial}{\partial y}(\overline{\rho v}) = 0 \tag{10-1}$$

$$\overline{\rho u}\,\frac{\partial \bar{u}}{\partial x} + \overline{\rho v}\,\frac{\partial \bar{u}}{\partial y} = \frac{\partial}{\partial y}\left[(\mu + \epsilon_\mu)\,\frac{\partial \bar{u}}{\partial y}\right] - \frac{d\bar{p}}{dx} \tag{10-2a}$$

$$\frac{\partial \bar{p}}{\partial y} = 0 \tag{10-2b}$$

$$\overline{\rho u}\,\frac{\partial \bar{h}}{\partial x} + \overline{\rho v}\,\frac{\partial \bar{h}}{\partial y} = (\mu + \epsilon_\mu)\left(\frac{\partial \bar{u}}{\partial y}\right)^2 + \frac{\partial}{\partial y}\left[(k + \epsilon_k)\,\frac{\partial \bar{T}}{\partial y}\right] + \bar{u}\,\frac{d\bar{p}}{dx} \tag{10-3}$$

where $\epsilon_\mu$ and $\epsilon_k$ are the eddy coefficients of friction and heat transfer defined by

$$-\overline{(\rho v)'u'} = \epsilon_\mu\,\frac{\partial \bar{u}}{\partial y} \quad \text{and} \quad \overline{(\rho v)'h'} = \epsilon_{k_1}\,\frac{\partial \bar{h}}{\partial y} = \epsilon_k\,\frac{\partial \bar{T}}{\partial y} \tag{10-4}$$

respectively. The bars indicate temporal mean values. The ratio $c_p(\mu + \epsilon_\mu)/(k + \epsilon_k)$ is designated the mixed Prandtl number $Pr_{\mathrm{m}}$, which reduces to the molecular Prandtl number $Pr_{\mathrm{lam}}(= c_p\mu/k)$ in the sublayer at the plate and contains the turbulent Prandtl number $Pr_{\mathrm{t}}(= c_p\epsilon_\mu/\epsilon_k)$ of the outer region of the turbulent boundary layer. Thus Eq. 10-3 can be rewritten as

$$\overline{\rho u}\,\frac{\partial \bar{h}}{\partial x} + \overline{\rho v}\,\frac{\partial \bar{h}}{\partial y} = (\mu + \epsilon_\mu)\left(\frac{\partial \bar{u}}{\partial y}\right)^2 + \frac{\partial}{\partial y}\left[\frac{(\mu + \epsilon_\mu)}{Pr_{\mathrm{m}}}\,\frac{\partial \bar{h}}{\partial y}\right] + \bar{u}\,\frac{d\bar{p}}{dx} \tag{10-5}$$

Since the above equations have the same form as Eq. 3-1, 3-2, and 3-4 for laminar flow, the independent variables $x$ and $y$ are likewise transformed to $x$ and $\bar{u}$ by the Crocco transformation $\bar{u} = \bar{u}(x, y)$ and $x = x$. Hence, Eq. 10-1, 10-2a, and 10-5 become, after elimination of $\overline{\rho v}$,

$$\frac{\partial}{\partial x}\left(\overline{\rho u}\,\frac{\mu + \epsilon_\mu}{\tau}\right) + \frac{\partial^2 \tau}{\partial \bar{u}^2} - \frac{d\bar{p}}{dx}\,\frac{\partial}{\partial \bar{u}}\left(\frac{\mu + \epsilon_\mu}{\tau}\right) = 0 \tag{10-6}$$

$$\tau^2\left[\frac{\partial}{\partial \bar{u}}\left(\frac{1}{Pr_{\mathrm{m}}}\,\frac{\partial \bar{h}}{\partial \bar{u}}\right) + 1\right] + (1 - Pr_{\mathrm{m}})\left(\frac{1}{Pr_{\mathrm{m}}}\,\frac{\partial \bar{h}}{\partial \bar{u}}\right)\frac{\partial \tau}{\partial \bar{u}}\,\tau - \overline{\rho u}(\mu + \epsilon_\mu)\,\frac{\partial \bar{h}}{\partial x} + (\mu + \epsilon_\mu)\left(\frac{\partial \bar{h}}{\partial \bar{u}} + \bar{u}\right)\frac{d\bar{p}}{dx} = 0 \tag{10-7}$$

in which $\tau = (\mu + \epsilon_\mu)\partial\bar{u}/\partial y$. In order to simplify the problem and still arrive at a practical solution, it is assumed that $\partial\bar{h}/\partial x = 0$ and $d\bar{p}/dx = 0$. Eq. 10-6 and 10-7 then reduce to

$$\frac{\partial}{\partial x}\left[\frac{\overline{\rho u}(\mu + \epsilon_\mu)}{\tau}\right] + \frac{\partial^2 \tau}{\partial \bar{u}^2} = 0 \tag{10-8}$$

$$\tau\left[\frac{d}{d\bar{u}}\left(\frac{1}{Pr_{\mathrm{m}}}\,\frac{d\bar{h}}{d\bar{u}}\right) + 1\right] + (1 - Pr_{\mathrm{m}})\left(\frac{1}{Pr_{\mathrm{m}}}\,\frac{d\bar{h}}{d\bar{u}}\right)\frac{\partial \tau}{\partial \bar{u}} = 0 \tag{10-9}$$

Rearrangement of Eq. 10-9 gives

$$\left(\frac{\bar{h}'_*}{Pr_m}\right)' + (1 - Pr_m)\frac{\tau'}{\tau}\left(\frac{\bar{h}'_*}{Pr_m}\right) = -\frac{u_e^2}{h_e} \tag{10-10}$$

which is linear and first order in $\bar{h}_*/Pr_m$ as a function of $u_*$ at const $x$. Symbols $\bar{h}_*$ and $\bar{u}_*$ denote $\bar{h}/h_e$ and $\bar{u}/u_e$, respectively, and the primes indicate differentiation with respect of $\bar{u}_*$ alone. Integration of Eq. 10-10 at const $x$ results in [22]

$$\bar{h}_*(\bar{u}_*) = \bar{h}_*(0) - [\bar{h}_*(0) - 1]\frac{S(u_*)}{S(1)} + \frac{u_e^2}{h_e}\left[\frac{S(u_*)}{S(1)}R(1) - R(\bar{u}_*)\right] \tag{10-11}$$

in which

$$S(\bar{u}_*) = \int_0^{\bar{u}_*} Pr_m \cdot \exp\left[-\int_{\tau(0)}^{\tau}(1 - Pr_m)\frac{d\tau}{\tau}\right]d\bar{u}_* \tag{10-12}$$

and

$$R(\bar{u}_*) = \int_0^{\bar{u}_*} Pr_m \cdot \exp\left[-\int_{\tau(0)}^{\tau}(1 - Pr_m)\frac{d\tau}{\tau}\right] \left\{\int_0^{\bar{u}_*}\exp\left[\int_{\tau(0)}^{\tau}(1 - Pr_m)\frac{d\tau}{\tau}\right]d\bar{u}_*\right\}d\bar{u}_* \tag{10-13}$$

Eq. 10-11 gives the enthalpy distribution all the way across the turbulent boundary layer. As expected, the equation is identical in form to Eq. 3-17 for laminar flow.

**F,11. Heat Transfer.** Since the equation for enthalpy distribution for a turbulent boundary layer has the same form as for a laminar boundary layer, the heat transfer characteristics will also have the same form, viz.

(Heat transfer) $$q_w = -St\rho_e u_e(h_r - h_w) \tag{11-1}$$

(Stanton number) $$St = \frac{1}{s}\frac{c_f}{2} \tag{11-2}$$

(Recovery enthalpy) $$h_r = h_e + r\frac{u_e^2}{2} \tag{11-3}$$

where $s = S(1)$ and $r = 2R(1)$.

In order to compute the local heat transfer $q_w$, it is therefore necessary to determine the recovery factor $r$, the Reynolds analogy factor $s$, and the local skin friction coefficient $c_f$.

*Recovery factor.* As suggested by experimental data [23], the velocity profile can be conveniently divided into three parts: a laminar sublayer, a transition or buffer zone, and a fully turbulent region [24]. With this artifice, an algebraic formula for the recovery factor as a function of laminar Prandtl number, turbulent Prandtl number, and Reynolds number can be derived.

The general expression for recovery factor is [22]

$$r = 2R(1) = 2\int_0^1 Pr_m \exp\left[-\int_{\tau(0)}^{\tau}(1 - Pr_m)\frac{d\tau}{\tau}\right] \left\{\int_0^{\bar{u}_*}\exp\left[\int_{\tau(0)}^{\tau}(1 - Pr_m)\frac{d\tau}{\tau}\right]d\bar{u}_*\right\}d\bar{u}_* \quad (11\text{-}4)$$

with variable Prandtl number. However, before the integral can be evaluated, it is necessary to have information on the shear distribution across the layer, except for the case of $Pr = 1$ when $r = 1$. Now for turbulent boundary layers, there is no analytical expression for $\tau$ as there is in the case of laminar boundary layers. Therefore, with turbulent flow, it is necessary to assume a shear distribution which conforms with experiment. In the first place, owing to the experimental fact that the sublayer and transition regions are very small compared to the turbulent part of the boundary layer, it is certainly sufficient to assume that the total shear is constant across those subregions. Hence, Eq. 11-4 becomes, for averaged (constant) $Pr_{lam}$ and $Pr_t$,

$$r = 2Pr_{lam}\int_0^{\bar{u}_{*lam}}\bar{u}_*d\bar{u}_* + 2\int_{\bar{u}_{*lam}}^{\bar{u}_{*t}}Pr_m\bar{u}_*d\bar{u}_* + 2Pr_t\int_{\bar{u}_{*t}}^{1}\tau_*^{Pr_t-1}d\bar{u}_*\int_0^{\bar{u}_{*t}}\tau_*^{1-Pr}\,du_* + 2Pr_t\int_{\bar{u}_{*t}}^{1}\tau_*^{Pr_t-1}\int_{\bar{u}_{*t}}^{\bar{u}_*}\tau_*^{1-Pr_t}\,d\bar{u}_*d\bar{u}_* \quad (11\text{-}5)$$

where $\bar{u}_{*lam}$ indicates the outer edge of the laminar sublayer, $\bar{u}_{*t}$ the inner edge of the turbulent zone, and $\tau_* = \tau/\tau(0)$.

Experimentally [25], the shear distribution may be well approximated by a straight line over the turbulent region of the boundary layer, whence

$$\tau_* = 1 - \frac{y}{\delta} \quad (11\text{-}6)$$

Therefore $\tau_*(\bar{u}_*)$ is represented by the ordinate above the $y_*(= y\bar{u}_*/\delta)$ profile. Typical velocity and shear profiles for a turbulent boundary layer are plotted in Fig. F,11a. The Blasius velocity and shear distribution for laminar flow are also plotted in the figure for comparison. It is seen that the turbulent shear $\tau_*$ as a function of relative velocity $\bar{u}_*$ is much fuller than the laminar shear, and therefore tends to justify the assumption usually made in turbulent flow analysis that the shear is constant across the layer. Also, the assumption that the turbulence Prandtl number $Pr_t$ is near unity tends further to diminish the shear effect. If the semi-logarithmic law for velocity is used, then the shear distribution as a function of $\bar{u}_*$ becomes

$$\tau_* = 1 - \exp\left[1 - \frac{K}{\sqrt{c_f/2}}(1 - \bar{u}_*)\right] \tag{11-7}$$

in which $K$ is the universal mixing-length constant.

The next step in the evaluation of Eq. 11-5 is to place values on the limits $\bar{u}_{*\text{lam}}$ and $\bar{u}_{*\text{t}}$. This is done by following von Kármán [24], who stipulated for the velocity profile: (1) a laminar sublayer between the limits $0 \leqq y^* \leqq 5$ where $y^* = \rho\sqrt{\tau(0)/\rho}\, y/\mu$, whence $u^* = y^*$, where

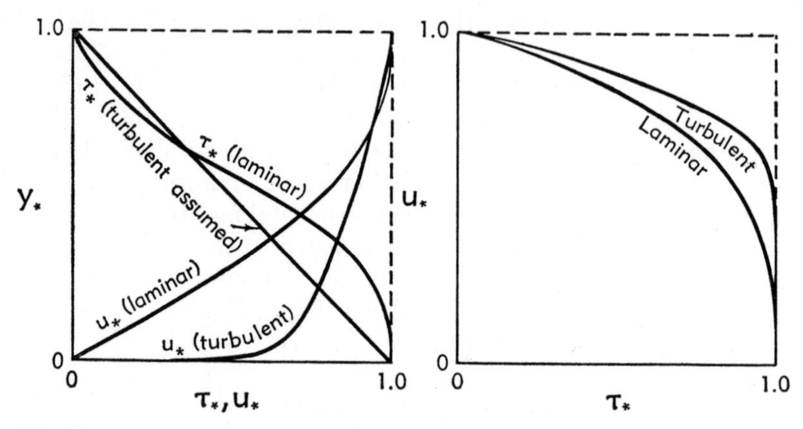


Fig. F,11a. Velocity and shear distributions for laminar and turbulent flow.

$u^* = u/\sqrt{\tau(0)/\rho}$; and (2) a transition or buffer zone between the limits $5 \leqq y^* \leqq 30$ and following the law $u^* = 5[1 + \ln (y^*/5)]$.[1] Therefore,

$$\bar{u}_{*\text{lam}} = 5\sqrt{\frac{c_f}{2}} \tag{11-8}$$

and

$$\bar{u}_{*\text{t}} = 5(1 + \ln 6)\sqrt{\frac{c_f}{2}} \tag{11-9}$$

[1] A more significant velocity profile that fits the flow all the way to the wall is given by van Driest [26].)

$$u* = \int_0^{y*} \frac{2dy*}{1 + \sqrt{1 + 4k^2 y*^2[1 - \exp(-y*/A*)]^2}}$$

in which $A* = 26$. Now

$$\frac{\epsilon}{\mu} = \left[\frac{1}{(\partial u*/\partial y*)}\right] - 1$$

so that for small $y*$

$$\frac{\epsilon}{\mu} \to \frac{k^2}{A*^2}\, y*^4$$

Thus the ratio of the turbulent to the molecular momentum transport coefficient starts out as $y*^4$.

since $\sqrt{\tau(0)/\rho} = u_e \sqrt{c_f/2}$. Because these velocity profile assumptions are based on the incompressible flow experiments of Nikuradse [23], the present development is essentially for incompressible flow of gases, although, as demonstrated later, compressibility will not alter the results appreciably.

The first term of Eq. 11-5 becomes, with the aid of Eq. 11-8,

$$2Pr_{\text{lam}} \int_0^{\bar{u}_{*\text{lam}}} \bar{u}_* d\bar{u}_* = Pr_{\text{lam}} \bar{u}_*^2 = 25 \frac{c_f}{2} Pr_{\text{lam}} \tag{11-10}$$

Since

$$Pr_{\text{m}} = c_p \frac{\mu + \epsilon_\mu}{k + \epsilon_k} = \frac{\mu + \epsilon_\mu}{\dfrac{\mu}{Pr_{\text{lam}}} + \dfrac{\epsilon_\mu}{Pr_{\text{t}}}} \tag{11-11}$$

and

$$\mu + \epsilon_\mu = \frac{\tau}{\partial \bar{u}/\partial y} \tag{11-12}$$

it will be found that the second term of Eq. 11-5 may be written, through the use of Eq. 11-8 and 11-9, as

$$2 \int_{\bar{u}_{*\text{lam}}}^{\bar{u}_{*\text{t}}} Pr_{\text{m}} \bar{u}_* d\bar{u}_* = 2 \times 25 \frac{c_f}{2} Pr_{\text{t}} \ln\left(5 \frac{Pr_{\text{lam}}}{Pr_{\text{t}}} + 1\right) + 2 \times 25 \frac{c_f}{2} Pr_{\text{t}} \int_1^6 \frac{\ln (y^*/5)}{\dfrac{Pr_{\text{t}}}{Pr_{\text{lam}}} - 1 + \dfrac{y^*}{5}} d\left(\frac{y^*}{5}\right) \tag{11-13}$$

Now, the integral on the right-hand side of Eq. 11-13 cannot be evaluated in closed form; however, it can be expressed accurately, according to numerical calculation, by

$$\int_1^6 \frac{\ln (y^*/5)}{\dfrac{Pr_{\text{t}}}{Pr_{\text{lam}}} - 1 + \dfrac{y^*}{5}} d\left(\frac{y^*}{5}\right) \cong \frac{\ln 6}{2} \ln \left[\frac{\frac{3}{4}\left(\frac{Pr_{\text{t}}}{Pr_{\text{lam}}} - 1\right) + 6}{\frac{3}{4}\left(\frac{Pr_{\text{t}}}{Pr_{\text{lam}}} - 1\right) + 1}\right] \tag{11-14}$$

for $-1 \leqq Pr_{\text{t}}/Pr_{\text{lam}} - 1 \leqq \infty$.

Next, Eq. 11-7 is substituted into the last two terms of Eq. 11-5, and the integrals are obtained by expanding the integrands by means of the binomial theorem and obtaining the limit of the sum of the integrated terms. The result can be represented accurately by

$$Pr_{\text{t}} \left[1 - \bar{u}_{*\text{t}}^2 + \frac{\pi^2}{6} \frac{2}{K} \sqrt{\frac{c_f}{2}} (1 - Pr_{\text{t}})\right] \tag{11-15}$$

for $Pr_{\text{t}} \to 1$, and by

$$Pr_{\text{t}} \left\{1 - \bar{u}_{*\text{t}}^2 + \frac{2}{K} \sqrt{\frac{c_f}{2}} (1 - Pr_{\text{t}}) \left[\frac{\pi^2}{6} + \frac{3}{2} (1 - Pr_{\text{t}})\right]\right\} \tag{11-16}$$

for $0.7 \leqq Pr_t \leqq 1$, where the term $\frac{3}{2}(1 - Pr_t)$ is a numerical approximation.

Collecting Eq. 11-10, 11-13, 11-14, and 11-16 into Eq. 11-5 gives finally, for the recovery factor:

$$r = Pr_t\left[1 + \frac{2}{K}\sqrt{\frac{c_f}{2}}(1 - Pr_t)\left[\frac{\pi^2}{6} + \frac{3}{2}(1 - Pr_t)\right]\right.$$
$$+ 25\frac{c_f}{2}\left\{\left(\frac{Pr_{\mathrm{lam}}}{Pr_t} - 1\right) + 2\ln\left[1 + \frac{5}{6}\left(\frac{Pr_{\mathrm{lam}}}{Pr_t} - 1\right)\right]\right.$$
$$\left.\left. + (\ln 6)\ln\left[1 + \frac{7}{8}\left(\frac{Pr_{\mathrm{lam}}}{Pr_t} - 1\right)\right] - (\ln 6)\ln\left[1 + \frac{1}{4}\left(\frac{Pr_{\mathrm{lam}}}{Pr_t} - 1\right)\right]\right\}\right] \tag{11-17}$$

This formula should be valid for normal gases.

In order to utilize Eq. 11-17 to calculate the recovery factor, one requires numerical values for the molecular and turbulent Prandtl numbers. While data on the molecular Prandtl number are readily available in the NBS-NACA Tables of Thermal Properties of Gases, yet only a few direct measurements [*27,28*] of the turbulent Prandtl number have been made, and the accuracy of such measurements is apparently not sufficient to establish a definitive value for the turbulent Prandtl number.

Since it is much simpler to take temperature recovery measurements than direct turbulent Prandtl number measurements, Eq. 11-17 might well be used to determine indirectly the turbulent Prandtl number from measured turbulent recovery factors. However, it is first necessary to state that, while the above-derived expression for recovery factor is essentially an incompressible flow formula, the measurements of recovery factors are obtained only with supersonic flows on insulated surfaces [*20,29,30*]. Certainly, it is only for supersonic flow that the recovery factor has value. Fortunately, it appears from measurements with air that the turbulent recovery factor is fairly independent of Mach number and Reynolds number. Now, it is expected that the turbulent Prandtl number should also be independent of Mach number and Reynolds number. Hence, if Eq. 11-17 is correct, there should be one value of $Pr_t$ such that $r = \text{const}$. Indeed, it is seen in Fig. F,11b that for $r = \text{const}$, the turbulent Prandtl number must be 0.86, using incompressible flow friction coefficients. Furthermore, it is of great interest to observe that the corresponding recovery factor has a theoretical value of 0.88, which checks well with experiment. A laminar Prandtl number of 0.71, corresponding to 100°F for air, was used in the calculations. Squire's $Pr^{\frac{1}{3}}$ is also indicated in Fig. F,11b.

Since the turbulent Prandtl number is a molar characteristic of the turbulent motion itself, it appears that the value $Pr_t = 0.86$ should apply to all fluids.

In order to show that Eq. 11-17 gives recovery factors which are also independent of Mach number, at least in the first approximation, it is necessary to introduce the Mach number into the friction coefficient. Thus, assuming that Eq. 11-17 can be used to represent compressible flow if wall conditions are substituted into the equation, the factor

$$\left(1 + r\frac{\gamma - 1}{2} M_e^2\right)$$

should be multiplied into $c_f/2$ wherever $c_f/2$ appears. It must then be remembered that the friction coefficient becomes the compressible flow coefficient.

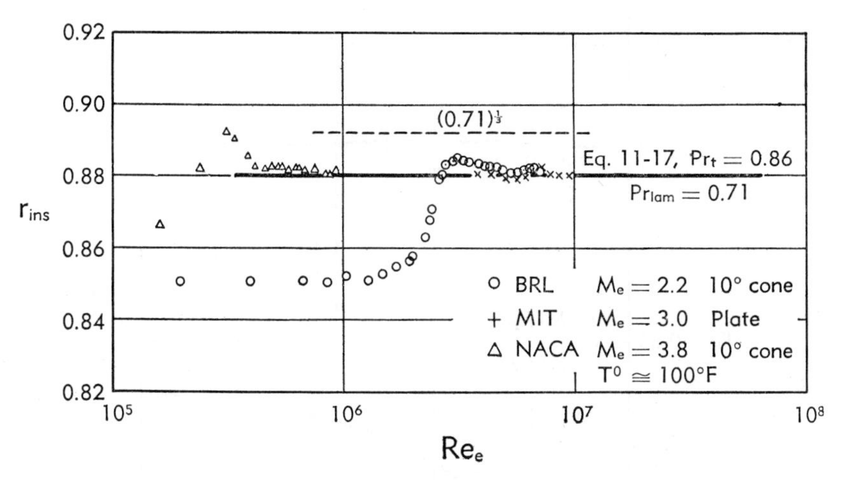


Fig. F,11b. Recovery factor for a turbulent boundary layer on a flat plate as a function of Reynolds number for air. $M_e = 0$.

That the turbulent recovery factor given by Eq. 11-17 is essentially independent of Mach number for a flat plate (or a cone) in a wind tunnel with $Re = 10^7$ is seen in Fig. F,11c, in which some data of MIT and NACA (1 by 3-ft No. 1 tunnel) are also plotted. The values of $c_f/2$ used for the calculation were obtained from the data of Coles [*31*]. This apparent independence further justifies the analysis leading to Eq. 11-17. Fig. F,11d indicates the turbulent recovery factor variation during free flight. The difference between Fig. F,11c and F,11d is due to the difference between the molecular Prandtl number variation in wind tunnel and free flight. The NBS-NACA molecular Prandtl number variation was assumed [*5*]. The laminar flow recovery factors are shown in Fig. F,11c and F,11d for the purpose of comparison.

Owing to the method of calculation, it is hardly expected that the curves of Fig. F,11c and F,11d are meaningful at the higher Mach numbers. Indeed, more information on the laminar sublayer and transition region in supersonic flow is necessary for further progress.

The effect of heat transfer on the turbulent recovery factor can be estimated by substitution of the factor $T_w/T_e$ for the above factor

$$\left(1 + r\frac{\gamma - 1}{2} M_e^2\right)$$

The same trend as with Mach number is found to appear. Thus $r$ is essentially independent of $T_w/T_e$ also.

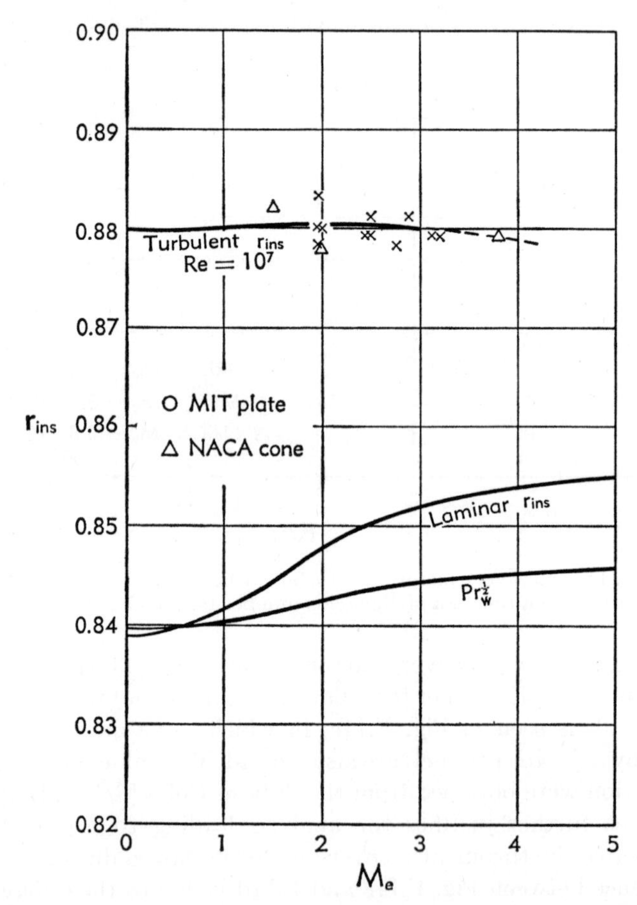


Fig. F,11c. Recovery factor for a turbulent boundary layer on a flat plate in air in a wind tunnel as a function of Mach number. $T_0$ = 100°F.

*Reynolds analogy factor.* Another item that must be known before a heat transfer calculation can be made is the Reynolds analogy factor, so called because it was Reynolds who concluded in 1874 that heat transfer was proportional to fluid friction. The general expression for the Reynolds analogy factor is [22]

$$s = S(1) = \int_0^1 Pr_m \cdot \exp\left(-\int_{\tau(0)}^{\tau} (1 - Pr)\frac{d\tau}{\tau}\right) d\bar{u}_* \qquad (11\text{-}18)$$

in which $Pr$ varies across the boundary layer.

An algebraic formula can be derived for $s$ if the same assumptions concerning velocity and shear distribution are stipulated as in the de-

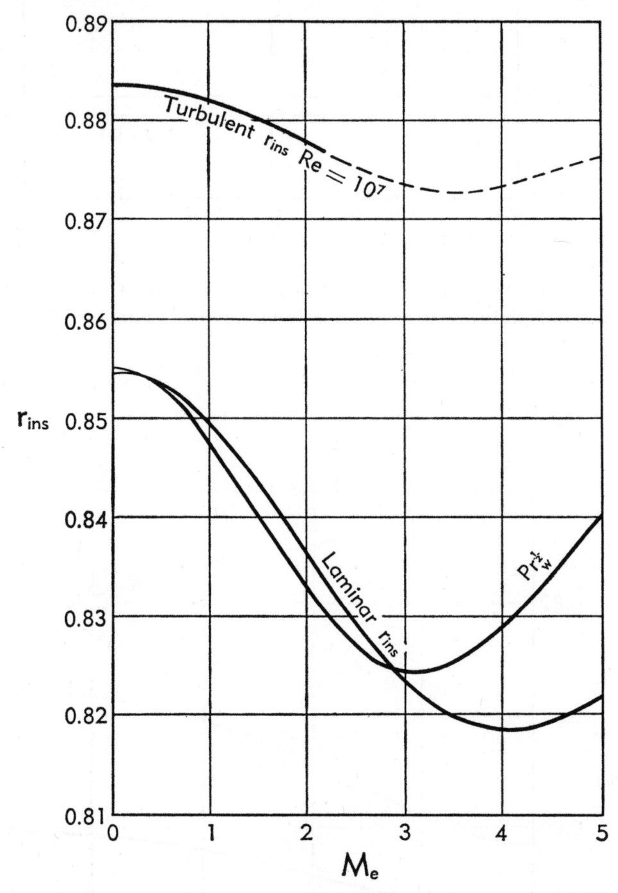


Fig. F,11d. Recovery factor for a turbulent boundary layer on a flat plate in free flight in air as a function of Mach number. $T_e$ = 400°R.

velopment of the recovery factor $r$. The derivation is considerably simpler than for $r$ and leads to

$$s = Pr_t\left[1 + 5\sqrt{\frac{c_f}{2}}\left\{\frac{1}{5K}(1 - Pr_t)\left[\frac{\pi^2}{6} + \frac{3}{2}(1 - Pr_t)\right]\right.\right.$$
$$\left.\left. + \left(\frac{Pr_{lam}}{Pr_t} - 1\right) + \ln\left[1 + \frac{5}{6}\left(\frac{Pr_{lam}}{Pr_t} - 1\right)\right]\right\}\right] \qquad (11\text{-}19)$$

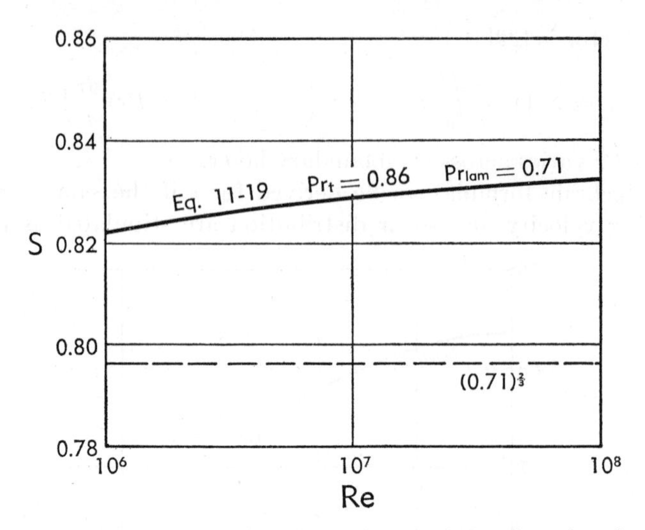


Fig. F,11e. Reynolds analogy factor for a turbulent boundary layer on a flat plate in air as a function of Reynolds number. $M_e = 0$.

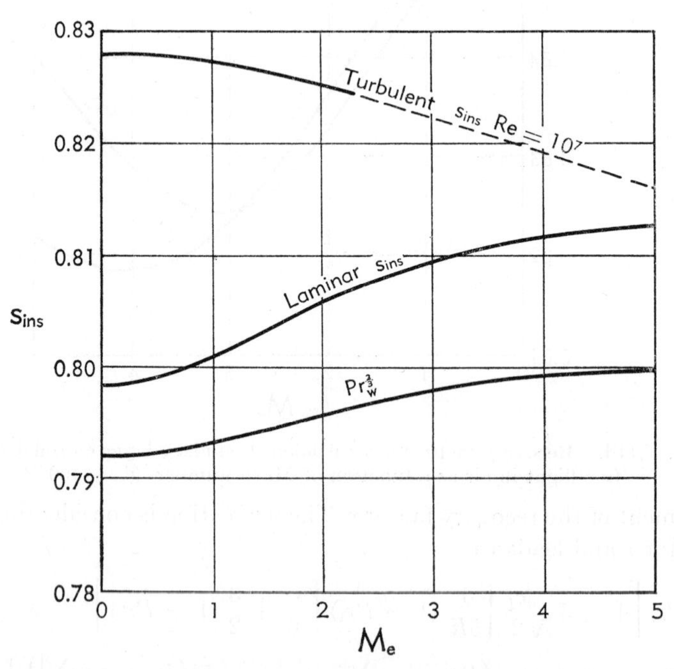


Fig. F,11f. Reynolds analogy factor for a turbulent boundary layer on a flat plate in air in a wind tunnel as a function of Mach number. $T_0 = 100°F$.

valid for $0.7 \leqq Pr_t \leqq 1$. This formula reduces to von Kármán's formula when it is assumed that $Pr_t = 1$. For $Pr_{lam} = Pr_t = 1$, then $s = 1$, which gives the basic Reynolds analogy, viz. $St = c_f/2$.

The turbulent Prandtl number of 0.86, obtained above by making Eq. 11-19 compatible with experiment, should be used in Eq. 11-19.

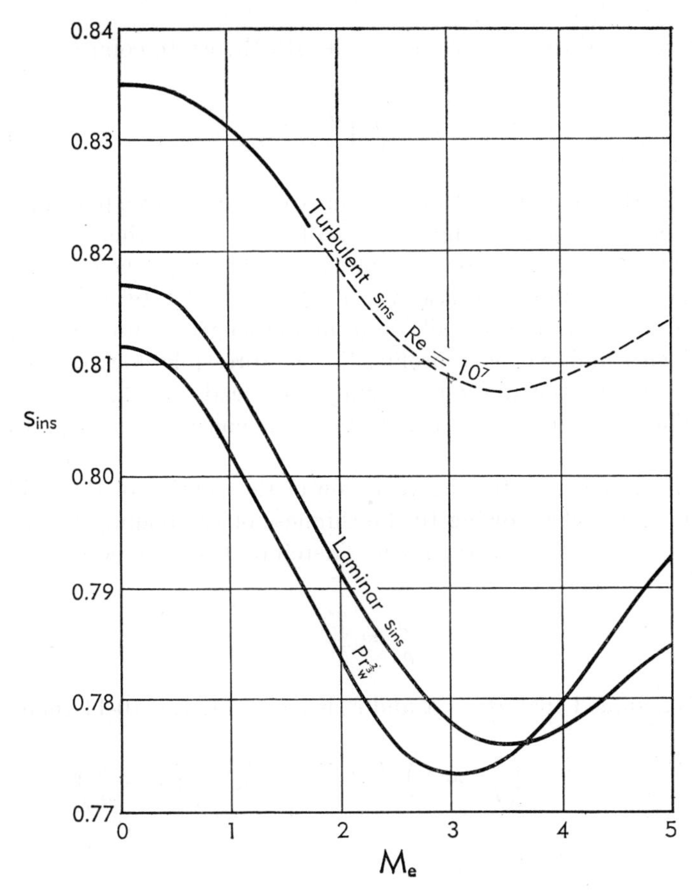


Fig. F,11g. Reynolds analogy factor for a turbulent boundary layer on a flat plate in free flight in air as a function of Mach number. $T_e = 400°R$.

Fig. F,11e shows the effect of Reynolds number on $s$ for air at low speed (incompressible flow), using $Pr_t = 0.86$ and $Pr_{lam} = 0.71$. Colburn's [32] $Pr^{\frac{2}{3}}$ is also plotted in this figure.

Fig. F,11f and F,11g indicate that the effect of compressibility on $s$ for moderate heating or cooling of flat plates (or cones) in a wind tunnel and in free flight is small.

It appears that for air a reasonable value for $s$ is 0.825.

*Local skin friction coefficient.* Analytically, it would be desirable to obtain from Eq. 10-8 a shear distribution across the turbulent boundary layer. However, the situation is complicated by the presence of the eddy viscosity $\epsilon_\mu$, which is a function of the eddying process itself, rather than a function of temperature like the molecular viscosity $\mu$. As a result, the simplest procedure to calculate the wall shear is to use the von Kármán integral method based upon a velocity profile obtained from the Prandtl mixing-length theory.

Application of the Prandtl mixing-length theory to compressible flow leads to [21]

$$\tau = \bar{\rho} l^2 \left(\frac{d\bar{u}}{dy}\right)^2 \tag{11-20}$$

in which $l$ is the mixing length analogous to the mean free path in kinetic theory. Near the wall, one may assume that $l = Ky$ where $K$ is a constant equal to about 0.40; however, away from the wall, one might assume the von Kármán similarity law, viz. $l = -K(d\bar{u}/dy)/(d^2\bar{u}/dy^2)$. For incompressible flow near the wall, both mixing-length assumptions lead to the semilogarithmic velocity profile. For compressible flow, on the other hand, the use of the different assumptions leads to slightly different results. The shear stress $\tau$ is usually taken as constant and equal to the wall value $\tau_w$.

In order to account for the variation of the density of the fluid, it is first remembered that, owing to the thinness of the boundary layer, the pressure is constant across the layer. Therefore, from the perfect gas law, when $\overline{\rho' T'}$ is neglected,

$$\frac{\bar{\rho}}{\rho_w} = \frac{T_w}{\bar{T}} \tag{11-21}$$

Next it is assumed that $Pr = 1$ and $c_p$ is constant. Eq. 10-11 then yields

$$\frac{\bar{T}}{T_e} = \frac{T_w}{T_e} - \left(\frac{T_w}{T_e} - 1\right)\frac{\bar{u}}{u_e} + \frac{\gamma - 1}{2} M_e^2 \frac{\bar{u}}{u_e}\left(1 - \frac{\bar{u}}{u_e}\right) \tag{11-22}$$

or, upon rearrangement,

$$\frac{\bar{T}}{T_w} = 1 + \left[\left(1 + \frac{\gamma - 1}{2} M_e^2\right)\frac{T_e}{T_w} - 1\right]\frac{\bar{u}}{u_e} - \frac{\gamma - 1}{2} M_e^2 \frac{T_e}{T_w}\left(\frac{\bar{u}}{u_e}\right)^2 \tag{11-23}$$

Hence, upon substitution of Eq. 11-23 in Eq. 11-21, the density relation becomes

$$\frac{\bar{\rho}}{\rho_w} = \frac{1}{1 + B(\bar{u}/u_e)^2 - A(\bar{u}/u_e)^2} \tag{11-24}$$

where

$$A^2 = \frac{\dfrac{\gamma - 1}{2} M_e^2}{T_w/T_e} \quad \text{and} \quad B = \frac{1 + \dfrac{\gamma - 1}{2} M_e^2}{T_w/T_e} - 1 \tag{11-25}$$

Finally, taking $l = Ky$ and putting Eq. 11-24 into Eq. 11-20, with $\tau = \tau_w$, yields the following velocity distribution result:

$$\frac{1}{A}\sin^{-1}\frac{2A^2\frac{\bar{u}}{u_e} - B}{(B^2 + 4A^2)^{\frac{1}{2}}} + \frac{1}{A}\sin^{-1}\frac{B}{(B^2 + 4A^2)^{\frac{1}{2}}} = \frac{1}{u_e}\sqrt{\frac{\tau_w}{\rho_w}}\left[F + \frac{1}{K}\ln\left(\sqrt{\frac{\tau_w}{\rho_w}}\frac{y}{\nu_w}\right)\right] \tag{11-26}$$

where $F$ is a constant and $\nu_w$, the kinematic viscosity at the wall, is introduced because of its influence in the laminar sublayer.

Eq. 11-24 and 11-26 can now in turn be substituted into the von Kármán momentum integral relation for a flat plate with zero pressure gradient, viz.

$$\tau_w = \frac{d}{dx}\int_0^\delta \bar{\rho}\bar{u}(u_e - \bar{u})dy \tag{11-27}$$

to yield a complicated integral which, however, can be expanded into a series by means of integration by parts. Upon neglect of terms of higher order, the resulting series can be approximated by a simple expression which leads to an engineering formula for the local skin friction coefficient in terms of Reynolds number, Mach number, and wall-to-free stream temperature ratio when the final constant involving $F$ is adjusted to reduce the formula to the von Kármán friction law for incompressible flow. In this way van Driest [*21*] obtained the formula

$$\frac{0.242}{Ac_f^{\frac{1}{2}}(T_w/T_e)^{\frac{1}{2}}}(\sin^{-1}\alpha + \sin^{-1}\beta) = 0.41 + \log(Re \cdot c_f) - \left(\frac{1}{2} + n\right)\log\left(\frac{T_w}{T_e}\right) \tag{11-28}$$

where

$$\alpha = \frac{2A^2 - B}{(B^2 + 4A^2)^{\frac{1}{2}}} \quad \text{and} \quad \beta = \frac{B}{(B^2 + 4A^2)^{\frac{1}{2}}}$$

and $n$ is the exponent in the viscosity law $\mu = \text{const} \cdot T^n$. For air, the exponent $n$ ranges from 0.76 at ordinary room temperature to 0.5 at higher temperatures.

If, now, one assumes the similarity law for mixing length, viz. $l = -K(d\bar{u}/dy)/(d^2\bar{u}/dy^2)$, instead of $l = Ky$, then, following the same procedure given above, one obtains

$$\frac{0.242}{Ac_f^{\frac{1}{2}}(T_w/T_e)^{\frac{1}{2}}}(\sin^{-1}\alpha + \sin^{-1}\beta) = 0.41 + \log(Re \cdot c_f) - n\log\frac{T_w}{T_e} \tag{11-29}$$

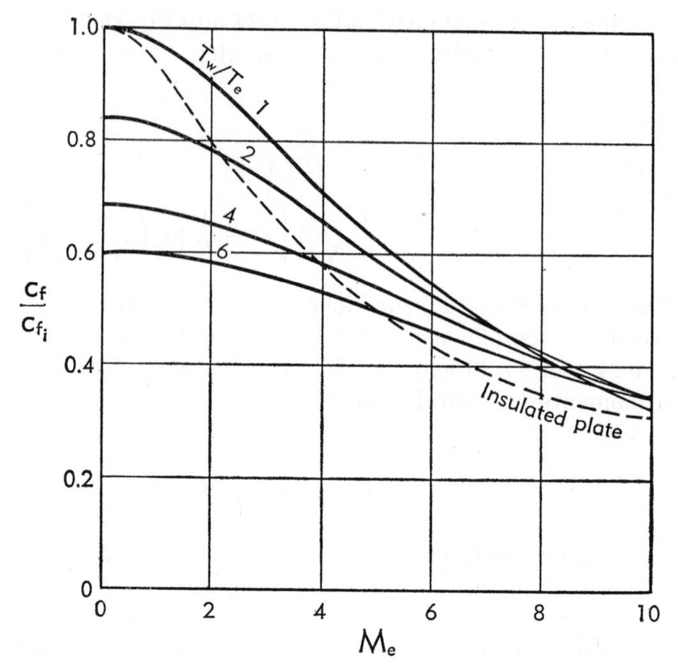


Fig. F,11h. Effect of heat transfer and Mach number on local skin friction coefficient according to Eq. 11-28 for a Reynolds number of $10^7$.

which is different from Eq. 11-28 by the term $\frac{1}{2}\log(T_w/T_e)$. When the plate is insulated, Eq. 11-29 reduces to the formula derived by Wilson [33].

Other formulas are readily derivable. For example, Cope [34] held the density constant and equal to the wall value in Eq. 11-20, so that, with $l = Ky$, he obtained for the velocity profile

$$\frac{\bar{u}}{u_e} = \frac{1}{u_e}\sqrt{\frac{\tau_w}{\rho_w}}\left[F + \frac{1}{K}\ln\left(\sqrt{\frac{\tau_w}{\rho_w}}\frac{y}{\nu_w}\right)\right] \tag{11-30}$$

When the density is allowed to vary according to Eq. 11-24, the von Kármán integral (Eq. 11-27) then leads to the following expression:

$$\frac{0.242}{c_f^{\frac{1}{2}}(T_w/T_e)^{\frac{1}{2}}} = 0.41 + \log(Re \cdot c_f) - (1 + n)\log\frac{T_w}{T_e} \tag{11-31}$$

Cope originally derived this formula for the case of the insulated plate only, where

$$\frac{T_w}{T_e} = 1 + \frac{\gamma - 1}{2}M_e^2$$

i.e. $B = 0$ in Eq. 11-24.

The most simple approach (and the first attempted) was that used by von Kármán [35], who allowed the density to remain constant and equal to the wall value in both Eq. 11-20 (with $l = Ky$) and 11-27, i.e. throughout the entire analysis. One obtains, then, for the heat transfer case,

$$\frac{0.242}{c_f^{\frac{1}{2}}(T_w/T_e)^{\frac{1}{2}}} = 0.41 + \log\,(Re \cdot c_f) - n \log \frac{T_w}{T_e} \tag{11-32}$$

which differs from Eq. 11-31 by the factor log $(T_w/T_e)$. Von Kármán also originally derived his equation for the insulated-plate case, because he (like Cope later) desired to find the effect of speed, only, upon drag.

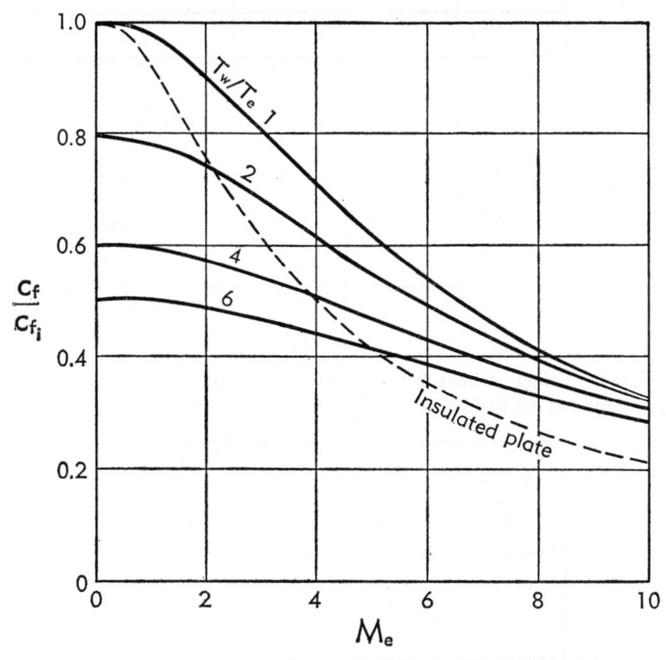


Fig. F,11i. Effect of heat transfer and Mach number on local skin friction coefficient according to Eq. 11-29 for a Reynolds number of $10^7$.

The general question that must now be answered is: Which of the above formulas is the most valid for engineering purposes? Although the question can best be answered by experimental data, a preliminary check on the form of the equations can be made upon observation of the effect of heat transfer $(T_w/T_e)$ on the local skin friction coefficient. Eq. 11-28, 11-29, 11-31, and 11-32 are plotted in Fig. F,11h, F,11i, F,11j, and F,11k where the ratio of the compressible to the incompressible flow coefficient for one Reynolds number and $n = 0.76$ is shown as a function of Mach number for various wall-to-free stream temperature ratios. It is immediately seen from Fig. F,11h and F,11i that, regardless of mixing-length theory assumed, Eq. 11-28 and 11-29 yield friction coefficients which are definite functions of Mach number for a constant wall temperature. On

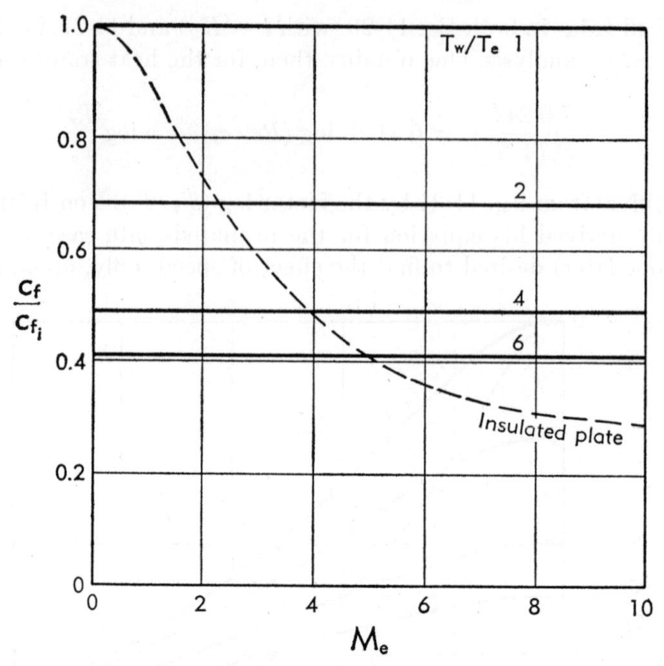


Fig. F,11j. Effect of heat transfer and Mach number on local skin friction coefficient according to Eq. 11-31 for a Reynolds number of $10^7$.

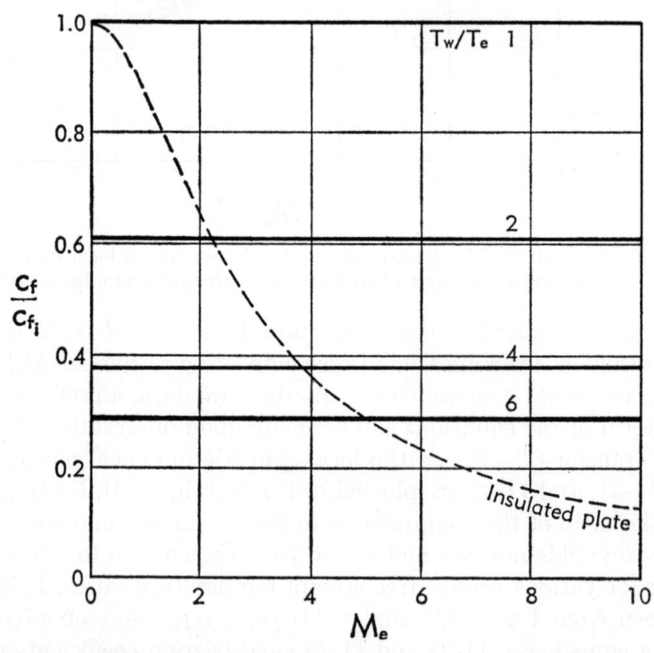


Fig. F,11k. Effect of heat transfer and Mach number on local skin friction coefficient according to Eq. 11-32 for a Reynolds number of $10^7$.

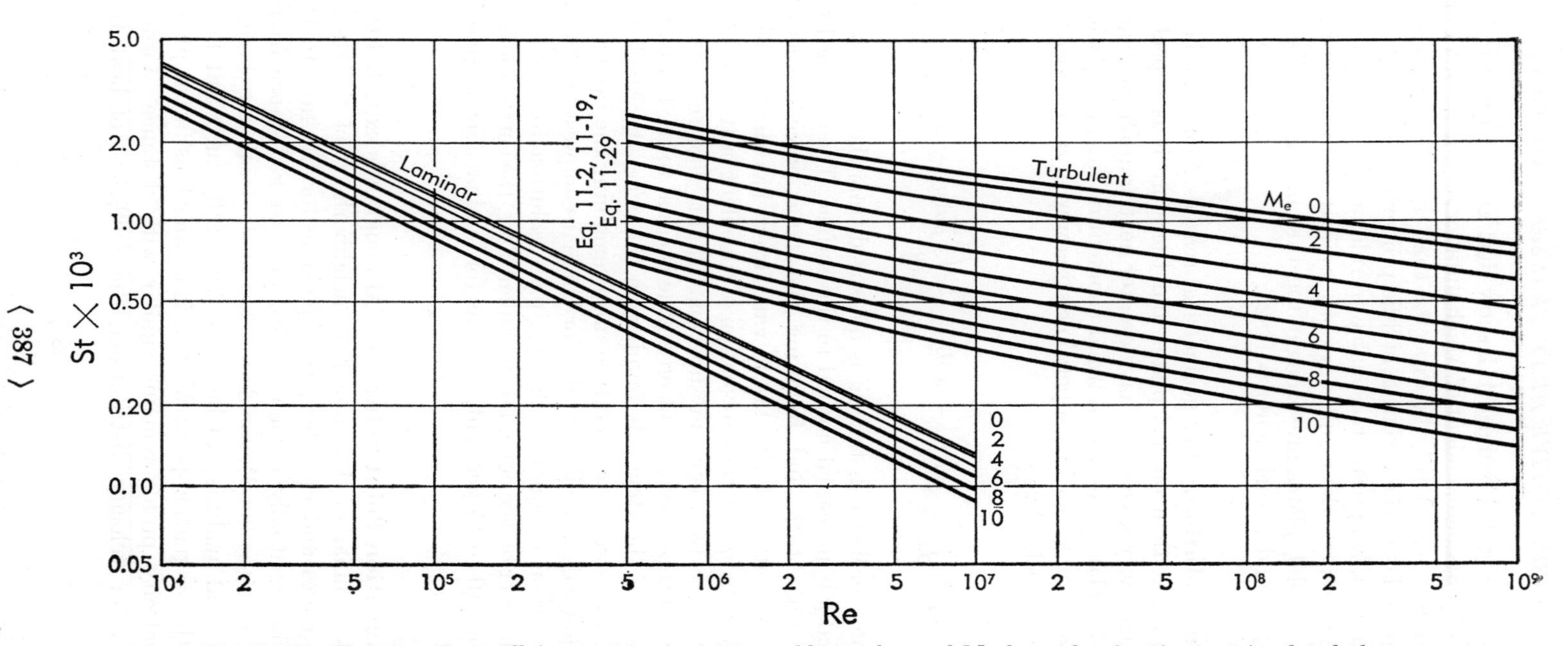


Fig. F,11l. Heat transfer coefficient as function of Reynolds number and Mach number for air on an insulated plate.

the other hand, Fig. F,11j and F,11k show that Eq. 11-31 and 11-32 yield friction coefficients independent of Mach number for a constant wall temperature. Since it can hardly be expected that the wall temperature has complete control over the variation of fluid properties, i.e. that dissipation can be neglected, it appears reasonable to rule out Eq. 11-31 and 11-32.

For completeness, the results for both laminar and turbulent flow for near-insulated flat plates are brought together in Fig. F,11l using Eq. 11-2 and 11-29 and $s$ (turbulent) = 0.825.

**F,12. Cone Solution.** For geometrical reasons, boundary layers are thinner on cones than on flat plates and therefore it is expected that turbulent boundary layers will have greater heat transfer coefficients for cones than for plates. The von Kármán momentum integral relation for a boundary layer on a cone in a supersonic stream with zero angle of attack and attached shock wave is

$$\tau_w = \frac{d}{dx}\int_0^\delta \overline{\rho u}(u_e - \bar{u})dy + \frac{1}{x}\int_0^\delta \overline{\rho u}(u_e - \bar{u})dy \tag{12-1}$$

in which the coordinate distance $x$ is measured from the cone apex along the cone and $y$ is measured normal to the surface. Then, using Eq. 12-1 instead of Eq. 11-27, and following the same procedure as carried out in the derivation of Eq. 11-28, van Driest has shown [*36*] that a simple rule exists for the transformation of turbulent heat transfer results from a flat plate to a cone in supersonic flight. The rule states that the local heat transfer coefficient on a cone is equal to the flat plate solution for one half the Reynolds number on the cone, the Mach number and wall-to-free stream temperature ratio remaining the same; thus the turbulent flow rule is similar to that for laminar compressible flow where the cone solution is equal to the flat plate solution for one-third the Reynolds number on the cone. For turbulent flow, the correction amounts to only about 10 to 15 per cent, whereas for laminar flow it amounts to 73 per cent.

**F,13. Stagnation Point Solution.** Although it is expected that the flow will be laminar in the immediate neighborhood of the stagnation region of spheres and cylinders, it is possible for the flow to become unstable and eventually turbulent with increasing distance from that region, owing to the low Reynolds number of the local flow there.

A theoretical analysis can be made for a fully turbulent boundary layer near the stagnation point when it is assumed, as in flat plate flow, that the velocity profile remains similar with distance. Assuming a $\frac{1}{7}$-power law for velocity distribution, the coefficient of heat transfer

$St_\infty$ in the formula

$$q_w = -St_\infty \rho_\infty U(h_r - h_w)$$

becomes [37]:

$$St_\infty = 0.042 \left(\frac{\beta D}{U}\right)^{\frac{4}{5}} \left(\frac{\rho_\infty u_\infty D}{\mu_\infty}\right)^{-\frac{1}{5}} \left(\frac{c_{pe}\mu_e}{k_e}\right)^{-\frac{2}{3}} \left(\frac{\rho_e}{\rho_\infty}\right)^{\frac{4}{5}} \left(\frac{\mu_e}{\mu_\infty}\right)^{\frac{1}{5}} \left(\frac{x}{D}\right)^{\frac{3}{5}} \quad (13\text{-}1)$$

for spheres. For cylinders, the constant is 0.040.

For an approximate calculation over the face of a sphere, the constant 0.042 may be apportioned linearly with $\beta$ to 0.030 for flat plates,

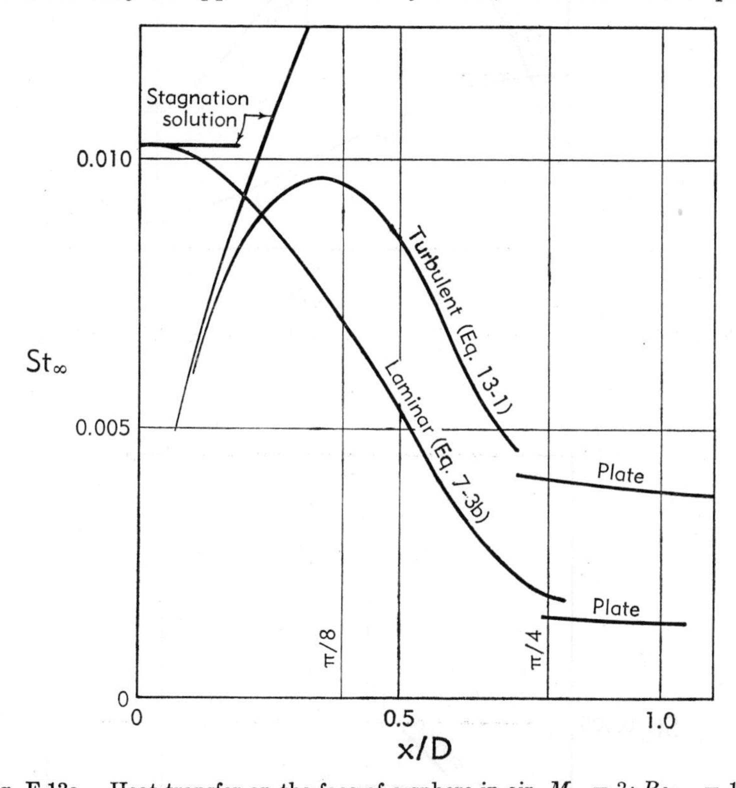


Fig. F,13a. Heat transfer on the face of a sphere in air. $M_\infty = 3$; $Re_{D_\infty} = 10^5$.

and the ratios $\rho_e/\rho_\infty$, $\mu_e/\mu_\infty$, as well as $\beta$ computed from Newtonian pressure calculations and isentropic expansion from the stagnation region. The heat transfer rate then becomes a maximum at about 40 degrees. Fig. F,13a, F,13b, and F,13c show the heat transfer on the face of a sphere in air with $M_\infty = 3$ and $Re_{D_\infty} = \rho_\infty UD/\mu_\infty = 10^5$, $10^6$, and $10^7$, respectively. Also shown in the figures are the variations of heat transfer for completely laminar flow using Eq. 7-3b. It is seen that the maximum turbulent heat transfer rate increases relative to the maximum laminar rate as Reynolds number increases.

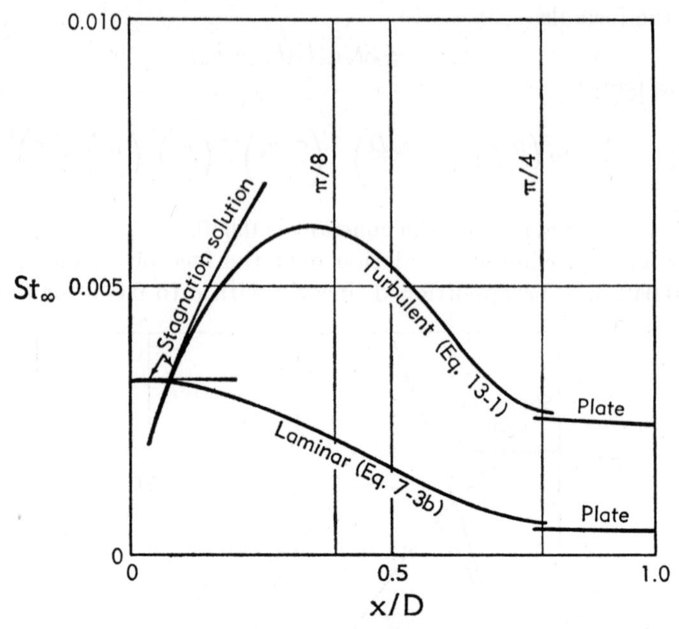


Fig. F,13b. Heat transfer on the face of a sphere in air. $M_\infty = 3$; $Re_{D\infty} = 10^6$.

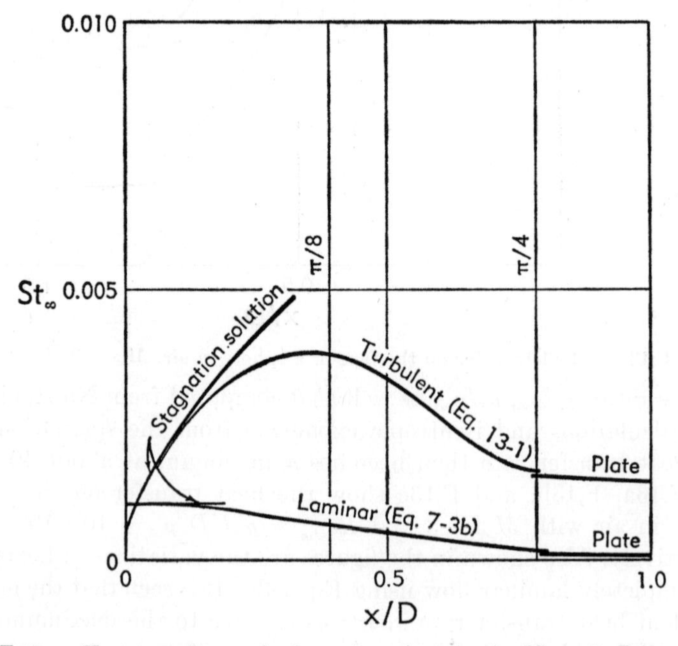


Fig. F,13c. Heat transfer on the face of a sphere in air. $M_\infty = 3$; $Re_{D\infty} = 10^7$.

**F,14. Effects of Variable Free Stream Pressure, Wall Temperature, Etc.** The effects of variable free stream pressure and variable wall temperature are generally qualitatively the same but relatively less for turbulent than for laminar boundary layers. Two references are Rubesin [*38*] for surface temperature variation and Clauser [*39*] for pressure gradients.

Fluid injection in the stream through the wall is effective in reducing heat transfer to the surface from the boundary layer. For example, Rubesin [*40*] has developed a theory for gas injection into a high speed turbulent boundary layer; comparison of the theory at Mach number zero with data of Mickley, et al. [*41*] shows good agreement. (For detailed discussion see Sec. *G*.)

**F,15. Rough Walls.** All of the aforementioned analyses had to do with smooth walls. However, the following formula, derived in the same manner as Eq. 11-28, will be indicative of local skin friction (and therefore heat transfer) on rough plates [*37*]:

$$\frac{0.242}{Ac_f^{\frac{1}{2}}(T_w/T_e)^{\frac{1}{2}}}(\sin^{-1}\alpha + \sin^{-1}\beta) = 1.40 + \log\left(\frac{x}{\epsilon}c_f^{\frac{1}{2}}\right) \qquad (15\text{-}1)$$

where $\epsilon$ is the plate roughness and $x$ is the distance from the plate leading edge. It is assumed, of course, that the roughness projections are great enough to disrupt the viscous influence of the wall and that the projections do not reach the sonic line. As with skin friction, heat transfer rates for rough plates should be significantly greater than for smooth plates.

**F,16. Status of Experimental Knowledge.**

*Skin friction.* Since heat transfer is proportional to skin friction, and since friction is apparently easier to measure than heat transfer, it is proper to glean first the experimental data on skin friction so that more data may be made available to verify the theory.

The data of Coles [*31*] and Korkegi [*42*] for local friction on insulated plates is plotted in Fig. F,16a. The data were obtained by direct force measurements. Also plotted are Eq. 11-28 and 11-29 for $n = 0.76$. Apparently both Eq. 11-28 and 11-29 are adequate for engineering purposes. However, for more precision when more definitive data are available, and assuming that Eq. 11-28 and 11-29 have the proper form, it may be suggested that an equation be written as follows:

$$\frac{0.242}{Ac_f^{\frac{1}{2}}(T_w/T_e)^{\frac{1}{2}}}(\sin^{-1}\alpha + \sin^{-1}\beta) = 0.41 + \log(Re \cdot c_f) - (p+n)\log\frac{T_w}{T_e} \qquad (16\text{-}1)$$

where $p$ is an arbitrary constant to be adjusted to the data.

The mean skin friction data of Sommer and Short [43] and Chapman and Kester [44] are plotted in Fig. F,16b. The former data were obtained from deceleration measurements of hollow cylinders in free flight, and therefore the wall-to-free stream temperature ratio remained low (ranging from 1.03 at Mach number 2.81 to 1.75 at Mach number 7). The latter data were the result of steady state, direct total force measurements of

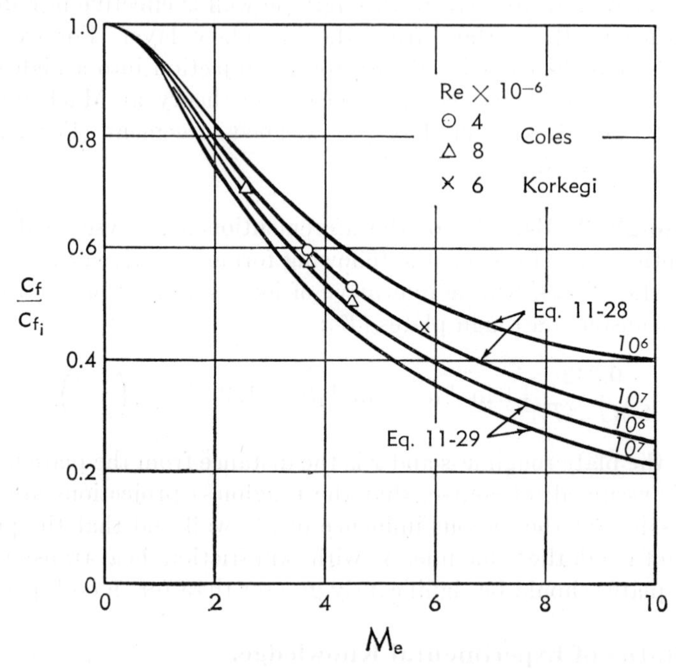


Fig. F,16a. Comparison of theory and experiment on local skin friction coefficient for turbulent boundary layers on insulated flat plates.

the cylinder of a cone-cylinder combination under zero heat transfer conditions. The mean skin friction equation, viz.

$$\frac{0.242}{AC_f^{\frac{1}{2}}(T_w/T_e)^{\frac{1}{2}}}(\sin^{-1}\alpha + \sin^{-1}\beta) = \log(Re \cdot C_f) - n \log\frac{T_w}{T_e} \quad (16\text{-}2)$$

corresponding to Eq. 11-29, is also plotted in Fig. F,16b for $n = 0.76$. It is readily apparent that Eq. 16-2 is verified and that the ruling out of Eq. 11-31 and 11-32 is justified.

It will be noted (see Fig. F,16a) that the data of Coles show an effect of Reynolds number as predicted by theory, whereas the data of Chapman and Kester yielded practically no effect of Reynolds number.

Although the above data of Sommer and Short were gathered for supersonic speeds, it should be pointed out that heat transfer effects on skin friction can be studied at low speeds without a supersonic wind tunnel. For example, when the Mach number is zero, Eq. 16-1 becomes

$$\frac{0.242}{c_f^{\frac{1}{2}}(T_w/T_e)^{\frac{1}{2}}}\frac{2}{B}(\sqrt{1+B}-1) = 0.41 + \log(Re \cdot c_f) - (p+n)\log\left(\frac{T_w}{T_e}\right) \tag{16-3}$$

in which $p = \frac{1}{2}$ for $l = Ky$ and $p = 0$ for $l = -K(d\bar{u}/dy)/(d^2\bar{u}/dy^2)$, but may be adjusted by the data. Experimental data under these conditions are apparently not available as yet.

*Heat transfer.* The necessary ingredients, viz. $r$, $s$, and $c_f$, have now been presented for the calculation of heat transfer $q_w$ from Eq. 11-1.

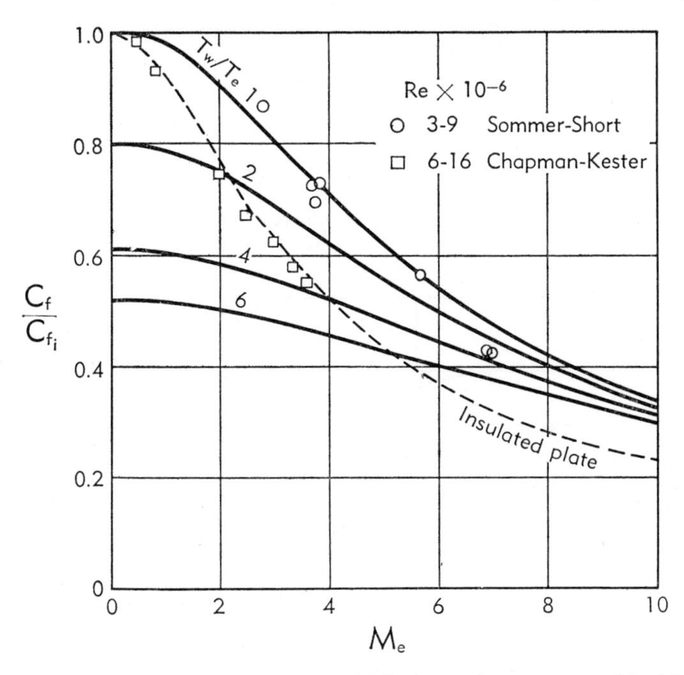


Fig. F,16b. Effect of heat transfer and Mach number on mean skin friction coefficient according to Eq. 16-2 for a Reynolds number of $10^7$.

They have also been checked against experiment. Therefore, it is expected that the resulting heat transfer calculations will be adequate for engineering purposes.

A final check on the theory may be made by measuring the heat transfer rate into or out of the boundary layer, thus obtaining the value of $St$ directly. In Fig. F,16c, F,16d, and F,16e are plotted some heat transfer coefficients obtained by Shoulberg and others [*45*] at the Massachusetts Institute of Technology for $M_e = 2.0$ at $T_w/T_e = 2.1$, $M_e = 2.5$ at $T_w/T_e = 2.7$, and $M_e = 3.0$ at $T_w/T_e = 3.3$. Theoretical curves, derived from Eq. 11-2, 11-19 (corrected for Mach number and heat transfer effect, say $s = 0.825$) and 11-29, are also drawn in the figures. Good agreement

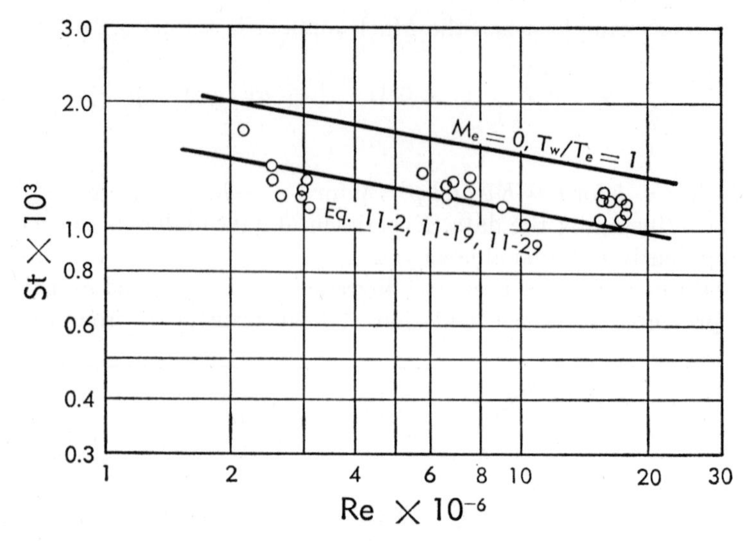


Fig. F,16c. Local heat transfer coefficient for a turbulent boundary layer on a heated flat plate. $M_e = 2.0$ and $T_w/T_e = 2.1$.

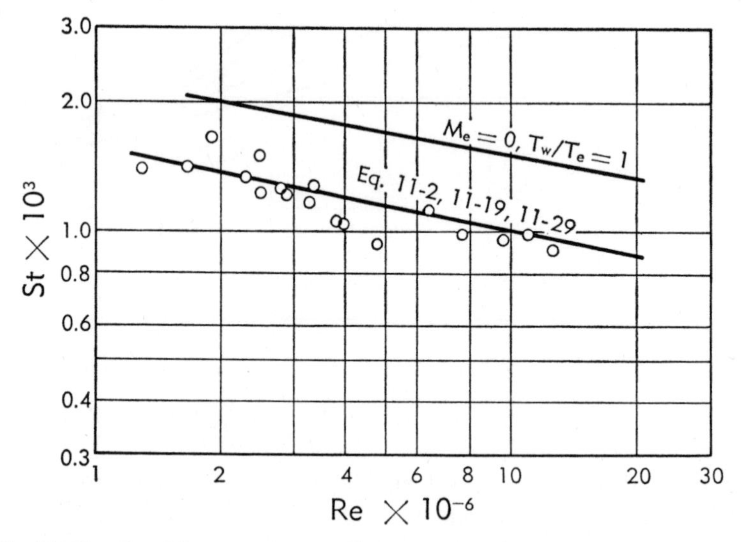


Fig. F,16d. Local heat transfer coefficient for a turbulent boundary layer on a heated flat plate. $M_e = 2.5$ and $T_w/T_e = 2.7$.

is noted, which seems to justify the entire heat transfer analysis. However, there is some variance in the experimental data of various laboratories [*45*,*46*,*47*,*48*], as seen in Fig. F,16f, and therefore additional definitive data is needed. Fig. F,16f represents the condition of moderate (small) heat transfer. Further check with greater heat transfer rates would be useful.

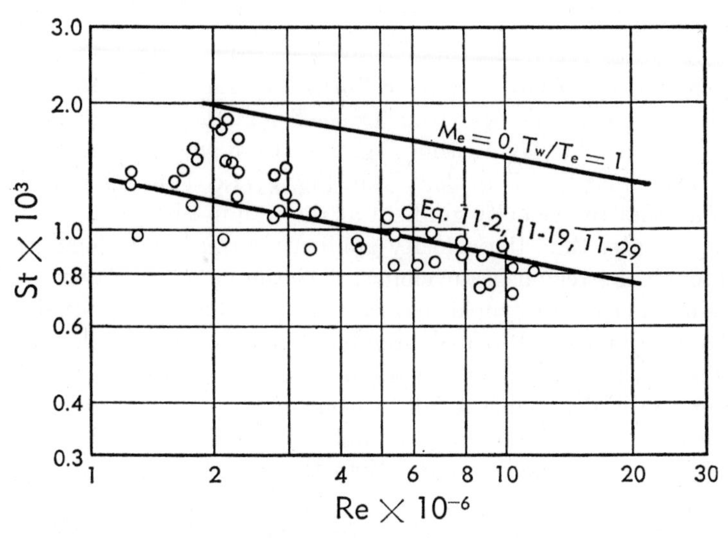


Fig. F,16e. Local heat transfer coefficient for a turbulent boundary layer on a heated flat plate. $M_e = 3.0$ and $T_w/T_e = 3.3$.

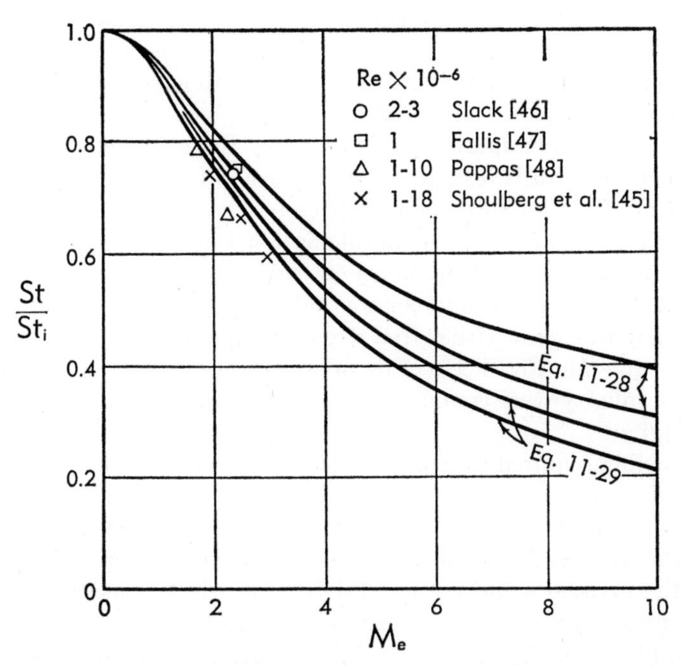


Fig. F,16f. Comparison of theory and experiment on local heat transfer coefficient for turbulent boundary layers on near-insulated flat plates.

*TRANSITION*

**F,17. Stability of the Laminar Boundary Layer and Relation to Transition.** That the heat transfer coefficient for turbulent flow is an order of magnitude (say 10 times) greater than the heat transfer coefficient for laminar flow is evident from Fig. F,11k. This difference is due to the fact that the velocity gradient at the wall in turbulent flow is considerably greater than the velocity gradient at the wall in laminar flow.

Although the region of development of the boundary layer between the minimum critical Reynolds number (neutral stability for infinitesimal disturbances) and the Reynolds number of fully turbulent flow is truly the transition region, yet in this discussion the expression "transition" will refer to the beginning of fully turbulent flow. It will be found that the transition Reynolds number so defined will be many times greater (again perhaps 10 times or more) than the minimum critical Reynolds number.

Since the heat transfer coefficients for turbulent flow are much greater than those for laminar flow, it is desirable to employ ways and means of delaying transition as much as possible. One method of delaying transition is to draw heat out of the laminar boundary layer at the wall. By this means the minimum critical Reynolds number is increased. For two-dimensional infinitesimal disturbances, it was demonstrated by Lees [*49*] that (1) with subsonic free stream flow, cooling the boundary layer was stabilizing, although the layer would always become unstable for sufficiently high Reynolds number, whereas (2) with supersonic free stream flow, cooling was again stabilizing, yet it was possible through sufficient practical cooling to maintain stability for any Reynolds number however large. When the wall is insulated, an increase in free stream Mach number is destabilizing for subsonic or supersonic flow. It was next shown by van Driest [*50*], through numerical calculation, that the region of complete stability (infinite Reynolds number) extended from Mach number 1 to 9 for air when the Prandtl number was taken as 0.75 and the Sutherland viscosity law was used with a free stream temperature of −67.6°F. The results are given in Fig. F,17a. The minimum critical Reynolds numbers other than infinity were computed using an estimation formula given by Lees in [*49*].

The cooling required for complete stabilization of the laminar boundary layer for air under various conditions is plotted in Fig. F,17b. The solid curves (the viscous solution) are the more accurate in that they include the viscous forces in the stability analysis, whereas the dotted curves (the inviscid solution) are stability criteria because they include only the pressure forces and not the viscous forces in the analysis. The condition ($Pr = 0.75$, $\rho_* \mu_* = 1$) should be used for ordinary wind tunnel work because at low temperatures the Prandtl number is approximately

0.75 and the viscosity is proportional to the temperature. The condition (variable $Pr$ (see Fig. F,5a), Sutherland law, $T_e = 400°R$) would best be used for slender bodies and thin surfaces in free flight. The condition ($Pr = 0.715$, $\rho_*^{\frac{1}{2}}\mu_* = 1$) is applicable to cones or blunt bodies where the

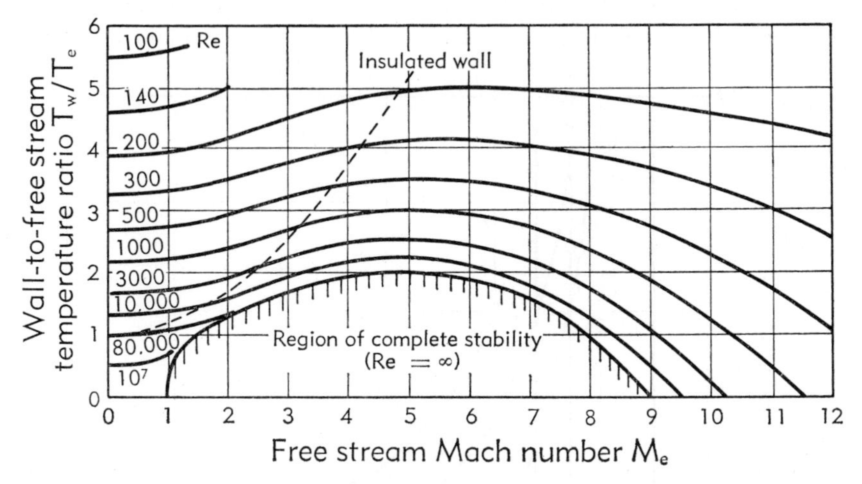


Fig. F,17a. Minimum critical Reynolds number as a function of free stream Mach number and wall-to-free stream temperature ratio. Prandtl number 0.75 and Sutherland viscosity law.

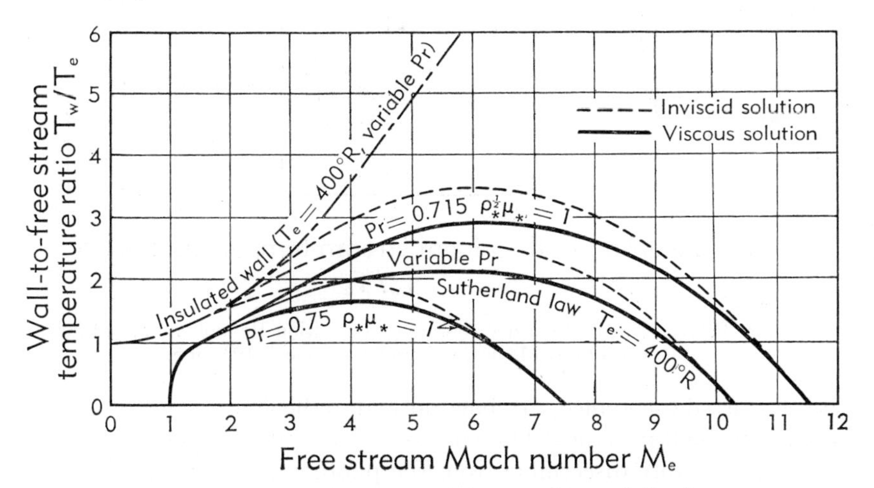


Fig. F,17b. Cooling required for complete stabilization of the laminar boundary layer for air.

ambient temperature (just outside the boundary layer) is great so that $Pr = 0.715$ and $\mu_* = T_*^{\frac{1}{2}}$. The calculations resulting in the above curves were based on analyses of the boundary layer as given in [*1*,*2*,*3*].

Since transition from a laminar to a turbulent boundary layer is a consequence of instability of the laminar flow, heating the boundary layer should promote, and cooling retard, transition. That this is the case has been shown experimentally by Scherrer [51], Higgins and Pappas [52], and Czarnecki and Sinclair [53] of the National Advisory Committee for Aeronautics, Eber [54] of the Naval Ordnance Laboratory, and van Driest and Boison [55,56] of North American Aviation, Inc. Plate F,17 is a set of photographs by van Driest and Boison showing the boundary layer when

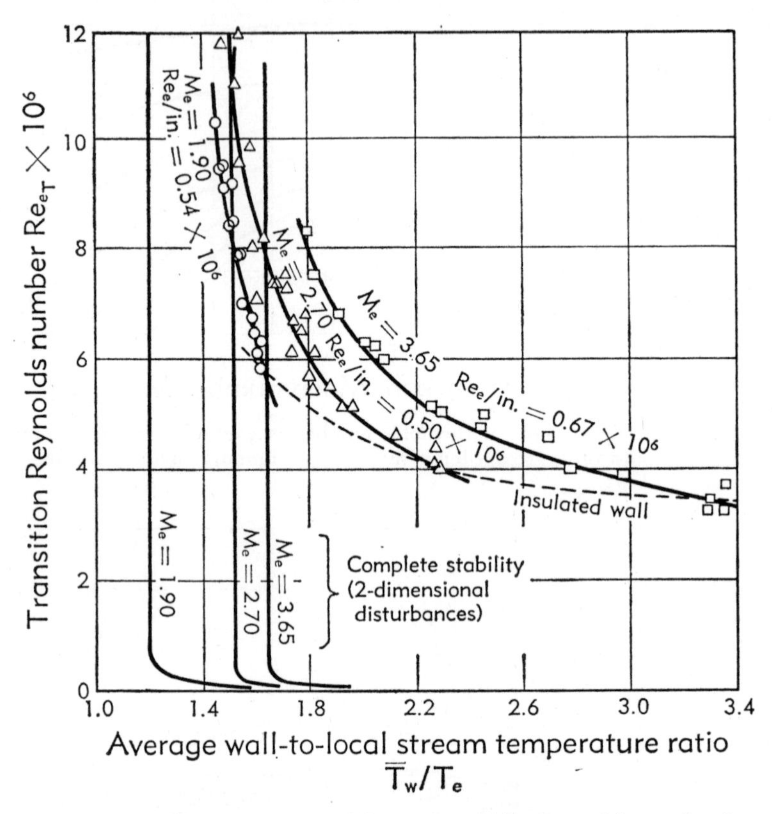


Fig. F,17c. Effect of surface cooling on transition Reynolds number for several local Mach numbers on a smooth 10° cone.

it is distorted (magnified) 20 times normal to the flow by means of a cylindrical lens built into the Schlieren system [57]. Transition and its delay by cooling is readily discernible from the photographs. The length of each photograph represents 16 inches of a smooth 10° (apex angle) cone, cooled internally with gaseous nitrogen; the left-hand edge of each photograph is located 4.5 inches from the apex of the cone. The Reynolds number per inch is 500,000. The effect of surface cooling [56] on the transition Reynolds number for several local Mach numbers on the cone in a low turbulence tunnel is indicated in Fig. F,17c. Lines of infinite minimum critical Reynolds number are also plotted in the figure. The dashed line of Fig. F,17c shows the effect of Mach number on transition for the zero heat transfer case. It is thus generally seen from the figure that transition seems to follow the same trends predicted for the stability of the laminar boundary layer, not only with cooling, but also with increase in Mach number for an insulated surface.

**F,18. Effect of Supply Tunnel Turbulence.** The data in Fig. F,17c are for a smooth model (10-micro-inches) in a wind tunnel with

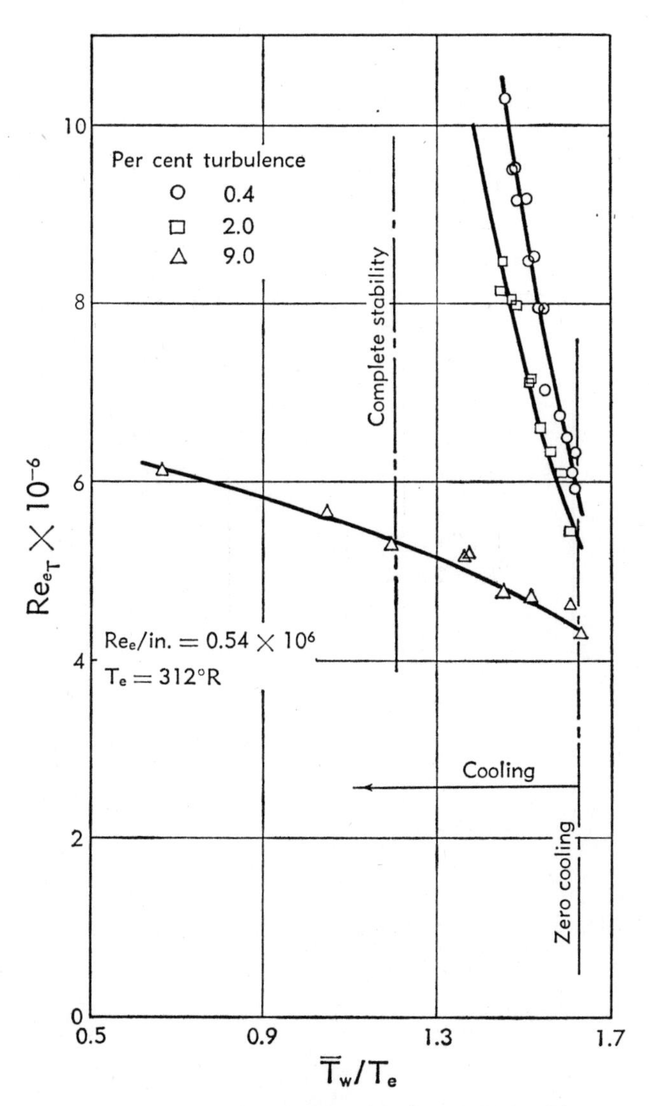


Fig. F,18a. Effect of supply turbulence on transition with cooling. $M_e = 1.90$; 10° smooth cone.

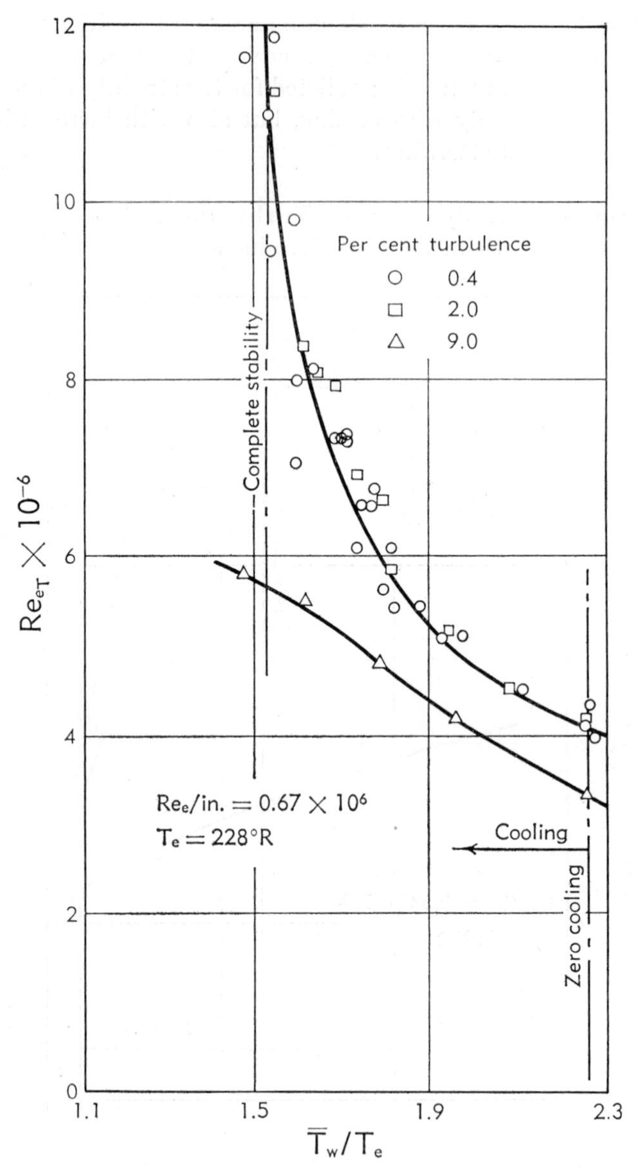


Fig. F,18b. Effect of supply turbulence on transition with cooling. $M_e = 2.70$; 10° smooth cone.

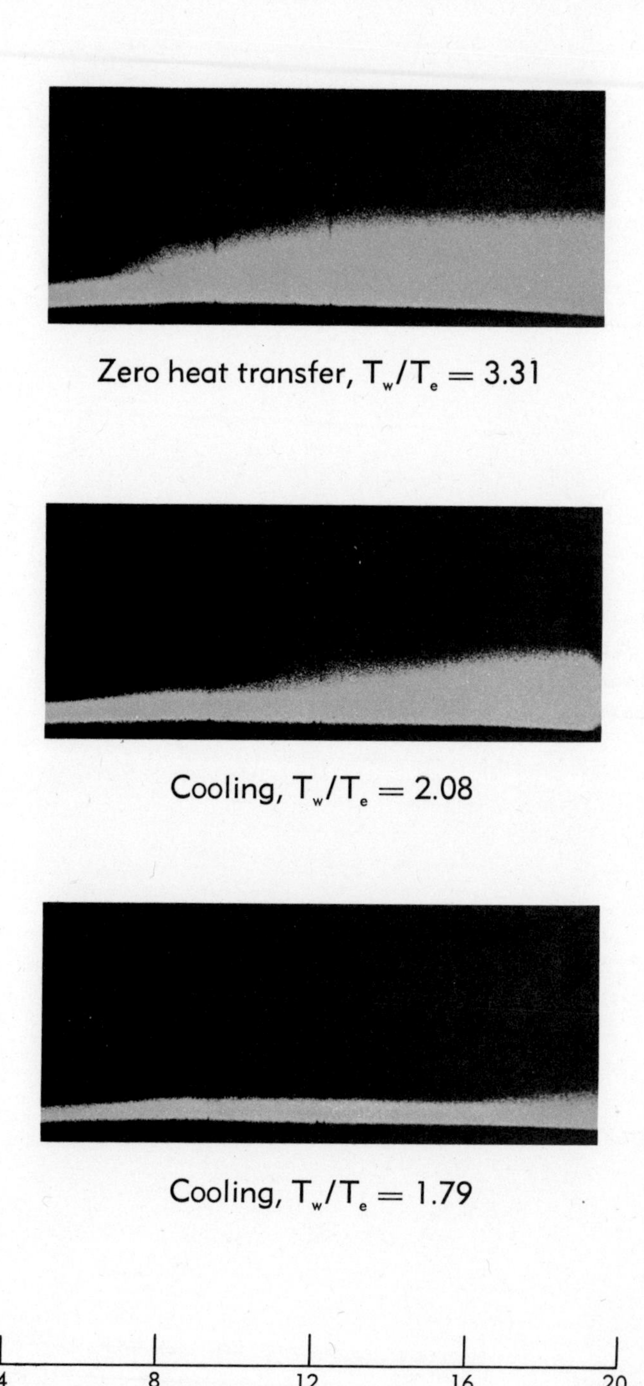


Plate F,17. Schlieren photographs showing delay of transition on a smooth $10^{\circ}$ cone by surface cooling. $M_e = 3.65$, $Re_e/\text{in.} = 0.50 \times 10^6$.

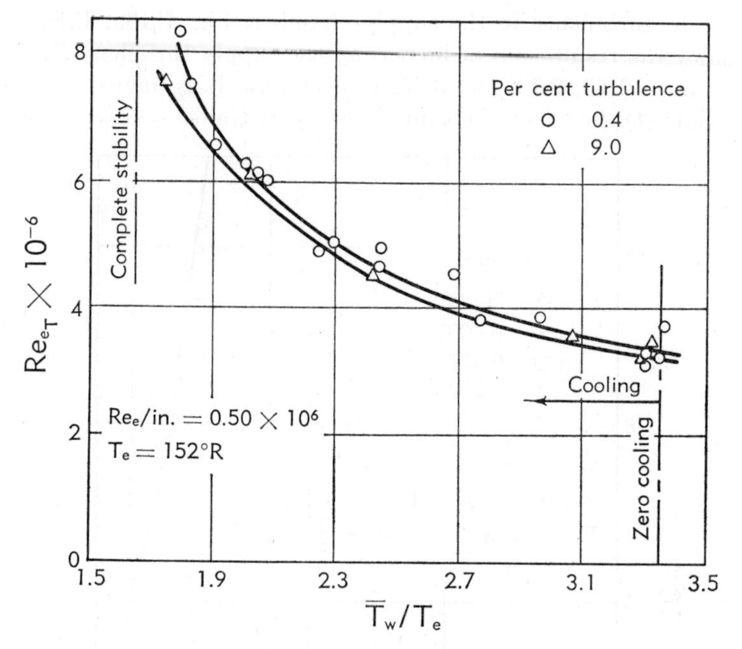


Fig. F,18c. Effect of supply turbulence on transition with cooling. $M_e = 3.65$; 10° smooth cone.

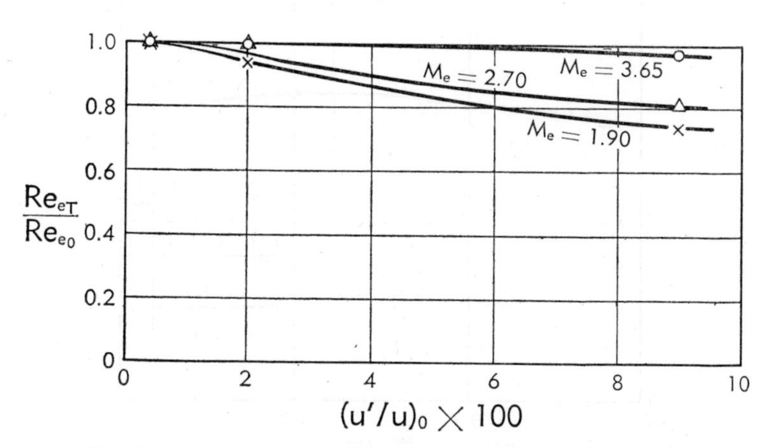


Fig. F,18d. Effect of supply-stream turbulence on transition as a function of Mach number. Zero heat transfer.

0.4 per cent turbulence in the supply chamber. Fig. F,18a, F,18b, and F,18c show the results [56] of increasing the supply turbulence to 9 per cent for $M_e = 1.90$, 2.70, and 3.65, respectively. It is immediately concluded that: (1) the effect of cooling in delaying transition decreases with

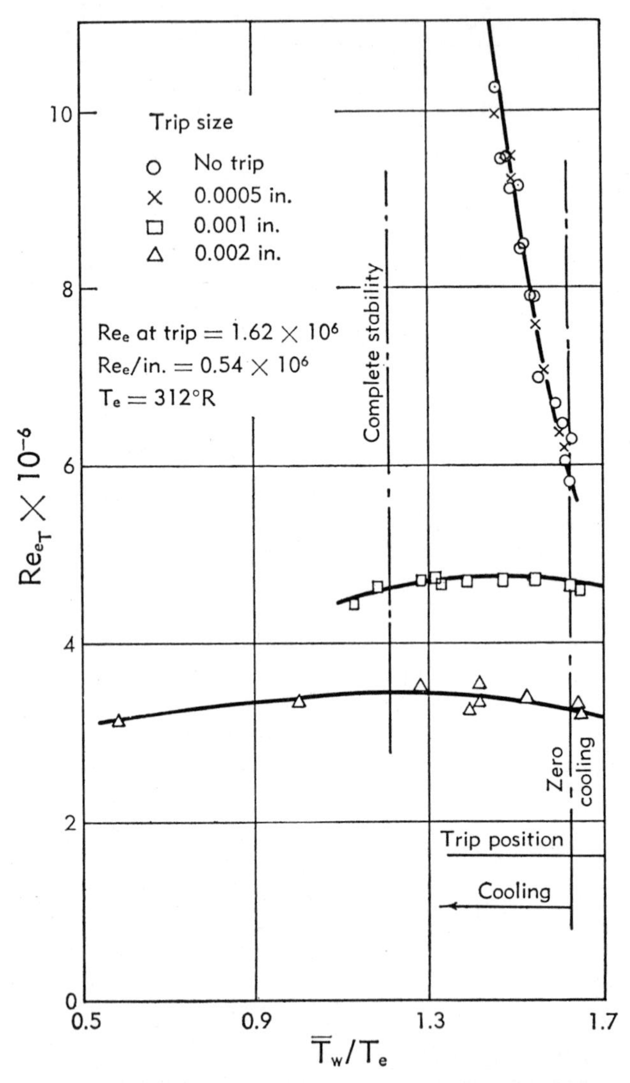


Fig. F,19a. Effect of roughness on transition with cooling. $M_e = 1.90$. Wire trips at $Re_e = 1.62 \times 10^6$; 10° cone.

increasing turbulence, (2) the effect of supply-tunnel turbulence in promoting transition decreases as Mach number increases. The second conclusion is again drawn from Fig. F,18d, which is a cross plot of Fig. F,18a, F,18b, and F,18c for zero cooling. The ordinate of Fig. F,18d is the ratio of tho transition Reynolds number with variable turbulence $Re_{e_T}$ to that with 0.4 per cent turbulence $Re_{e_0}$, and the abscissa is the percentage ratio of the root-mean-square velocity fluctuation $u'$ to the mean velocity $u$ in the supply chamber.

**F,19. Effect of Surface Roughness.** Transition promoted by surface roughness can still be controlled by cooling, depending, however, upon the roughness size. Data [*56*] obtained for wire rings 3 inches from the tip of a 10-degree smooth cone at local Mach number 1.90, 2.70, and 3.65

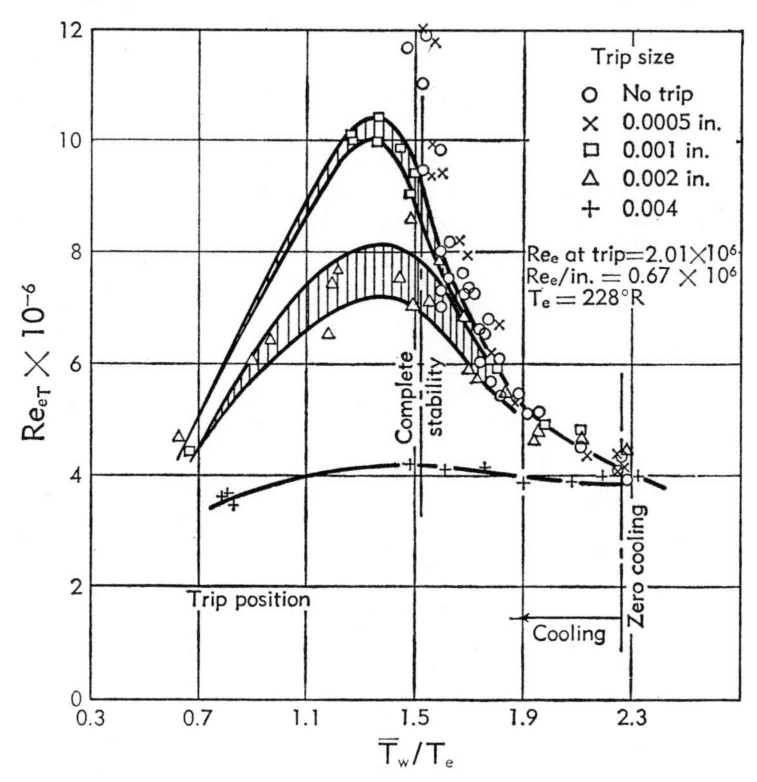


Fig. F,19b. Effect of roughness on transition with cooling. $M_e = 2.70$. Wire trips at $Re_e = 2.01 \times 10^6$; 10° cone.

are shown in Fig. F,19a, F,19b, and F,19c, respectively. These data show that: (1) for sufficiently small two-dimensional roughness, cooling can still delay transition as though the body were smooth, (2) sufficiently large roughnesses disrupt the flow to such an extent that cooling is no longer effective, (3) for intermediate roughnesses, a reversal in transition is apparently possible, during which transition is first delayed and then promoted by cooling, and (4) the effect of roughness in promoting transition decreases as Mach number increases. The reversal may be explained by the argument that cooling first tends to stabilize the flow until the

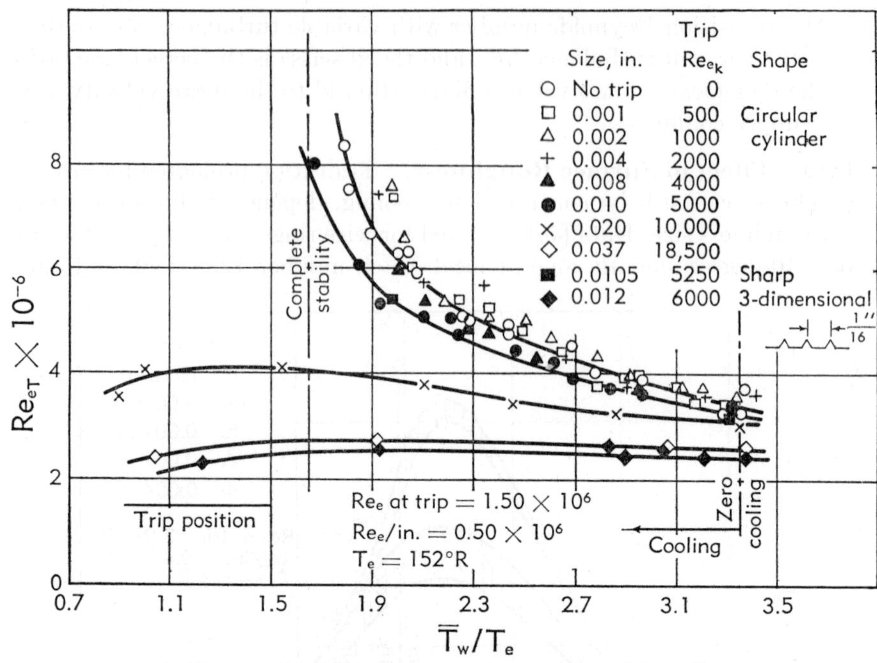


Fig. F,19c. Effect of roughness on transition with cooling. $M_e = 3.65$. Wire trips at $Re_e = 1.50 \times 10^6$; 10° cone.

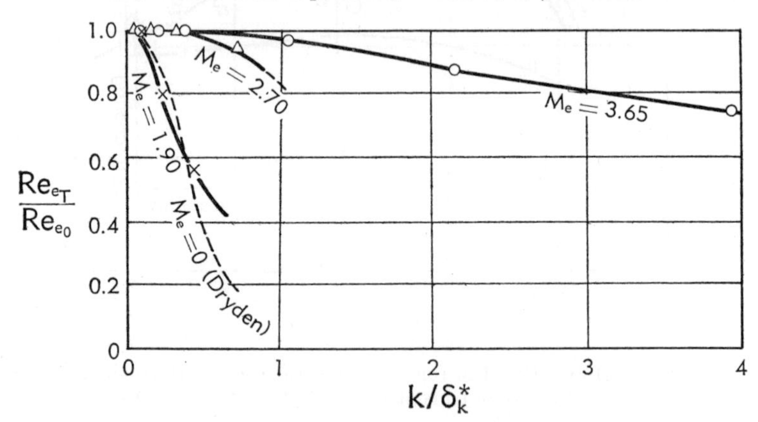


Fig. F,19d. Effect of roughness on transition as a function of Mach number. Zero heat transfer.

boundary layer becomes sufficiently thin that the roughness shows its effect. The fourth conclusion is again seen in Fig. F,19d, which is a cross-plot of Fig. F,19a, F,19b, and F,19c for zero heat transfer. The ordinate of Fig. F,19d is the ratio of the transition Reynolds number with a trip $Re_{e_T}$ to that for the smooth cone $Re_{e_0}$, whereas the abscissa is the ratio of the roughness height $k$ to the boundary layer displacement thickness $\delta_k^*$ at the trip, in accordance with the procedure of Dryden [58].

# *CHAPTER 2. APPLICATION OF THEORY TO ENGINEERING PROBLEMS AT HIGH SPEEDS*

**F,20. Aerodynamic Heating of High Speed Vehicles.** The rise in temperature of the air in immediate contact with the surface of a vehicle as a result of high speed causes transfer of heat into the vehicle, thus the expression "aerodynamic heating." The temperature rise of the contact air may be caused by direct compression, such as at the nose of a blunt body, or friction in a boundary layer, or both. The glowing of meteorites is a manifestation of the high temperatures associated with aerodynamic heating.

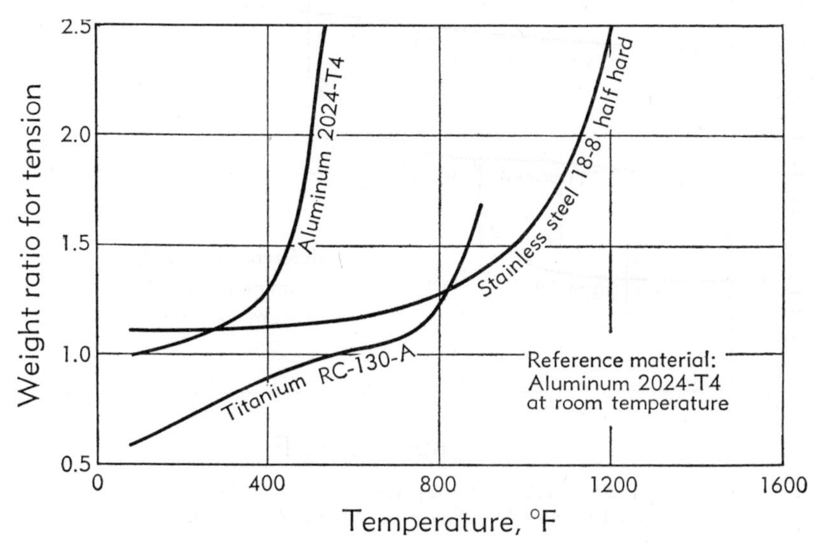


Fig. F,20a. Effect of temperature on the weight ratio for the same tensile load for various metals.

At low speeds, aerodynamic heating is usually objectionable only to the pilot. However, at high speeds, such heating actually dictates the design of the vehicle, not only for structural reasons, but also because of the problem of insulating vital compartments, such as for fuel and guidance equipment. Indeed, the design of hypersonic missiles, such as glide or ballistic rockets, awaits further research on boundary layer heat transfer rates and high temperature insulating and structural materials.

Fig. F,20a and F,20b show the effect of temperature on the strength of aluminum alloy, stainless steel, and titanium using aluminum alloy at room temperature as the base [*59*]. While the loss in tensile yield-strength with temperature is indicated in Fig. F,20a, a more significant presentation is given in Fig. F,20b, which gives the relative weights of metal required to carry the same load for buckling. According to Fig. F,20a it is apparent, from a tension-load standpoint, that titanium is most suitable all the way up to about 800°F, above which stainless steel would be preferable. On the other hand, from a plate-buckling standpoint, Fig. F,20b shows that aluminum alloy is preferable up to a temperature of about 600°F, titanium is most suitable up to about 900°F, after which stainless steel would be desirable. At any rate, regardless of loading condition, it may be concluded that titanium should be the most useful of the three metals between about 600°F and 900°F. (Mach number ranges, corresponding to full boundary layer temperature rise from an ambient

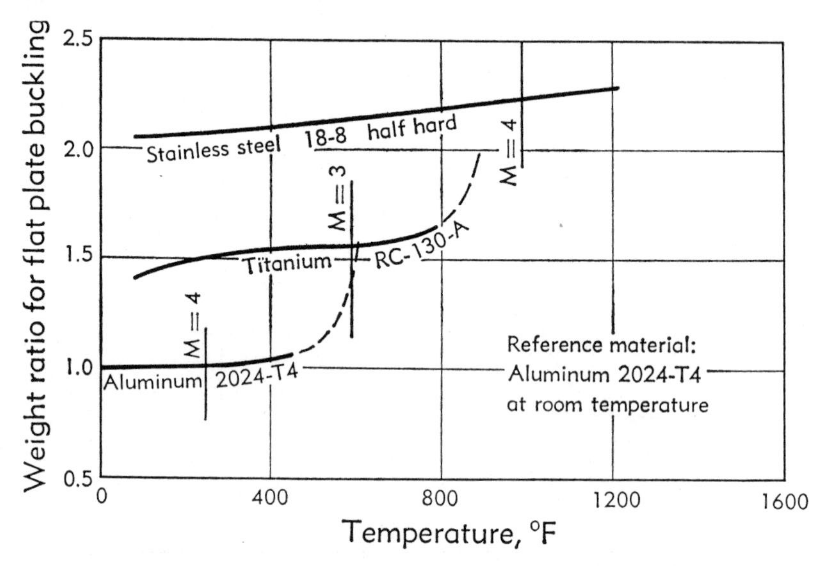


Fig. F,20b. Effect of temperature on the weight ratio for the same buckling load for various metals.

temperature of −60°F, are also indicated in Fig. F,20b.) At higher temperatures, say 1500°F, other heat-resistant alloys must be considered. For example, Hastelloy C is a recently developed high temperature, nickel-base alloy which has good inherent section properties and therefore may prove suitable for the design of the main structure of high Mach number vehicles. Because the temperature of a body is greatest at the nose as well as at other protruding parts, it may be necessary to use an insulating material of low structural value, such as a ceramic, in those regions, especially when such regions may be backed up with sufficient supporting structure. The leading edges of wings may be treated likewise.

*Calculation of skin temperature.* In the engineering calculation of the skin temperature of a high speed vehicle, the usual assumptions are: (1) the skin is so thin that the temperature gradient in the skin normal to the surface is negligible, (2) heat conduction along the skin is negligible, (3) no heat transfer takes place to or from other parts of the missile, (4) the specific heat of the air in the boundary layer is constant, and (5) radiation emissivity and absorptivity of the skin are equal. Accordingly, the differential equation for skin temperature is

$$c_w \rho_w \delta_w \frac{dT_w}{dt} = St c_p \rho_e u_e (T_r - T_w) - \epsilon(\sigma T_w^4 - G) \qquad (20\text{-}1)$$

where, on the left-hand side of the equation, $T_w$, $c_w$, $\rho_w$, and $\delta_w$ are the

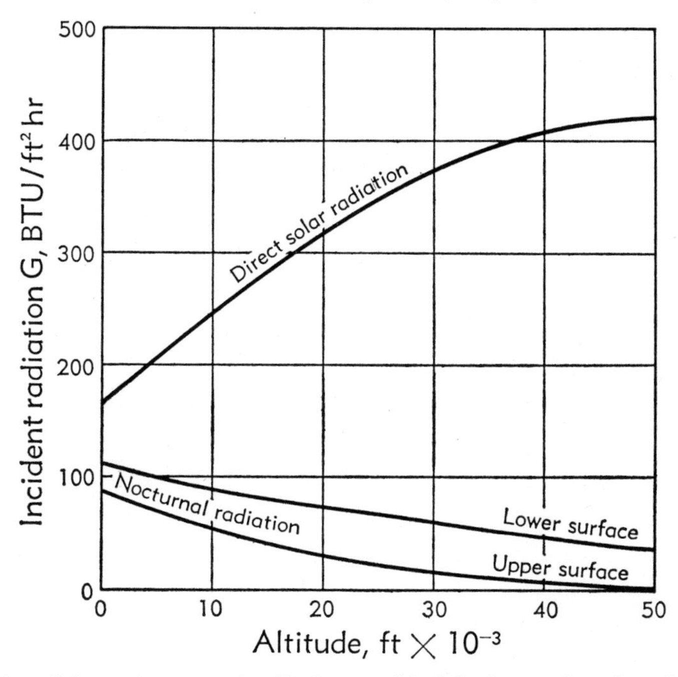


Fig. F,20c. Solar and nocturnal radiation to a black body as a function of altitude.

temperature, specific heat, density, and thickness of the skin, respectively, and $t$ is time. On the right-hand side, the symbols $T_r$, $\epsilon$, and $\sigma$ represent the insulated-skin (recovery) temperature, skin emissivity, and the Stefan-Boltzmann radiation constant ($0.173 \times 10^{-8}$ BTU/ft$^2$ hr ($^\circ$R)$^4$), respectively. $G$ signifies the incident radiation from solar, terrestrial, and interstellar sources. The specific heat at constant pressure of the air is $c_p$, while the density and velocity at the outer edge of the boundary layer are $\rho_e$ and $u_e$, respectively. $St$ is the Stanton number for either laminar or turbulent flow or mixed. Fig. F,20c shows the variation of incident radiation with altitude [*60*]. Owing to orientation of the aircraft in flight, only a fraction of such radiation is received. If heat transfer to other parts of the vehicle is considered, then the rate of that heat transfer must be subtracted from the right-hand side of Eq. 20-1; if heat

*Table F,20.* Emissivities of a few materials.

| Emissivity | Material | Temperature range, °F |
|---|---|---|
| 0.11 to 0.19 | Aluminum oxidized at 1110°F | 390 to 1110 |
| 0.55 to 0.60 | Smooth sheet iron | 1650 to 1900 |
| 0.66 | Oxidized rolled sheet steel | 70 |
| 0.62 to 0.73 | Stainless steel (8 per cent Ni, 18 per cent Cr) after 42 hr heating at 980°F | 420 to 980 |

is transferred to the skin from other parts, then such transfer must be added to the right-hand side of the equation. The emissivities of a few important materials are given in Table F,20 [*61*].

The solution of Eq. 20-1 is usually carried out by successive approximation because $St$ is an implicit function of $T_w$, $Re_e$, and $M_e$.

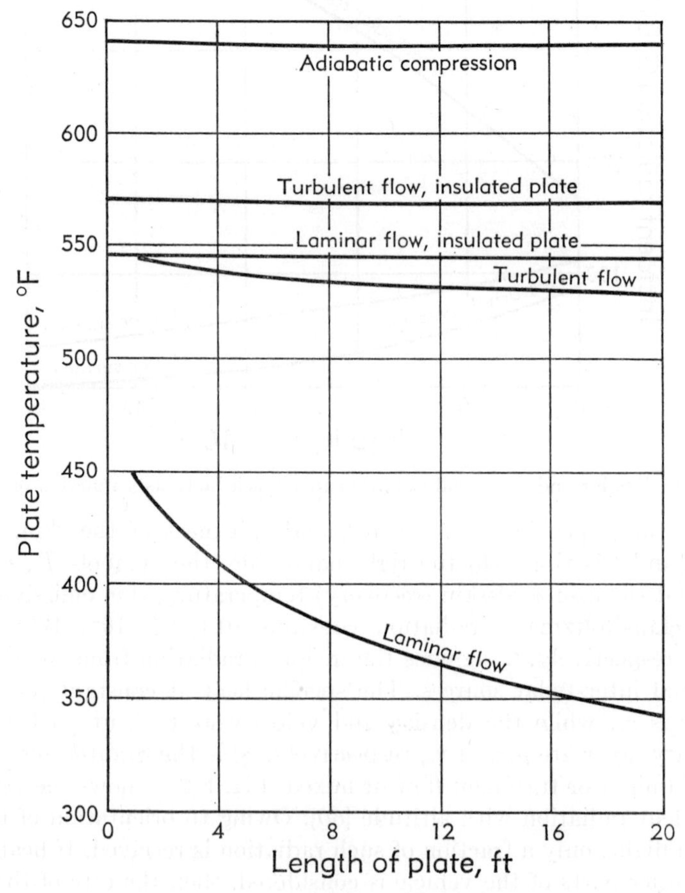


Fig. F,20d. Temperature distribution along a flat plate moving at Mach number 3.

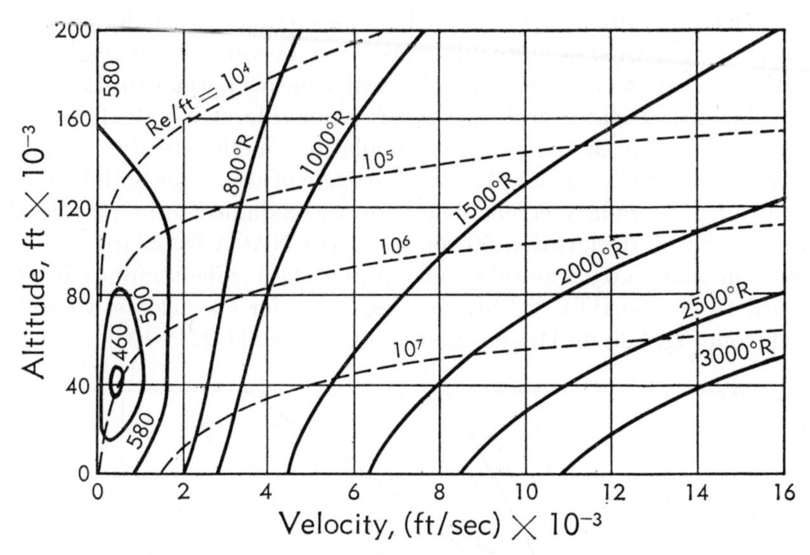


Fig. F,20e. Flat plate flight temperature at point 5 ft from leading edge. Laminar boundary layer.

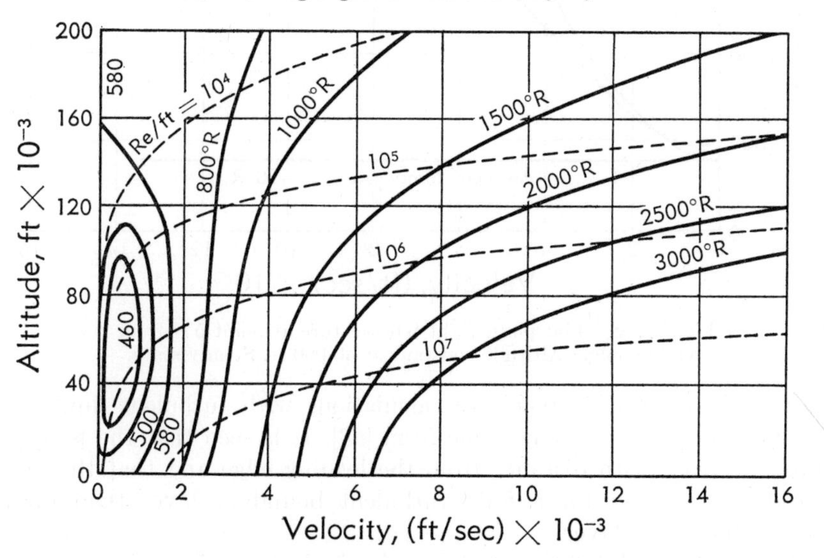


Fig. F,20f. Flat plate flight temperature at point 5 ft from leading edge. Turbulent boundary layer.

Eq. 20-1 presupposes relatively slow change in motion of the vehicle, depending of course on how thick the skin really is. Apparently the method is satisfactory for the boosting of missiles (such as the V-2) when the skin thickness is of the order $\frac{1}{32}$ inch and the acceleration is about 5 g's. For highly transient conditions, such as with ballistic dive-ins, it would be necessary to allow for the variation of temperature across the skin. Such a procedure becomes quite laborious because it usually involves the numerical method of finite differences [*62*]. Fortunately, it is still sufficiently accurate to consider only the heat transfer normal to the plate.

In the steady state (cruise), the left-hand side of Eq. 16-1 is zero. The results of typical temperature calculations in the steady state are shown in Fig. F,20d for a flat plate at zero angle of attack for both laminar and turbulent boundary layers. The plate was assumed to be moving at Mach number 3 at elevation 50,000 ft. in the NACA Standard Atmosphere. The emissivity was taken at 0.5 and the incident radiation was assumed to be 200 BTU/ft$^2$ hr. The heat transfer coefficients were obtained from Fig. F,5i for laminar flow and from Eq. 11-2, 11-19, and 11-29

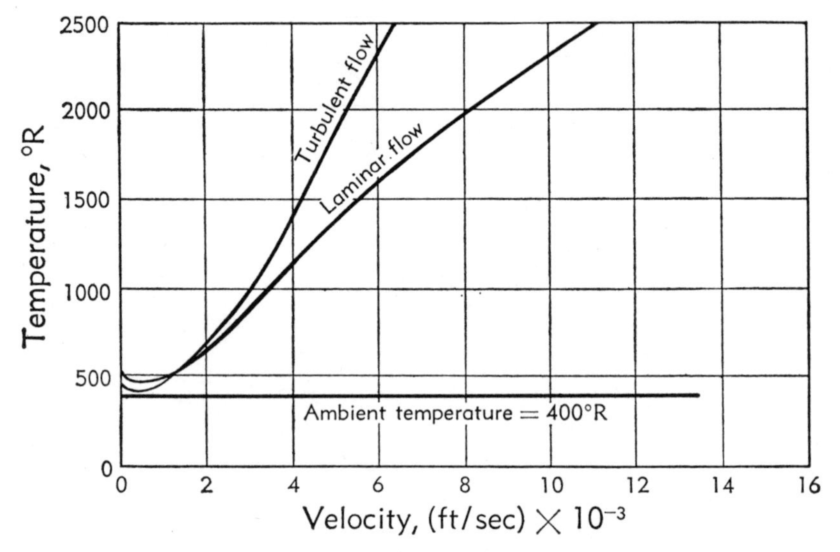


Fig. F,20g. Flat plate flight temperature at point 5 ft from leading edge. Altitude constant at 40,000 ft. Steady state.

for turbulent flow. To facilitate calculations with turbulent flow, Eq. 11-29 can be put in nomographic form [*63*]. It is seen that the temperatures decrease with distance from the leading edge and that they are considerably higher for a fully turbulent boundary layer than for a laminar boundary layer.

Fig. F,20e and F,20f may be useful in hypersonic cruising-missile design, because they show at what altitude a missile must cruise in order to maintain a given temperature at a distance 5 ft aft of the leading edge, assuming the missile can be represented by a flat plate. The plate is at zero angle of attack, the radiation emissivity was again taken at 0.5, and the NACA Standard Atmosphere was used. Fig. F,20e is for laminar flow and Fig. F,20f for turbulent flow. Lines of constant Reynolds number per foot of length are also indicated in the figures. The temperature contour 580°R represents the case where the radiation just balances the absorption of heat from the sun. This temperature (580°R) is then the temperature of a body at rest in the atmosphere or in motion out in space. It may also be the temperature of a body in motion in the atmosphere when the speed is such that the boundary layer temperature is 580°R. The fact that there are lower temperature contours within the

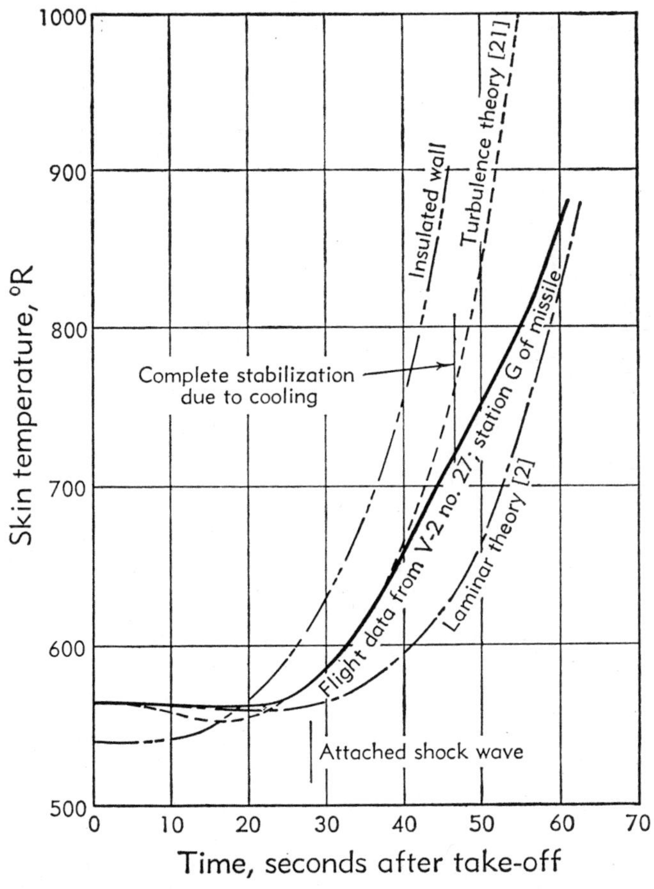


Fig. F,20h. Correlation of theory with skin-temperature data from a V-2 rocket. Boundary layer not tripped. Data of Fischer and Norris.

580°R contour means that as a body starts from rest the temperature falls at first, because the ambient air is at a lower temperature than the body temperature, and then rises as the friction within the boundary layer increases. At a certain speed, the boundary layer temperature becomes equal to the wall temperature, whereupon the wall radiates heat at exactly that rate at which it receives it from space. At higher speeds, the friction increases the boundary layer temperature and heat is transferred into the wall from the layer, thereby increasing the wall temperature. The fall and rise in temperature of a flat plate increasing its speed from subsonic to supersonic speed while remaining at 40,000 ft altitude is shown in Fig. F,20g. It appears that the solar heat is balanced at about Mach number 1.5 for 50 per cent of direct solar radiation. The skin tem-

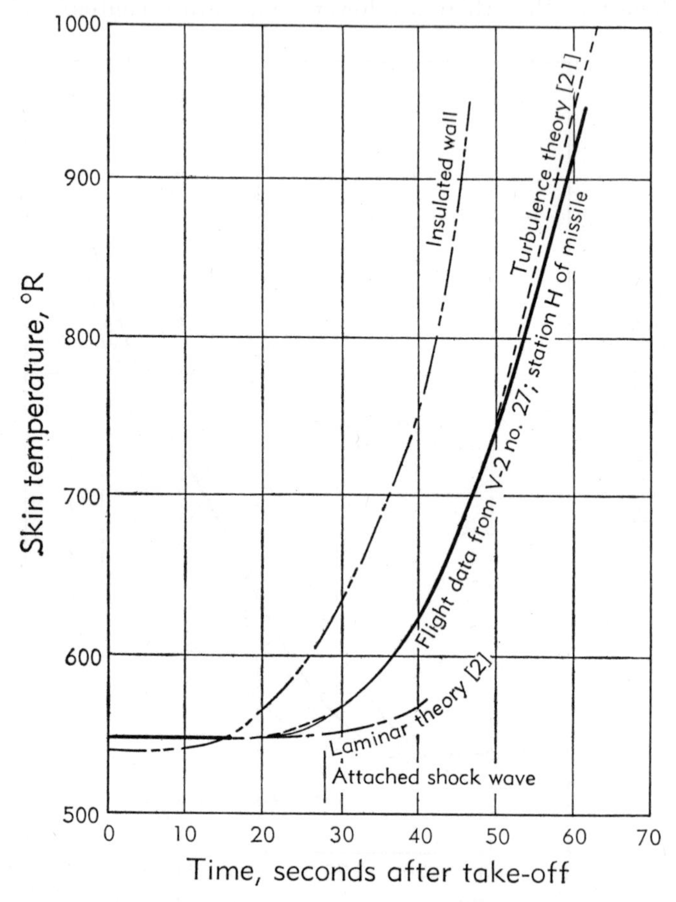


Fig. F,20i. Correlation of theory with skin-temperature data from a V-2 rocket. Boundary layer tripped. Data of Fischer and Norris.

perature then is about 120°F which would begin to produce discomfort for the pilot if one were present.

*Correlation of theory and experiment.* Considerable skin-temperature data have been recorded during the flight of supersonic missiles. Of particular interest are the data reported by Fischer and Norris [*64*,*65*], measured at several points on the nose of a V-2 (German A-4) rocket during ascent at White Sands, New Mexico, on October 9, 1947. Fig. F,20h and F,20i show the experimental temperature variation with time for stations

G and H located on opposite sides of the nose cone and 12 in. from the tip. The temperatures are plotted up to 61 sec, when the rocket motor burned out. Stations G and H were chosen for study because station H was located aft of a strip of two-dimensional boundary layer trip, whereas station G was not; therefore, the temperature data at those stations should show the difference between the normal boundary layer and a fully turbulent layer. For the purpose of comparing the data with the theory, theoretical temperature curves for laminar and turbulent layers are plotted in the figures. The heat transfer coefficients for the cone were obtained from flat plate theory by use of the rules stated above. During

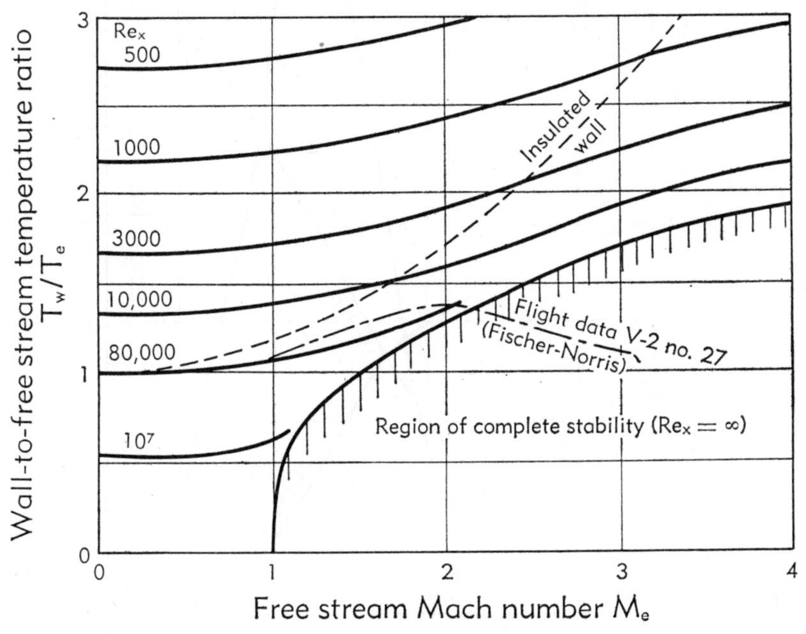


Fig. F,20j. Course of V-2 flight data.

the period of the measurements, radiation was practically negligible. Also shown in Fig. F,20h is the theoretical time at which the laminar boundary layer becomes completely stable (regardless of Reynolds number) for infinitesimal two-dimensional disturbances due to cooling caused by skin-temperature lag. This limit was obtained by following the course of the wall-to-free-stream temperature ratio in Fig. F,20j and using Fig. F,20k, which is included to show the variation of pertinent properties necessary in the heat transfer study for station G. The instant of absolute stabilization seems to correspond to the intersection of the temperature ratio and the stabilization curve in the figure. However, it is suspected that stabilization began before that time, as apparently happened in Fig. F,20h.

That the theory for turbulent flow follows the data quite satisfactorily is shown in Fig. F,20i. Perhaps the slight deviation after 45 sec is caused by the strong stabilization effect of cooling in spite of the boundary layer trip.

Fig. F,20h is generally interesting because it shows clearly the course of events which is typical of boundary layer development as a function of

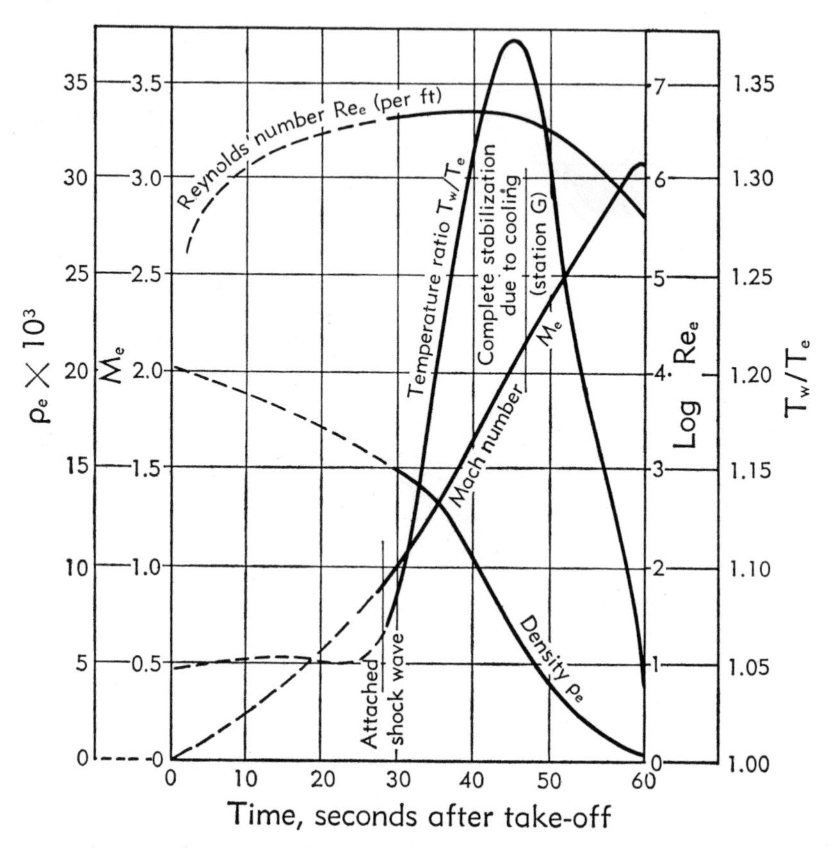


Fig. F,20k. Variation of flow parameters on nose cone of V-2 rocket in Fig. F,20h and F,20i.

Reynolds number and wall-to-free stream temperature ratio (heat transfer). At first, the Reynolds number soon becomes large enough to make the boundary layer turbulent; therefore the data follow the turbulent trend for a while. However, as the speed increases, the boundary layer temperature increases, thus bringing about heat flow into the missile skin owing to heat capacity of the skin. The boundary layer cooling then tends to stabilize the layer; in fact, a rate of cooling is finally reached after which a laminar boundary layer is stable for any Reynolds number. The transition from turbulent to laminar flow is clearly seen in Fig. F,20h.

It is to be emphasized that the strong tendency for stabilization exhibited in Fig. F,20h is caused by the transient heat lag of the skin and not by radiation, since radiation was almost negligible compared to the heat absorption of the skin. Thus, transient firings of the above type are of great importance in the study of boundary layer characteristics at supersonic speeds. However, steady state temperature data, when available, will check radiation rates of cooling and their effect on boundary layer stability. Reliable data at hypersonic speeds and higher altitudes will be useful for studying the effect of slip flow on heat transfer. It is of interest to note in Fig. F,20l that after 70 sec of flight the flow for the one-foot station of the above-discussed V-2 had already entered the slip-flow regime defined by Tsien [*66*].

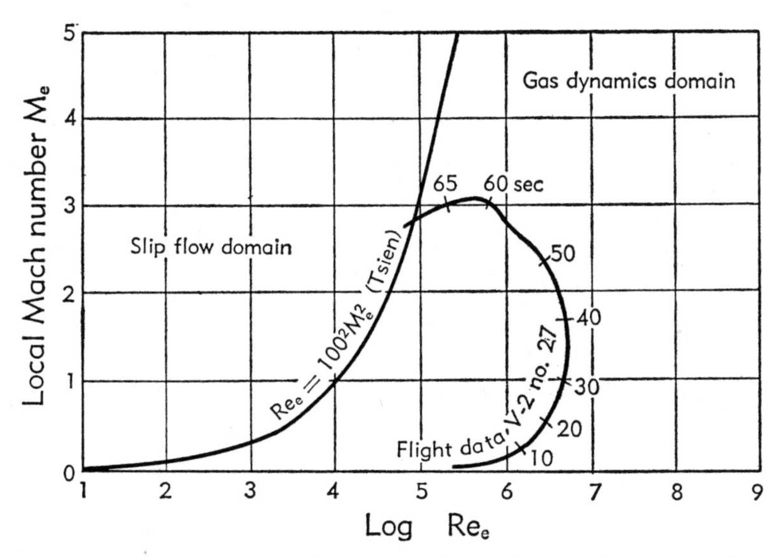


Fig. F,20l. Flow domain during flight of V-2 rocket no. 27 for 1 ft station.

**F,21. Heat Transfer in Rocket Motors.** Another important heat transfer problem is that of the rocket motor in which the metallic walls must be protected against the high temperatures of the propellant gases. The problem is essentially the same as in the aerodynamic heating of high speed vehicles, except that in rocket motors the flow properties change much more rapidly. The ambient temperatures in the nozzle are always high, so that the nozzle wall, particularly at the throat, must be continually protected by either regenerative or film cooling. Only at hypersonic speeds does the boundary layer temperature on the outside of a vehicle become comparable to that in the nozzle. Regenerative cooling is brought about by circulating some of the fuel in the motor jacket before injecting it into the combustion chamber. Film cooling is a technique, first used by the Germans in the V-2 rocket motor, by which small quantities of fluid, say the regenerative coolant, are permitted to enter the nozzle at many points on the interior surface and spread over the wall in a thin film. When the coolant is introduced in the nozzle through the porous wall, the process is called sweat cooling.

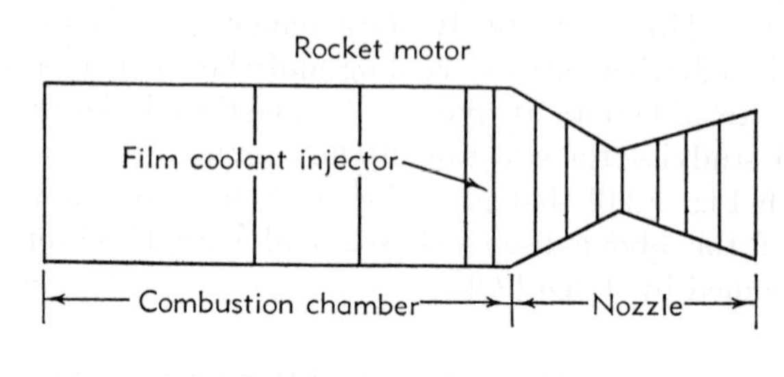


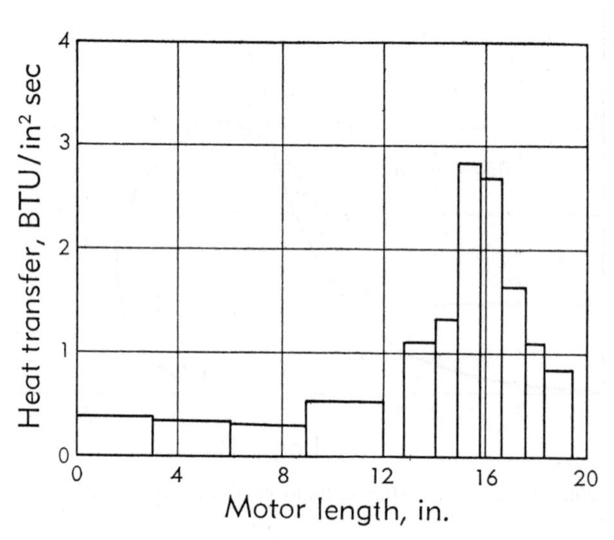


Fig. F,21a. Heat transfer distribution in acid-aniline rocket motor.

*Experimental investigations.* Because of the large variation of flow properties within the rocket nozzle, theoretical calculation of heat transfer in rocket motors has given way to experiment.

A rather complete experimental investigation has been carried out by Boden [67] to determine the effect of many factors, including film cooling, on the heat transfer in a 1000-lb thrust rocket motor using $6\frac{1}{2}$ per cent red fuming nitric acid for the oxidizer and a mixed fuel of 80 per cent aniline and 20 per cent furfuryl alcohol. The combustion-chamber temperature was about 5000°F. The rate of heat transfer was obtained at various sections of the motor, including the combustion chamber, by measuring the change in bulk temperature of the jacket coolant. The film coolant used in these experiments was water.

Fig. F,21a shows a typical distribution of heat transfer through the walls of the motor using fresh oxidizing acid in the propellant and no film cooling. It is at once observed that the rate of heat transfer is highest just upstream of the nozzle throat, probably because in that vicinity the boundary layer is the thinnest owing to the favorable pressure gradient. It is also seen that the heat transfer in the combustion chamber is relatively low. In this region where the gases are very hot, radiation from the gas contributes a good share (up to 30 per cent) of the heat transmitted to the walls, the remainder being caused by convection. In the nozzle where ambient temperatures are lower, radiation is considered unimportant.

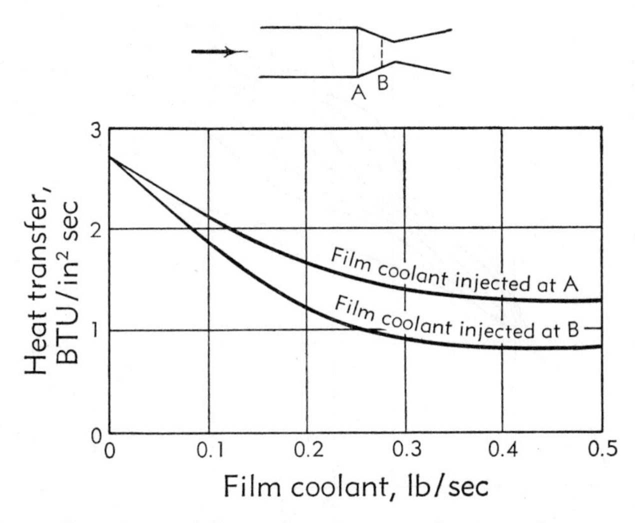


Fig. F,21b. Effect of rate of film-coolant flow upon heat transfer at nozzle throat.

It was found that fresh acid always produced low heat transfer. Also, the presence of iron, chromium, and nickel dissolved from the shipping containers could increase the heat transfer as much as 50 per cent. A factor which decreased the heat transfer rate was, of course, a decrease in temperature as indicated by a decrease in oxidizer-fuel mixture ratio. No significant loss in motor performance was observed with change in mixture ratio. The design of the propellant injector as well as the nozzle shape were other more or less important factors.

How film cooling affects the rate of heat transfer at the throat section of the nozzle is shown in Fig. F,21b. Fresh acid was used in the experiments represented in this figure. The upper curve shows the decrease in heat transfer through the wall when film coolant is injected tangentially to the circumference of the combustion chamber at the entrance to the nozzle. The lower curve indicates an even greater reduction when the coolant was injected midway between the entrance and throat of the nozzle where the heat transfer was increasing rapidly. Observations of the nozzle after the tests showed that film cooling persisted throughout the nozzle throat. For the particular motor used, maximum cooling was attained when the coolant flow rate was 5 per cent of the propellant consumption rate. From the results of his experiments, Boden concluded that film cooling reduces the heat transfer in rocket motors up to 70 per cent, and that proper control of the operating mixture ratio and the propellant

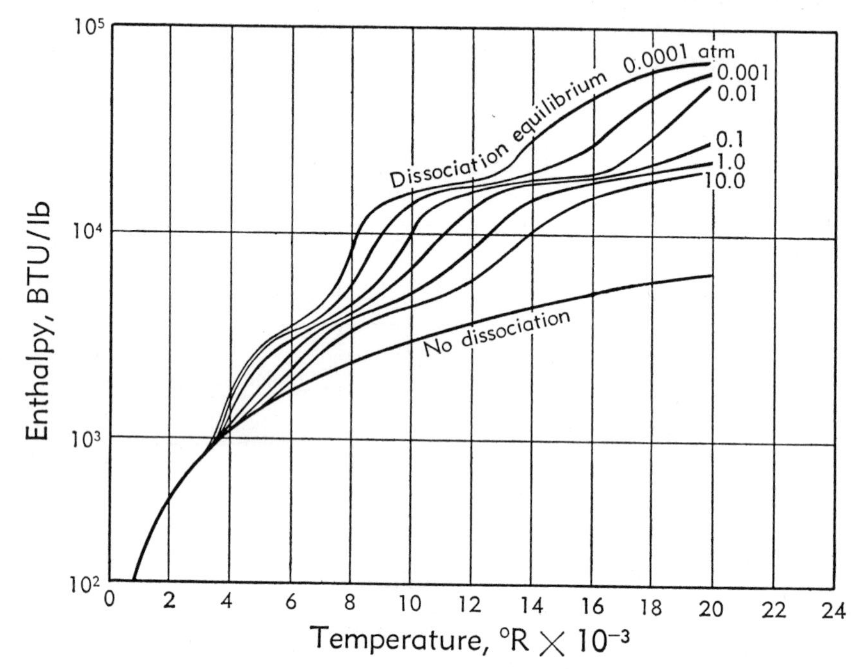


Fig. F,22a. Enthalpy of air as a function of temperature and pressure.

composition would gain an additional 10 to 15 per cent reduction. Although the above results were obtained using water as the film coolant, other data indicated that fuel was equally effective.

A similar set of experiments was conducted by Greenfield [*68*] to determine the coefficients of heat transfer in a rocket motor designed to produce a 1000-lb thrust with a liquid oxygen-ethyl alcohol propellant. The experimental procedure for measuring the heat transfer rate utilized the transient temperature rise of the five uncooled segments which comprised the walls of the motor nozzle. Two series of tests were carried out: one series using the liquid oxygen-ethyl alcohol propellant which developed an estimated 3000°F, the other using high pressure air at 1400°F. No film cooling was attempted. The following empirical formula fitted fairly well the data from the five nozzle-wall segments:

$$h = 0.029 \frac{G^{0.8}}{D^{0.2}} c_p \mu^{0.2} \tag{21-1}$$

where $h$ is the heat transfer coefficient in BTU/ft² hr (°F) and is equal to the product $Stc_{p_e}\rho_e u_e$. Also in Eq. 21-1, $G$ is the mass velocity (at midpoint of a segment) in lb mass/ft² hr, $D$ the inside nozzle diameter at a segment midpoint in feet, $c_p$ the specific heat of the gas at the insulated-wall temperature in BTU/lb mass F, $\mu$ the viscosity of the gas at the insulated-wall temperature in lb mass/ft hr. It is interesting to note that in spite of the rapid changes in the flow properties throughout the rocket nozzle, Eq. 21-1 has the same form as empirical laws for turbulent flow in straight pipes [*59*].

**F,22. Dissociation Effects.** When the speed of an aircraft becomes so great that the temperature of the surrounding air (owing to com-

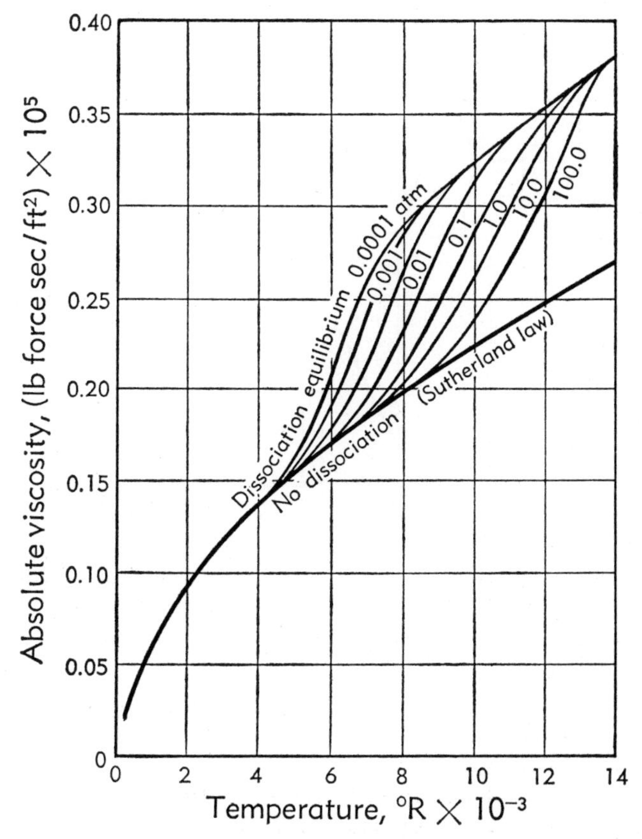


Fig. F,22b. Absolute viscosity of air as a function of temperature and pressure.

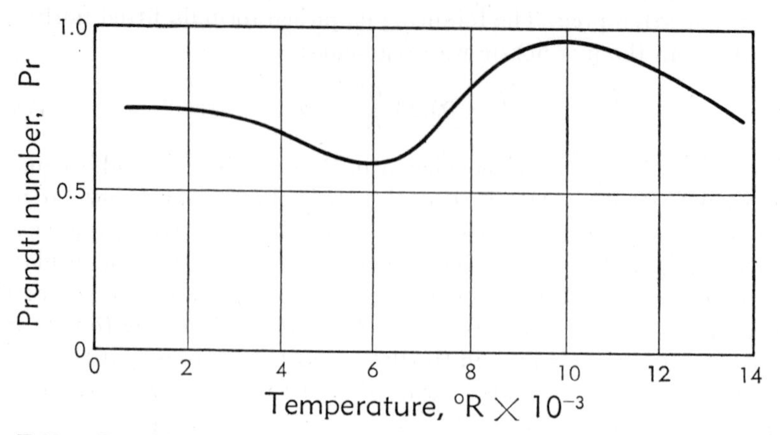


Fig. F,22c. Prandtl number of air as a function of temperature at 0.1-atm pressure.

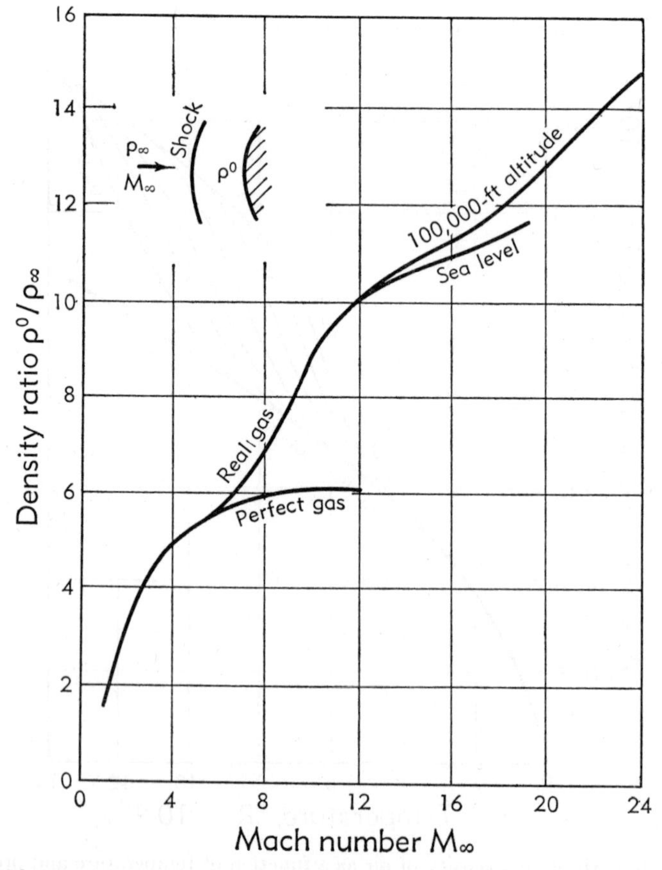


Fig. F,22d. Ratio of stagnation to ambient density across a normal shock for air.

pression behind shock waves or friction in the boundary layer) becomes sufficiently high, the air components partially dissociate, and the composition of the new air will be entirely different from that at low temperature conditions. For example, at a speed of about Mach 20 at 100,000 feet altitude, the composition of the air behind a normal shock would be

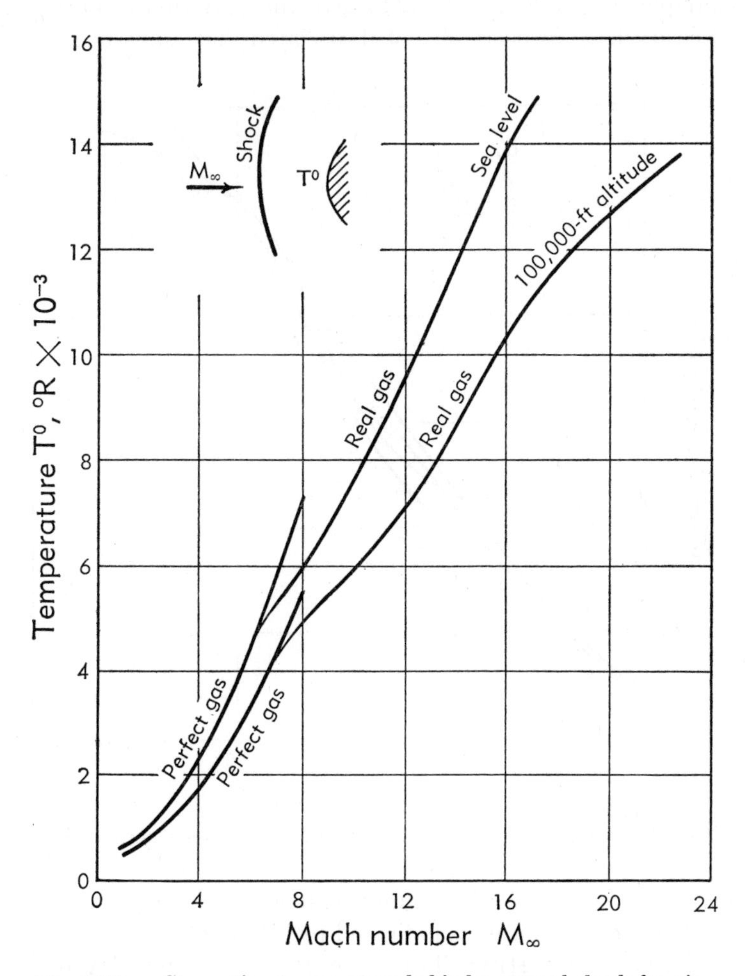


Fig. F,22e. Stagnation temperature behind a normal shock for air.

approximately 50 per cent atomic nitrogen, 24 per cent molecular nitrogen, and 26 per cent atomic oxygen, compared to 78 per cent molecular nitrogen and 21 per cent molecular oxygen at low temperature. The degree of dissociation increases with decrease in pressure; hence the resulting composition of the air is a function of pressure as well as temperature.

An important effect of dissociation is an increase in specific heat resulting from the absorption of energy in the breaking apart of the air components.

PROPERTIES OF DISSOCIATED AIR. Before any calculation of heat transfer under conditions conducive to dissociation can be undertaken, the thermodynamic, as well as transport, properties must be determined. For example, Fig. F,22a and F,22b give the variation of enthalpy [*69*] and viscosity [*70*], respectively, of dissociated and undissociated air for

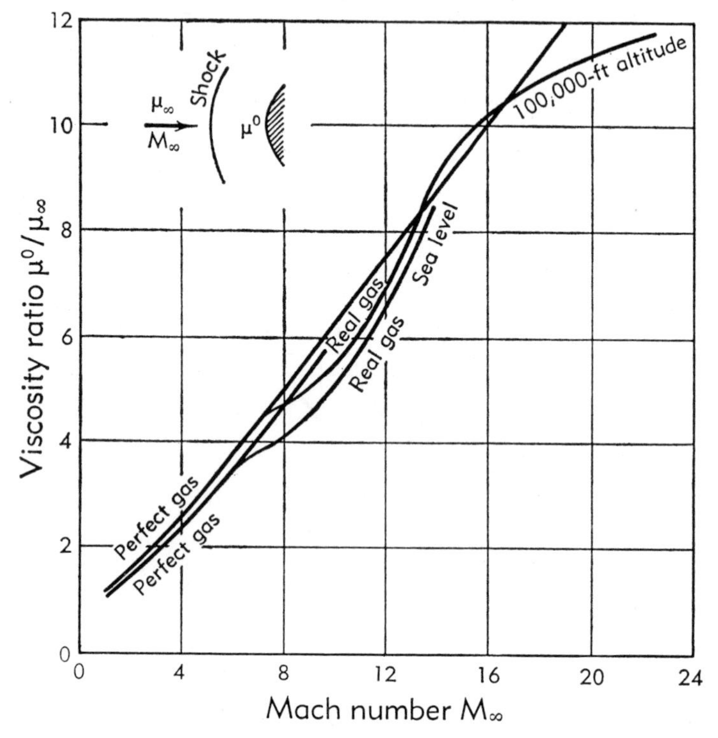


Fig. F,22f. Ratio of stagnation to ambient pressure across a normal shock for air.

various pressures. The Prandtl number, however, is not altered appreciably by high temperature, as indicated in Fig. F,22c [*71*].

CALCULATION OF HEAT TRANSFER NEAR THE STAGNATION POINT INCLUDING DISSOCIATION.

*Laminar flow.* As mentioned in Art. 7, the results expressed in Eq. 7-1b, 7-2b, and 7-3b for laminar flow heat transfer at the stagnation point of a body at supersonic speed can be applied with some approximation to hypersonic flow.

In Eq. 7-2b and 7-3b, $\beta$ is again obtained from Fig. F,7a. The Prandtl number $(c_p\mu/k)^0$ is taken from Fig. F,22c where it is seen to remain at a value of about 0.7 for air. The density ratio $\rho^0/\rho_\infty$ value of about 0.7 for air. The density ratio $\rho^0/\rho_\infty$ across a normal shock in free flight is plotted in Fig. F,22d; this ratio was computed through simultaneous solution of the continuity, momentum, and energy equations, along with the equation of state in [*69*]. Out of this calculation also comes the temperature ratio (Fig. F,22e). From Fig. F,22e and Fig. F,22b is determined the viscosity ratio $\mu^0/\mu_\infty$ plotted in Fig. F,22f. The temperature ratio in Fig. F,22e is of extra interest because it indicates immediately what

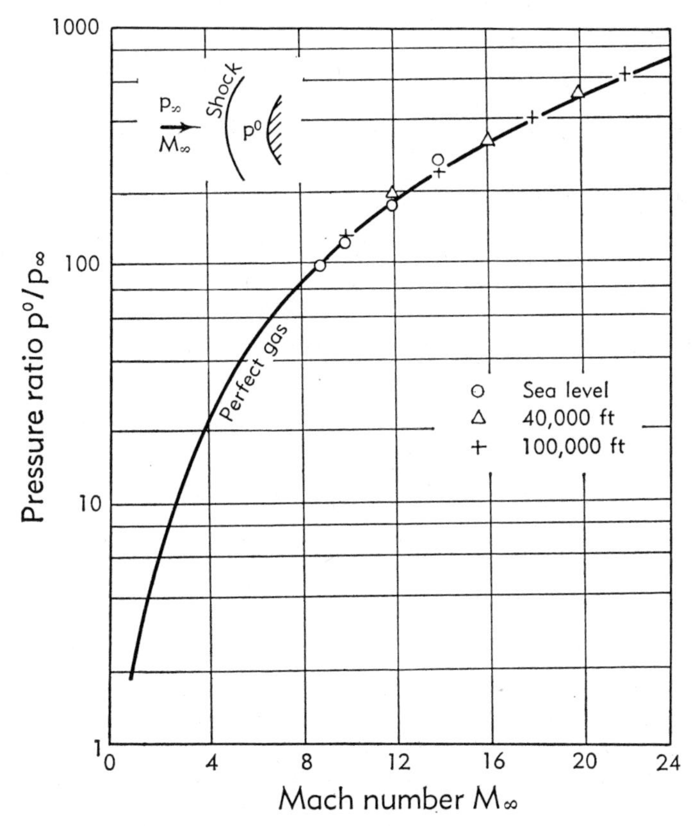


**Fig. F,22g.** Ratio of stagnation to ambient viscosity across a normal shock for air.

temperature an insulated body would acquire, or rather, what temperature a body is subjected to, at very high speeds.

The stagnation enthalpy $h^0$ is readily computed from

$$h^0 = h_\infty + \frac{U^2}{2} \tag{22-1}$$

and is therefore independent of dissociation. It is noteworthy that the stagnation pressure behind a shock wave is apparently also independent of dissociation (see Fig. F,22g).

The above simple procedure using Eq. 7-1b, 7-2b, and 7-3b checks shock tube experimental data of Rose and Riddell [*72*] very well for the stagnation point of a sphere as seen in Fig. F,22h. A more elaborate theory of Fay and Riddell [*73*], taking into account the effects of diffusion and atomic recombination, also fits the data well, so that it would seem that these latter effects do not significantly influence the heat transfer rate, at least according to the above experiments.

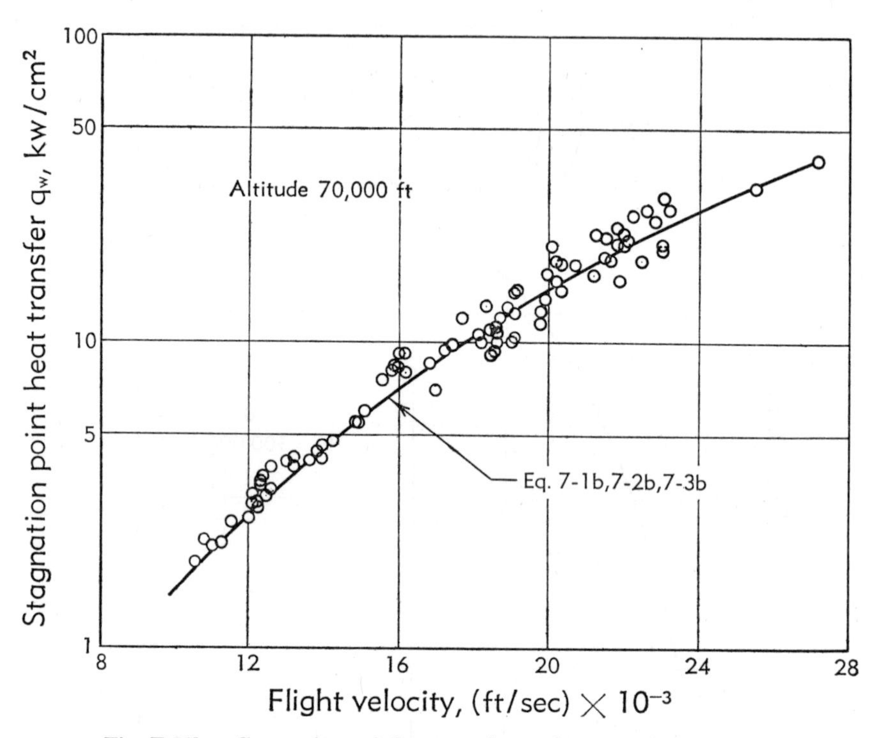


Fig. F,22h. Comparison of theory and experiment on heat transfer at the stagnation point of a sphere.

While the above procedure produces good results for the calculation of heat transfer from a dissociated gas, the actual over-all effect of dissociation on the heat transfer rate for a perfect gas is shown in Fig. F,22i. The calculation was made for a sphere at 100,000-feet altitude in the ICAO (International Civil Aviation Organization) atmosphere, and the wall temperature was assumed to be 2500°R. It is concluded that the effect of dissociation (real gas) on heat transfer, compared to the perfect gas solution, is not great.

*Turbulent flow.* As with laminar flow, it can be shown that for turbulent flow the effect of dissociation, compared to the perfect gas solution, will also not be very great [*74*].

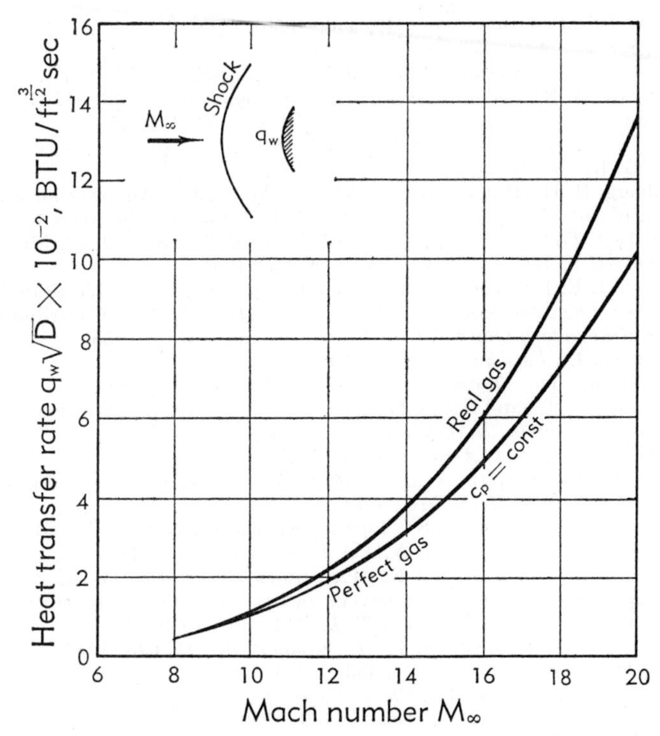


Fig. F,22i. Effect of dissociation on heat transfer at the stagnation point of a sphere at 100,000-ft altitude in the ICAO atmosphere. Wall temperature at 2500°R.

## F,23. Cited References.


1. Crocco, L. Lo strato limite laminare nei gas. *Ministero della Difesa-Aeronautica, Roma., Monografie Scientifiche di Aeronautica 3*, 1946. Transl. in *Aerophys. Lab., North Amer. Aviation Rept. AL-684*, 1948.
2. van Driest, E. R. Investigation of laminar boundary layer in compressible fluids using the Crocco method. *NACA Tech. Note 2597*, 1952.
3. van Driest, E. R. The laminar boundary layer with variable fluid properties. *Heat Transfer and Fluid Mech. Inst.*, Berkeley, 1954.
4. Keyes, F. G. The heat conductivity, viscosity, specific heat, and Prandtl numbers for thirteen gases. *Mass Inst. Technol. Project SQUID Tech. Rept. 37*, 1952.
5. *Tables of the Thermal Properties of Gases*. Natl. Bur. Standards Circular 564, U.S. Government Printing Office, 1955.
6. Hantzsche, W., and Wendt, H. *Jahrbuch deut. Luftfahrtforschung 76*, 1941.
7. Goldstein, S. *Modern Developments in Fluid Dynamics, 1st ed., Vol. 2*. Oxford Univ. Press, 1938.
8. Homann, F. *Z. angew Math. u. Mech. 16*, 159 (1936).
9. Sibulkin, M. *J. Aeronaut. Sci. 19*, 570 (1952).
10. Grimminger, G., Williams, E. P., and Young, G. B. W. *J. Aeronaut. Sci. 17*, 675 (1950).
11. Korobkin, I. Laminar heat-transfer characteristics of a hemisphere for the Mach number range 1.9 to 4.9. *Nav. Ord. Lab. Rept. 3841*, 1954.
12. Stine, H. A., and Wanlass, K. Theoretical and experimental investigation of aerodynamic-heating and isothermal heat-transfer parameters on a hemispherical nose with laminar boundary layer at supersonic Mach numbers. *NACA Tech. Note 3344*, 1954.

13. Goland, L. *J. Aeronaut. Sci. 17*, 436 (1950).
14. Levy, S. *J Aeronaut. Sci. 21*, 459 (1954).
15. Morris, D. N., and Smith, J. W. *J. Aeronaut. Sci. 20*, 805 (1953).
16. Chapman, D. R., and Rubesin, M. W. *J. Aeronaut. Sci. 16*, 547 (1949).
17. Lighthill, M. J. *Proc. Roy. Soc. London A202*, 359 (1950).
18. Smith, J. W. *J. Aeronaut. Sci. 21*, 154 (1954).
19. Eber, G. R. *J. Aeronaut. Sci. 19*, 1 (1952).
20. Shoulberg, R. H., Hill, J. A. F., and Rivas, M. A., Jr. An experimental determination of flat plate recovery factors for Mach numbers between 1.90 and 3.14. *Mass. Inst. Technol. Nav. Supersonic Lab. Wind Tunnel Rept. 36*, May 1952.
21. van Driest, E. R. *J. Aeronaut. Sci. 18*, 145 (1951).
22. van Driest, E. R. The turbulent boundary layer with variable Prandtl number. *Aerophys. Lab., North Amer. Aviation Rept. AL-1914*, 1954. Contributed to *Fifty Years of Boundary Layer Theory*. Vieweg, Braunschweig, 1955.
23. Nikuradse, J. *Forschungsheft 356*, 1932.
24. von Kármán, Th. *Trans. Am. Soc. Mech. Engrs. 61*, 705 (1939).
25. Schubauer, G. B., and Klebanoff, P. S. Investigation of separation of the turbulent boundary layer. *NACA Tech. Note 2133*, 1950.
26. van Driest, E. R. *J. Aeronaut. Sci. 23*, 1007 (1956).
27. Landis, F., and Shapiro, A. H. The turbulent mixing of co-axial gas jets. *Heat Transfer and Fluid Mech. Inst.*, 1951.
28. Corrsin, S., and Uberoi, M. S. Further experiments on the flow and heat transfer in a heated turbulent air jet. *NACA Tech. Note 1865*, 1949.
29. Stine, H. A., and Scherrer, R. Experimental investigation of the turbulent-boundary-layer temperature-recovery factor on bodies of revolution at Mach numbers from 2.0 to 3.8. *NACA Tech. Note 2664*, 1952.
30. des Clers, B., and Sternberg, J. *J. Aeronaut. Sci. 19*, 645 (1952).
31. Coles, D. *J. Aeronaut. Sci. 21*, 433 (1954).
32. Colburn, A. P. *Trans. Am. Chem. Engrs. 29*, 174 (1933).
33. Wilson, R. E. *J. Aeronaut. Sci. 17*, 585 (1950).
34. Cope, W. F. The turbulent boundary layer in compressible flow. *Brit. Aeronaut. Research Council Repts. and Mem. 7634*, 1943.
35. von Kármán, Th. The problem of resistance in compressible fluids. *V. Convengo della Foundazione Alessandro Volta*, Rome, 1935.
36. van Driest, E. R. *J. Aeronaut. Sci. 19*, 55 (1952).
37. van Driest, E. R. *Aeronaut. Eng. Rev. 15*, 26 (1956).
38. Rubesin, M. W. The effect of an arbitrary surface-temperature variation along a flat plate on the convective heat transfer in an incompressible turbulent boundary layer. *NACA Tech. Note 2345*, 1951.
39. Clauser, F. H. *J. Aeronaut. Sci. 21*, 91 (1954).
40. Rubesin, M. W. An analytical estimation of the effect of transpiration cooling on the heat-transfer and skin-friction characteristics of a compressible, turbulent boundary layer. *NACA Tech. Note 3341*, 1954.
41. Mickley, H. S., et al. Heat, mass and momentum transfer for flow over a flat plate with blowing or suction. *NACA Tech. Note 3208*, 1954.
42. Korkegi, R. H. *Transition Studies and Skin Friction Measurements on an Insulated Flat Plate at a Hypersonic Mach Number. Ph.D. Thesis*, Calif. Inst. Technol., 1954.
43. Sommer, S. C., and Short, B. J. *J. Aeronaut. Sci. 23*, 536 (1956).
44. Chapman, D. R., and Kester, R. H. *J. Aeronaut. Sci. 20*, 441 (1953).
45. Shoulberg, R. H., et al. An experimental investigation of flat plate heat-transfer coefficients at Mach numbers of 2, 2.5 and 3 for a surface-temperature-to-stream total temperature ratio of 1.18. *Mass. Inst. Technol. Nav. Supersonic Lab. Wind Tunnel Rept. 39*, 1953.
46. Slack, E. G. Experimental investigation of heat transfer through laminar and turbulent boundary layers on a cooled flat plate at a Mach number of 2.4 *NACA Tech. Note 2686*, 1952.
47. Fallis, W. B. Heat transfer in the transitional and turbulent boundary layers of a

flat plate at supersonic speeds. *Inst. Aerophys., Univ. Toronto, UTIA Rept. 19*, 1952.

48. Pappas, C. C. Measurement of heat transfer in the turbulent boundary layer on a flat plate in supersonic flow and comparison with skin-friction results. *NACA Tech. Note 3222*, 1954.
49. Lees, L. The stability of the laminar boundary layer in a compressible fluid. *NACA Rept. 876*, 1947.
50. van Driest, E. R. *J. Aeronaut. Sci. 19*, 801 (1952).
51. Scherrer, R. Boundary layer transition on a cooled 20° cone at Mach numbers of 1.5 and 2.0. *NACA Tech. Note 2131*, 1950.
52. Higgins, R. W., and Pappas, C. C. An experimental investigation of the effect of surface heating on boundary-layer transition on a flat plate in supersonic flow. *NACA Tech. Note 2351*, 1951.
53. Czarnecki, K. R., and Sinclair, A. R. An extension of the effects of heat transfer on boundary-layer transition on a parabolic body of revolution (NACA RM-10) at a Mach number of 1.61. *NACA Tech. Note 3166*, 1954.
54. Eber, G. R. *J. Aeronaut. Sci. 19*, 55 (1952).
55. van Driest, E. R., and Boison, J. C. *J. Aeronaut. Sci. 22*, 70 (1955).
56. van Driest, E. R., and Boison, J. C. *J. Aeronaut. Sci. 24*, 885 (1957).
57. Buchele, D. R., and Goossens, H. R. *Rev. Sci. Instr. 25*, 262 (1954).
58. Dryden, H. L. *J. Aeronaut. Sci. 20*, 477 (1953).
59. Strength of metal aircraft elements. *Munitions Board Aircraft Comm. U.S. Dept. of Defense, Rept. ANC-5a.* Revised June 1951.
60. A design manual for determining the thermal characteristics of high-speed aircraft. *Air Force Tech. Rept. 5632*, Wright Field, Ohio, 1947.
61. McAdams, W. H. *Heat Transmission.* McGraw-Hill, 1942.
62. Kaye, J. *J. Aeronaut. Sci. 17*, 787 (1950).
63. Martin, J. J. *J. Aeronaut. Sci. 20*, 147 (1953).
64. Fischer, W. W., and Norris, R. H. *Trans. Am. Soc. Mech. Engrs. 71*, 457 (1949).
65. Fischer, W. W., and Norris, R. H. Supersonic convective heat transfer correlations from skin temperature. *General Electric Project Hermes Rept. 55258*, 1949.
66. Tsien, H. S. *J. Aeronaut. Sci. 13*, 653 (1946).
67. Boden, R. H. *Trans. Am. Soc. Mech. Engrs. 73*, 385 (1951).
68. Greenfield, S. *J. Aeronaut. Sci. 18*, 512 (1951).
69. Hilsenrath, J., and Beckett, C. W. Tables of thermodynamic properties of argon-free air to 15,000°K. *Natl. Bur. Standards MIPR-AEDC-1*, 1956.
70. Moore, L. L. *J. Aeronaut. Sci. 19*, 505 (1952).
71. Hansen, C. F. *J. Aeronaut. Sci. 20*, 789 (1953).
72. Rose, P. H., and Riddell, F. R. An investigation of stagnation point heat transfer in dissociated air. *AVCO Research Lab. Research Note 32*, Apr. 1957.
73. Fay, J. A., and Riddell, F. R. Stagnation point heat transfer in dissociated air. *AVCO Research Lab. Research Note 18*, June 1956.
74. van Driest, E. R. Transition and turbulent heating, including possible real gas effects. *OSR-Convair Astronautics Symposium*, Feb. 1957.

# SECTION G

## *COOLING BY PROTECTIVE FLUID FILMS*

S. W. YUAN

**G,1. Introduction.** One of the most important current problems in aeronautical engineering is concerned with the flow of high energy gases. Such flow has been experienced in engines of the turbine or ramjet type, rocket motors, and nuclear reactors which use gases with high temperatures but relatively low velocities to develop power and/or thrust. The combustion chambers, turbine blades, and afterburners are examples of components exposed to high temperature gases. Recently, much attention is being given to the problem of aerodynamic heating in high speed flight, in which exterior surfaces of aircraft and missiles are exposed to gases with low temperatures but high relative velocities. In steady flight at Mach numbers of four or higher, such surfaces become heated to temperatures at which the strength properties of the strongest-known alloys deteriorate markedly. Moreover, the pilot and such critical cargo as instruments and explosives must be protectively cooled.

In rocket motors, where combustion temperatures of 4000 to 5000°F are easily reached, cooling has been used for some time. The conventional method of cooling rocket motors is to use one of the propellants as a regenerative coolant which circulates in ducts around the motor and is then injected into the combustion chamber. This method limits the choice of many high energy propellant combinations such as the hydrogen-oxygen and hydrogen-fluorine systems, because they do not possess the desired physical properties for a satisfactory regenerative coolant. Furthermore, the inherent disadvantage of this method is that it is difficult to increase the heat transfer coefficient of motor wall-to-coolant to a value much higher than those values which exist in motors of current design. This is so because, in order to increase the liquid film coefficient, the velocity of the coolant must be increased at the sacrifice of increasing the pressure drop through the motor. Since the allowable value of pressure drop in the cooling jacket of a jet motor is limited, the coolant velocity and the liquid film coefficient are also limited.

The heat transmitted from the combustion gas to the chamber wall can be considerably reduced by placing some thermally insulating material on the hot gas surface of the wall. Such an insulation has been tried in the form of ceramic coating, but the limited lifetime of refractory materials so far developed for chamber wall coatings has made it impractical for rocket motors. Furthermore, there appears to be a limit to the improvement in materials. It is generally accepted that, ultimately, methods of cooling exposed surfaces must be used. A method of coating the chamber wall with a layer of fluid would insulate the wall better than a ceramic coating because of the much lower thermal conductivity of fluid.

A promising means for controlling the heat flow to the wall of a rocket motor (first used by Germans in the V-2) is the technique of introducing small quantities of liquid at many points, distributed uniformly over the interior surface of the combustion chamber. The liquid so introduced is spread over the chamber wall in a thin film and eventually evaporates. The essential advantage of this film-cooling method is that the screening film of coolant fluid is permitted to vaporize, thus increasing its heat-absorbing capacity many times over that of a system in which the fluid remains in the liquid phase. It has a further advantage in that the fluid will form a heat-resistant layer which separates the hot gases from the chamber wall surface and in this way diminishes the heat transfer rate from the hot gases to the wall.

A logical extension of the film-cooling process is to increase the number of cooling orifices infinitely, i.e. to use a porous wall. The combustion chamber walls to be cooled can be made porous by powder metallurgy or the Poroloy process. A coolant in the form of a gas or liquid can be forced through the pores. Such a technique is often referred to as *sweat or transpiration cooling*. As the fluid passes through the porous wall in a direction opposite to the heat flow, heat will be transmitted from the wall to the fluid, the fluid forming a protective layer on the surface exposed to the hot gases similar to the case of film cooling. In the method of film cooling, the fluid film is gradually destroyed by turbulent mixing with the hot gases so that the effectiveness of the film decreases in the downstream direction from the point of injection. This disadvantage is eliminated in the transpiration-cooling method where the coolant is continuously injected along the entire chamber wall. In addition to this advantage, the method of transpiration cooling provides much greater surface area for heat transfer. It can be seen that the coolant absorbs heat as soon as it enters the abundant region of the porous wall. Because of the great surface area available for heat transfer, the method of transpiration cooling is particularly desirable when nuclear energy is used as the power source for rocket and jet motors.

The purpose of this section is to present a critical review of the fundamental aspects of cooling by protective fluid films. It must be realized that neither the theoretical nor the experimental aspects of this subject have been sufficiently developed to permit a logical presentation, starting from a basic assumption and progressing to the solution for engineering applications. Instead, it is found necessary to review the progress of this demanding subject made along several independent lines of attack which may serve as basic references for further research and exploration. Since the basic theories on heat transfer and fluid dynamics problems are treated at length in other sections of this volume, only the application of such theories to heat transfer in transpiration cooling is discussed in detail in the present section.

## G,2. Flow through Porous Metal.

*Porous metal.* The porosity of a specimen may be defined by

$$\text{Porosity (per cent)} = \frac{\text{specific gravity of the alloy} - \text{specific gravity of the specimen}}{\text{specific gravity of the alloy}}$$

The specific gravity of the specimen can be determined by weighing and measuring the specimen after sintering. An ideal porous medium is a medium which is composed of innumerable voids of varying sizes and shapes termed *pore spaces.* Pores are interconnected to one another by constricted channels through which the contained fluid may flow under the influence of a driving pressure. A clear way to comprehend the porous medium is to visualize a body of ordinary unconsolidated sand.

Porous metals can be produced by the powder metallurgy process. A method adopted by German scientists is to sinter the metal powder in a refractory container without any previous compacting pressure. The advantage of this method is that porous parts having complicated shapes which would be difficult to press in dies can be produced. However, the porosity of the finished product is very difficult to control due to the fact that only one variable, namely the particle size of the powder, seems to have a great influence on the porosity after sintering.

An alternative method of preparing porous metals was developed by Duwez [*1*] at the Jet Propulsion Laboratory of the California Institute of Technology early in 1945. This method consists of mixing the metal powder with a certain amount of porosity-producing agent which is compacted at high pressure and then sintered at a high temperature. The formation of pores in the compact, interconnected by constricted channels, is due to the fact that the porosity-producing agent decomposes into a gaseous state and must escape through the grain of the metal powder. Because of the shrinkage of the compact during sintering, some of these channels may close. However, a sufficient number of channels remain open to make the metal permeable.

The technical details of the methods of preparation of porous metal have been described in [*1*]. As an illustration, the technique used for preparing porous stainless steel by the use of ammonium bicarbonate may be briefly reviewed. The porous specimens were prepared by mixing the metal powder with a certain amount of ammonium bicarbonate, compacting the mixture at 80,000 lb/in.$^2$, and sintering in an atmosphere of pure hydrogen for 4 hours at 2300°F. The variation in porosity is from about 18 to approximately 52 per cent, for a variation of ammonium bicarbonate from 0 to 15 per cent. According to the results of experiments [*1*], the main variable factor is the amount of ammonium bicarbonate which controls porosity. The tensile strength of the porous specimens varies from 45,000 to 8000 lb/in.$^2$, with the variation in porosity from about 17 to 54 per cent. From the viewpoint of strength it is advisable to use the maximum practical compacting pressure and to adjust the amount of ammonium bicarbonate in order to produce the required porosity.

Recently a sintered-wire porous metal known as *Poroloy* was developed by Wheeler and Duwez [*2*] at the California Institute of Technology. The wound-wire porous metal is made by wrapping a very thin and narrow ribbon of flattened wire (composed of any sinterable metal) around a mandrel of any arbitrary cross section. After the wire has been wound on the mandrel to the desired depth, the mandrel and wire, as a unit, are placed in a controlled-atmosphere furnace and then sintered. Following sintering the mandrel is removed and the metallic shape is processed into a finished form. The porosity is formed by the space between the individual strands of wire, and with proper control the pores, of predetermined size, are interconnected and uniformly distributed, and form a predetermined passage for fluid flow through the metal.

The advantages of Poroloy over ordinary sintered powder-porous metals are a higher strength for a given permeability because of its wire construction and a higher ductility because of the continuous strands of fine wire which bear a large portion of applied loads. In sintered porous metals, on the other hand, the entire load must be carried by the individual sinter bonds between the particles of powder. Furthermore, Poroloy can be made like plywood, a nonisotropic material having greatest strength in the direction of the bisection of the acute crossing angle, and the lowest strength at right angles to this direction. When the wire strands cross at right angles the material exhibits a uniform strength in all directions.

*Permeability of porous metal.* An important problem in the design of transpiration-cooled parts is the study of the flow of fluids through porous metals. In other words, the permeability of the metal of which the parts are to be made must be known. The permeability of the metal expresses the capacity of a porous material to pass fluids when pressure differences exist. As a result of the complexity of the structure of porous metals, a complete analytical study of the problem of predicting the permeability is precluded. The following discussion is based on the experimental study of the flow of gas through porous metals [*3,4*].

For low values of velocity, Darcy's law

$$\frac{\Delta p}{L} = \text{const}\,\frac{\mu v_{\mathrm{w}}}{d^2} \tag{2-1}$$

gives the relationship between the pressure difference $\Delta p$ acting on the two surfaces of a plain porous wall of thickness $L$, the viscosity $\mu$, the velocity $v_{\mathrm{w}}$ of the coolant flowing through the porous wall, and the length $d$ characterizing the pore openings. This law is valid only if the pressure drop is the result of viscous shear in laminar flow. It gives a linear relationship between pressure drop and velocity analogous to Poiseuille flow in a pipe. For high Reynolds numbers the pressure drop is proportional to the density of the coolant and the square of the velocity which can be expressed as follows:

$$\frac{\Delta p}{L} = \text{const}\,\frac{\rho v_{\mathrm{w}}^2}{d} \tag{2-2}$$

In the flow through a porous medium, unlike the flow in pipes, there is no definite small range of Reynolds number to distinguish the laws given in Eq. 2-1 and 2-2. The gradual transition from the Darcy regime is due to the inertia of the fluid contracting and expanding through the pores. The inertia factor becomes progressively more important with increasing velocity. Hence, in the pressure drop equation, the loss due to both viscous shear and inertia effects must be included. The two foregoing equations can be combined in the following manner if the weight rate of flow $G$ is introduced to take account of the compressibility effect. It becomes

$$\frac{\Delta p^2}{L} = \alpha\left(\frac{2p_0\mu}{\sigma_0}\right)G + \beta\left(\frac{2p_0}{\sigma_0 g}\right)G^2 \tag{2-3}$$

in which $\sigma_0$ is the specific weight of the fluid at a reference pressure $p_0$. The two coefficients, $\alpha$ and $\beta$, defined by Eq. 2-3, are independent of the nature of the fluid and have only the dimension of some unknown length characterizing the structure of the porous medium itself.

Fig. G,2a gives typical curves of pressure-squared difference vs. the weight rate of flow from experimental results made with fine iron and fine ammonium bicarbonate powders. Fig. G,2b gives the relation between the strength, the flow rate, the relative density, and the pressure for Poroloy stainless steel with a 35° crossing angle, where $p_1$ and $p_2$ are in absolute pressure (lb/in.$^2$) and $L$ is the thickness in inches. The viscous resistance coefficient $\alpha$ and the inertia resistance coefficient $\beta$ of Eq. 2-3 can be determined from these experimental curves. The viscous resistance coefficient $\alpha$ is found to be inversely proportional to approximately the seventh power of the porosity. The variation of the inertial resistance coefficient $\beta$ with porosity is rather complex and the only conclusion to be drawn is that it decreases with increasing porosity. The relation between the coefficients $\alpha$ and $\beta$ and the percentage porosity of porous metals can therefore be established only for a given metal. A more general correlation of the measured permeability values obtained from different metals cannot yet be obtained.

The complexity of the permeability problem of porous metals so far obtained lies in the fact that not all of the pores or channels are neces-

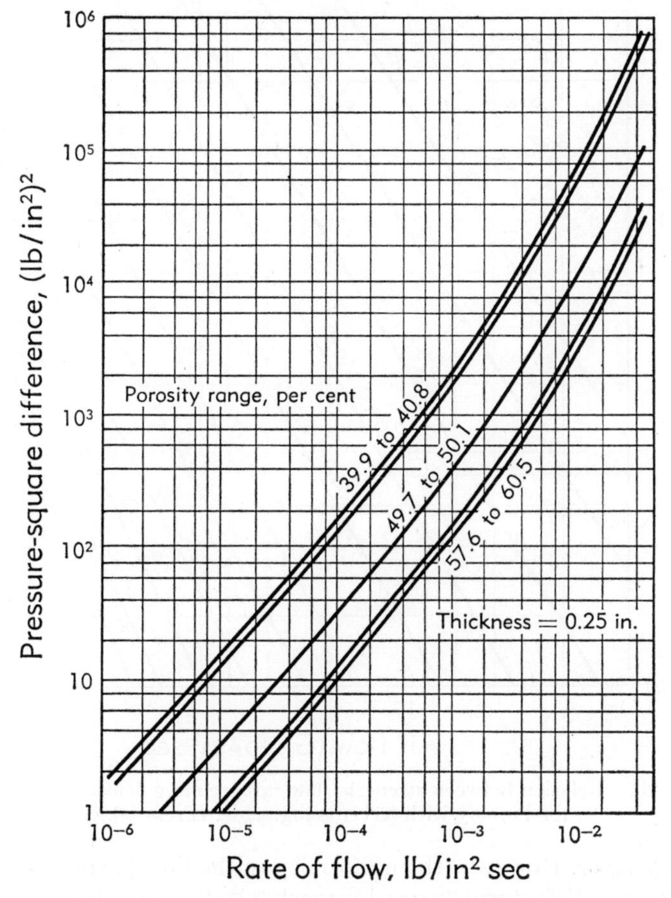


Fig. G,2a. Pressure-square difference vs. rate of flow of nitrogen for porous iron specimens prepared with fine iron and fine ammonium bicarbonate powders. Air at $T_0$ = 540°R, $\mu_0$ = 0.017 centipoise. (From [*4*].)

sarily continuous throughout the metal specimen. Furthermore the vague knowledge of the distribution of the pores and the complex passages interconnecting the pores in porous metals makes it very difficult to obtain any quantitative correlation between the permeability coefficient and the porosity of porous metals.

The pattern of the flow of gases leaving a porous metal surface was investigated experimentally at the Jet Propulsion Laboratory [*5*]. The results indicate that the fluid leaves a porous surface in the form of a number of small jets which coalesce almost immediately to form a uniform outward-moving layer. On the other hand, there is another type of flow pattern in which the fluid leaves the porous surface in the form of isolated jets which maintain their identity and create a very turbulent

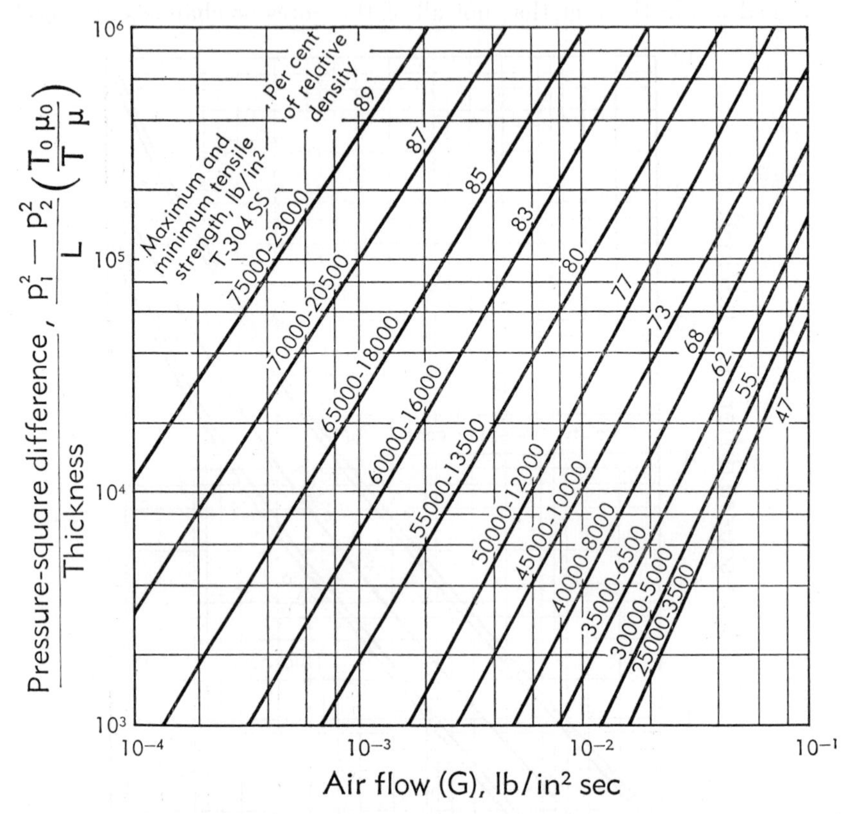


Fig. G,2b. Relation between strength, flow rate, relative density and pressure for Poroloy with 35° crossing angle. (From [2].)

boundary layer. However, the uniformity of the flow pattern can be controlled to a satisfactory degree by mechanical means during the fabricating process of a sintered-wire porous metal.

**G,3. Physical Nature of Transpiration-Cooling Process.** In discussing the problem of heat transfer inside transpiration-cooled porous walls, it is desirable to consider the simplest possible case. Since the pattern of the porous passages is a very complicated three-dimensional network, the assumption of a network consisting of identical cylindrical channels running from one end of the specimen to the other is made. Fig. G,3 shows the variation of the temperature throughout the porous wall and through the boundary layers. A cold medium flowing along the bottom surface of the porous wall is pressed through the pores in the wall represented by cylindrical channels in Fig. G,3 and leaves the wall on the upper side. Hot gas with a free stream temperature $T_\infty$ flows along the upper surface of the porous wall and builds up a boundary layer which is usually turbulent. Within this turbulent boundary layer, a laminar sublayer forms in the immediate vicinity of the surface where the temperature drops rapidly to the value $T_w$ (temperature of the upper wall surface). The amount of heat flow $q$ per unit of time and surface area entering the wall through the upper surface is determined by the temperature gradient on the wall. Since the layers adjacent to the wall are

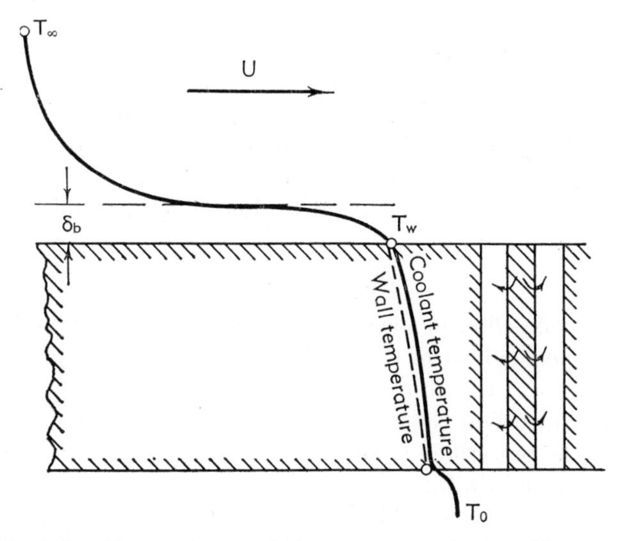


Fig. G,3. Temperature variation between coolant and hot fluid.

at rest, heat is transferred to the surface of the wall, essentially by conduction. The heat transfer in the boundary layers is discussed in detail later.

The investigation of heat transfer inside the transpiration-cooled porous wall was made by Weinbaum and Wheeler [*6*]. In this study it is taken that no change of state of cooling fluid occurs and that its direction of flow is opposite to that of the heat flow through the cylindrical bars of porous metal. It is further assumed that a steady state of heat flow is attained. The time rate of heat flow is, in the case of solid metal, given by the familiar Fourier equation

$$\dot{q} = -kA \frac{dt}{dz} \tag{3-1}$$

where $A$ is the cross-sectional area of the porous wall, $k$ is the thermal conductivity of the metal, and $t$ is the temperature of the metal at any given point inside the wall. This expression must be corrected to take into account the fact that the wall consists only partially of solid metal. If $s$ denotes the porosity of the metal, then Eq. 3-1 can be rewritten as follows:

$$q = -k(1 - s)A \frac{dt}{dz} \tag{3-2}$$

The rate of heat transfer from metal to fluid is proportional to the area of contact and to the difference between the temperature $t$ of the metal and the temperature $T$ of the fluid. Since both $t$ and $T$ vary along the cylindrical bars, this heat transfer changes continuously along the width of the porous metal. For an infinitesimally small length $dz$, the following expression holds:

$$dq = -hA\pi Nd(t - T)dz \tag{3-3}$$

where $h$ is the heat transfer coefficient, $N$ is the number of passages per unit cross-sectional area, $d$ is the diameter of the cylindrical pore, and $\pi Nd$ is the total circumference at any cross section.

The heat conduction from metal to fluid is used in raising the temperature of the fluid, hence

$$dq = Qc_p dT \tag{3-4}$$

where $Q$ is the mass flow of the cooling fluid through the cylindrical pores and $c_p$ is the specific heat of the cooling fluid at constant pressure.

The solutions of the above three simultaneous differential equations give the temperature of the metal and the fluid at any point within the porous wall. The prescribed values of the temperature of the cooling fluid before its entrance into the cylindrical bars and the temperatures of the metal at both the hot and cold ends are used to determine the constants of integration. The resulting expressions show that the temperatures of the metal and the fluid become almost indistinguishable except within a very narrow range near the cold end of the wall. The temperature distribution along the width of the porous wall is not linear, as in the case of a solid metal, but is an exponential function.

The indistinguishable difference in temperature between the cooling fluid on its flow through the pores and the wall material can be realized from the fact that the metal surface area in contact with the cooling fluid is very great in the porous wall. The cooling fluid therefore leaves the porous wall with the wall temperature $T_w$ and with small velocity normal to the surface. In passing away from the surface, the cooling fluid picks up momentum from the gas flow until it finally reaches the outside gas velocity. At the same time its temperature increases either by conduction or by turbulent mixing until at some distance the gas temperature is reached. A counterflow is thus created between the heat flowing from the hot gas toward the wall and the cooling fluid flowing away from the wall.

The cooling fluid continuously absorbs heat from the hot gas and in this process the over-all heat transfer from hot gas to the wall is diminished.

In the foregoing discussion the cooling medium is assumed to be a gas. If a liquid coolant is used and the mass flow of the coolant is great enough, then the liquid evaporates from the upper surface of the wall. The heat transfer from the hot gas to the wall is essentially the same as in the case when a gas coolant is used. It is evident that cooling with a liquid is more effective than cooling with a gas since considerable heat is absorbed by the vaporization process. There is a boundary layer on the coolant entrance side of the wall within which the coolant temperature increases from the initial value $T_0$ to the temperature with which the coolant enters the pores. The thickness of this boundary layer and the temperature increase within it, however, are much smaller than on the hot side of the wall.

## G,4. Heat Transfer in Transpiration-Cooled Boundary Layer.

General Problems. It is well known that fluid flowing along a solid wall builds up a boundary layer along the surface of the wall. When a temperature difference exists between the fluid and the wall, a thermal boundary layer is built up along the wall, which, for gases, has a thickness of the same order of magnitude as a hydrodynamic boundary layer. The transfer of heat between a fluid stream and wall mainly takes place within this boundary layer. The boundary layers may be laminar or turbulent. Since the amount of coolant injection necessary to keep the same wall temperature is, for the turbulent boundary layer, about twice that for the laminar one, it is important to study the conditions of flow for each particular case.

In the combustion chamber of jet motors, due to the rough combustion process, the flow is certainly of the turbulent type. Considering the high negative pressure gradient in the flow through the nozzle, the flat plate solution is assumed to yield some indication of heat transfer in transpiration-cooled turbulent boundary layer in combustion chambers and nozzles. Furthermore, due to the extremely high accelerations at the throat of the nozzle, the flow in the nozzle might be laminar in some cases. In addition to reducing turbulence, a negative pressure gradient tends to increase the stability of the laminar boundary layer in the nozzle.

On the other hand, the flow along a gas turbine blade is expected to be laminar in the region around the nose of the blade. Due to the existence of pressure gradient along the blade surface, the boundary layer solution for the flat plate can no longer be applied here. Although a positive pressure gradient in the flow direction would decrease the heat transfer from the hot fluid to wall, the stability of the laminar layer is decreased. The exact location of the transition to turbulent flow cannot be exactly predicted yet by calculation, although a reasonable indication can be expected from the stability analysis which is discussed later. The influence of a pressure gradient in transpiration-cooled turbulent boundary layer theory is still uncertain; however, it is believed that the influence is less on a turbulent layer than on a laminar one.

Another important application of transpiration cooling is in reducing the aerodynamic heating problem in high speed flight. Since both heat transfer and drag coefficients are known to be lower for laminar than for turbulent flows, it is more advantageous to have a laminar boundary layer than the turbulent type. The solution of a transpiration-cooled boundary layer on a flat plate can be employed here with reasonably good approximation.

The treatments in the subsequent articles are divided into approximate methods for the solution of the laminar boundary layer, exact solutions of the laminar boundary layer, and approximate solutions of the turbulent boundary layer. The stream fluid and the injected fluid are assumed to be homogeneous.

Approximate Methods for the Solution of Heat Transfer in the Laminar Boundary Layer. The heat transfer in the laminar boundary layer of a transpiration-cooled wall in a flow can be solved by the von Kármán momentum and energy equations for the boundary layer. The basic derivation of these equations is treated at length in Vol. IV. For two-dimensional compressible flow with a pressure gradient and a uniform injection (or suction) at the wall, the momentum and energy equations for the boundary layer are given, respectively, as

$$\frac{\partial}{\partial x}\int_0^{\delta_u} \rho u(u_e - u)dy + \frac{\partial u_e}{\partial x}\int_0^{\delta_u} (\rho_e u_e - \rho u)dy = \rho_w u_e v_w + \left(\mu \frac{\partial u}{\partial y}\right)_w \tag{4-1}$$

$$\frac{\partial}{\partial x}\int_0^{\delta_h} \rho u c_p(T_e - T)dy + \frac{\partial(c_p T_e)}{\partial x}\int_0^{\delta_h} u(\rho_e - \rho)dy + \int_0^{\delta_h} \mu\left(\frac{\partial u}{\partial y}\right)^2 dy$$

$$= \rho_w v_w c_p(T_e - T_w) + \left(k \frac{\partial T}{\partial y}\right)_w \tag{4-2}$$

where the subscript $_e$ represents quantities at the outer edge of the laminar layer and $_w$ quantities at the wall. The other symbols are standard and a sketch of velocity and temperature fields within the boundary layer along a transpiration-cooled wall is shown in Fig. G,4a.

*Incompressible boundary layer on a porous flat plate.* It was mentioned in the previous article that in many of the applications of heat transfer the boundary layer is turbulent. Nevertheless, it is interesting and important to understand the mechanism of heat transfer qualitatively, as well as to clarify some physical quantities involved which cannot be easily interpreted in complicated cases. The following analysis is made by the investigation of the flow of a hot gas over a porous flat plate under the condition of uniform gas injection from the bottom of the plate. The assumptions made in the present investigation are: (1) the mass density and viscosity of the fluid are assumed to be constant, (2) the flow is assumed to be laminar, and the fluid along the wall and the coolant flowing through the pores are assumed homogeneous, and (3) the wall temperature in the direction of flow is constant.

In accordance with the above assumptions, Eq. 4-1 and 4-2 can be simplified considerably by dropping both the second terms on the left-hand side and taking out $\rho$, $\mu$, and $c_p$ from the integrals. Furthermore, both $u_e$ and $T_e$ are equal to the constant quantities $U$ and $T_\infty$ in the free stream. The term giving the heat produced through internal friction in Eq. 4-2 can be neglected because it is comparatively small at the low speed considered here.

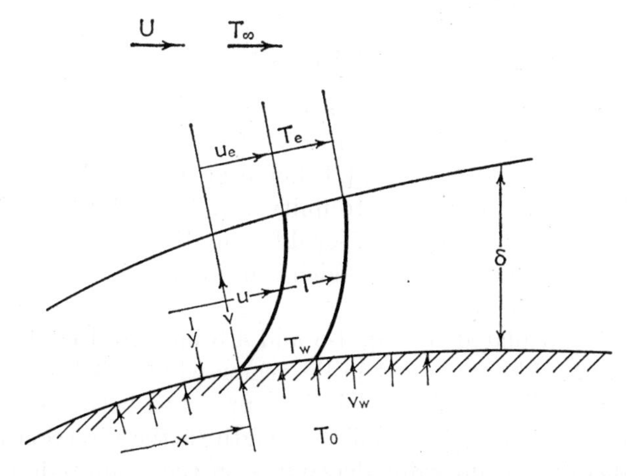


Fig. G,4a. Boundary layer along a porous transpiration-cooled wall.

In order to solve these two simplified momentum and energy equations for the boundary layer, polynomials of the fourth degree as approximations of the velocity and temperature profiles are assumed. The coefficients of the fourth degree polynomials are calculated from the boundary conditions used by Pohlhausen, except that at the wall the velocity perpendicular to the main flow is equal to the injection velocity $v_w$ instead of zero value. The results are, for velocity profile,

$$\frac{u}{U} = \left[2\left(\frac{y}{\delta_u}\right) - 2\left(\frac{y}{\delta_u}\right)^3 + \left(\frac{y}{\delta_u}\right)^4\right] - \frac{2\lambda}{1+\lambda}\left[\left(\frac{y}{\delta_u}\right) - 3\left(\frac{y}{\delta_u}\right)^2 + 3\left(\frac{y}{\delta_u}\right)^3 - \left(\frac{y}{\delta_u}\right)^4\right] \quad (4\text{-}3)$$

and for temperature profile,

$$\frac{T - T_w}{T_\infty - T_w} = \left[2\left(\frac{y}{\delta_h}\right) - 2\left(\frac{y}{\delta_h}\right)^3 + \left(\frac{y}{\delta_h}\right)^4\right] - \frac{2\lambda_h}{1+\lambda_h}\left[\left(\frac{y}{\delta_h}\right) - 3\left(\frac{y}{\delta_h}\right)^2 + 3\left(\frac{y}{\delta_h}\right)^3 - \left(\frac{y}{\delta_h}\right)^4\right] \quad (4\text{-}4)$$

where $\lambda = v_w\delta_u/\nu$ and $\lambda_h = v_w\delta_h/\nu$; $\delta_u$ and $\delta_h$ are thicknesses of the hydrodynamic and the thermal boundary layers, respectively.

With the aid of Eq. 4-3 and 4-4, the analytical solutions of the momentum and energy equations for boundary layers are obtained. The results can be expressed as follows:

$$\xi = \frac{2}{35}\left[ 31.18 + 12\lambda - \frac{10}{1+\lambda} + \frac{9}{2}\ln\frac{(1+\lambda)^2}{1+3\lambda+3\lambda^2} - \frac{35\sqrt{2}}{3}\tan^{-1} 2\sqrt{3}\left(\lambda + \frac{1}{2}\right)\right] \tag{4-5}$$

for the momentum equation and

$$\xi = f(\lambda_h, \zeta, Pr) \tag{4-6}$$

for energy equation where $\xi = (Ux/\nu)(v_w/U)^2$, $\zeta = \delta_h/\delta_u$ and $Pr$ is the Prandtl number. The complete expression for Eq. 4-6 is much too complicated to be presented here and [7] should be consulted.

For a Prandtl number equal to unity Eq. 4-5 and 4-6 are identical. It is noted that the changes of $\lambda_h$ for different Prandtl numbers are not appreciable within the range of $\xi$ which is of interest in the investigation of transpiration cooling.

The results calculated by Eq. 4-5 and 4-6 indicate that the relation between $\xi$ and $\lambda_h$ is linear except in the region where $\xi$ is less than unity. In other words, a linear relationship is approached between the boundary layer thickness ($\delta_u$ or $\delta_h$) and the length in the direction of flow $x$ when $\delta_u$ reaches a certain value depending on the magnitude of $v_w$. The Blasius solution reveals, for an impermeable flat plate, that the boundary layer thickness is directly proportional to the square root of the length in the direction of flow as well as the viscosity of the fluid. In the case of flow over a flat plate with injection when $\delta_u$ reaches a certain thickness, the effect of viscosity on the boundary layer becomes negligibly small, and the formation of the boundary layer is mainly due to the additional mass fluid injected into the main fluid. Hence the ratio of the boundary layer thickness to the length in the direction of flow is linearly proportional to the ratio of injected velocity to the main stream velocity. The instability of the laminar boundary layer may be interpreted from the inflection points occurring in the velocity and temperature profiles. It is found that the larger the value of $v_w/U$ the farther the inflection points move outward from the plate. A discussion on stability considerations of the laminar boundary layer is given later on in this article.

The temperature field in the laminar boundary layer described in the previous paragraphs may be used to determine the amount of coolant required to cool the wall to a predesignated temperature. From the balance between the heat flow to the wall from the hot gas and the heat absorbed by the coolant, one gets

$$k\left(\frac{\partial T}{\partial y}\right)_w = \rho_w v_w c_p (T_w - T_0) \tag{4-7}$$

Since the fluid layers adjacent to the wall are at rest, the heat flow from the hot gas to the wall must be transferred by conduction through these layers. This is represented by the term on the left-hand side of Eq. 4-7. The term on the right-hand side of Eq. 4-7 is the heat absorbed by the coolant. In the case where variation of wall temperature in the direction of flow is considered, an additional term representing the heat flow in the metal must be added in Eq. 4-7. Hence the thermal conductivity of the metal enters into the energy balance equation.

At the suggestion of the author, Ness [*8*] made a theoretical investigation of the temperature distribution along a semi-infinite porous flat plate under the condition of uniform coolant injection. A heat-balance differential equation of the second order, including a term containing the physical parameters of the plate, is used in conjunction with the solution of the equations of continuity, momentum, and energy. The temperature distribution along the plate is obtained for the respective cases of thermal conductivity not equal to, and equal to, zero. Results show that the inclusion of the thermal conductivity term in the heat-balance equation eliminates the infinite temperature gradient at the leading edge.

The total heat flow to the plate can be obtained by integrating Eq. 4-7 over the entire plate of length $l$. The relation between the wall temperature and the amount of coolant needed is then determined as follows:

$$\frac{T_\infty - T_w}{T_w - T_0} = \frac{105}{2}\left(\frac{v_w}{U}\right)^2\left(\frac{Ul}{\nu}\right)\left[\left\{\frac{19}{1+\lambda} + \frac{5}{(1+\lambda)^2} - \frac{27}{2}\ln\frac{(1+\lambda)^2}{1+3\lambda+3\lambda^2} + 35\sqrt{3}\tan^{-1}2\sqrt{3}\left(\lambda+\frac{1}{2}\right)\right\}_0^{\lambda_l}\right]^{-1} \tag{4-8}$$

where $\lambda_l$ can be determined from the curve $\lambda$ vs. $\xi$ for a corresponding value of $\xi_l$, i.e. $(Ul/\nu)(v_w/U)^2$. For a predesignated wall temperature and given Prandtl number and Reynolds number, the amount of coolant required per unit time can be determined from Eq. 4-8, provided that the temperature of the hot fluid and of the coolant are known. The expression in Eq. 4-8 is derived for $Pr = 1$ and [*7*] should be consulted for $Pr \neq 1$.

In Fig. G,4b the ratio of the temperature difference, $(T_\infty - T_w)/(T_w - T_0)$ is plotted against the coolant velocity ratio $v_w/U$ for $Pr = 1$. The influence of the Reynolds number on the coolant discharge and the wall temperature is rather appreciable. As the Reynolds number increases the coolant discharge decreases for a given wall temperature. The opposite is found to be the case for the Prandtl number. The above phenomena can be explained by the fact that heat transfer from a hot gas to the wall is inversely proportional to the thickness of the thermal boundary layer adjacent to the wall. Since the thickness of the thermal boundary layer is directly proportional to the Reynolds number of length in the direction of flow, the first phenomenon is clear. As mentioned in the previous article the increase of Prandtl number does not increase appreciably the thickness of the thermal boundary layer. On the other hand, the increase in fluid viscosity due to the increases in the Prandtl number may give a sufficiently low Reynolds number of boundary layer thickness to increase the final heat transfer to the wall.

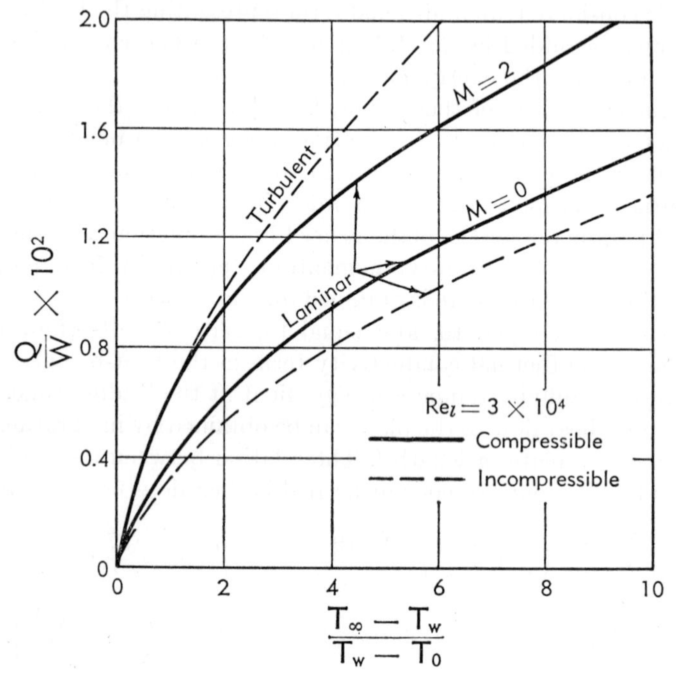


Fig. G,4b. Temperature ratio vs. mass flow ratio. (From [7,9].)

The film heat transfer coefficient $h_i$ between the hot gas and the wall can be determined by Eq. 4-8. The ratio of film heat transfer coefficient $h_i$ with transpiration cooling to the film heat transfer coefficient $h$ with impermeable plate under the same conditions of flow over the plate as a function of $v_w/U$ ratio is given in Fig. G,4c. It is interesting to see that for an injected coolant velocity equal to 1 per cent of the hot gas velocity, the heat transfer to the wall can be reduced to about one-fifth of the value without transpiration cooling.

*Compressible boundary layer on a porous flat plate.* In order to understand the phenomena of heat transfer in transpiration cooling in which large temperature differences occur across the boundary layer [9], the physical properties of the fluid must be taken into consideration. The assumptions made in the present article are: (1) the inverse proportion between the mass density and the temperature inside the boundary layer is used, and the viscosity is assumed to be proportional to both the square root and three-fourths power of the temperature; (2) the flow is assumed to be laminar, and the fluid flowing along the wall and the coolant flowing through the pores are assumed homogeneous; (3) the Prandtl number is assumed to be equal to unity; and (4) the wall temperature in the direction of flow is constant.

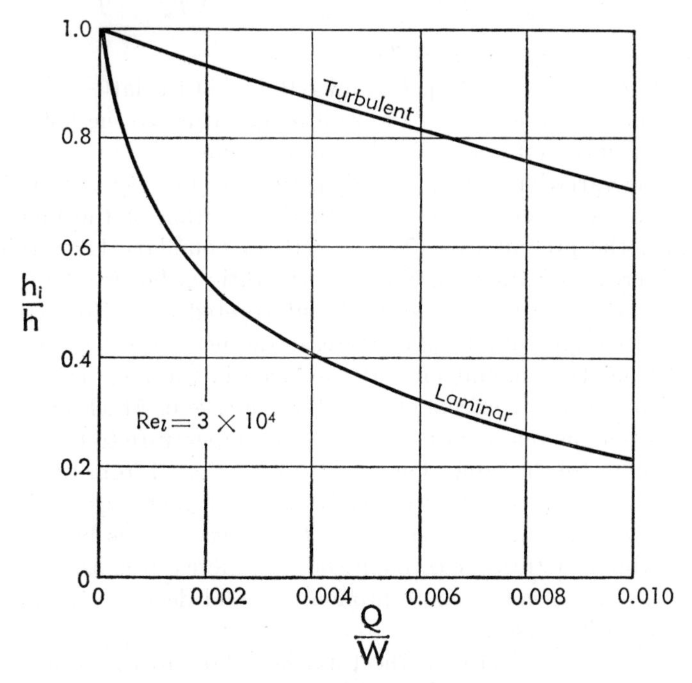


Fig. G,4c. Ratio of heat transfer coefficient with and without transpiration-cooled plate vs. mass flow ratio.

Crocco [*10*] has shown that, for a Prandtl number equal to unity, the equation of motion in the boundary layer of a flat plate in steady compressible flow and the corresponding energy equation can be satisfied by equating the temperature $T$ to a certain parabolic function of the velocity $u$ only. This relation between $T$ and $u$ is

$$\frac{T}{T_\infty} = \frac{T_w}{T_\infty} - \left(\frac{T_w}{T_\infty} - 1\right)\frac{u}{U} + \frac{\gamma - 1}{2} M^2 \frac{u}{U}\left(1 - \frac{u}{U}\right) \qquad (4\text{-}9)$$

With the aid of Eq. 4-9 the variation of mass density and viscosity inside the boundary layer can then be expressed as a function of the velocity $u$ only. As in the case of incompressible flow a polynomial of the fourth degree as an approximation to the velocity profile is assumed and its coefficients are calculated from the boundary conditions as described previously. Eq. 4-1 can then be solved upon substitution of the velocity profile and the expressions for mass density and viscosity. The results can be expressed as follows:

$$\xi = \frac{\text{const}}{M^2} \frac{\mu_w}{\mu_\infty} f\left(\lambda, \frac{T_w}{T_\infty}, M^2\right) \tag{4-10}$$

where

$$\xi = \frac{Ux}{\nu_\infty} \left(\frac{\rho_w v_w}{\rho_\infty U}\right)^2, \quad \lambda = \frac{\rho_w v_w \delta_u}{6\mu_w} - f\left(\frac{T_\infty}{T_w}, M^2\right)$$

depending on $\mu \sim \sqrt{T}$ or $\mu \sim T^{\frac{3}{4}}$.

The difference between Eq. 4-5 and 4-10 is that the latter contains the Mach number and the ratio of the wall temperature to the hot gas temperature which do not appear in the former equation. This is due to the fact that the variation of the mass density and viscosity as functions of temperature are taken into account in the solution of the momentum equation in the present case. The growth in boundary layer thickness with the increase of Mach number and the ratio of hot gas temperature to the wall temperature can be easily interpreted from Eq. 4-10. Since the effect of compressibility is to increase the heat transfer through the wall, and since the amount of heat produced in the boundary layer increases with speed, the effects of both the increase of Mach number and the ratio of hot gas temperature to the wall temperature to the boundary layer thickness are the same. The results as calculated from Eq. 4-10 also reveal that the temperature gradient at the wall increases as the Mach number increases, and decreases as $v_w/U$ increases. This behavior indicates that the heat transfer through the wall increases as the compressibility of the flow becomes more pronounced and decreases as the injection of coolant increases.

From the balance between the total heat flow to the wall from the hot gas and the total heat absorbed by the coolant, one obtains

$$\int_0^l k_w \left(\frac{\partial T}{\partial y}\right)_w dx = \rho_w v_w c_p (T_w - T_0) l \tag{4-11}$$

The temperature gradient at the wall can be obtained from Eq. 4-9 and 4-10. The relation between the wall temperature and the rate of coolant injection is then determined by the following expression:

$$\frac{T_\infty - T_w}{T_w - T_0} = Pr_w Re_l \left(\frac{T_\infty}{T_w} - 1\right) \frac{\mu_\infty}{\mu_w} \frac{Q}{W} f\left(\lambda_l, \frac{T_\infty}{T_w}, M^2\right) \tag{4-12}$$

where

$$\frac{Q}{W} = \frac{\rho_w v_w}{\rho_\infty U}$$

The influence of variation in the physical properties of the gas across the boundary layer to the transpiration cooling can be seen in Fig. G,4b.

It indicates that for zero Mach number, unless the temperature difference across the boundary layer is large, say $T_\infty/T_w > 3$, the increase of the rate of the coolant injection in order to maintain a predesignated wall temperature is about 10 per cent over the case in which constant physical properties of the gas are assumed. On the other hand, an appreciable increase of the rate of the coolant injection for maintaining a predesignated wall temperature is found between the case of $M = 2$ and $M = 0$. This leads to the conclusion that for a flow of subsonic speed and in which the temperature difference of the hot gas relative to the wall is not large, the physical properties of the gas may be regarded as constant in the application of transpiration cooling.

As already mentioned, the relation between the rate of the coolant injection and the wall temperature is based on the average value in a flow of gas over a plate with a given Reynolds number. It must be borne in mind that the boundary layer thickness increases almost linearly with the length in the direction of flow, and the heat transfer to the wall decreases proportionally from the leading edge of the plate to downstream. This results in a longitudinal temperature gradient along the transpiration-cooled wall and, naturally, heat flow through the thermally conductive plate occurs. For this reason, as far as the laminar flow is concerned, the efficient method in transpiration cooling is to vary the rate of the coolant injection along the plate in accordance with the local heat transfer at the wall [*11*].

*Compressible boundary layer on a porous wall with a pressure gradient.* Flows with pressure gradients (favorable and/or adverse) are of considerable practical importance in connection with the transpiration cooling of turbine blades or airfoil surfaces in high speed flow (aerodynamic heating problem) [*12*]. The flow along a gas turbine blade is expected to be laminar at least in the region around the nose of the blade, while at supersonic speeds it may be possible to maintain a laminar boundary layer along aircraft and missile surfaces. Since the presence of an adverse pressure gradient has an effect similar to that of a normal injection mass flow, i.e. they both tend to increase the boundary layer thickness, it is the purpose of this article to determine the net effect of these parameters on the flow over a transpiration-cooled surface. The present investigation is based on the assumption that the coefficient of viscosity is linearly proportional to the absolute temperature and the Prandtl number is unity.

In order to solve the momentum equation (Eq. 4-1) and the energy equation (Eq. 4-2) for the hydrodynamic and thermal boundary layer thickness $\delta_u$ and $\delta_h$, respectively, it is convenient to replace the normal distance $y$ by the variable $t$, defined as follows:

$$y = \int_0^t \left(\frac{T}{T_e}\right) dt \tag{4-13}$$

Eq. 4-2 can be further simplified if the stagnation enthalpy $h^0 = (u/2)^2 + c_pT$ is used instead of the absolute temperature $T$. If, with the above assumptions, both the velocity and stagnation enthalpy profiles are assumed as fourth degree polynomials in $t$, satisfying appropriate conditions at the outer edge of the boundary layer and at the wall, and these profiles are substituted into the modified equations (Eq. 4-1 and 4-2), then two ordinary differential equations in the nondimensional hydrodynamic and thermal thicknesses are obtained. On the basis of a uniform wall temperature, general approximate solutions of these differential equations for the boundary layer thicknesses are derived. These solutions are valid for a prescribed external flow as given by $u_e/U$ and $M_\infty$, and for a given wall temperature and mass flow injection distribution. By this means the boundary layer characteristics can then be calculated with comparative ease. The following general conclusions are drawn from the above analysis: (1) in the region of an adverse pressure gradient, the cooling of the wall tends to delay the separation of the flow, (2) for a fixed wall temperature, normal mass flow injection tends to promote separation, although in the absence of an adverse pressure gradient, injection alone cannot cause separation; and (3) the effect of the wall temperature on the boundary layer characteristics depends on whether the axial pressure gradient is adverse or favorable. The skin friction tends to be diminished by a decrease in the wall temperature (for fixed injection) in a favorable pressure gradient, but tends to be increased in an adverse pressure gradient. Similar conclusions hold for the Nusselt number but it is less sensitive to change in the wall temperature than the skin friction.

In the preceding analysis, the wall temperature and the injection mass flow have been treated as independent quantities. Actually, however, a consideration of the heat balance at the wall indicates that the wall temperature and the amount of injection mass flow are related to each other through the temperature of the coolant. Thus, by considering such a heat balance, a new parameter involving the coolant temperature is introduced. The details of this analysis can be found in [*13,14*].

Exact Solution of Heat Transfer in the Laminar Boundary Layer. In the preceding articles, approximate methods for the solution of heat transfer in laminar boundary layers on a transpiration-cooled wall have been discussed. The solutions obtained by approximate methods have explained most of the physical phenomena in the transpiration-cooling problems, even though they satisfy the differential equations of boundary layer flow only on the average.

The present article considers some exact solutions of the equations of boundary layer flow. The essential restrictions of the exact solutions are that they are based on the case in which the velocity outside of the boundary layer is proportional to a power of the distance along the main flow (wedge flow) and that the velocity of fluid injection is proportional to the reciprocal of the square root of the distance from the leading edge of a flat plate. However, the velocity and temperature profiles obtained by this method are quite accurate. They can be used in a laminar boundary layer stability analysis.

The equations of the laminar boundary layer for steady state flow of a viscous compressible fluid with heat transfer may be obtained from Vol. IV as

*Momentum equation:*

$$\rho u \frac{\partial u}{\partial x} + \rho v \frac{\partial u}{\partial y} = \frac{\partial}{\partial y}\left(\mu \frac{\partial u}{\partial y}\right) - \frac{\partial p}{\partial x} \tag{4-14}$$

*Continuity equation:*

$$\frac{\partial(\rho u)}{\partial x} + \frac{\partial(\rho v)}{\partial y} = 0 \tag{4-15}$$

*Energy equation:*

$$c_p\left(\rho u \frac{\partial T}{\partial x} + \rho v \frac{\partial T}{\partial y}\right) = \frac{\partial}{\partial y}\left(k \frac{\partial T}{\partial y}\right) + \mu\left(\frac{\partial u}{\partial y}\right)^2 + u \frac{\partial p}{\partial x} \tag{4-16}$$

The boundary conditions are: when $y = 0$,

$$\left.\begin{aligned} &u = 0; \quad v = v_w(x); \quad T = T_w \\ &\text{and when } y = \infty, \\ &u = u_e; \quad \frac{\partial u}{\partial y} = 0; \quad T = T_e; \quad \frac{\partial T}{\partial y} = 0 \end{aligned}\right\} \tag{4-17}$$

*Incompressible boundary layer with constant fluid properties.* In the case of incompressible laminar boundary layer flow with constant fluid properties ($\rho$ = constant and $\mu$ = constant) [*15*], the last two terms in Eq. 4-16 can be neglected. When the velocity outside the boundary layer is assumed to be proportional to a power of distance along the wall from the stagnation point ($u_e = cx^m$), the transformation methods of Schlichting [*16*] and of Falkner and Skan [*17*] can be applied. With the following changes in variables:

$$\left.\begin{aligned} \eta &= y\sqrt{\frac{m+1}{2}}\sqrt{\frac{u_e}{\nu x}} \\ f &= \sqrt{\frac{m+1}{2}}\frac{\psi}{\sqrt{\nu x u_e}} \\ \theta &= \frac{T - T_w}{T_e - T_w} \end{aligned}\right\} \tag{4-18}$$

where $u = \partial\psi/\partial y$, $v = -\partial\psi/\partial x$ and $m$ is the Euler number, the momentum equation (Eq. 4-14) and the energy equation (Eq. 4-16) are transformed into the following two ordinary differential equations with $f$ and $\theta$ as functions of $\eta$ only:

$$\frac{d^3f}{d\eta^3} + f\frac{d^2f}{d\eta^2} - \frac{2m}{1+m}\left[\left(\frac{df}{d\eta}\right)^2 - 1\right] = 0 \tag{4-19}$$

and

$$\frac{d^2\theta}{d\eta^2} + Prf\frac{d\theta}{d\eta} = 0 \tag{4-20}$$

With the boundary conditions given in Eq. 4-17 the above transformation is based on the assumption that the temperature of the wall is constant and the normal injection velocity at the wall is given by

$$-\sqrt{\frac{m+1}{2}}\,f_w = \frac{v_w}{u_e}\sqrt{\frac{u_e x}{\nu}} = \text{const} \tag{4-21}$$

and $v_w \sim 1/\sqrt{x}$ for a constant $u_e$.

The differential equation (Eq. 4-19) can be solved only numerically and Eq. 4-20 can readily be integrated if the function $f$ is known from the solution of Eq. 4-19.

Numerical results for a laminar boundary layer flow on a flat plate ($m = 0$) and for flow near a stagnation point ($m = 1$) were given in [*16*]. With the aid of these solutions the heat transfer phenomena in the above two cases for Prandtl number equal to unity were calculated in [*15*]. The results can be briefly summarized as follows:

1. In the case of flow on a flat plate, the heat transfer coefficient $h$ decreases rapidly for an increase in $(v_w/u_e)\sqrt{Re_x}$. It is reduced to one tenth of the value without transpiration cooling for an average ratio of $v_w/u_e = 1$ per cent ($Re_x = 10^4$).
2. For flow near the stagnation point ($m = 1$) it is found that the point of inflection does not appear in the velocity profiles. This is understandable because the flow in the neighborhood of the stagnation point is under the influence of a favorable pressure gradient and therefore becomes more stable than the case on the flat plate. The heat transfer coefficient $h$ diminishes practically to zero when the coolant injection parameter $v_w/\sqrt{\nu c}$ reaches 3.2.
3. It appears that the required coolant injection to maintain a given wall temperature is much less in the present case than the result obtained in the approximate solution. This result is expected because in the approximate solution a uniform coolant injection was assumed, whereas in the present exact solution the coolant injection is proportional to the reciprocal of the square root of the distance from the leading edge of a flat plate.

*Compressible boundary layer with variable fluid properties.* The simultaneous effects of pressure gradient in the main stream flow over a porous wall and property changes in the fluid due to large temperature differences between the wall and the free stream [18] will be treated in the present article. In order to simplify the analysis, the following assumptions are made: (1) The Mach number $M$ is small, (2) the Euler number $m$ is constant, (3) the wall temperature $T_w$ is constant, and (4) the fluid property variation is expressible as some power of the absolute temperature.

$$\mu \sim T^{\omega}, \quad k \sim T^{\epsilon}, \quad c_p \sim T^{\alpha}, \quad \rho \sim T^{-1} \tag{4-22}$$

On the basis of assumption 1, the last two terms in Eq. 4-16 can be neglected and the quantities $\rho_w$ and $T_e$ can be treated as constants.

It was mentioned in the previous article that, for a wedge-type flow, the transformation methods of Pohlhausen [19] and of Falkner and Skan [20] can be applied. With the following changes in variables:

$$\left.\begin{aligned} \eta &= y\sqrt{\frac{\rho_w u_e}{\mu_w x}} \\ \theta &= \frac{T - T_w}{T_e - T_w} \\ f &= \frac{\rho_w \psi}{\sqrt{\mu_w \rho_w u_e x}} \end{aligned}\right\} \tag{4-23}$$

the momentum equation (Eq. 4-14) and the energy equation (Eq. 4-16) can be transformed into two ordinary differential equations with $f$ and $\theta$ as functions of $\eta$ only. With the boundary conditions given in Eq. 4-17 the above two equations can be solved numerically for any prescribed Euler number $m$, Prandtl number $Pr$, temperature ratio (stream temperature divided by wall temperature), and coolant flow parameter $f_w$. From the boundary condition at the wall, the following expression gives for a dimensionless measure of the coolant flow in terms of the coolant velocity:

$$f_w = -\frac{2}{1 + m}\frac{v_w}{u_e}\sqrt{Re_x} \tag{4-24}$$

where $f_w$ is considered to be a constant which yields a constant wall temperature if the conduction along the wall and the radiation are neglected. The expressions for the local skin friction coefficient at the wall and the local heat transfer coefficient (Nusselt number) to the wall are obtained, respectively, as follows:

$$c_f\sqrt{Re_x} = 2\left(\frac{\partial^2 f}{\partial \eta^2}\right)_w \tag{4-25}$$

and

$$\frac{Nu}{\sqrt{Re_x}} = \left(\frac{\partial \theta}{\partial \eta}\right)_w \tag{4-26}$$

A balance between the heat flow to the wall from the hot fluid and the heat absorbed by the coolant at the wall yields

$$\frac{T_e - T_w}{T_w - T_0} = -\frac{1+m}{2} Pr_w \frac{f_w}{(\partial\theta/\partial\eta)_w} \tag{4-27}$$

For a predesignated wall temperature and given Prandtl number, Euler number, and Reynolds number, the amount of coolant required can be determined from Eq. 4-27 provided that the temperatures of the hot fluid and of the coolant are known. In Fig. G,4d the ratio of the temperature difference, $(T_e - T_w)/(T_w - T_0)$, is plotted against the coolant mass flow ratio $(Q/W)\sqrt{Re_x}$ for $Pr = 0.7$. It is seen that the influence of the

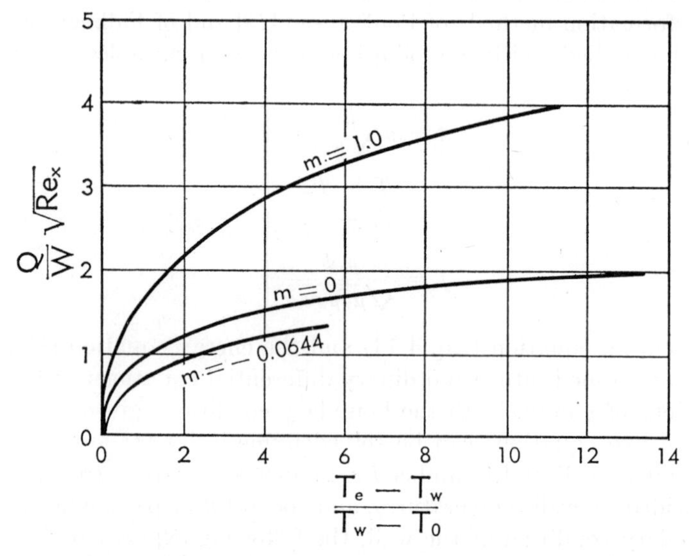


Fig. G,4d. Temperature ratio vs. mass flow ratio for favorable, zero, and adverse pressure gradients.

pressure gradient on the coolant discharge and the wall temperature is appreciable. For a favorable pressure gradient ($m = 1$) the heat transfer to the wall is increased almost twice the value of the flat plate case ($m = 0$). On the other hand, the heat transfer to the wall is diminished by 25 per cent of the flat plate value with a small adverse pressure gradient. The wall skin friction behaves in a similar manner but it will be more sensitive to change with the pressure gradient than the heat transfer to the wall. Furthermore, the displacement and momentum thicknesses are reduced to approximately one third of their flat plate values in the favorable pressure gradient, but the thermal boundary layer thickness is changed only slightly in this case.

Calculations of 58 velocity and temperature distributions were made for air which include the simultaneous effects of pressure gradients in the main stream, the flow through a porous wall, and the large temperature variations through the boundary layer ($Pr = 0.7$, $\omega = 0.7$, $\epsilon = 0.85$, and $\alpha = 0.19$ were used in Eq. 4-22). A complete tabulation of these calculations can be found in [21]. An extension of the above wedge-type solution to the heat transfer in flow around cylinders of arbitrary cross section for transpiration-cooled surfaces was made in [22].

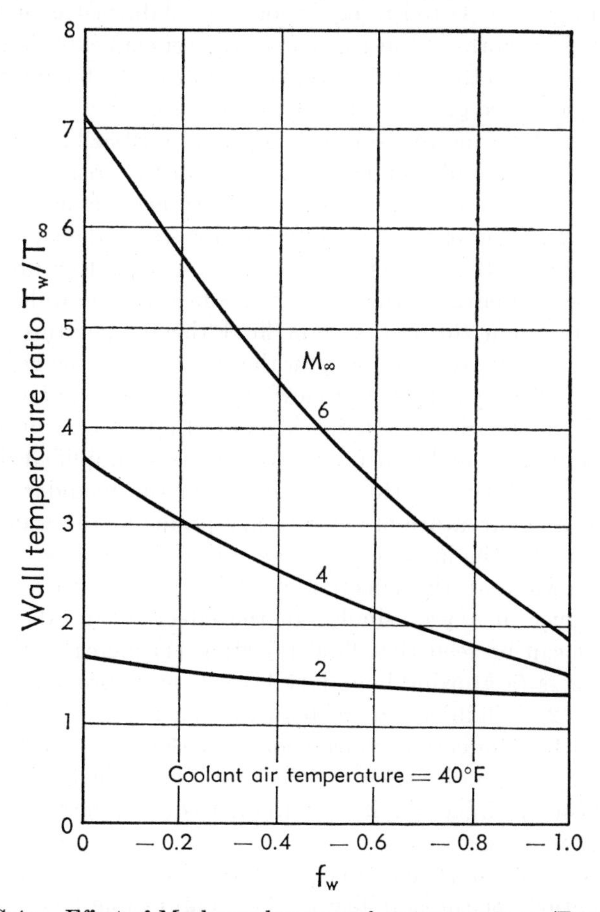


Fig. G,4e. Effect of Mach number on surface temperature. (From [23].)

An exact solution of the heat transfer of the compressible laminar boundary on a transpiration-cooled flat plate is made in [23]. The effect of Mach number on surface temperature for different rates of coolant injection are shown in Fig. G,4e. It is interesting to note that, for large rates of coolant injection, the wall temperature is less dependent on Mach number than for small rates of injection.

STABILITY CONSIDERATIONS OF THE LAMINAR BOUNDARY LAYER WITH COOLANT INJECTION. The stability theory for the laminar boundary layer on an impermeable surface was developed by Tollmien, Schlichting, and Lin for an incompressible fluid. Lees and Lin [24] extended the theory to include the effect of compressibility. By application of the stability theory it is possible to determine, from the velocity distribution in the boundary layer, the local Reynolds number at which a flow with such a velocity distribution becomes unstable. Transition to a turbulent boundary layer may be expected to occur somewhere downstream of the point of stability. The works of the above investigators indicate that an adverse pressure gradient in the flow direction destabilizes the boundary layer and a favorable pressure gradient increases the stability.

In the analyses of the stability of compressible laminar boundary layers [24,25], the results indicate that stability is greatly influenced by the heat transfer from the wall to the gas. In accordance with Eq. 4-14 at the wall condition of the flat plate it follows that the curvature of the velocity profile at the wall is proportional to a negative product of the temperature gradient and the velocity gradient at the wall. Then if the wall is hotter than the free stream fluid the temperature gradient at the wall will be negative, and in turn, the curvature of the velocity profile at the wall will be positive. It follows that in the boundary layer on a heated wall the velocity profile has a point of inflection which is a necessary and sufficient condition for the existence of amplified disturbance, hence, its instability. On the other hand, in the boundary layer on a cooled wall, the curvature of the velocity profile at the wall is negative and consequently the limit of complete stability increases.

It is known that the effect of fluid injection is to destabilize the boundary layer in a way similar to the effect of an adverse pressure gradient. It can be seen that fluid injection (1) increases the boundary layer thickness (a growing boundary layer is more prone to become turbulent) and (2) fluid injection creates a velocity profile which is less stable than one without injection. Since cooling of the wall and fluid injection at the wall have opposite effects on the stability of the laminar boundary layer with coolant injection, it is desirable to determine the simultaneous effects on transition.

Based on the improved viscous solutions of the stability equations [26], calculations of the stability of the compressible laminar boundary layer with coolant injection are made in [23] for the reduction of aerodynamic heating in high speed flight. The results apply at moderate supersonic speeds and indicate the complete stability limits for two-dimensional disturbances. In Fig. G,4f, the complete stability curves for several rates of coolant injection are shown. For a given rate of coolant injection, each of the curves depicts the region of complete stability. For any given Mach number, the wall temperature must be below the curve in order to attain a completely stable laminar boundary layer.

Sublayer Theory in Turbulent Flow. The heat transfer in the

turbulent boundary layer is of much greater importance than in the laminar because it is more often encountered in engineering problems, yet little progress has been made in the development of methods for the calculation of turbulent boundary layer even without transpiration cooling. The difficulty in this problem is that no precise knowledge of the surface shear and the shearing-stress distribution across the turbulent boundary

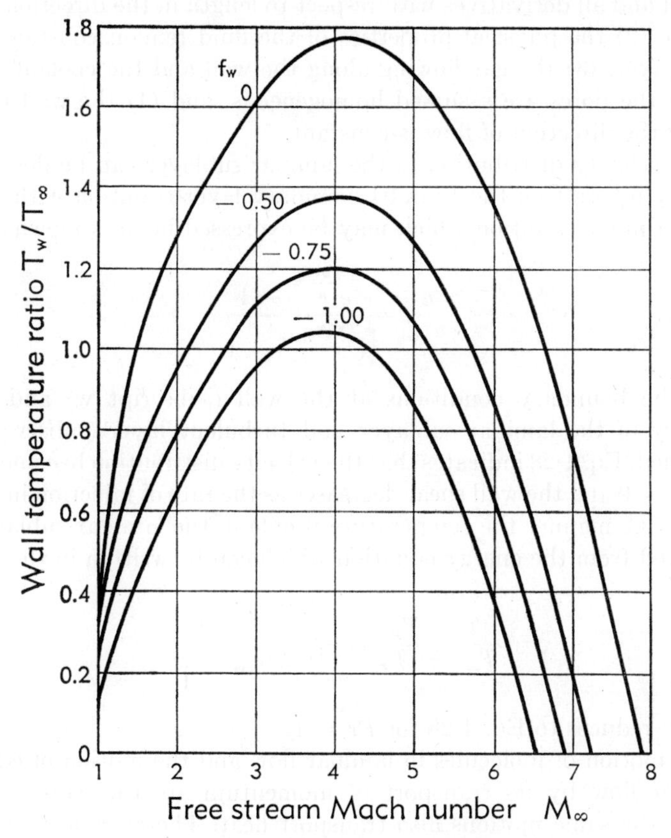


Fig. G,4f. Limiting wall temperature required for complete stabilization of boundary layer. (From [*23*].)

layer (essential quantities in connection with the solution of boundary layer equations) is available.

It has long been recognized that the momentum exchange in turbulent flow is impossible when the fluid stream approaches the vicinity of a solid wall where a thin laminar sublayer exists and that the transfer of shearing stress must depend on viscous action. Outside of this thin sublayer only the turbulent exchange mechanism is effective while the transfer by molecular action may be neglected. In a like manner, the rate of heat transfer between a fluid stream in turbulent flow and a smooth wall is largely controlled by the relatively high resistance of the laminar sublayer next to the wall.

The above concept was used by Prandtl in the investigation of turbulent flow in a pipe. Rannie's extension of the concept [27] to heat transfer in transpiration cooling is discussed here.

The assumptions made in this investigation are: (1) steady flow is assumed and all derivatives with respect to length in the direction of flow are zero, (2) the physical properties of the fluid remain constant across the sublayer, (3) the gas flowing along the wall and the coolant flowing through the pores are assumed homogeneous, and (4) the wall temperature in the direction of flow is constant.

The velocity distribution in the laminar sublayer can be determined easily by integrating the Prandtl boundary layer equation with the aid of a continuity equation which may be expressed in the following form:

$$\frac{u}{u_{\mathrm{lam}}} = \frac{e^{\frac{\rho_{\mathrm{w}} v_{\mathrm{w}}}{\mu} y} - 1}{e^{\frac{\rho_{\mathrm{w}} v_{\mathrm{w}}}{\mu} \delta_{\mathrm{lam}}} - 1} \tag{4-28}$$

where the boundary conditions at the wall (subscript w) and at the boundary of the laminar sublayer and turbulent layer (subscript lam) are applied. Eq. 4-28 indicates that the velocity distribution becomes linear when $v_{\mathrm{w}} = 0$ and the wall shear decreases as the rate of injection increases.

In a like manner the temperature profile in the laminar sublayer can be derived from the energy equation which can be written in the form

$$\frac{T - T_{\mathrm{w}}}{T_{\mathrm{lam}} - T_{\mathrm{w}}} = \frac{e^{\frac{Pr \rho_{\mathrm{w}} v_{\mathrm{w}}}{\mu} y} - 1}{e^{\frac{Pr \rho_{\mathrm{w}} v_{\mathrm{w}}}{\mu} \delta_{\mathrm{lam}}} - 1} \tag{4-29}$$

Eq. 4-29 reduces to Eq. 4-28 for $Pr = 1$.

The motion of molecules in laminar flow and the motion of eddies in turbulent flow by its transport of momentum are the causes of skin friction; the same motions also transport heat. Therefore a relationship should exist between skin friction and heat transport. Reynolds used this approach to obtain the following relation between momentum transfer and heat transfer across a turbulent stream:

$$\frac{q_{\mathrm{lam}}}{c_p(T_{\mathrm{g}} - T_{\mathrm{lam}})} = \frac{\tau_{\mathrm{lam}}}{(u_{\mathrm{c}} - u_{\mathrm{lam}})} \tag{4-30}$$

where $q_{\mathrm{lam}}$ and $\tau_{\mathrm{lam}}$ are the heat transfer and shearing stress at the boundary between the laminar sublayer and turbulent layer and $T_{\mathrm{g}}$ and $u_{\mathrm{c}}$ are the temperature and velocity at the center of the pipe. These can be evaluated from Eq. 4-29 and 4-28, respectively. Upon the substitution for quantities $q_{\mathrm{lam}}$, $\tau_{\mathrm{lam}}$, and $T_{\mathrm{lam}}$ in Eq. 4-30, the relation between the wall temperature and the rate of coolant injection is determined as

$$\frac{T_w - T_0}{T_g - T_0} = \frac{e^{-Pr\frac{\rho_w v_w}{\mu}\delta_{lam}}}{1 + \frac{c_{p_w}}{c_p}\left(\frac{u_c}{u_{lam}} - 1\right)\left(1 - e^{\frac{-\rho_w v_w \delta_{lam}}{\mu}}\right)} \tag{4-31}$$

Since experimental information on transpiration-cooled turbulent boundary layers has not been achieved, the variation of laminar-sublayer thickness with the velocity of injection remains unknown. It is assumed that the flow in the turbulent case is not affected by the velocity of injection, and hence that the shearing stress and the velocity $u_{lam}$ at the edge of the core are the same as for flow in a smooth pipe. The thickness of the laminar sublayer has been measured in smooth pipe and found to satisfy the relation

$$\frac{\delta_{lam} u_\tau}{\nu} = y^* \tag{4-32}$$

where $u_\tau^2 = \tau_w/\rho$ and $y^* = 5.6$ is taken by Prandtl after examination of the velocity profile measured close to a wall. On the basis of Eq. 4-32 the following expressions are obtained:

$$\begin{aligned} \delta_{lam} &= \nu y^* \sqrt{\frac{\rho}{\tau_w}} \\ u_{lam} &= y^* \sqrt{\frac{\tau_w}{\rho}} \end{aligned} \tag{4-33}$$

where $\tau_w = c_f \rho u_c^2/2$. For the Reynolds number range $5000 < Re < 200{,}000$ the friction coefficient $c_f$ for smooth pipes satisfies the empirical relation $c_f = 0.046(Re)^{-\frac{1}{5}}$.

The relation between the wall temperature and the rate of coolant flow is calculated from Eq. 4-31 and shown in Fig. G,4b. The result reveals that for a designated wall temperature the rate of coolant required for transpiration-cooled turbulent flow is almost twice as much as in the case of laminar flow. For an injected velocity equal to 1 per cent of the hot fluid velocity, the heat transfer to the wall is reduced to 70 per cent of the value without transpiration cooling. The comparison of this result with the result obtained under the same conditions in laminar flow is shown in Fig. G,4c.

Approximate Solution of Heat Transfer in Turbulent Boundary Layer on a Flat Plate. The treatment above may be extended to the case of the effect of coolant injection on the behavior of a compressible turbulent boundary layer [*28,29*]. In order to simplify the analysis, the following assumptions are made: (1) the coolant fluid is the same as the boundary layer fluid, (2) the wall temperature in the direction of flow is constant, and (3) the Prandtl number is equal to unity.

The basic equations, which represent the principles of conservation of momentum, conservation of mass, and conservation of energy, for the compressible turbulent boundary over a flat plate, can be expressed as follows [Sec. B]:

The momentum equation in the $x$ direction is

$$\overline{\rho u}\,\frac{\partial \bar{u}}{\partial x} + \overline{\rho v}\,\frac{\partial \bar{u}}{\partial y} = \frac{\partial}{\partial y}\left(\mu\,\frac{\partial \bar{u}}{\partial y} - \overline{\rho v' u'}\right) = \frac{\partial \bar{\tau}}{\partial y} \tag{4-34}$$

The continuity equation is

$$\frac{\partial(\overline{\rho u})}{\partial x} + \frac{\partial(\overline{\rho v})}{\partial y} = 0 \tag{4-35}$$

The energy equation is

$$\overline{\rho u}\,\frac{\partial(c_p\overline{T})}{\partial x} + \overline{\rho v}\,\frac{\partial(c_p\overline{T})}{\partial y} = \frac{\partial}{\partial y}\left(k\,\frac{\partial \overline{T}}{\partial y} - c_p\overline{\rho v' T'}\right) + (\mu + \epsilon_\mu)\left(\frac{\partial \bar{u}}{\partial y}\right)^2 \tag{4-36}$$

The quantities with bars represent time-average quantities, while primed quantities represent instantaneous values of fluctuating quantities. The specific heat is assumed to be a constant and the fluid properties of density, viscosity, and thermal conductivity are considered to vary with temperature. The boundary conditions are

$$\begin{aligned} &\text{At } y = 0; && \overline{T} = T_w; \quad \bar{u} = 0 \\ & && \bar{\rho} = \rho_w; \quad \overline{\rho v} = \rho_w v_w \\ &\text{At } y = \delta; && \overline{T} = T_\infty; \quad \bar{u} = U \\ & && \bar{\rho} = \rho_\infty; \quad \overline{\rho v} = \rho_\infty v_\infty \end{aligned} \tag{4-37}$$

For a Prandtl number equal to unity, the relation between $\overline{T}$ and $\bar{u}$ can be expressed as in Eq. 4-9 in the following manner:

$$\frac{\overline{T}}{T_\infty} = \frac{T_w}{T_\infty} + \left(1 - \frac{T_w}{T_\infty}\right)\frac{\bar{u}}{U} + \frac{\gamma - 1}{2}\,M_\infty^2\,\frac{\bar{u}}{U}\left(1 - \frac{\bar{u}}{U}\right) \tag{4-38}$$

In order to make the solution of Eq. 4-34 possible, at least for practical purposes, certain nonrigorous assumptions are made which are analogous to those used in the case of low speed, incompressible turbulent flow along a smooth wall without injection. The first simplification is to assume that the dependency of variable quantities with respect to $x$ is negligible compared to their variations with respect to $y$ in the neighborhood of a permeable wall. Secondly, Prandtl's mixing-length hypothesis is assumed to apply for the present problem. Then in the turbulent region, Eq. 4-34 can be simplified as follows:

$$\rho_w v_w\,\frac{du}{dy} = \frac{d\tau}{dy} = \frac{d}{dy}\left[\rho K^2 y^2 \left(\frac{du}{dy}\right)^2\right] \tag{4-39}$$

The bars representing time-average quantities have been dropped since all the terms in Eq. 4-39 are mean values. The two boundary conditions are: (1) the shearing stress $\tau = \tau_w$ when $y \to 0$, and (2) the velocity distribution from the solution of Eq. 4-39 must reduce to von Kármán's logarithmic velocity distribution law for $T_w/T_\infty = 1$, $M_\infty = 0$, and $v_w = 0$.

The equation of state for zero pressure gradient in $y$ direction leads to

$$\frac{\rho_\infty}{\rho} = \frac{T}{T_\infty} \tag{4-40}$$

Upon the substitution of Eq. 4-40 and Eq. 4-38 into Eq. 4-39, the solution which represents the velocity distribution of a compressible turbulent boundary layer with fluid injection at the wall is obtained:

$$\frac{\delta_u \rho_w U}{\mu_\infty}\left(\frac{T_w}{T_\infty}\frac{c_f}{2}\right)^{\frac{1}{2}}\frac{y}{\delta_u} = e^{(I_1 - DK)} \tag{4-41}$$

where

$$I_1 = \int_0^{u/U} \frac{E dz}{\left[\left(1 + \frac{2}{c_f}\frac{\rho_w v_w}{\rho_\infty U_\infty} z\right)(1 + Bz - A^2 z^2)\right]^{\frac{1}{2}}} \tag{4-42}$$

$$\left[\left(\frac{T_w}{T_\infty}\right)\left(\frac{c_f}{2}\right)\right]^{\frac{1}{2}} E = K \tag{4-43}$$

$$c_f = \frac{2\tau_w}{\rho_\infty U^2} \tag{4-44}$$

and

$$A^2 = \left(\frac{T_\infty}{T_w}\right)\left(\frac{\gamma - 1}{2}\right) M_\infty^2; \quad B = \left(\frac{T_\infty}{T_w} - 1\right) + \frac{T_\infty}{T_w}\left(\frac{\gamma - 1}{2}\right) M_\infty^2 \tag{4-45}$$

The empirical constants $K$ and $D$ can only be determined from the proper experimental velocity distribution.

The skin friction coefficient can be determined from the momentum integral given in Eq. 4-1 as follows:

$$c_f = 2\frac{d}{dx}\left[\delta_u \int_0^1 \frac{\rho u}{\rho_\infty U}\left(1 - \frac{u}{U}\right) d\frac{y}{\delta_u}\right] - 2\frac{\rho_w v_w}{\rho_\infty U} \tag{4-46}$$

Eq. 4-46 can be simplified by substituting the expression for $d(y/\delta_u)$ from Eq. 4-41, after its differentiating with respect to $u/U$, along with the relation between $\rho$, $T$, and $u$ given in Eq. 4-38 and 4-40. The final expression for local and average skin friction coefficient is

$$\ln\left[\left(C_f + \frac{2}{x}\int_0^x \frac{\rho_w v_w}{\rho_\infty U} dx\right) R_x\right] + \ln\left(\frac{K}{2}\right) - \omega \ln\left(\frac{T_w}{T_\infty}\right) + DK = \ln I_2 \tag{4-47}$$

where

$$I_2 = E^2 \int_0^1 \frac{\frac{u}{U}\left(1 - \frac{u}{U}\right) e^{I_1} d\left(\frac{u}{U}\right)}{\left[1 + \frac{2}{c_f}\frac{\rho_w v_w}{\rho_\infty U}\left(\frac{u}{U}\right)\right]^{\frac{1}{2}}\left[1 + B\frac{u}{U} - A^2\left(\frac{u}{U}\right)^2\right]^{\frac{3}{2}}} \tag{4-48}$$

$$\mu_w = \mu_\infty \left(\frac{T_w}{T_\infty}\right)^\omega \tag{4-49}$$

and

$$C_f = \frac{1}{x}\int_0^x c_f dx \tag{4-50}$$

From the assumption that the Prandtl number is equal to unity it can be shown that the simple relation between skin friction and heat transfer is

$$c_h = \frac{h}{c_p \rho_\infty U} = \frac{c_f}{2} \tag{4-51}$$

and

$$C_h = \frac{C_f}{2} \tag{4-52}$$

Once local or average skin friction is determined from Eq. 4-47, the appropriate heat transfer coefficients can be determined from Eq. 4-51 and 4-52. In the case where the Prandtl number is not equal to unity the effect of transpiration cooling on the relation between the coefficients of skin friction and heat transfer may be found in [*29*].

In [*30*] the heat transfer and skin friction coefficients have been obtained from measured data for turbulent boundary layers at very low Mach numbers. In these tests both suction and injection were applied at the plane boundary of the stream. Skin friction coefficients were determined from plots of the momentum thickness against longitudinal station, where the momentum thickness was determined by obtaining the velocity profiles at various stations. The heat transfer was determined by direct measurement. The Reynolds number range of this data was about $9 \times 10^4$ to $3.3 \times 10^6$ and the temperature difference between the wall and the free stream was about 30°F.

In order to make a comparison between the theoretically derived local skin friction and heat transfer coefficients and the appropriate data in [*30*], the empirical constants $K$ and $D$ in Eq. 4-47 are determined by letting $C_f = c_f$, $T_w/T_\infty = 1$, $M_\infty = 0$, and $v_w = 0$ and comparing the resulting expression with the following von Kármán incompressible local skin friction law

$$4.15 \log (c_f Re_x) + 1.7 = c_f^{-\frac{1}{2}} \tag{4-53}$$

from which $K = 0.393$ and $D = 6.53$.

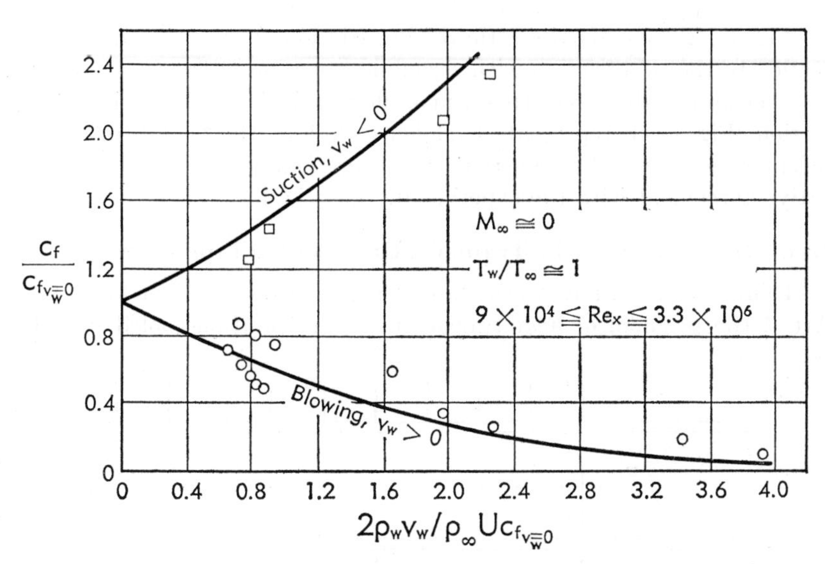


Fig. G,4g. Ratio of local skin friction coefficient with and without transpiration-cooled plate vs. mass flow ratio parameter compared with experiments. (From [*28*].)

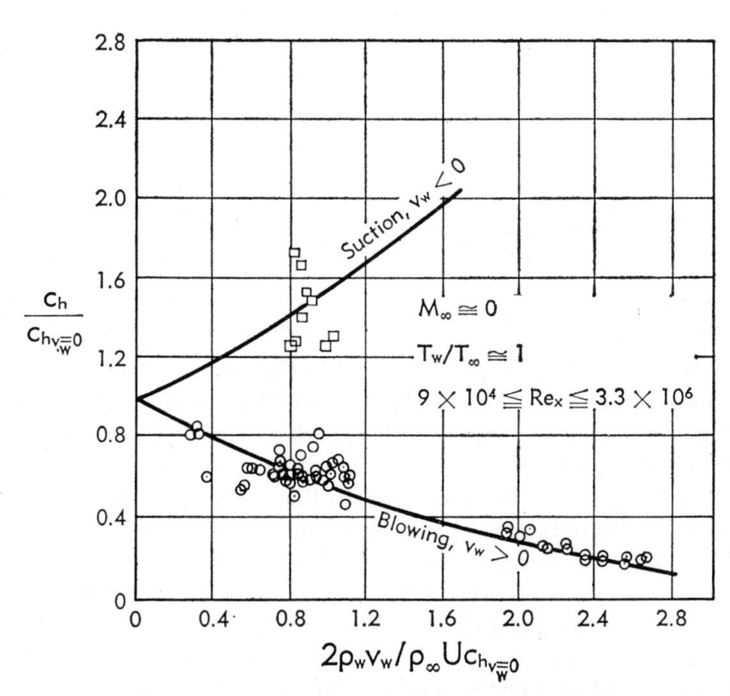


Fig. G,4h. Ratio of local heat transfer coefficient with and without transpiration-cooled plate vs. coolant flow ratio parameter compared with experiment. (From [*28*].)

Fig. G,4g presents the ratio of skin friction coefficient with fluid injection to the skin friction with zero fluid injection at the same Reynolds number and wall-to-free-stream mass flow ratio for both suction and injection. Fig. G,4h represents analogous plots of the heat transfer coefficient ratio. It can be seen that the theoretical curves give good qualitative agreement with the experimental data [*30*].

## G,5. Heat Transfer in Transpiration-Cooled Pipe Flow.

Laminar Pipe Flow with Coolant Injection at Wall [*31,32*]. In Art. 4 the problem of heat transfer in a transpiration-cooled boundary

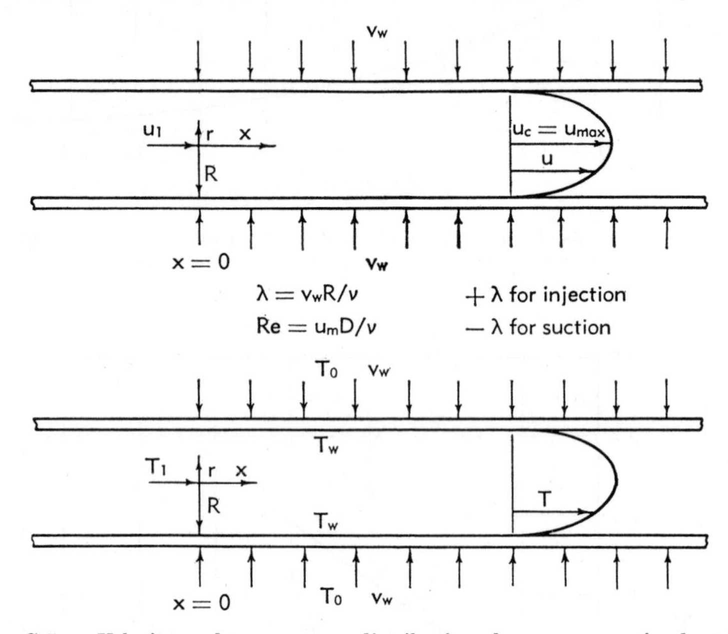


Fig. G,5a. Velocity and temperature distribution along a porous circular pipe.

layer has been treated to a great extent in the case of a laminar flow over a porous plate. For flows in a conduit, such as the combustion chambers, afterburners of jet motors, and the nozzles of rocket motors, it is not exactly clear whether the results obtained from the transpiration-cooled boundary layer can be directly applied. Because of the unclarified status it is desirable to obtain the basic phenomena of the nonisothermal fully developed flow through a porous-wall pipe with coolant injection.

The problem of heat transfer of a steady laminar flow in a circular pipe has been studied (Graetz [*33*] and Nusselt [*34*]) since the latter part of the last century. In these studies it was assumed that the wall temperature is constant and changes discontinuously at $x = 0$ (see Fig. G,5a). The physical properties of the fluid are independent of temperature and the Poiseuille velocity distribution is maintained throughout the motion.

In the present treatment, exact solutions of the Navier-Stokes equations, the continuity equation, and the energy equation in cylindrical coordinates are obtained. The assumptions made here are: (1) the fluid is incompressible, i.e. the mass density and the viscosity of the fluid are assumed to be constant, (2) the fluid flowing in the axial direction and the fluid flowing through the porous wall are assumed homogeneous, (3) the maximum axial velocity at the entrance of the porous-wall pipe is equal to the maximum axial velocity in the Poiseuille flow, (4) the fluid flowing through the porous wall is uniform throughout, (5) the free convection, radiation, and dissipation are neglected, and (6) the wall temperature is constant and changes discontinuously at $x = 0$ (see Fig. G5,a).

If a curvilinear coordinate system is introduced (see Fig. G,5a) with the origin at the center of the cross section of a circular pipe, where $x$ is taken in the direction of the flow, $r$ in the radial direction, and $\vartheta$ the azimuthal angle, then with axial symmetry of flow the Navier-Stokes equations become

$$u\frac{\partial u}{\partial x} + v\frac{\partial u}{\partial r} = -\frac{1}{\rho}\frac{\partial p}{\partial x} + \nu\left(\frac{\partial^2 u}{\partial r^2} + \frac{1}{r}\frac{\partial u}{\partial r} + \frac{\partial^2 u}{\partial x^2}\right) \tag{5-1}$$

$$u\frac{\partial v}{\partial x} + v\frac{\partial v}{\partial r} = -\frac{1}{\rho}\frac{\partial p}{\partial r} + \nu\left(\frac{\partial^2 v}{\partial x^2} + \frac{\partial^2 v}{\partial r^2} + \frac{1}{r}\frac{\partial v}{\partial r} - \frac{v}{r^2}\right) \tag{5-2}$$

*The continuity equation:*

$$\frac{\partial(ru)}{\partial x} + \frac{\partial(rv)}{\partial r} = 0 \tag{5-3}$$

*The energy equation:*

$$\rho c_p\left(v\frac{\partial T}{\partial r} + u\frac{\partial T}{\partial x}\right) = -u\frac{\partial p}{\partial x} + k\left[\frac{1}{r}\frac{\partial}{\partial r}\left(r\frac{\partial T}{\partial r}\right) + \frac{\partial^2 T}{\partial x^2}\right] + \phi \tag{5-4}$$

The boundary conditions are

$$r = 0: \qquad v = \frac{\partial u}{\partial r} = 0 \tag{5-5}$$

$$r < R \text{ and } x = 0: \qquad T = T_1 \tag{5-6}$$

$$r = R: \qquad u = 0, \quad v = -v_w = \text{const} \tag{5-7}$$

$$r = R \text{ and } x > 0: \qquad T = T_w \tag{5-8}$$

*Velocity distribution and skin friction.* For two-dimensional incompressible flow a stream function exists such that

$$ru = \frac{\partial \psi}{\partial r}, \qquad -rv = \frac{\partial \psi}{\partial x} \tag{5-9}$$

and the continuity equation (Eq. 5-3) is satisfied. For a constant fluid injection or suction at the porous wall and the given boundary conditions, the following stream function is introduced

$$\psi = \frac{R^2}{2}\left[\frac{u_1}{f'(0)} + 4v_w \frac{x}{R}\right] f(z) \tag{5-10}$$

where $z = (r/R)^2$.

Introducing the expressions of $u$ and $v$ from Eq. 5-9 and 5-10 into Eq. 5-1 and 5-2 results in

$$-\frac{1}{\rho}\frac{\partial p}{\partial x} = \frac{4u_1}{R^2}\left[\frac{1}{(f'0)} + 4\frac{\lambda}{Re}\frac{x}{R}\right][Rv_w(f'^2 - ff'') - \nu(zf''' + f'')] \tag{5-11}$$

$$\frac{1}{\rho}\frac{\partial p}{\partial z} = \frac{2v_w}{R}\left[Rv_w\left(\frac{f^2}{z^2} - \frac{2ff'}{z}\right) - 2\nu f''\right] = F(z) \tag{5-12}$$

where $\lambda = v_w R/\nu$ and $Re = u_m D/\nu$ and $u_1$ is the maximum velocity for $v_w = 0$. Since the right-hand side of Eq. 5-12 is a function of $z$ only, differentiation of both sides of it with respect to $x$ yields

$$\frac{\partial^2 p}{\partial x \partial z} = 0 \tag{5-13}$$

Hence, differentiating Eq. 5-11 with respect to $z$ gives zero on the left-hand side, and integrating the right-hand side of the equation, one obtains

$$zf''' + f'' - \lambda(f'^2 - ff') = c \tag{5-14}$$

for $\lambda \leqq 1$ and

$$f'^2 - ff'' - \frac{1}{\lambda}(zf''' + f'') = k \tag{5-15}$$

for $\lambda > 1$, where $c$ and $k$ are the constants of integration to be determined.

Eq. 5-14 is an ordinary nonlinear differential equation of the third order which resulted from the Navier-Stokes equations and the continuity equation by the similarity transformation. With the aid of the four given boundary conditions an exact solution can be obtained and the constant of integration $c$ determined.

It can be seen that the limiting form of Eq. 5-14, by letting $v_w$ approach zero, is the equation describing a flow through a circular pipe with impermeable walls. The solution of this equation which satisfies all the four boundary conditions given in Eq. 5-5 and 5-7 is the well-known Poiseuille law for pipe flow. If small values of $\lambda$ are treated as a perturbation parameter, a solution of Eq. 5-14 can be obtained, which is discussed later.

On the other hand, if large values of $\lambda$ are treated as a perturbation parameter the third order differential equation (Eq. 5-15) is reduced to a second order one. The solution of Eq. 5-15 can also be obtained in the same manner since all four boundary conditions given in Eq. 5-5 and 5-7 can be satisfied.

The solution of Eq. 5-14 can be expressed for small values of $\lambda$ ($\lambda \leqq 1$) by a power series developed near $\lambda = 0$ as follows:

$$f = f_0 + \lambda f_1 + \lambda^2 f_2 + \cdots + \lambda^n f_n \tag{5-16}$$

and

$$c = c_0 + \lambda c_1 + \lambda^2 c_2 + \cdots + \lambda^n c_n \tag{5-17}$$

where $f_n$'s and $c_n$'s are taken to be independent of $\lambda$. By substituting Eq. 5-16 and 5-17 into Eq. 5-14 and equating coefficients of like power of $\lambda$, one obtains the following set of equations:

$$zf_0''' + f_0'' = c_0 \tag{5-18}$$

$$zf_1''' + f_1'' - f_0'^2 + f_0 f_0'' = c_1 \tag{5-19}$$

$$zf_2''' + f_2'' - 2f_0'f_1' + f_0''f_1 + f_0 f_1'' = c_2 \tag{5-20}$$

The boundary conditions to be satisfied by $f_n$'s are

$$f_n(0) = f_n'(1) = 0; \qquad \lim_{z\to 0} \sqrt{z}\, f_n''(z) = 0$$

for all $n$ (5-21)

$$\left.\begin{aligned} f_0(1) &= \tfrac{1}{2} \\ f_n(1) &= 0 \qquad n \geqq 1 \end{aligned}\right\}$$

The second order perturbation solution of Eq. 5-14 obtained by solving Eq. 5-18, 5-19, and 5-20 is given as follows:

$$f(z) = \left(z - \frac{1}{2}z^2\right) + \lambda\left(-\frac{z}{18} + \frac{z^2}{18} - \frac{z^3}{12} + \frac{z^4}{72}\right)$$

$$+ \lambda^2\left(\frac{83}{5400}z - \frac{19}{540}z^2 + \frac{11}{432}z^3 - \frac{1}{144}z^4 + \frac{1}{720}z^5 - \frac{1}{10800}z^6\right) \tag{5-22}$$

$$c = -1 - \tfrac{3}{4}z + \tfrac{11}{270}z^2 \tag{5-23}$$

It is seen from the foregoing equations that the second order perturbation solution is sufficiently accurate even for $\lambda = 1$. The velocity components in the axial and radial directions are obtained by substituting Eq. 5-22 and 5-10 into Eq. 5-9 as follows:

$$\frac{u}{u_1} = \left[\frac{1}{1 - \frac{\lambda}{18} + \frac{83}{5400}\lambda^2} + 4\frac{\lambda}{Re}\frac{x}{R}\right]\left[1 - z + \frac{\lambda}{36}(-2 + 9z - 9z^2 + 2z^3)\right.$$

$$\left. + \frac{\lambda^2}{10800}(166 - 760z + 825z^2 - 300z^3 + 75z^4 - 6z^5)\right] \tag{5-24}$$

$$\frac{v}{u_1} = -\frac{2\lambda}{Re\sqrt{z}}\left[z - \frac{1}{2}z^2 + \frac{\lambda}{72}(-4z + 9z^2 - 6z^3 + z^4)\right.$$

$$\left. + \frac{\lambda^2}{10800}(166z - 380z^2 + 275z^3 - 75z^4 + 15z^5 - z^6)\right] \tag{5-25}$$

The pressure drop in the flow direction can be obtained upon the substitution of Eq. 5-22 into Eq. 5-11 and 5-12, i.e.

$$\frac{p(0, r) - p(x, r)}{\frac{1}{2}\rho u_1^2} = \frac{8}{Re}\left[1 + \frac{3}{4}\lambda - \frac{11}{270}\lambda^2\right]\left[\frac{1}{f'(0)} + 2\frac{\lambda}{Re}\frac{x}{R}\right]\frac{x}{R} \quad (5\text{-}26)$$

The coefficient of skin friction at the wall can also be obtained from Eq. 5-24, and can be written

$$c_f = \frac{2\tau_w}{\rho u_1^2} = \frac{4}{Re}\left[\frac{1}{1 - \frac{\lambda}{18} + \frac{83\lambda^2}{5400}} + 4\frac{\lambda}{Re}\frac{x}{R}\right]\left[1 + \frac{\lambda}{12} - \frac{13\lambda^2}{540}\right] \quad (5\text{-}27)$$

In a like manner, the solution of Eq. 5-15 can be expressed for large values of $\lambda$ ($\lambda > 1$) by a power series developed near $1/\lambda = 0$. The complete treatment of this part of the work is given in [*31*].

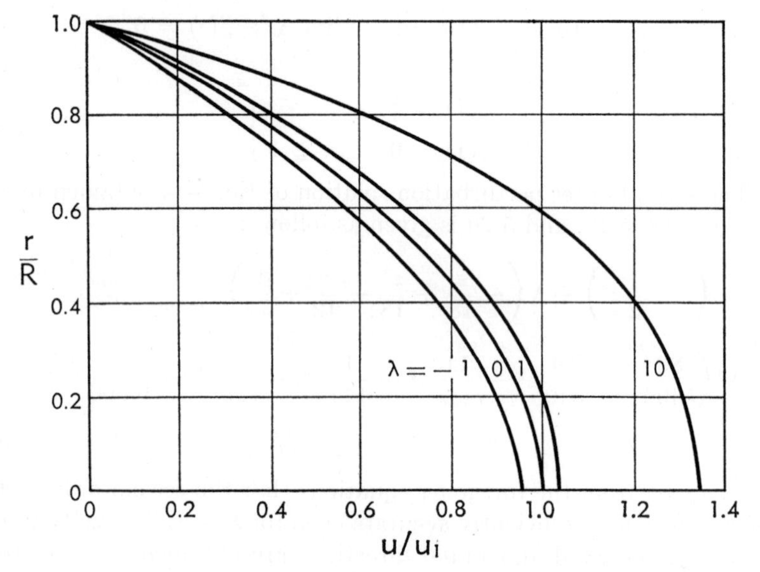


Fig. G,5b. Velocity profiles vs. length in radial direction for various $\lambda$($Re$ = $10^3$, $x/R$ = 10). (From [*31*].)

The velocity distributions in the main flow direction at an arbitrary cross section of the pipe for $\lambda = \pm 1$ and $\lambda = 10$ are shown in Fig. G,5b. It was noted that when $\lambda = 0$, the profile becomes Poiseuille's paraboloid, and for $\lambda > 0$ (fluid being injected through the wall) the axial velocity increases and the velocity gradient at the wall increases. For $\lambda < 0$ (fluid being withdrawn through the wall) both the axial velocity and the velocity gradient at the wall decrease as compared with Poiseuille's case. The above phenomenon follows the law of conservation of matter. In the present case the radial velocity, which vanishes in Poiseuille's case, has a finite magnitude except at the center of the pipe where it vanishes.

One of the essential parameters in the present investigation is the skin friction at the wall. In Poiseuille's flow the skin friction coefficient at the wall $c_f$ has a constant value of $4/Re$. The wall friction coefficient as calculated from this analysis indicates that the effect of injection in a pipe flow is to increase the wall friction coefficient. In a boundary layer flow on a

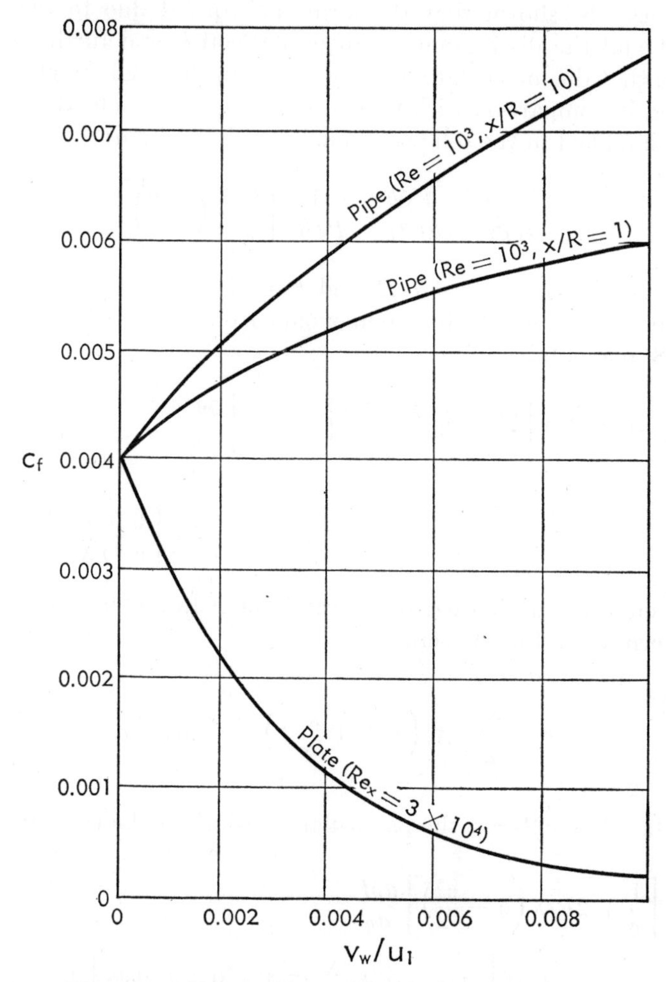


Fig. G,5c. Variation of local wall frictional coefficient with fluid injection. (From [31].)

porous flat plate the effect of fluid injection at the wall is to increase the thickness of the boundary layer and to decrease the velocity gradient at the wall. Hence the wall friction decreases in this case. On the other hand, in a pipe flow the effect of fluid injection at the wall is to accelerate the main stream velocity. Hence the velocity gradient at the wall, which determines the wall friction, increases. For a fluid injection ratio $v_w/u_1 =$

0.01 the wall friction coefficient increases by 85 per cent over the Poiseuille flow case. A comparison of the variation of local wall friction coefficient with fluid injection between the case of flow in a porous-wall pipe and on a flat plate was shown in Fig. G,5c.

*Temperature distribution and heat transfer.* For an incompressible fluid, it can be shown that the terms in Eq. 5-4 due to the pressure gradient and the dissipation $\phi$ can be neglected, and furthermore it is assumed that the molecular heat conduction in the axial direction may be neglected in comparison with that in the radial direction. Hence Eq. 5-4 can be simplified in the following nondimensional form:

$$\frac{v}{u_1}\frac{\partial\theta}{\partial\eta} + \frac{u}{u_1}\frac{\partial\theta}{\partial\xi} = \frac{1}{PrRe}\left[\frac{1}{\eta}\frac{\partial}{\partial\eta}\left(\eta\frac{\partial\theta}{\partial\eta}\right)\right] \tag{5-28}$$

where $\xi = x/R$, $\eta = \sqrt{z} = r/R$, and $\theta = (T - T_w)/(T_1 - T_w)$. Upon substitution of the velocity components from Eq. 5-24 and 5-25 into Eq. 5-28, one obtains

$$\left[\frac{1}{1 - \frac{\lambda}{18}} + 4\frac{\lambda}{Re}\xi\right]\frac{\partial\theta}{\partial\xi} = 2\frac{\lambda}{Re}\frac{1}{f'(\eta)}\left[\eta - \frac{\eta^3}{2}\right]\frac{\partial\theta}{\partial\eta} + \frac{1}{PrRe}\frac{1}{f'(\eta)}\left[\frac{1}{\eta}\frac{\partial}{\partial\eta}\left(\eta\frac{\partial\theta}{\partial\eta}\right)\right] \tag{5-29}$$

The energy equation written in the form of Eq. 5-29 yields a solution in the form of an infinite series

$$\theta = \sum_{j=1}^{\infty} A_j\left(1 + 4\frac{\lambda}{Re}\xi\right)^{-\frac{c_j^2}{4Pr\lambda}} M_j(\eta, c_j) \tag{5-30}$$

where the $M_j(\eta, c_j)$'s are the particular solutions of the equation.

$$\frac{d^2M}{d\eta^2} + \left[\frac{1}{\eta} + 2Pr\lambda\left(\eta - \frac{\eta^3}{2}\right)\right]\frac{dM}{d\eta} + c^2\left[(1 - \eta^2) + \frac{\lambda}{36}(7\eta^2 - 9\eta^4 + 2\eta^6)\right]M = 0 \tag{5-31}$$

and $c_j$'s are the eigenvalues of Eq. 5-31 which correspond to the boundary condition $\theta_{\eta=1} = 0$. The series solution of Eq. 5-31 corresponding to the eigenvalue $c_j$, which is free from singularities at $\eta = 0$ is

$$M_j = 1 - \frac{c_j^2}{4}\eta^2 + \frac{1}{16}\left[\frac{c_j^4}{4} + c_j^2\left(Pr\lambda - \frac{7}{36}\lambda + 1\right)\right]\eta^4 + \cdots \tag{5-32}$$

Multiplying both sides of Eq. 5-31 by the appropriate factor, Eq. 5-31 can be written as the following Sturm-Liouville equation:

$$\frac{d}{d\eta}\,[m(\eta)M_j'] + c_j p(\eta) M_j = 0 \tag{5-33}$$

where

$$m(\eta) = \eta e^{Pr\lambda\left(\eta^2 - \frac{\eta^4}{4}\right)}$$

$$p(\eta) = m(\eta)\left[(1-\eta^2) + \frac{\lambda}{36}\,(7\eta^2 - 9\eta^4 + 2\eta^6)\right]$$

Hence $M_i(\eta, c_i)$ and $M_j(\eta, c_j)$ for $i \neq j$ are orthogonal functions with respect to the weight function $p(\eta)$; i.e.

$$\int_0^1 p(\eta) M_i M_j d\eta = 0 \tag{5-34}$$

The coefficients of the series expansion, $A_j$'s (Eq. 5-30) are determined from the boundary condition (Eq. 5-6) applied to Eq. 5-30, which is

$$\sum_{j=1}^{\infty} A_j M_j(\eta, c_j) = 1 \tag{5-35}$$

Then multiplying both sides of Eq. 5-35 by $p(\eta)M_j(\eta, c_j)$ and integrating from 0 to 1

$$A_j = \frac{\int_0^1 p(\eta) M_j(\eta, c_j) d\eta}{\int_0^1 p(\eta) M_j^2(\eta, c_j) d\eta} \tag{5-36}$$

From the differential equation (Eq. 5-33), it can be seen that

$$\int_0^1 p(\eta) M_j(\eta, c_j) d\eta = \frac{1}{c_j^2}\, e^{\frac{3}{4}Pr\lambda} \left(\frac{dM_j}{d\eta}\right)_{\eta=1} \tag{5-37}$$

and

$$\int_0^1 p(\eta) M_j^2(\eta, c_j) d\eta = \frac{1}{2c_j}\, e^{\frac{3}{4}Pr\lambda} \left(\frac{dM_j}{d\eta}\right)_{\eta=1} \left(\frac{\partial M}{\partial c}\right)_{c=c_j,\,\eta=1} \tag{5-38}$$

Thus

$$A_j = -\frac{2}{c_j \left(\frac{\partial M}{\partial c}\right)_{c=c_j,\,\eta=1}} \tag{5-39}$$

The heat transfer coefficient for the flow in a pipe is usually calculated with the difference between the mean temperature of the fluid and the wall temperature. The mean temperature over the cross section considered, weighted with respect to the axial velocity, may be defined by the equation

$$\theta_M = \frac{T_M - T_w}{T_1 - T_w} = \frac{\int_0^R \theta u r dr}{\int_0^R u r dr} \tag{5-40}$$

The heat transfer coefficient is then defined by

$$q = h(T_M - T_w) \tag{5-41}$$

where heat flow per unit area at the wall is

$$q = -k\left(\frac{\partial T}{\partial r}\right)_{r=R} = -\frac{k}{R}(T_1 - T_w)\left(\frac{\partial \theta}{\partial \eta}\right)_{\eta=1} \tag{5-42}$$

In nondimensional form, the heat transfer coefficient or Nusselt number $Nu$ is

$$Nu = \frac{hD}{k} = -\frac{2}{\theta_M}\left(\frac{\partial \theta}{\partial \eta}\right)_{\eta=1}$$

$$= \frac{-2}{\theta_M}\left\{A_1\left[1 + 8Pr\lambda\left(\frac{1}{PrRe}\frac{x}{D}\right)\right]^{-\frac{c_1^2}{4Pr\lambda}} M_1'(1)\right.$$

$$\left. + A_2\left[1 + 8Pr\lambda\left(\frac{1}{PrRe}\frac{x}{D}\right)\right]^{-\frac{c_2^2}{4Pr\lambda}} M_2'(1) + \cdots\right\} \tag{5-43}$$

The temperature distribution given in Eq. 5-30 may be used to determine the amount of coolant required to cool the wall to a predesignated temperature. From the condition of heat balance at the wall, one obtains

$$\int_0^l k\left(\frac{\partial T}{\partial r}\right)_{r=R} dx = -\rho v_w c_p (T_w - T_0) l \tag{5-44}$$

Upon substitution of Eq. 5-30 into the above equation, one obtains the temperature difference ratio as follows:

$$\frac{T_1 - T_w}{T_w - T_0} = 4Pr\lambda\left(\frac{v_w l}{u_m D}\right)\left[\frac{A_1 M_1'(1)}{1 - \frac{c_1^2}{4Pr\lambda}}\left\{1 - \left(1 + 4\frac{v_w}{u_m}\frac{l}{D}\right)^{1-\frac{c_1^2}{4Pr\lambda}}\right\}\right.$$

$$\left. + \frac{A_2 M_2'(1)}{1 - \frac{c_2^2}{4Pr\lambda}}\left\{1 - \left(1 + 4\frac{v_w}{u_m}\frac{l}{D}\right)^{1-\frac{c_2^2}{4Pr\lambda}}\right\}\right]^{-1} \tag{5-45}$$

where

$$M_j'(1) = \left[\frac{\partial M_j(\eta)}{\partial \eta}\right]_{\eta=1}$$

In Fig. G,5d the heat transfer coefficient or Nusselt number is plotted against the coolant Reynolds number. It indicates that the Nusselt number decreases almost linearly with an increase of the coolant Reynolds number. This is due to the fact that the range of coolant Reynolds numbers considered in the present investigation is rather small ($\lambda \leqq 1$). As the coolant Reynolds number increases further, the Nusselt number then decreases more gradually. The above phenomenon was also obtained in the case of nonisothermal flow over a plate with coolant injection.

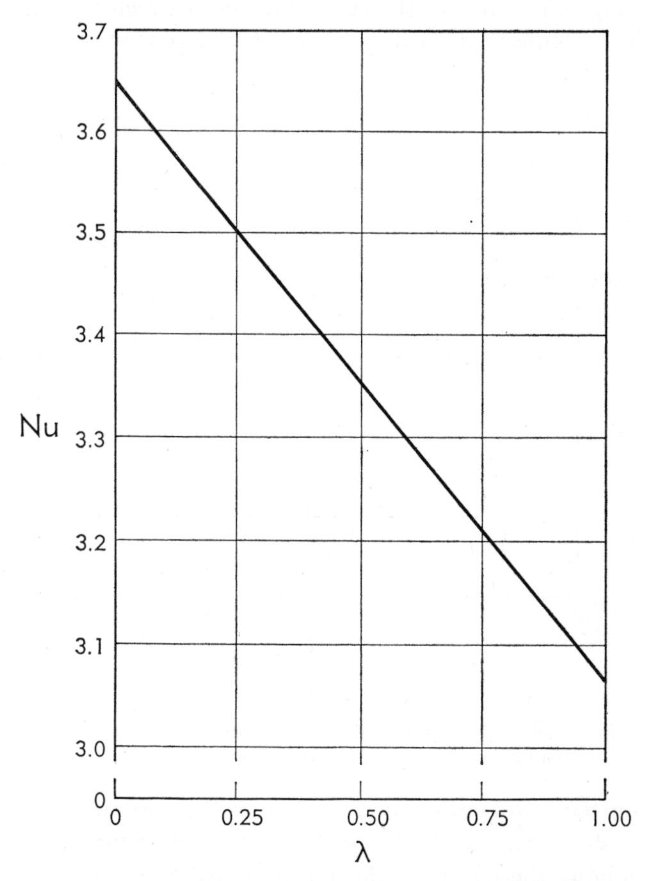


Fig. G,5d. Local heat transfer coefficient for various rates of coolant injection ($(1/PrRe)(1/D) = 0.075$). (From [*32*].)

The ratio of temperature difference $(T_1 - T_w)/(T_w - T_0)$ is plotted against the coolant flow ratio $v_w l/u_m D$ in Fig. G,5e. For a predesignated wall temperature the amount of coolant required per unit time can readily be determined provided that the entrance temperature $T_1$ and the coolant temperature $T_0$ are known.

The results obtained from the studies of nonisothermal laminar flow over a plate with coolant injection show that the friction coefficient at the wall decreases with the increase of coolant injection. They also indicate that the heat transfer coefficient decreases with the increase of coolant injection. Thus there is a definite direct relationship between the friction coefficient and the heat transfer coefficient. On the other hand, the results obtained here indicate that in a pipe flow the effect of fluid injection at the wall is to accelerate the main stream velocity. Hence the velocity gradient at the wall, which determines the wall friction, increases. This phenomenon indicates that the analogue between the heat transfer and the momentum transfer does not exist in porous-wall cooling of pipe flow.

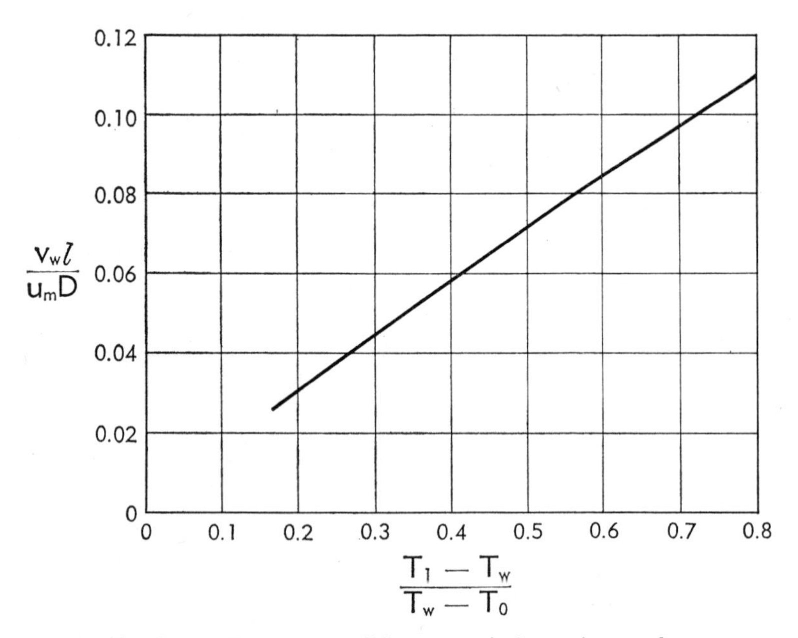


Fig. G,5e. Temperature difference ratio for various coolant parameters $((1/PrRe)(l/D) = 0.075)$. (From [*32*].)

Approximate Solution of Turbulent Pipe Flow with Coolant Injection at Wall. In the present treatment an approximate analysis for determining the effect of transpiration cooling on a fully developed turbulent flow in a circular pipe is given [*35*]. In order to simplify the analysis it is assumed that: (1) the fluid is incompressible, i.e. the fluid properties remain constant, (2) the fluid flowing in the axial direction and the fluid flowing through the porous wall are assumed homogeneous, (3) the fluid flowing through the porous wall is uniform throughout, and (4) the wall temperature is constant.

If a curvilinear coordinate system is introduced with the origin at the center of the cross section of a circular pipe where $x$ is taken in the direction of the flow and $r$ in the radial direction and $\varphi$ is the azimuthal angle, then with axial symmetry of flow the Reynolds equations for the time-average velocities become

$$u\frac{\partial u}{\partial x} + v\frac{\partial u}{\partial r} = -\frac{1}{\rho}\frac{\partial p}{\partial x} - \frac{1}{\rho}\frac{1}{r}\frac{\partial}{\partial r}(r\tau) \tag{5-46}$$

$$u\frac{\partial v}{\partial x} + v\frac{\partial v}{\partial r} = -\frac{1}{\rho}\frac{\partial p}{\partial r} + \frac{1}{\rho}\frac{\partial \tau}{\partial x} \tag{5-47}$$

where $\tau = -\mu\partial u/\partial r - \rho\overline{u'v'}$. The continuity equation is

$$\frac{\partial(ru)}{\partial x} + \frac{\partial(rv)}{\partial r} = 0 \tag{5-48}$$

The eddy heat transfer equation excluding the dissipation term is

$$\rho c_p u\frac{\partial T}{\partial x} + \rho c_p v\frac{\partial T}{\partial r} = \frac{1}{r}\frac{\partial}{\partial r}\left[kr\frac{\partial T}{\partial r} - \rho c_p r\overline{v'T'}\right] \tag{5-49}$$

The boundary conditions are

$$r = 0: \qquad u = u_c; \qquad \tau = 0 \tag{5-50}$$

$$T = T_g; \quad \left(\frac{\partial T}{\partial r}\right) = 0 \tag{5-51}$$

*Velocity distribution and skin friction.* The first simplification necessary in achieving an approximate solution for Eq. 5-46, 5-47, and 5-48 is to assume that $v = -v_w r/R$ and that in the region close to the wall

$$\frac{\partial u}{\partial r} \gg \frac{u}{R}$$

is valid. With the above assumptions and with the aid of the continuity equation, Eq. 5-46 and 5-47 are reduced to

$$\frac{v_w}{R}\frac{\partial(r^2u)}{\partial r} = \frac{r}{\rho}\frac{\partial p}{\partial x} + \frac{1}{\rho}\frac{\partial(r\tau)}{\partial r} \tag{5-52}$$

and

$$\frac{\partial p}{\partial r} = 0 \tag{5-53}$$

According to momentum transfer theory this gives

$$-\overline{u'v'} = l^2\left|\frac{du}{dy}\right|^2 \tag{5-54}$$

where $l = K(R - r)$. After neglecting the viscous shearing stress and combining Eq. 5-54 and 5-52, one obtains, after integration with the aid of Eq. 5-50

$$K^2(R - r)^2\left(\frac{du}{dr}\right)^2 = \frac{r}{R}(u_p^2 + v_w u) \tag{5-55}$$

where $u_p^2 = -(R/2\rho)(\partial p/\partial x)$ has the dimension of the square of a velocity. The closed form solution for velocity distribution in a fully developed turbulent pipe flow with fluid injection at the wall is obtained from Eq. 5-55 with boundary conditions given in Eq. 5-50. This is

$$\frac{u_c - u}{u_p} = \frac{1}{K}\left[\ln\frac{1+\zeta}{1-\zeta} - 2\zeta\right] - \frac{1}{4K^2}\frac{v_w}{u_p}\left[\ln\frac{1+\zeta}{1-\zeta} - 2\zeta\right]^2 \qquad (5\text{-}56)$$

where $\zeta = (r/R)^{\frac{1}{3}}$, $u_c$ is the velocity at the center of the pipe, and $K$ is an empirical constant to be discussed later. For a zero injection velocity Eq. 5-56 reduces to the form expressing the velocity distribution in flow through a circular pipe [*36*, pp. 340–344].

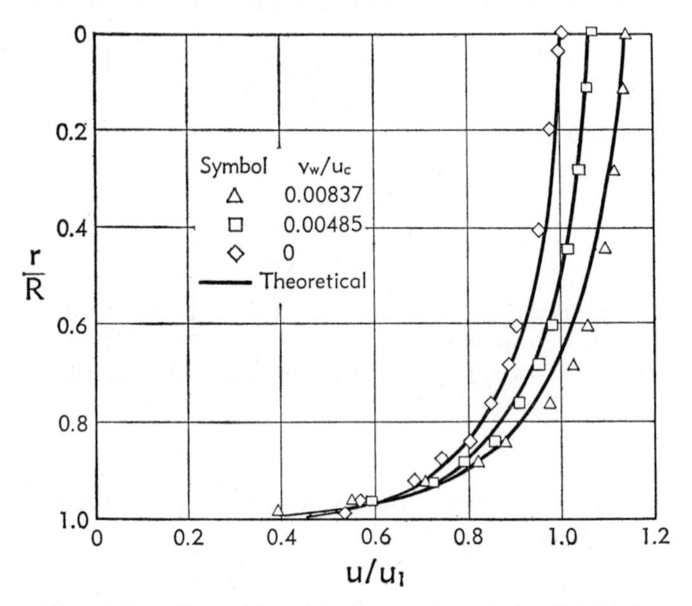


Fig. G,5f. Effect of fluid injection on the velocity distribution in turbulent pipe flow. (From [*35*].)

From Eq. 5-56 the mean flow velocity $u_m$ can be determined by integration over the cross section. It is

$$u_m = \frac{2}{R^2}\int_0^R urdr = u_c - \frac{16}{15}\frac{u_p}{K} + 0.541\frac{v_w}{K^2} \qquad (5\text{-}57)$$

Hence the empirical constant $K$ can be readily calculated from Eq. 5-57 if the measured velocity distribution and pressure gradient are known. The average value of $K$ is about 0.24 for the case of zero injection. However, the values of $K$ tend to increase with the increase of fluid injection. Additional data from further tests (now being conducted at the Polytechnic Institute of Brooklyn) are needed in order to form a definite relationship between the above two parameters. In Fig. G,5f the effect of fluid injection on the velocity distribution of a fully developed turbulent flow in a circular pipe was shown. The theoretical curves were calculated from Eq. 5-56. The experimental data were taken from a porous stainless steel pipe with a 5-inch diameter and a length of 20 inches. The range of Reynolds numbers was from $10^5$ to $3 \times 10^5$. The comparison between the theoretical curve and the experimental data shows close agreement.

The momentum integral equation for the turbulent flow through a pipe with fluid injection at the wall is obtained by integrating Eq. 5-46 over the cross section from $r = 0$ to $r = R$. This yields

$$c_f = \frac{2\tau}{\rho u_m^2} = -\frac{R\dfrac{dp}{dx}}{\rho u_m^2} - \frac{2}{u_m^2}\frac{d}{d(x/R)}\left[u_c^2\int_0^1\left(\frac{u}{u_c}\right)^2\left(\frac{r}{R}\right)d\left(\frac{r}{R}\right)\right] \tag{5-58}$$

The integral in Eq. 5-58 can be evaluated by substituting the expression for the velocity profile from Eq. 5-56. After a very tedious integration, the resulting expression for the skin friction coefficient becomes

$$c_f = 2\left(\frac{u_p}{u_m}\right)^2 - \frac{1}{u_m^2}\frac{d}{d(x/R)}\left[u_c^2\left\{1 - \frac{32}{15K}\frac{u_p}{u_c} + \frac{9.66}{K^4}\left(\frac{v_w}{u_c}\right)^2 + \frac{2.159}{K^2}\left(\frac{u_p^2}{u_c^2} + \frac{1}{2}\frac{v_w}{u_c}\right) - \frac{3.235}{K^3}\frac{u_p}{u_c}\frac{v_w}{u_c}\right\}\right] \tag{5-59}$$

*Temperature distribution and heat transfer.* In order to achieve an approximate solution for the temperature distribution in a fully developed turbulent flow in a pipe with coolant injection at the wall it is necessary to make some simplifications of Eq. 5-49. It is assumed that $v = -v_w r/R$ and that in the region close to the wall

$$\frac{\partial T}{\partial r} \gg \frac{T}{R}$$

holds. The temperature distribution may be written

$$T = A\left(\frac{x}{R}\right) + \theta\left(\frac{r}{R}\right) \tag{5-60}$$

According to the mixture length theory, the eddy heat transfer term

$$\overline{v'T'} = -K_1^2(R - r)^2\left|\frac{du}{dr}\right|\frac{dT}{dr} \tag{5-61}$$

Following the above hypothesis and assumptions Eq. 5-49 can be simplified, after integration, as follows:

$$\left[\frac{k}{\rho c_p} + K_1^2(R - r)^2\frac{du}{dr}\right]\frac{dT}{dr} + v_w\left(\frac{r}{R}\right)T = \frac{A}{Rr}\int_0^r rudr \tag{5-62}$$

The condition at $r = 0$ gives the zero constant of integration.

Upon substitution of the term of the velocity gradient from Eq. 5-56 into Eq. 5-62 it may be integrated to give

$$T = [e^{-\int_0^\zeta g(\zeta)d\zeta}] \int_0^\zeta [e^{\int_0^\zeta g(\zeta)d\zeta}]\, h(\zeta)d\zeta + T_g e^{-\int_0^\zeta g(\zeta)d\zeta} \tag{5-63}$$

where

$$g(\zeta) = 2\frac{v_w}{u_c}\zeta^3 \left[\frac{u_m}{u_c}\frac{2}{PrRe} + K_1^2(1-\zeta^2)\zeta\left\{-\frac{u_p}{Ku_c} + \frac{v_w}{2u_cK^2}\left(\ln\frac{1+\zeta}{1-\zeta} - 2\zeta\right)\right\}\right]^{-1}$$

$$h(\zeta) = \left[\frac{4A}{\zeta}\int \frac{u}{u_c}\zeta^3 d\zeta\right]\frac{g(\zeta)}{2\frac{v_w}{u_c}\zeta^3} \tag{5-64}$$

The term $(u_m/u_c)(2/PrRe)$ is due to heat transfer by molecular conductivity which is negligibly small in comparison with the eddy heat transfer term except very close to the wall. The empirical constant $K_1$ may be determined from the measured temperature profiles.

In Fig. G,5g the effect of coolant injection on the temperature distribution of a fully developed turbulent flow in a circular pipe was shown. The comparison between the theoretical curve calculated from Eq. 5-63

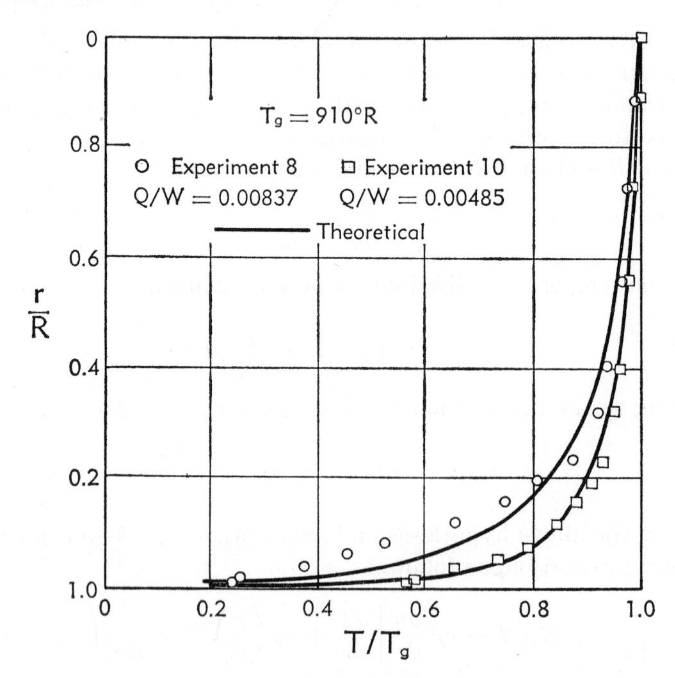


Fig. G,5g. Effect of coolant injection on the temperature distribution in turbulent pipe flow. (From [35].)

and the experimental data show close agreement for small coolant injection. Since the variation of the fluid properties was not taken into consideration in the theory it might be the main reason for the discrepancy between the theory and experiment, especially in the case of large coolant injection.

The rate of heat transfer per unit area radially outwards at the wall can be calculated by integrating the energy equation (Eq. 5-49) across the radius of the circular pipe.

$$q_w = \frac{1}{R}\frac{d}{dx}\int_0^R \rho c_p T u r \, dr - \rho_w c_{p_w} v_w T_w \tag{5-65}$$

From the condition of heat balance at the wall (the heat transfer by the hot gas to the wall is absorbed by the coolant) one obtains

$$q_w = \rho_w v_w c_{p_w}(T_w - T_0) \tag{5-66}$$

Combining Eq. 5-65 and 5-66, after integrating between two cross sections, $l_1$ and $l_2$, one obtains the temperature difference ratio as follows:

$$\frac{T_g - T_w}{T_g - T_0} = \left(1 - \frac{T_w}{T_g}\right)\left[1 - \frac{1}{2}\frac{R}{l}\frac{C_{p_m}}{C_{p_w}}\frac{W_1}{Q}\left\{\frac{W_2}{W_1}\left(\frac{U_m}{U_c}\right)_2 - \left(\frac{U_m}{U_c}\right)_1\right]^{-1} \tag{5-67}$$

where $W = \rho_c U_c$, $Q = \rho_w v_x$, and the quantities $(\ )_1$ and $(\ )_2$ represent the values at stations, $l_1$ and $l_2$, respectively.

## G,6. Comparison with Experimental Results on Transpiration Cooling.

EXPERIMENTAL RESULTS VS. THEORY. The systematic experimental study of transpiration cooling was initiated at the Jet Propulsion Laboratory by Duwez and Wheeler in 1946 [*37,38,39,40,41,42*]. The experimental investigation was limited to the case of a cylindrical duct made of porous material through the walls of which the coolant was injected. The test section containing the porous-wall duct was one inch in diameter and eight inches long and a gasoline-air flame served as the source of hot gas. The gas temperature ranged from 1100 to 1900°F with Mach numbers approaching 1.0 and Reynolds numbers up to 140,000. For the detailed description of experimental equipment, [*38*] should be consulted.

The main object of the experiments is to establish a relation between the surface temperature of the porous material and the weight rate of coolant flow for different conditions of temperature and velocity in the main stream of hot gas. Four significant variables were measured in the experiments, namely the temperature $T_g$ of the main stream of gas, the weight rate of flow of the hot gas $W$, the weight rate of flow of coolant $Q$, and the surface temperature $T_w$ of the porous wall at several points along the tube. For a given porous material and a given coolant, all the measurements can be reduced to the ratio $(T_g - T_w)/(T_w - T_0)$ as a function of $Q/W$.

A comparison of the experimental data with the theoretical results of [27] is given in Fig. G,6a in which $(T_g - T_w)/(T_g - T_0)$ is plotted against $Q/W$. For a given porous material the measured values of $(T_g - T_w)/(T_g - T_0)$ and $Q/W$ obtained within the range of temperatures and velocities covered in the experiments fall more or less on a single curve having the shape of the theoretical curves. But the theoretical curves indicate there is small dependency on the Reynolds number. This can be

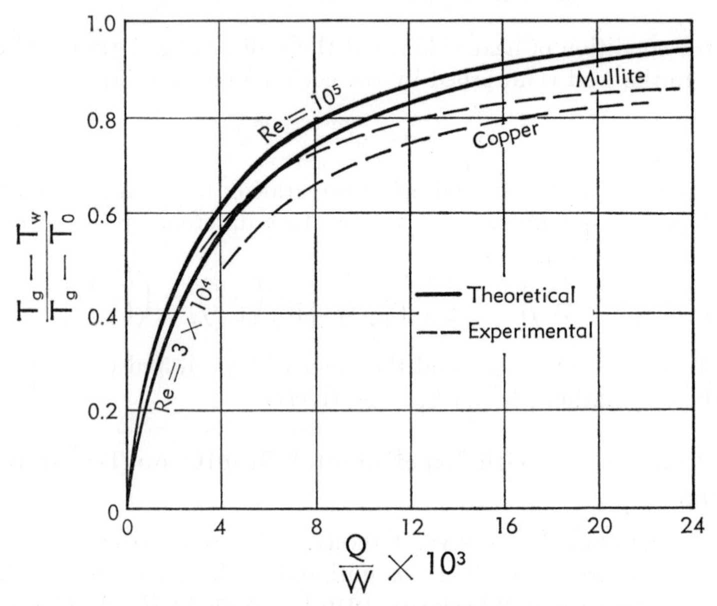


Fig. G,6a. Comparison of theoretical and experimental results on temperature difference ratio vs. mass flow ratio. (From [27].)

seen in Fig. G,6a. Since the theoretical analysis does not include the conductivity of the porous material, the result shows a fair agreement with the measured values obtained with a porous ceramic specimen and the poorest agreement with a porous copper specimen.

Perhaps it should be mentioned that a very good agreement has been obtained between the experimental results of a stainless steel specimen and the theoretical curve computed from the laminar boundary layer theory by Yuan [7] for a Reynolds number of $3 \times 10^4$. This is given in Fig. G,6b. Although the agreement is for a particular case, it is interesting to note that qualitatively there is very good agreement between theory and experiment in transpiration cooling.

An experimental investigation of the isothermal laminar boundary layer on a porous flat plate (injection begins at a distance parameter from the leading edge) was made at the Polytechnic Institute of Brooklyn [*43*]. Fig. G,6c shows that good agreement has been obtained between the measured velocity profiles and those calculated from the theoretical results given in [*7*]. The heat transfer theory in the laminar boundary layer can therefore be considered to have been verified, at least for a low rate of heat transfer. Due to the roughness and jet effect of the injected velocity of the porous plate, only qualitative agreement is obtained between the measured transition Reynolds number and those predicted from the laminar boundary layer stability theory [*25*].

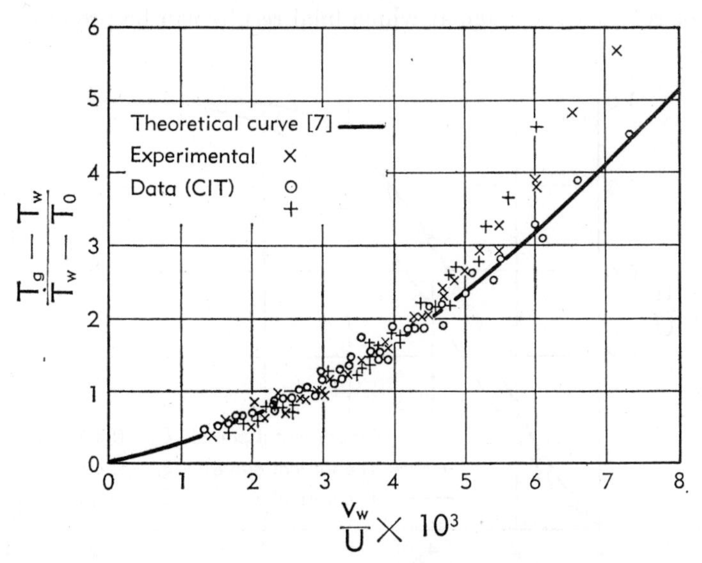


Fig. G,6b. Comparison of measured data in a stainless-steel specimen with theoretical result [*7*]. (From [*37*].)

An extensive experimental study of transpiration cooling of turbulent pipe flow with injection is being conducted at the Polytechnic Institute of Brooklyn under the auspices of Project Squid. The investigation has been guided by the theory discussed in Art. 5. The experimental apparatus for this investigation was designed and so arranged that fully developed turbulent flow would be established upstream of the test section. Hence any change in the flow conditions in the porous test section would be due to mass injection. The porous stainless steel segment, made by the Poroloy method, is a five-inch-diameter circular pipe, 24 inches in length. The velocity and pressure surveys were made at six stations along the axial direction of the porous-wall pipe. For zero injection at the wall the measured velocity profiles ($10^5 \leqq Re \leqq 5 \times 10^5$) are in good agreement with Nikuradse's measurement for the smooth pipe. A comparison of the measured velocity profiles with various injection velocities to the theoretically calculated velocity profiles is given in Fig. G,5f.

Radial temperature profiles were also measured at six stations along the axis of the porous-wall pipe. The inner temperature of the porous wall was measured at six axial stations by thermocouples of the integrating type. The results of the measured temperature profiles were also used in a comparison with those of the theoretically calculated temperature profiles. This comparison was given in Fig. G,5g. The results of the present temperature-profile surveys for a fully developed turbulent pipe flow with coolant injection at the wall will be used to develop a semiempirical relation of the heat transfer coefficient for transpiration cooling. The study has not reached the stage at which final results can be presented at this time.

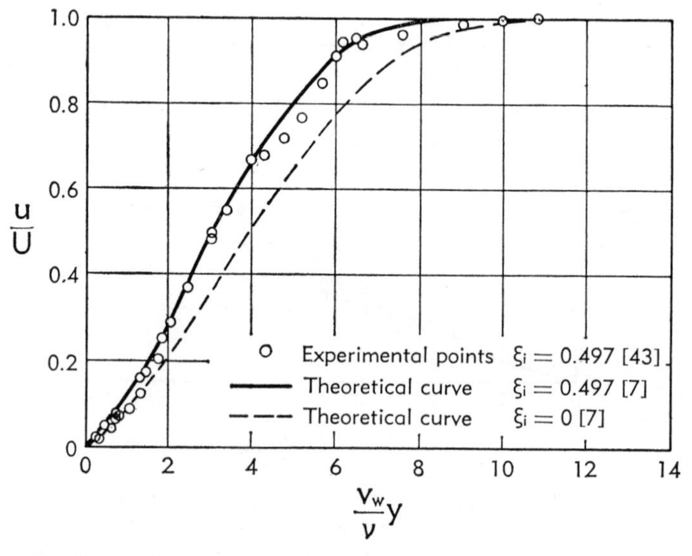


Fig. G,6c. Comparison of theoretical and experimental velocity profiles with injection for $\xi = (v_w/U)^2 Re_x = 1.0$. (From [43].)

Question of Skin Friction and Heat Transfer Coefficient. As pointed out in Art. 4 the rate of change of momentum in the boundary layer due to mass fluid injection at the wall has the same effect as the rise of pressure gradient in the flow direction. Hence it is clear that the increase of fluid injection at the wall increases the thickness of boundary layer and decreases the slope of the velocity profile at the wall in the boundary layer. In the case of laminar boundary layer it is evident that the wall shearing stress and heat transfer from the hot gas to the wall decreases as the injected coolant increases. Since the heat flow from hot gas to the wall can be expressed by the following forms:

$$q = k\left(\frac{\partial T}{\partial y}\right)_w = h_i(T_g - T_w) \tag{6-1}$$

and the wall temperature decreases with the increase of coolant injection, it can be seen that the film heat transfer coefficient $h_i$ decreases as the coolant injection increases. This is shown in Fig. G,4c.

The above phenomena were also observed in the case of heat transfer in the turbulent boundary layer on a flat plate with coolant injection at the wall. This can be seen in Fig. G,4g and G,4h.

The result obtained from the study of laminar pipe flow with fluid injection at the wall has shown that the effect of fluid injection at the wall is to accelerate the main stream velocity. Hence the velocity gradient at the wall, which determines the wall friction, increases. On the other hand, the result of the study of heat transfer of a laminar pipe flow with coolant injection shows that the heat transfer coefficient at the wall decreases with an increase in the rate of coolant injection. This phenomenon thus indicates that the analogy between the heat transfer and momentum transfer does not exist in transpiration-cooled pipe flow.

For turbulent pipe flow the connection between the pressure drop and the flow volume which, in turn, determines the wall shearing stress must be obtained from tests. Wheeler [*44*] has made some preliminary pressure-drop studies in a transpiration-cooled pipe. From the test data an empirical expression is formulated

$$\frac{\Delta p^2}{W^2L} = f\frac{RT_g}{g^2D} + B\left(\frac{Q}{W}\right)^n \frac{RT_g}{g^2D} \tag{6-2}$$

where $W$ is the weight rate of flow in the main stream, $R$ is the gas constant, $T_g$ is the main stream temperature, $g$ is the acceleration of gravity, and $D$ is the diameter of the pipe. The first term on the right-hand side of Eq. 6-2 represents the head loss, which was observed with no coolant flow where $f$ is the friction factor corresponding to Blasius formula for a smooth pipe. The second term expresses the additional loss which occurred when coolant was added. For isothermal flow the exponent $n$ becomes unity. The parameter $B$ seems to depend somewhat on the initial value of $f$ and on the nature of the cooling gas, being greater for the less dense gas. The exact factors which control the parameter $B$ and $n$ cannot be determined from the present preliminary data.

The importance of Eq. 6-2 is realized when one considers that the shearing stress at the wall $\tau_w$ may be determined experimentally by the measurement of the pressure drop. Once Eq. 6-2 is exactly established the shearing stress at the wall $\tau_w$ and the heat flow to the wall from the hot gas $q_w$ can be determined in the transpiration-cooled turbulent boundary layer.

General Discussion on Transpiration Cooling. On comparing the theoretical curves computed from [*27*] with the experimental results, it is seen that the shape of the curves is correct but that the theoretical wall temperature for a given coolant flow is lower than the measured values. The deviation appears to be more pronounced when the coolant flows become larger. It is believed that the discrepancies between theories and experimental data can be interpreted by the following discussions.

*Assessment of experimental errors.* The errors inherent in the measurements of the main stream gas temperature were probably the most serious. It can be realized that the application of proper thermometric techniques is difficult without disturbing the velocity profile of the gas stream. The deterioration of thermocouples at high gas stream temperatures creates another serious problem. Furthermore the radiation heat loss from the thermocouple to the straightening-tube wall, the uncertainty as to the recovery factor of the probe, the error in the location of the thermocouple with respect to the temperature and velocity profiles, and the changes in the calibration of the thermocouple due to chemical reaction between the couple and the gas stream may contribute to error in the measurement of the true gas temperature.

Next, the error in the measurement of the wall temperature due to the presence of the thermocouple tends to block off the flow of coolant between itself and the hot wall of the specimen. Thus the thermocouple indicates temperatures which are higher than those that would actually exist on the surface of an undisturbed wall.

Disposition of carbonaceous materials on the specimen surface may cause the difficulty in obtaining reproducible experimental results. Since carbon deposition decreases the permeability of the specimen it would affect the coolant discharge pattern, the thermal conductivity of the specimen surface, and therefore the measured wall temperature. There is some radial heat loss from the back of the specimen to the holder which was not measured. The effect of this loss in general is to decrease the value of wall temperature for a given value of $Q/W$.

*Error arising from assumptions in the theory.* As previously mentioned, the theory assumed that there is no wall temperature gradient in the flow direction and hence no heat conducted along the wall. Actually, there is an "inlet length" for the porous material where the temperature distribution changes from that typical of flow in an uncooled pipe to the final distribution for porous-wall cooling. This inlet length depends on the conductivity of the porous material and is large for a material of high conductivity. Hence the theoretical results show a better agreement with measured values obtained with porous ceramic specimens than a porous copper specimen. Furthermore the measured data indicates that the discrepancy among various porous materials is reduced considerably when a longer specimen is used.

In the theory the coolant flow normal to the wall was assumed uniformly distributed over the surface of the specimen. It has been found in experiments that the coolant leaves the surface in the form of a number of isolated jets. Thus the transpiration-cooling process will be less efficient in practice than in theory and the values of measured wall temperatures are correspondingly higher for a given coolant flow.

It has been found in the experiments that the velocity of a stream of gas passing through a transpiration-cooled tube increases rapidly along the length of the tube. The rate of increase depends on the mass flow ratio $Q/W$ and the density of the gas. The main stream velocity used in the theory is independent of the length in the direction of flow.

Fundamentally, the influence of the rate of coolant flow to the shearing stress at the wall, to the main stream velocity profiles, and to the laminar sublayer thickness must be thoroughly investigated experimentally before an accurate theory in transpiration cooling can be realized.

Different Physical Properties Between Coolant and Hot Gas. When the physical properties of the coolant gas differ from those of the main stream gas, Eq. 4-31 can also be used to approximate the relation between the wall temperature and the coolant flow. It can be seen from Eq. 4-31 that the specific heat is the most important property, with a secondary effect due to the Prandtl number. The theoretical results computed for nitrogen and hydrogen coolants give a fair agreement with experimental data.

The results of the experimental investigation of transpiration cooling by injecting water as a coolant indicate that there is a critical value in the amount of coolant, above which the surface temperature of the porous material remains near or below the boiling point of water, and below which the surface temperature increases very rapidly with decreased flow. The instability of water coolant flow may be explained by the evaporation of water inside the porous metal just below the hot surface. A film of vapor rather than a film of water was formed on the surface exposed to heat. It is undoubtedly true that this phenomenon would occur in the use of other kinds of liquid coolant. Unless some means of controlling the evaporation of the liquid coolant inside the porous metal is developed, a liquid coolant cannot be successfully used in transpiration cooling.

## G,7. Film Cooling and Its Comparison with Transpiration Cooling.

*General description.* It was mentioned in the introduction that film cooling is a method of protecting a surface from a high temperature gas stream by separating the surface and the hot gas stream with a thin continuous film of a liquid or gaseous coolant. The coolant is discharged by slots or orifices to the surface where the hot gas is flowing and is carried downstream by the flowing hot gas. In this way an insulating film is formed along the surface; however, the film is gradually destroyed on its way downstream by turbulent mixing. The coolant film has to be renewed at a certain distance downstream by injecting a new coolant through additional slots, because otherwise the wall temperature would eventually approach the temperature of the hot gas. The insulating effect of liquid film layer is better than the gas film layer due to the fact that the liquid coolant is evaporated by the heat from the flowing hot gas. The heat required for evaporation keeps the temperatures of the liquid film and the wall to the evaporation temperature, until a point downstream from the slot is reached where the liquid is completely evaporated.

In early work in Germany certain scientists employed the method of film cooling in rocket motors by injecting a coolant through small holes into the chamber and nozzle walls of a regeneratively cooled motor to cool the predetermined "hot spots." A series of holes generally uniformly spaced around the circumference of the wall has been employed if a complete wall is needed to be film-cooled. A different injection method is to introduce the coolant through inclined holes along the motor walls. This method has the advantage over the injection through radial holes in that it retains most of the coolant along the wall that is to be cooled, while injection through radial holes cannot avoid discharging a portion of the coolant directly into the main gas stream. Tangential holes which inject the coolant around the circumference of the motor, thereby taking advantage of centrifugal force to hold the coolant on the wall, have also been employed.

An investigation of film cooling based on the injection of the coolant through a slot around the circumference of the combustion chamber or nozzle is presented in [*45*]. The advantages of the radial injection of the coolant through a slot are: (1) the coolant flow rate may be accurately predicted in any section of the motor, and (2) a uniform film can be established at all sections of the motor.

*Film-cooling problems.* The heat transfer process in film cooling is essentially the same as the process in transpiration cooling. One of the most important problems in film cooling is to determine the length of the fluid film along the wall. This depends on the quantity of fluid injected and the stability of the fluid film. Up to the present time there are neither theoretical analyses nor experimental investigations which yield a definite and general answer in regard to this important phenomenon. Hence it is limited only to particular results which will be presented here. In Fig. G,7a the wall temperature of a particular liquid-film-cooled tube is shown. The liquid-film-cooled length is indicated between the points $A$ and $C$. At point $C$ the wall temperature reaches the boiling temperature of the liquid and beyond the point $C$ the liquid is completely evaporated, while the wall temperature increases rapidly to a value approaching the gas temperature. If a gas coolant is used instead of a liquid the length of the film would only exist for a short distance between $B$ and $C$. This makes the use of a gas coolant in film cooling inadequate since numerous slots would be required.

Tsien [46] has indicated that, when the friction drag of a gas passing over a liquid film is of appreciable magnitude, the flow of a film coolant on a solid surface can be compared to the flow of the liquid near the wall of a pipe completely filled with a turbulent flowing liquid. Furthermore, when the film is of sufficient thickness to include a turbulent layer of coolant on the gaseous side of the film, instability occurs and some of the coolant breaks away in the form of droplets. The criterion of the instability of the coolant film can be completely described by $y^*$, a parameter indicating flow conditions near the wall. The above phenomenon was also interpreted by Rannie [47]. Knuth [48] has calculated some NACA experimental results on film cooling by Sloop and Kinney [49] and found that a definite value of $y^*$ exists for the criterion of the instability of coolant film.

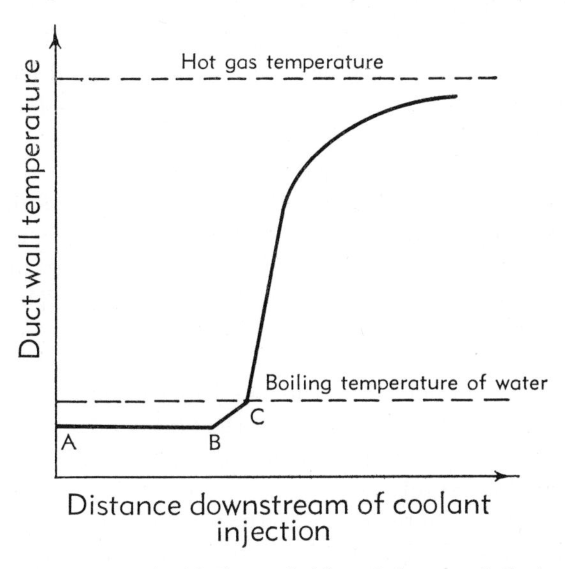


Fig. G,7a. Liquid-film-cooled length in smooth duct (injection begins at $A$). (From [49].)

An experimental study of the stability of the liquid film under various flow conditions is given in [45]. In this experiment, visual observation was made by injecting the liquid coolant through a slot into the test section where the air was blown through. At very low flow rates of the coolant, it entered the test section smoothly and flowed in a uniformly thin layer along the surface of the test section downstream from the injection slot. As the flow of liquid was increased, a point was reached where small air bubbles were formed immediately downstream of the slot. The mean velocity of the liquid in the slot corresponding to the condition where the bubbles first started to form was taken as the critical velocity of injection. If the liquid flow was increased beyond this critical velocity, the major portion of it separated from the wall of the test section.

The results of the experiments showed that the critical velocity of injection is increased when (1) the main stream air velocity is increased, (2) the coolant viscosity is increased, (3) the slot width is decreased, and (4) the density of the coolant is decreased. It further indicates that inclined injection of the coolant increases the critical velocity of injection considerably more than the case of injection perpendicular to the main stream flow.

*Comparison of the effectiveness of film and transpiration cooling.* Eckert [*50*] has made a comparison of the relative effectiveness of film and transpiration cooling which is based on a turbulent flow along a flat plate with constant gas velocity and temperature. The Reynolds number for the turbulent gas flow is assumed equal to $10^7$ and the Prandtl number is equal to 0.7. Air is considered as the coolant, as well as the outside flow gas. The parameters used in the comparison are the ratio of the temperature difference, the difference of wall temperature and coolant temperature to the difference of hot gas temperature and coolant temperature; and the ratio of coolant mass flow to the gas mass flow.

In the transpiration-cooling calculation the relation between the ratio of the temperature difference and the ratio of the mass flow is derived from the heat balance equation at the wall. The heat transfer coefficient used herein is obtained from sublayer theory in the turbulent flow [*51*]. In the film-cooling calculation the Wieghardt method [*52*] is used to determine the temperature difference ratio in relation to the mass flow ratio for a single slot. Although the temperature conditions within the boundary layer in [*52*] are opposite to the conditions found in film cooling, the results obtained in [*52*] can be used for the film-cooling process as long as the temperature differences are small enough to permit the gas property to be considered constant.

A comparison of the relative effectiveness of the two cooling methods considered is shown in Fig. G,7b. Transpiration cooling is much more effective than film cooling with a single slot and gives much lower wall temperature for a specified coolant flow. In other words, transpiration cooling requires a much smaller amount of coolant to cool the wall to a predesignated temperature. It must be borne in mind that in the film-cooling calculation the wall temperature cannot be made constant as in the case of transpiration cooling, and it represents the highest temperature occurring within the wall. At smaller downstream distances, the temperature decreases toward the value $T_0$ obtained immediately behind the slot. The effectiveness of the film cooling therefore is increased by increasing the number of slots along the plate, and it is expected that the film cooling eventually transforms into transpiration when the number of slots becomes very large.

There are, of course, other considerations, aside from that of a minimum of coolant, which influence the choice of the cooling method for a particular application. A distinct advantage of film cooling for practical applications is that it can be very easily adapted in most designs. In addition, film cooling, as explained above, appears to be a good method for thoroughly cooling a specific location. In this connection, further intensive research on the problems of methods of injection, stability of coolant film,

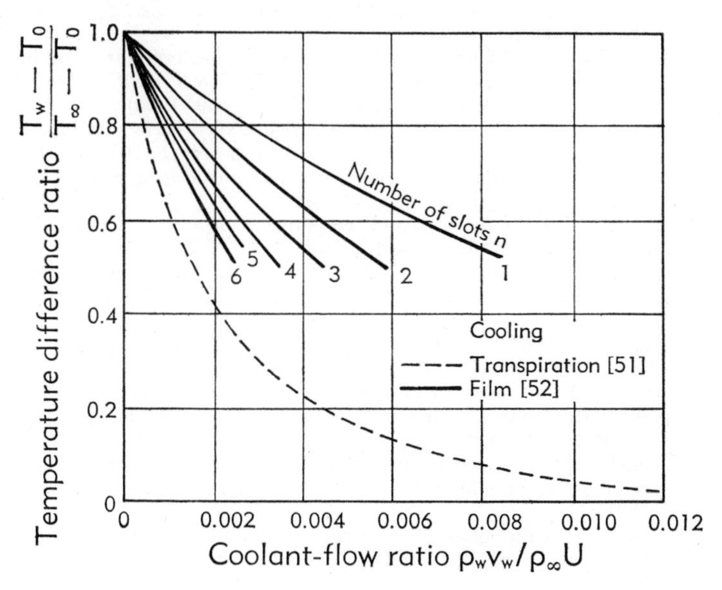


Fig. G,7b. Comparison of transpiration and film-cooling methods (turbulent flow $Re = 10^7$, $Pr = 0.7$). (From [*50*].)

and the mass and heat transfer between a hot gas and a coolant film in film cooling is needed.

## G,8. Cited References and Bibliography.

*Cited References*


1. Duwez, P., and Martin, H. F. Preparation and physical properties of porous metals for sweat cooling. *Calif. Inst. Technol. Jet Propul. Lab. Progress Rept. 3-14*, July 1946.
2. Wheeler, H. L., Jr. Private communication, Apr. 1956.
3. Duwez, P., and Wheeler, H. L., Jr. An experimental study of the flow of gas through porous metal. *Calif. Inst. Technol. Jet Propul. Lab. Progress Rept. 1-66*, Aug. 1947.
4. Green, L., Jr., and Duwez, P. The permeability of porous iron. *Calif. Inst. Technol. Jet Propul. Lab. Progress Rept. 4-85*, Feb. 1949.
5. Wheeler, H. L., Jr., and Myer, F. O. The pattern of flow of gas leaving porous metal surface. *Calif. Inst. Technol. Jet Propul. Lab. Progress Rept. 4-83*, Nov. 1948.
6. Weinbaum, S., and Wheeler, H. L., Jr. Heat transfer in sweat-cooled porous metal. *J. Appl. Phys. 20*, 113–122 (1949).
7. Yuan, S. W. A theoretical investigation of the temperature field in the laminar boundary layer on a porous flat plate with fluid injection. *Project Squid Tech. Rept. 4*, Sept. 1947.

8. Ness, N. On the temperature distribution along a semi-infinite sweat-cooled plate. *J. Aeronaut. Sci. 19,* 760–768 (1952).
9. Yuan, S. W. Heat transfer in laminar compressible boundary layer on a porous flat plate with fluid injection. *J. Aeronaut. Sci. 16,* 741–748 (1949).
10. Crocco, L. Sulla Transmissione del Calone de una Lamina Piana un fluido scorrente ad alta velocita. *Aerotecnica 12,* 181–197 (1932).
11. Yuan, S. W., and Ness, N. Heat transfer in a laminar compressible boundary layer on a porous flat plate with variable fluid injection. *Project Squid Tech. Mem. P.I.B.-15,* Sept. 1950.
12. Morduchow, M., and Galowin, L. The compressible laminar boundary in a pressure gradient over a surface cooled by fluid injection. *Proc. First Iowa Thermodynamics Symposium, State University of Iowa,* 143–169 (1953).
13. Morduchow, M. On heat transfer over a sweat-cooled surface in laminar compressible flow with a pressure gradient. *J. Aeronaut. Sci. 19,* 705–712 (1952).
14. Morduchow, M. Laminar separation over a transpiration-cooled surface in compressible flow. *NACA Tech. Note 3559,* 1955.
15. Eckert, E. R. G. Heat transfer and temperature profiles in laminar boundary layer on a sweat-cooled wall. *Army Air Force Tech. Rept. 5646,* 1947.
16. Schlicting, H., and Bussman, K. Exakte Losungen fur die laminare Grenzschicht mit Absangung und Ausblasen. *Schriften deut. Akad. Luftfahrtforschung 7B, 2,* 1943.
17. Falkner, V. N., and Skan, S. W. *Phil. Mag. 12,* 865 (1931). Also *Brit. Aeronaut. Research Council Repts. and Mem. 1314,* 1930.
18. Brown, W. B. Exact solution of the laminar boundary layer equations for a porous plate with variable fluid properties and a pressure gradient in the main stream. *Proc. First U.S. Natl. Congress Appl. Mech.,* Chicago, June 1951.
19. Pohlhausen, E. Der Warmeanstauch zwischen festen Korpen and Flussigkeiten mit kleiner Reibung and kleiner Warmeleitung. *Z. angew. Math. u. Mech. 1,* 115–121 (1921).
20. Hartree, D. R. On an equation occurring in Falkner and Skan's approximate treatment of equations of the boundary layer. *Proc. Cambridge Phil. Soc. 33,* 223 (1937).
21. Brown, W. B., and Donoughe, P. L. Table of exact laminar-boundary-layer solutions when the wall is porous and fluid properties are variable. *NACA Tech. Note 2479,* 1951.
22. Eckert, E. R. G., and Livingood, J. N. B. Method for calculation of heat transfer in laminar region of air flow around cylinders of arbitrary cross section (including large temperature difference and transpiration cooling). *NACA Rept. 1118,* 1953.
23. Low, G. M. The compressible laminar boundary layer with fluid injection. *NACA Tech. Note 3404,* 1955.
24. Lees, L., and Lin, C. C. Investigation of the stability of the laminar boundary layer in a compressible fluid. *NACA Tech. Note 1115,* 1946.
25. Lees, L. The stability of the laminar boundary layer in a compressible fluid. *NACA Rept. 876,* 1947.
26. Dunn, D. W., and Lin, C. C. On the stability of the laminar boundary layer in a compressible fluid, Part 1. *Mass. Inst. Technol. Math. Dept., Office Nav. Reserve Contract N5ori-07872 and N5ori-60,* Dec. 1953.
27. Rannie, W. D. A simplified theory of porous wall cooling. *Calif. Inst. Technol. Jet Propul. Lab. Progress Rept. 4-50,* Nov. 1947.
28. Dorrance, W. H., and Dore, F. J. The effect of mass transfer on the compressible turbulent boundary-layer skin friction and heat transfer. *J. Aeronaut. Sci. 21,* 404–410 (1954).
29. Rubesin, M. W. An analytical estimation of the effect of transpiration cooling on the heat transfer and skin friction characteristics of a compressible turbulent boundary layer. *NACA Tech. Note 3341,* 1954.
30. Mickley, H. S., Ross, R. C., Squyers, A. L., and Stewart, W. E. Heat, mass and momentum transfer for flow over a flat plate with blowing or suction. *NACA Tech. Note 3208,* 1954.

31. Yuan, S. W., and Finkelstein, A. B. Laminar pipe flow with injection and suction through a porous wall. *Trans. Am. Soc. Mech. Engrs. 78*, 719–724 (1956).
32. Yuan, S. W., and Finkelstein, A. B. Heat transfer of a laminar pipe flow with coolant injection. Presented at the *1956 Heat Transfer and Fluid Mech. Inst.*, Stanford Univ., 1956.
33. Graetz, L. *Ann. Phys. 18*, 79–94 (1883); *25*, 337–367 (1885).
34. Nusselt, W. *Z. Ver. deut. Ing. 54*, 1154–1158 (1910).
35. Yuan, S. W., and Galowin, L. S. Transpiration cooling in the turbulent flow through a porous-wall pipe. *Jet Propul. 28*, 178–181 (1958).
36. Goldstein, S. *Modern Development in Fluid Dynamics*, Vol. II. Oxford Univ. Press, 1938.
37. Duwez, P., and Wheeler, H. L., Jr. Experimental study of cooling by injection of a fluid through a porous material. *J. Aeronaut. Sci. 15*, 509–521 (1948).
38. Wheeler, H. L., Jr., and Duwez, P. A gasoline-air combustion chamber for the study of sweat cooling. *Calif. Inst. Technol. Jet Propul. Lab. Progress Rept. 1-59*, Nov. 1947.
39. Duwez, P., and Wheeler, H. L., Jr. Heat transfer measurements in a nitrogen sweat-cooled porous tube. *Calif. Inst. Technol. Jet Propul. Lab. Progress Rept. 4-48*, Nov. 1947.
40. Wheeler, H. L., Jr. Flow of gases through sweat-cooled tubes. *Calif. Inst. Technol. Jet Propul. Lab. Progress Report 4-87*, Dec. 1948.
41. Wheeler, H. L., Jr. Heat transfer in nitrogen and hydrogen sweat-cooled tubes. *Calif. Inst. Technol. Jet Propul. Lab. Progress Rept. 20-160*, Jan. 1952.
42. Wheeler, H. L., Jr., and Duwez, P. Heat transfer through sweat-cooled porous tubes. *Jet Propul. 25*, 519–524 (1955).
43. Libby, P. A., Kaufman, L., and Harrington, R. P. An experimental investigation of the isothermal laminar boundary layer on a porous flat plate. *J. Aeronaut. Sci. 19*, 127–134 (1952).
44. Wheeler, H. L., Jr. The influence of wall material on the sweat-cooled process. *Calif. Inst. Technol. Jet Propul. Lab. Progress Rept. 4-90*, May 1949.
45. Zacrow, M. J., Beighley, C. M., and Knuth, E. Progress report on the stability of liquid film for cooling rocket motors. *Project Squid Tech. Rept. 23*, Nov. 1950.
46. Tsien, H. S. Research in rocket and jet propulsion. *Aero. Digest 60*, 120–125 (1950).
47. Rannie, H. W. *Heat Transfer in Turbulent Shear Flow. Ph.D. Thesis*, Calif. Inst. Technol., 1951.
48. Knuth, E. L. Mechanics of film cooling. *Jet Propulsion 24*, 359–365 (1954).
49. Kinney, G. R., Jr., and Sloop, J. L. Internal film cooling experiments in a 4-inch duct with gas temperature to 2000°F. *NACA Research Mem. F50F19*, 1950.
50. Eckert, E. R. G., and Livingood, J. N. B. Comparison of effect of convection, transpiration and film cooling with air as coolant. *NACA Rept. 1182*, 1954.
51. Friedman, J. A theoretical and experimental investigation of rocket-motor sweat-cooling. *J. Am. Rocket Soc. 79*, 147–154 (1949).
52. Wieghardt, K. Hot-air discharge for de-icing. *Army Air Force Trans. F-TS-919-RE*, Dec. 1946.

*Bibliography*

Berman, A. Laminar flow in channels with porous wall. *J. Appl. Phys. 24*, 1232–1235 (1953).

Clarke, J. H., Menkes, H. R., and Libby, P. A. A provisional analysis of turbulent boundary layer with injection. *J. Aeronaut. Sci. 22*, 255–260 (1955).

Crocco, L. An approximate theory of porous, sweat, or film cooling with reactive fluids. *J. Am. Rocket Soc. 22*, 331–338 (1952).

Donoughe, P. L., and Livingood, J. N. B. Exact solution of laminar-boundary-layer equations with constant property values for porous wall and variable temperature. *NACA Tech. Note 3151*, 1954.

Dorrance, W. H. The effect of mass transfer on the compressible turbulent boundary-layer skin friction and heat transfer—An addendum. *J. Aeronaut. Sci. 23*, 283–284 (1956).

Duwez, P., and Wheeler, H. L., Jr. Preliminary experiments on the sweat-cooling method. *Calif. Inst. Technol. Jet Propul. Lab. Progress Rept. 3-13*, July 1946.

Eckert, E. R. G. One dimensional calculation of flow in a rotating passage with ejection through a porous wall. *NACA Tech. Note 3408*, Mar. 1955.

Eckert, E. R. G. Transpiration and film cooling. *Heat Transfer Symposium, Univ. Mich. Press*, 1953.

Eckert, E. R. G., Diaguila, A. J., and Donoughe, P. L. Experiments on turbulent flow through channels having porous rough surface with or without air injection. *NACA Tech. Note 3339*, 1955.

Ellerbrock, H. H., Jr. Some NACA investigation of heat transfer characteristics of cooled gas-turbine blades. General discussion on heat transfer. *Inst. Mech. Engrs. London*, Sept. 1952.

Emmons, H. W., and Leigh, D. Tabulation of the Blasius function with blowing and suction. *Harvard Univ. Combustion Aeronaut. Lab., Div. Appl. Sci., Interim Tech. Rept. 9*, Nov. 1953.

Green, L., Jr. Gas cooling of a porous heat source. *J. Appl. Mech. 19*, 173–178 (1952).

Grootenhuis, P., and Moore, N. P. W. Some observations on the mechanics of sweat cooling. *Seventh Intern. Congress Appl. Mech.*, London, 1948.

Grootenhuis, P., et al. Heat transfer to air passing through heated porous metals. General discussion on heat transfer. *Inst. Mech. Engrs. London*, 405–409 (1952).

Howarth, L. *Modern Developments in Fluid Dynamics, High Speed Flow*, Vol. II, Chap. XIV. Oxford Univ. Press, 1953.

Ivey, R. H., and Klunker, E. B. An analysis of supersonic aerodynamic heating with continuous fluid injection. *NACA Rept. 990*, 1950.

Jakob, M., and Fieldhouse, I. B. Cooling by forcing a fluid through a porous plate in contact with a hot gas stream. *Heat Transfer and Fluid Mech. Inst.*, June 1949.

Lees, L. Stability of the laminar boundary layer with injection of cool gas at the wall. *Project Squid Tech. Rept. 11*, May 1948.

Lew, H. G., and Fanucci, J. B. On the laminar compressible boundary layer over a flat plate with suction or injection. *J. Aeronaut. Sci. 22*, 589–597 (1955).

Livingood, J. N. B., and Eckert, E. R. G. Calculation of transpiration-cooled gas-turbine blade. *Trans. Am. Soc. Mech. Engrs. 75*, 1271–1278 (1953).

Mayer, E., and Baras, J. Q. Transpiration cooling in porous metal walls. *Jet Propulsion 24*, 366–368, 378, 386 (1954).

Muskat, M. *The Flow of Homogeneous Fluids Through the Porous Media*. McGraw-Hill, 1937.

Staniforth, R. Contribution to the theory of effusion cooling of gas turbine blades. General discussion on heat transfer. *Inst. Mech. Engrs. London*, Sept. 1951.

Yuan, S. W. Further investigation of laminar flow in channels with porous walls. *J. Appl. Phys. 27*, 267–269 (1956).

Yuan, S. W. Preliminary investigation of heat transfer in turbulent boundary layer on a porous wall. *Project Squid Tech. Rept. 19*, 29–36 (1950).

Yuan, S. W., and Barazotti, A. Experimental investigation of turbulent pipe flow with coolant injection. *Heat Transfer and Fluid Mech. Inst.*, June 1958.

Yuan, S. W., and Chin, C. Heat transfer in a laminar boundary layer on a partially sweat-cooled plate. *Project Squid Tech. Rept. 13*, Aug. 1949.

Yuan, S. W., and Whitford, C. Further investigation of heat transfer in a laminar compressible boundary layer on a porous plate with fluid injection. *Project Squid Tech. Rept. 14*, Sept. 1949.

# SECTION H

## *PHYSICAL BASIS OF THERMAL RADIATION*

S. S. PENNER

**H,1. Introduction.** The conventional and most successful approach to engineering calculations of radiant heat exchange is described in the following section. Included in the discussion are empirical rules and extrapolation procedures. In order to appreciate the limitations involved in the use of these empirical rules, it is essential to gain some understanding of the physical principles which determine emitted and absorbed radiant energies. Since a fundamental description of the phenomena involved is particularly simple for the equilibrium radiation of gases, we shall confine our attention to a brief survey of fundamental laws and to a qualitative outline of the methods used for calculations on the thermal radiation characteristics of gases.

**H,2. Black Body Radiation Laws.** A black body is defined as a body which neither transmits nor reflects any radiation which it receives; a black body absorbs all of the incident radiation. It can be shown that the equilibrium energy of radiation emitted from the unit area of a black body in unit time at a fixed temperature represents an upper limit for the thermally emitted energy from unit area for any substance which is at the same temperature as the black body. This definition of a black body and the quantum mechanics principle of equipartition of energy [*1*, Chap. 2; *2*, pp. 546–550; *3*, pp. 363–372] are sufficient to establish the Planck black body distribution law, which expresses the equilibrium rate at which radiant energy is emitted from a black body as a function of wavelength $\lambda$ and temperature $T$. The Planck black body distribution law has been abundantly confirmed by experiments.

The spectral (or monochromatic) radiancy $R_\lambda^0 d\lambda$ is defined as the energy emitted, per unit time, from unit area of a black body in the wavelength range between $\lambda$ and $\lambda + d\lambda$ at the absolute temperature $T$ (in °K), into a solid angle of $2\pi$ steradians. The Planck black body distribution law is

$$R_\lambda^0 d\lambda = \frac{c_1}{\lambda^5} \frac{d\lambda}{e^{c_2/\lambda T} - 1} \tag{2-1}$$

where $c_1/\pi$ and $c_2$ are known as the first and second radiation constants, respectively. The quantities $c_1$ and $c_2$ may be expressed in terms of the fundamental physical constants $c$ (velocity of light), $h$ (Planck's const), and $k$ (Boltzmann const). Thus $c_1 = 2\pi c^2 h \cong 3.742 \times 10^{-5}$ erg-cm²-sec⁻¹ and $c_2 = hc/k \cong 1.439$ cm-°K. For

$$\lambda T \leqq 0.3 \text{ cm-°K}, \qquad R_\lambda^0 d\lambda$$

is given, with an accuracy of better than one per cent, by Wien's radiation law

$$(R_\lambda^0)_{\text{Wien}} d\lambda = \frac{c_1}{\lambda^5} e^{-c_2/\lambda T} d\lambda$$

For $\lambda T \geqq 77$ cm-°K, the Rayleigh-Jeans radiation law

$$(R_\lambda^0)_{\text{RJ}} d\lambda = \left(\frac{c_1 T}{c_2 \lambda^4}\right) d\lambda$$

gives an accuracy of better than one per cent.

For a given temperature the maximum value of $R_\lambda^0$ is found from Eq. 2-1 to be

$$(R_\lambda^0)_{\max} = 21.20 c_1 \left(\frac{T}{c_2}\right)^5 \tag{2-2}$$

and to occur at the wavelength $\lambda_{\max}$ determined by Wien's displacement law

$$\lambda_{\max} T = \frac{c_2}{4.965} \cong 0.2898 \text{ cm-°K} \tag{2-3}$$

The total radiant energy emitted from unit area in unit time by a black body over all wavelengths into a solid angle of $2\pi$ steradians is

$$W = \int_0^\infty R_\lambda^0 d\lambda = \sigma T^4 \tag{2-4}$$

where $\sigma$ is known as the Stefan-Boltzmann constant and has the numerical value $\sigma \cong 5.670 \times 10^{-5}$ erg-cm$^{-2}$-(°K)$^{-4}$-sec$^{-1}$. The quantity $W$ is variously referred to as the radiant flux per unit area, total emissive power of a black body, or radiancy. The (normal) radiant intensity is the radiant energy emitted in a direction perpendicular to the black body, per unit solid angle, per unit area, per unit time; it is identified by the symbol $J$ and equals $W/\pi$.

The quantities $R_\lambda^0$, $(R_\lambda^0)_{\max}$, $R_\lambda^0/(R_\lambda^0)_{\max}$, $\int_0^\lambda R_{\lambda'}^0 d\lambda'$, $W$, and $(1/W)\int_0^\lambda R_{\lambda'}^0 d\lambda'$ have been tabulated [4] for the wavelengths and/or temperatures which are likely to be encountered in practice.

The frequency $\nu$ is related to the wavelength $\lambda$ through the expression

$$\nu = \frac{c}{\lambda} \tag{2-5}$$

where $c$ is the velocity of light ($c \cong 2.998 \times 10^{10}$ cm-sec$^{-1}$); the wave number $\omega$ is the reciprocal of the wavelength, i.e.

$$\omega = \frac{1}{\lambda} \tag{2-6}$$

From Eq. 2-1 and 2-5 it follows that the spectral radiancy in the frequency range between $\nu$ and $\nu + d\nu$ at the temperature $T$ is given by the expression

$$R_\nu^0 d\nu = \frac{2\pi h\nu^3}{c^2} \frac{d\nu}{e^{h\nu/kT} - 1} \tag{2-7}$$

Similarly $R_\omega^0 d\omega$ is determined according to the equation

$$R_\omega^0 d\omega = 2\pi hc^2\omega^3 \frac{d\omega}{e^{hc\omega/kT} - 1} \tag{2-8}$$

**H,3. Nonblack Radiators.** The (hemispherical) spectral emissivity $\epsilon_\lambda$ of a substance is defined as the ratio of the spectral radiancy for the given substance to the spectral radiancy of a black body. Thus the energy emitted from a nonblack substance, per unit area, per unit time, into a solid angle of $2\pi$ steradians in the wavelength range between $\lambda$ and $\lambda + d\lambda$ at the temperature $T$ is

$$R_\lambda d\lambda = \epsilon_\lambda R_\lambda^0 d\lambda$$

if the spectral emissivity of the substance is $\epsilon_\lambda$. The nonblack substance at temperature $T$ is said to have (total hemispherical) emissivity $\epsilon$ if the total emitted energy, per unit area, per unit time, into an angle of $2\pi$ steradians is

$$W' = \epsilon W = \epsilon\sigma T^4$$

The definitions of the spectral and total emissivities apply to distributed sources of radiation as well as to surfaces. A discussion of the thermal radiation characteristics of gases (Art. 5) involves essentially the development of basic procedures for the calculation of $\epsilon_\lambda$ and $\epsilon$ for equilibrium systems of pure gases and gaseous mixtures.

A simple example for the use of theoretical spectral emissivity relations is provided by Drude's law [*5*, Chap. 1] for pure metals, which holds within a few per cent for wavelengths longer than about $2\mu$.[1] Drude's law relates the spectral emissivity to the electrical resistivity $r$ (in cm) and the wavelength $\lambda$ (in cm), viz.

$$\epsilon_\lambda \cong 0.365 \sqrt{\frac{r}{\lambda}} \tag{3-1}$$

[1] The following wavelength units are often used in discussions of radiant heat transfer: Angstrom unit A (1 A = $10^{-8}$ cm) and micron $\mu$ ($1\mu = 10^{-4}$ cm). The wave number (reciprocal of the wavelength) is customarily expressed in cm$^{-1}$. The frequency is given in sec$^{-1}$.

Since the electrical resistivity is roughly proportional to the first power of the temperature for many metals, it follows that the total emissive power of many metals varies as $T$ within the range of validity of Eq. 3-1.

**H,4. Basic Laws for Distributed Radiators.** For thermodynamic equilibrium one can deduce Kirchhoff's law, which states that the spectral radiancy of any substance equals the product of the spectral absorptivity $P'_\omega$ and the spectral radiancy of a black body.[2] In other words, the spectral emissivity $\epsilon_\omega$ and the spectral absorptivity $P'_\omega$ are identically equal. It is convenient in practice to introduce the product of two-dimensional parameters for the dimensionless spectral absorptivity $P'_\omega$. Following customary procedure we write for distributed radiators

$$P'_\omega = P_\omega dX \tag{4-1}$$

where $P_\omega$ is termed the spectral absorption coefficient and is expressed in $\text{cm}^{-1}\text{-atm}^{-1}$ or in $\text{ft}^{-1}\text{-atm}^{-1}$, with the pressure referring to the actual

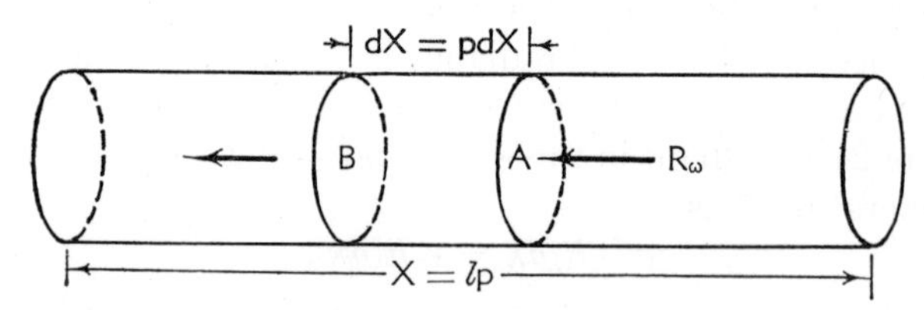


Fig. H,4. Schematic diagram for the determination of the basic spectral emission law for distributed isothermal radiators. (X represents optical density, $p$ equals the partial pressure of the radiator, and $l$ and $dx$ are geometric lengths.)

pressure of radiators responsible for absorption at the wave number $\omega$; correspondingly, the optical density $dX$, which represents the product of a geometric length and the partial pressure of the radiators, must have the dimensions of cm-atm or ft-atm, respectively.

Consider now a system of isothermal radiators at pressure $p$ distributed uniformly through a region of geometric length $l$. The optical density of a region of infinitesimal geometric length $dx$ is $dX = pdx$; the optical density of the region of geometric length $l$ is $X = pl$. A schematic diagram is shown in Fig. H,4 in which the abscissa has the dimensions of optical density. It is desired to obtain an expression for the total spectral radiancy from the isothermal distributed radiators located in a column of geometric length $l$. Let the spectral radiancy incident on the face $A$ be $R_\omega$. The change in spectral radiancy corresponding to the region of optical

[2] The choice of the wave number $\omega$ for identification of the spectral region is, of course, arbitrary. Either the wavelength $\lambda$ or the frequency $\nu$ may be used if desired. The statement that $P'_\omega$ is independent of the intensity of the incident radiation may be regarded as an experimentally established fact. This result follows also from molecular considerations concerning the relation between transition probabilities and absorption coefficients.

depth $dX$ is then

$$dR_\omega = (P_\omega dX)R^0_\omega - (P_\omega dX)R_\omega \tag{4-2}$$

where the first term on the right-hand side of Eq. 4-2 represents the emitted spectral radiancy in $dX$, and the second term measures the attenuation by the absorbers of radiation in $dX$. Since $R_\omega = 0$ for $X = 0$ it follows from Eq. 4-2 that

$$R_\omega = R^0_\omega(1 - e^{-P_\omega X}) \tag{4-3}$$

Eq. 4-3 is the basic phenomenological law for the emission of radiation from distributed sources. It is apparent that if an external light source is used such that $R_\omega = R'_\omega$ for $X = 0$, then Eq. 4-3 should be replaced by the expression

$$R_\omega = R^0_\omega(1 - e^{-P_\omega X}) + R'_\omega e^{-P_\omega X} \tag{4-4}$$

In those cases where the first term in Eq. 4-4 is negligibly small (i.e. negligible emission of radiation from the region under study), Eq. 4-4 reduces to the Bouguer-Lambert law of absorption

$$R_\omega = R'_\omega e^{-P_\omega X} \tag{4-5}$$

In absorption studies it is customary to choose $1/2\pi\omega$ as the unit of length and to introduce an extinction coefficient $\kappa$ through the relation

$$\kappa = \frac{P_\omega p}{4\pi\omega} \tag{4-6}$$

For absorbing liquids (and sometimes also for gases), a specific absorption coefficient $\beta$ may be introduced through the relation

$$\beta = \frac{P_\omega p}{c'} \tag{4-7}$$

where $c'$ is the concentration of the absorber. If $c'$ is expressed in mole $cm^{-3}$ and $P_\omega p$ in $cm^{-1}$, then $\beta$ has the dimensions $mole^{-1}$ $cm^2$ and the absorption law may be referred to as Beer's law of absorption. For ideal gases, sets of units involving mass absorption coefficients $k_\omega$ (in $cm^2$-$g^{-1}$) are sometimes used; in this case $k_\omega = P_\omega R'T$ where $R'$ is the gas const per gram. The quantity $P_\omega X$ is now replaced by $k_\omega \rho l$ with $\rho$ representing the gas density.

Reference to Eq. 4-3 shows that the spectral emissivity $\epsilon_\omega$ of the uniformly distributed radiators is given by the relation

$$\epsilon_\omega = 1 - e^{-P_\omega X} \tag{4-8}$$

Similarly, the total emissivity $\epsilon$ used in engineering calculations on radiant heat transfer is

$$\epsilon = \frac{1}{W}\int_0^\infty R^0_\omega(1 - e^{-P_\omega X})d\omega \tag{4-9}$$

Theoretical calculations of gas emissivities therefore require determination of $P_\omega$ in terms of atomic or molecular parameters, followed by evaluation of the integral appearing in Eq. 4-9. In this connection it is of particular importance to note that absorption coefficients $P_\omega$ for gas mixtures are additive but that neither spectral nor total emissivities can be added. As the result of this requirement, neither $\epsilon_\omega$ nor $\epsilon$ can exceed unity for equilibrium radiation.

**H,5. Theoretical Calculation of Gas Emissivities.** Theoretical calculations of gas emissivities require evaluation of $P_\omega$ from atomic or molecular parameters. The connection with basic theory is made conveniently through the Einstein theory [*6*] of absorption and emission of radiation, followed by introducing a precise description of the shape of spectral lines [*7,8,9,10*]. The details involved in establishing this connection between $P_\omega$ and fundamental physical principles are described elsewhere [*11,12*]. In the present discussion it appears desirable to summarize the physical notions and the conclusions reached as the result of more detailed studies. For quantitative calculations of gas emissivities the interested reader is referred to a series of journal articles [*13,14,15,16,17*] as well as to several survey papers [*11,12,18*].

Since gas emits radiation as the result of electronic, vibrational, and rotational transitions from excited energy levels to lower energy levels, the emitted radiant energy corresponding to these transitions is distributed over a well-defined wavelength region. In general, the radiation emitted as the result of electronic transitions is concentrated in the visible and ultraviolet regions of the spectrum, whereas vibration-rotation bands are responsible for the emission of light in the near infrared. Pure rotational transitions give rise to absorption bands at long wavelengths (i.e. $30\mu$ or more) in the infrared. As the temperature of the emitters is raised, the discrete emission lines or bands occurring at progressively shorter wavelengths make the more important contributions to the emitted radiant energy, because the black body distribution curve has its maximum value at progressively lower wavelengths (see below). At the temperatures of interest in connection with studies of equilibrium radiant heat transfer in combustion chambers, only the transitions corresponding to the infrared vibration-rotation bands make significant contributions to the observed radiant flux.

The physical principles involved in emissivity calculations can be understood by referring to Fig. H,5a, H,5b, and H,5c, where we have indicated the positions of the centers of vibration-rotation bands of $CO_2$ determined from room temperature absorption experiments, and calculable with great precision from expressions for energy levels derived by spectroscopists [*19,20,21*]. The abscissa in Fig. H,5a, H,5b, and H,5c is the wave number whereas the ordinate represents, in arbitrary units

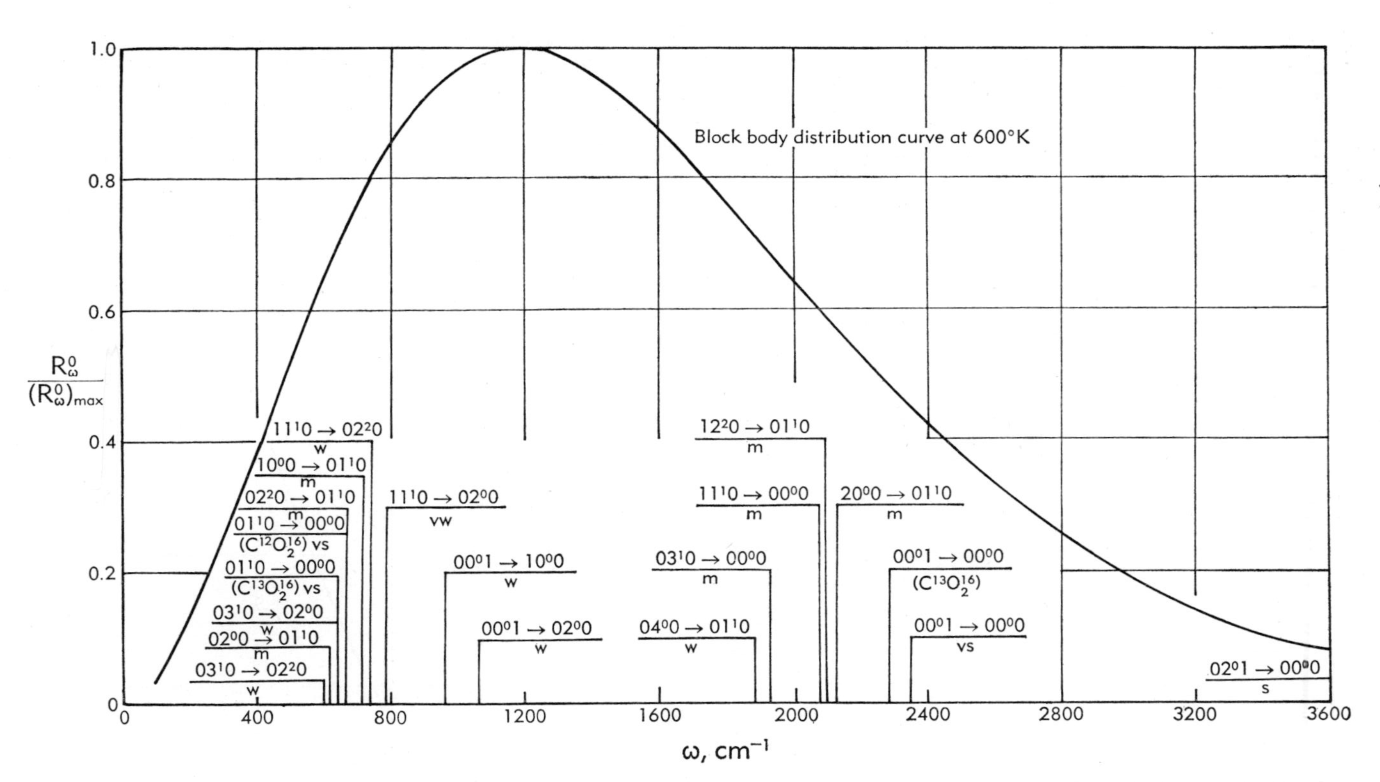


Fig. H,5a. Positions of centers of vibration-rotation bands observed at room temperature between 200 and 1800 cm$^{-1}$. The designations vs (very strong), s (strong), m (medium), w (weak), and vw (very weak) are those of Herzberg [*21*]. Also shown is the intensity ratio $R^0_\omega/R^0_{\omega\max}$ for a black body at 300°K.

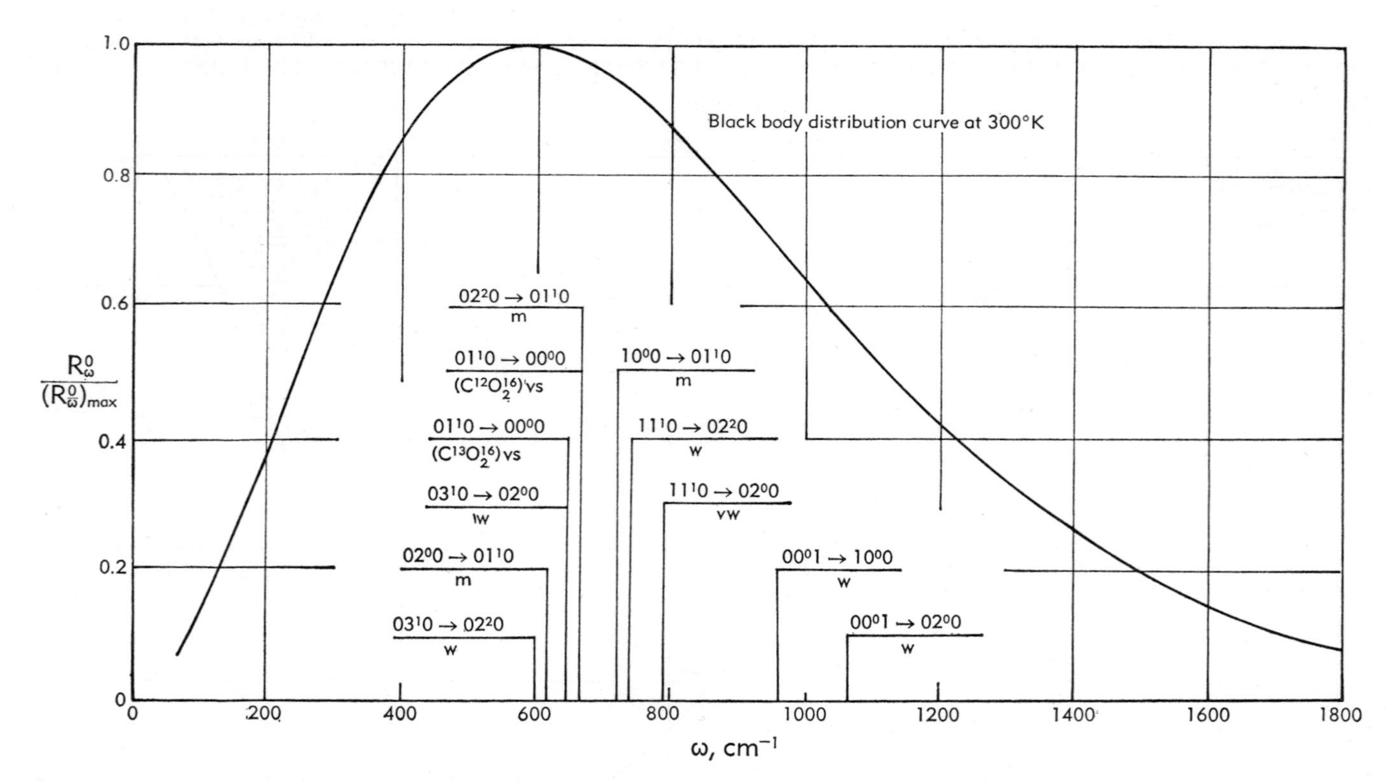


Fig. H,5b. Positions of centers of vibration-rotation bands observed at room temperature between 300 and 3600 $cm^{-1}$. Also shown is the intensity ratio $R^0\lambda/R^0\lambda_{max}$ for a black body at 600°K.

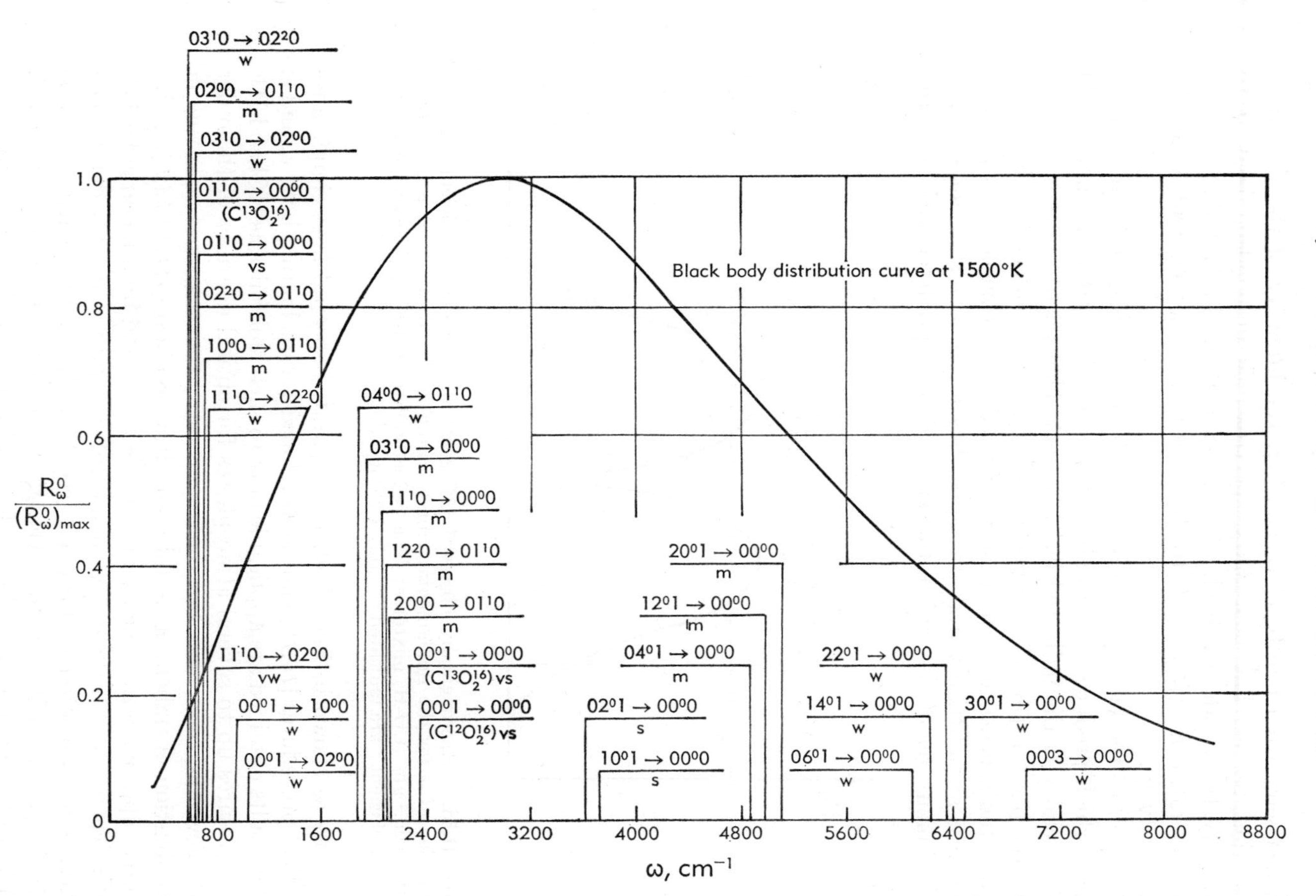


Fig. H,5c. Positions of centers of vibration-rotation bands observed at room temperature between 800 and 8,000 cm⁻¹. Also shown is the intensity ratio $R^0_\omega/R^0_{\omega\max}$ for a black body at 1500°K.

which vary from one band to another, the intensity of the vibration-rotation bands. The customary spectroscopic designation is used to identify the bands involved. Also shown in Fig. H,5a, H,5b, and H,5c is the ratio $R^0_\omega/(R^0_\omega)_{max}$ at temperatures of 300, 600, and 1500 °K, respectively.

Each of the vibration-rotation bands consists of a series of spectral lines which produce nonzero absorption coefficients at wave numbers in the vicinity of the indicated band centers. The spectral lines have finite widths [7,8,9,10] which increase with pressure. At sufficiently low pressures the spectral lines may be considered to be completely separated, whereas at sufficiently high pressures they merge to form a more or less continuous region in which the spectral absorption coefficient varies

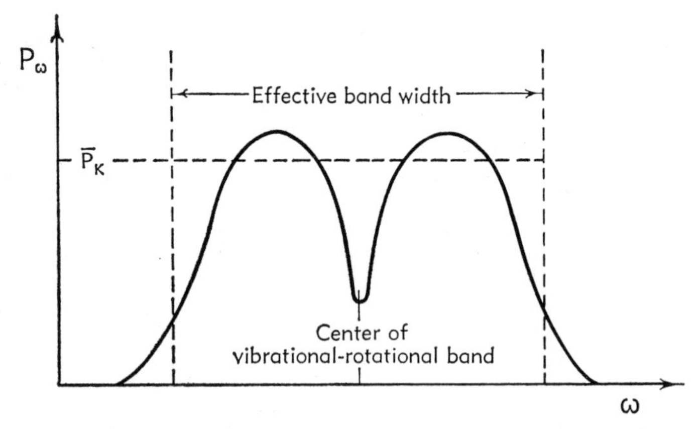


Fig. H,5d. Experimentally observed [23] spectral absorption coefficient $P_\omega$ as a function of $\omega$ for the fundamental vibration-rotation band of CO at a pressure of 700 lb/in.² abs (CO-$H_2$ mixtures). The "effective bandwidth" and "average absorption coefficient" are indicated roughly by dotted lines.

roughly as shown in Fig. H,5d. For separated spectral lines simple analytical procedures [15,16] can be developed for evaluating both $\epsilon_\omega$ and $\epsilon$; the results obtained are applicable only to such molecules as HCl and HF at pressures up to several atmospheres for optical densities of the order of a few cm-atm or less. For the important chemical species occurring in combustion chambers, a useful analytical procedure [11,12,13,14,17] involves approximating each vibration-rotation band by a rectangular box of calculable width ("effective band width") with a suitably determined "average absorption coefficient" (see Fig. H,5d). For regions of overlapping between bands, the average absorption coefficients are added. It is to be expected that an analysis utilizing average absorption coefficients and effective band widths will become better at elevated pressures. In general, for fixed values of the optical density, the emissivities increase with total pressure, approach, and then slowly exceed results calculated on the basis of effective band widths. At sufficiently high total pressures the calculated emissivities are too low, because the individual spectral lines become broadened in such a way that their tails "spill" effectively across the estimated widths of the bands. For overlapping spectral lines, using the concept of effective band widths, the emissivity $\epsilon$ at any temperature is given by an expression of the form

$$\epsilon = \sum_{\Delta\omega_K} (1 - e^{-\bar{P}_K X}) \left( \int_{\Delta\omega_K} \frac{R_\omega^0 d\omega}{W} \right) \tag{5-1}$$

where $\bar{P}_K$ is the average absorption coefficient for the spectral region of width $\Delta\omega_K$.

It is apparent from Fig. H,5a that at 300°K the principal contribution to $\epsilon$ must result from spectral lines in the regions between 600 and 800 $cm^{-1}$ and between 950 and 1050 $cm^{-1}$, because the factor $(1/W)\int_{\Delta\omega_K} R_\omega^0 d\omega$ will be very small for other vibration-rotation bands. Furthermore, for very small values of $X$ (i.e. $X < 0.1$ ft-atm), $\bar{P}_K X$ is effectively zero for all bands except the one identified as $01^10 \rightarrow 00^00$; thus, for small values of $X$, $\epsilon$ is practically determined by a single vibration-rotation band to which, however, the isotopic species $C^{13}O_2^{16}$ makes an appreciable contribution. As $X$ increases, other bands become important and may produce a complicated dependence of $\epsilon$ on $X$. On the other hand, as noted earlier in this discussion, $\epsilon$ will be relatively insensitive to total pressure above a limiting pressure where the spectral lines of a band are practically overlapping. For $CO_2$ this limiting pressure at room temperature is somewhat above 1 atm [*22*], for $H_2O$ about 3 atm, for CO about 10 atm [*18*], etc.

Fig. H,5b shows that, for $CO_2$ at 600°K, the major contributions are made by 600 to 1050 $cm^{-1}$ and 1800 to 2400 $cm^{-1}$ regions with, however, non-negligible contributions arising from the spectral region around 3600 $cm^{-1}$. Since the important contributions to $\epsilon$ are made by different vibration-rotation bands at different temperatures, the dependence of $\epsilon$ on $T$ for fixed values of $X$ and total pressure may be complicated, particularly for polyatomic gases and for gas mixtures. Hence any extrapolations to temperatures higher than those for which measurements are available lead to questionable results.

Fig. H,5c shows that at 1500°K the region between 1500 and 500 $cm^{-1}$ makes the important contributions to $\epsilon$, unless as-yet-unobserved combination and overtone bands of sizable intensity occur at larger values of $\omega$.

In view of the apparent dangers inherent in indiscriminate extrapolation of empirical data on gas emissivities, it is of importance to ask to what extent theoretical considerations can serve as a useful guide for gas mixtures of the type encountered in combustion devices. In answer to this question we may note that theoretical studies on diatomic gases [*11,12,13,14,15,16,18*] and basic spectroscopic studies for a number of these same gases [*23*] have been carried to the point where useful absolute calculations and extrapolations are feasible. For polyatomic gases, on the other hand, high temperature calculations are possible in principle but not yet feasible in practice because the required basic spectroscopic constants are not available [*17*]. For this reason, and because of the complexity of theoretical calculations for polyatomic gases and gas mixtures, the most fruitful approach at the present time to the problem of high temperature emissivity estimates must remain an empirical one. It appears very likely that the required basic data for radiant heat transfer calculations in combustion chambers can be obtained by the judicious use of spectroscopic studies on shock tube experiments. Details concerning emissivity calculations for such substances as CO, NO, $H_2O$, heated air, etc. are given elsewhere [*24*].

## H,6. Cited References.


1. Planck, M. *The Theory of Heat Radiation.* Transl. by M. Masius. P. Blakiston's Son and Co., Philadelphia, 1914.
2. Page, L. *Introduction to Theoretical Physics.* Van Nostrand, 1935.
3. Mayer, J. E., and Mayer, M. G. *Statistical Mechanics.* Wiley, 1940.
4. *Planck Radiation Functions and Electronic Functions.* Federal Works Agency, WPA, Natl. Bur. Standards, 1941.
5. Forsythe, W. E. *Measurements of Radiant Energy.* McGraw-Hill, 1937.
6. Einstein, A. On the quantum theory of radiation. *Physik. Z. 18,* 121 (1917).
7. Margenau, H., and Watson, W. W. Pressure effects on spectral lines. *Revs. Mod. Phys. 8,* 22 (1936).
8. Van Vleck, J. H., and Weisskopf, V. F. On the shape of collision-broadened lines. *Revs. Mod. Phys. 17,* 227 (1945).
9. Lindholm, E. *Dissertation,* Uppsala, 1942.
10. Anderson, P. W. Pressure broadening in the microwave and infrared regions. *Phys. Rev. 76,* 647 (1949).
11. Penner, S. S. The emission of radiation from diatomic gases. I. Approximate calculations. *Calif. Inst. Technol. Jet Propul. Lab. Progress Rept. 9-37,* May 1949.
12. Penner, S. S. Infrared emissivity of diatomic gases. In *Natl. Bur. Standards Circ. 523* (Energy transfer in hot gases), 1954.
13. Penner, S. S. The emission of radiation from diatomic gases. I. Approximate calculations. *J. Appl. Phys. 21,* 685 (1950).
14. Penner, S. S., and Weber, D. Emission of radiation from diatomic gases. II. Experimental determination of effective average absorption coefficients of CO. *J. Appl. Phys. 22,* 1164 (1951).
15. Penner, S. S., Ostrander, M. H., and Tsien, H. S. The emission of radiation from diatomic gases. III. Numerical emissivity calculations for carbon monoxide for low optical densities at 300°K and atmospheric pressure. *J. Appl. Phys. 23,* 256 (1952).
16. Penner, S. S. The emission of radiation from diatomic gases. IV. Emissivity calculations for CO and HCL for nonoverlapping rotational lines as a function of temperature and optical density. *J. Appl. Phys. 23,* 825 (1952).
17. Penner, S. S. Approximate emissivity calculations for polyatomic molecules. I. $CO_2$. *J. Appl. Phys. 25,* 660 (1954).
18. Penner, S. S. Emissivity calculations for diatomic gases. *J. Appl. Mech. 18,* 53 (1951).

19. Herzberg, G. *Atomic Spectra and Atomic Structure.* Dover, 1944.
20. Herzberg, G. *Molecular Spectra and Molecular Structure. I. Spectra of Diatomic Molecules.* Van Nostrand, 1950.
21. Herzberg, G. *Molecular Spectra and Molecular Structure. II. Infrared and Raman Spectra of Polyatomic Molecules.* Van Nostrand, 1951.
22. Hottel, H. C. Personal communication.
23. Penner, S. S., and Weber, D. Quantitative infrared intensity measurements. *J. Chem. Phys. 19,* 807, 817, 974 (1951); *21,* 649 (1953).
24. Penner, S. S. *Quantitative Molecular Spectroscopy and Gas Emissivities.* Addison-Wesley Press, 1959.

# SECTION I

## *ENGINEERING CALCULATIONS OF RADIANT HEAT EXCHANGE*

HOYT C. HOTTEL

**I,1. Radiating Characteristics of Surfaces.** Knowledge on the reader's part of the general nature of thermal radiation and the laws of black body radiation will be assumed in this section (see this volume, Sec. H). Fig. I,1a summarizes, for numerical use, the radiating characteristics of a black body in the form of a plot of monochromatic emissive power[1] $W_{b\lambda}$ divided by the fifth power of the absolute temperature versus the wavelength-temperature product. The curve may be visualized as an intensity-wavelength distribution at 1° absolute. An extra scale along the top permits a determination of the fraction of the spectral energy found below a given wavelength $\lambda$. The area under the curve is directly the Stefan-Boltzmann constant $\sigma[0.1713 \times 10^{-8}$ BTU/ft² hr (°R)⁴; $5.67 \times 10^{-5}$ ergs/cm² sec (°K)⁴; $4.88 \times 10^{-8}$ kg-cal/m² hr (°K)⁴; $1.00 \times 10^{-8}$ CHU/ft² hr (°K)⁴], for use in the relation

$$W_b = \sigma T^4 \tag{1-1}$$

where $W_b$ is the total emissive power, throughout a solid angle of $2\pi$ steradians, of a black body or "perfect" radiator.

In evaluating radiant heat transfer between surfaces, one could consider monochromatic radiation exchange and integrate throughout the spectrum; certain advantages would appear. For most engineering purposes, however, it is simpler to formulate total radiation exchange, expressing it in terms of the 4th power temperature law strictly applicable only to the black body or perfect radiator, and to let the more-or-less weak residual temperature function be taken care of by the variable total emissivity, absorptivity, or transmissivity of the pertinent bodies.

The emissivity $\epsilon$ of a surface (more properly the total hemispherical emissivity, to differentiate it from monochromatic emissivity $\epsilon_\lambda$ and from directional emissivity $\epsilon_\theta$, the ratio of radiating powers in a direction making the angle $\theta$ with the normal to the surface) varies with its temperature, its degree of roughness or grain size, and, if a metal, its degree of

[1] *Emissive power* refers to radiation throughout a full hemisphere of $2\pi$ steradians, and is $\pi J$ where $J$ is *intensity* (see Art. 2).

oxidation. The following generalizations may be made concerning the emissivity of surfaces: (1) The emissivities of metallic conductors are quite low and substantially proportional to the absolute temperature; and the proportionality constant for different metals varies as the square root of the electrical resistance at a standard temperature [*1*,*2*]. Unless

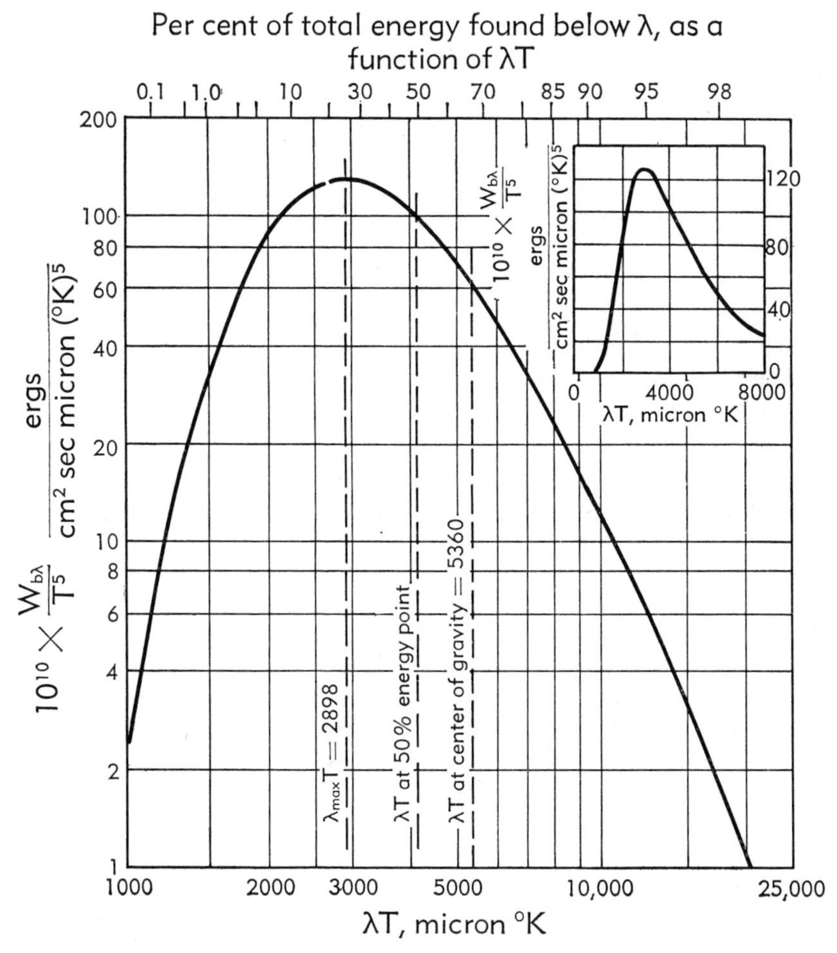


Fig. I,1a. Distribution of energy in the spectrum of a black body.

extraordinary pains are taken to prevent any possibility of oxidation or imperfection of polish, however, a specimen may exhibit several times this theoretical minimum emissivity. (2) The emissivities of nonconductors are much higher, depend on the refractive index, and, in contrast to metals, generally decrease with increase in temperature. Refractory materials may be expected to decrease in emissivity one-fourth to one-third as the temperature increases from 1850 to 2850°F; their grain structure and color are more important than their chemical composition [*3*]. (3) The emissivities of most nonmetals are above 0.8 at low temperatures and in the range 0.3 to 0.8 at furnace refractory temperatures. (4) Iron and steel vary widely with the degree of oxidation and roughness: clean metallic surfaces have an emissivity of 0.05 to 0.45 at low temperatures and of 0.4 to 0.7 at high temperatures; oxidized and/or rough surfaces, 0.6 to 0.95 at low temperatures and 0.9 to 0.95 at high temperatures. (5) Inconel, nichrome, and type 310 stainless steel all show a marked increase in emissivity when maintained at temperatures above 1500°F [*4*]. Table I,1, abstracted from a more comprehensive table appearing elsewhere with a bibliography [*5*, Chap. 4], gives the emissivities of various surfaces and emphasizes the large variation possible in a single material. Although the values in the table apply strictly to normal radiation from a surface (with few exceptions), they may be used with small error for hemispherical emissivity. Well-polished metal surfaces have a hemispherical emissivity 15 to 20 per cent higher, and well-polished nonmetals about 7 per cent less, than the normal value [*6*].

The absorptivity $\alpha$ of a surface depends on the factors affecting emissivity and, in addition, especially on the quality of the incident radiation, i.e. on its temperature. One may assign two subscripts to $\alpha$, the first to indicate the receiver and the second, the emitter of the radiation; more specifically, to indicate their respective temperatures. As seen in Sec. G, according to Kirchhoff's law, the emissivity of a surface at temperature $T_1$ is equal to the absorptivity $\alpha_{1,1}$ which the surface exhibits for black radiation from a source at the same temperature, i.e. a surface of low radiating power is also a poor absorber (or good reflector or transmitter) of radiation from a source at its own temperature. If the monochromatic absorptivity $\alpha_\lambda$ varies considerably with wavelength and much less with temperature (which is generally the case for nonmetals), it follows that the total absorptivity $\alpha_{1,2}$ will vary more with $T_2$ than with $T_1$. Data of Sieber [7] on $\alpha_{1,2}$ at $T_1 = 70°F$ for a large group of nonmetals appear in Fig. I,1b, indicating a decrease, with increase in $T_2$, from 0.8–0.95 at 500°R to 0.1–0.9 at 5000°R. The absorptivity of metallic conductors, on the other hand, increases approximately linearly with $\sqrt{T_1T_2}$.

If $\alpha_\lambda$ is a constant independent of $\lambda$, the surface is called *gray*, and its total absorptivity $\alpha$ will be independent of the spectral-energy distribution of the incident radiation; then $\alpha_{1,2} = \alpha_{1,1} = \epsilon_1$, i.e. emissivity $\epsilon$ may be used in substitution for $\alpha$ even though the temperatures of the incident radiation and the receiver are not the same.

Radiant interchange between a small nongray body of area $S_1$ and temperature $T_1$ in black surroundings at $T_2$ is plainly given by

$$q_{1\rightleftharpoons 2} = \sigma S_1(\epsilon_1 T_1^4 - \alpha_{1,2}T_2^4) \tag{1-2}$$

It has been seen that over a moderate temperature range $\alpha_{1,2}$ can be

*Table I,1.* The normal total emissivity of various surfaces.
(Selected items from a larger table [*5*, Chap. 4].)

| *Surface* | *T*, °F* | *Emissivity* |
|---|---|---|
| Metals and their oxides | | |
| Aluminum | | |
| Highly polished, pure | 440–1070 | 0.04–0.06 |
| Commercial sheet | 212 | 0.09 |
| Heavily oxidized | 200–940 | 0.20–0.31 |
| Aluminum alloys | | |
| 75 ST | 75 | 0.10 |
| 75 ST† | 450–900 | 0.22–0.16 |
| Calorized Cu, heated at 1110°F | 390–1110 | 0.18–0.19 |
| Calorized steel, heated at 1110°F | 390–1110 | 0.52–0.57 |
| Brass | | |
| Highly polished | 476–674 | 0.03 |
| Rolled plate, emeried | 72 | 0.20 |
| Oxodized by heating at 1110°F | 120–660 | 0.22 |
| Chromium, polished | 100–2000 | 0.08–0.36 |
| Copper | | |
| Electrolytic, polished | 176 | 0.02 |
| Commercial plate, emeried | 66 | 0.03 |
| Plate, heated at 1110°F | 390–1110 | 0.57 |
| Dow metal | | |
| Cleaned | 75 | 0.15 |
| Cleaned and polished† | 450–760 | 0.21–0.18 |
| Gold, pure polished | 440–1160 | 0.02–0.03 |
| Inconel | | |
| Types X and B, cleaned | 75 | 0.19–0.21 |
| Type X, cleaned† | 450–1575 | 0.60–0.75 |
| Type B, cleaned† | 450–1740 | 0.32–0.51 |
| Iron and steel (excluding stainless) | | |
| Electrolytic, polished | 350–440 | 0.05–0.06 |
| Iron, polished | 800–1880 | 0.14–0.38 |
| Wrought iron, polished | 100–480 | 0.28 |
| Smooth sheet iron | 1650–1900 | 0.55–0.60 |
| Rusted plate | 67 | 0.69 |
| Smooth oxidized iron | 260–980 | 0.78–0.82 |
| Strongly oxidized | 100–480 | 0.95 |
| Lead | | |
| Pure, polished | 260–440 | 0.06–0.08 |
| Oxidized at 300°F | 390 | 0.63 |
| Magnesium | | |
| Oxide | 530–1520 | 0.55–0.20 |
| Oxide | 1650–3100 | 0.20 |
| Monel metal | | |
| K Monel, cleaned | 75 | 0.17 |
| K Monel, cleaned† | 450–1610 | 0.46–0.65 |
| Nickel | | |
| Electrolytic, polished | 74 | 0.05 |
| Electroplated, not polished | 68 | 0.11 |
| Plate, oxidized at 1110°F | 390–1110 | 0.37–0.48 |
| Oxide | 1200–2290 | 0.59–0.86 |
| Nickel alloys | | |
| Chromnickel | 125–1894 | 0.64–0.76 |
| Copper-nickel, polished | 212 | 0.06 |
| Nichrome wire, bright | 120–1830 | 0.65–0.79 |
| Nichrome wire, oxidized | 120–930 | 0.95–0.98 |
| Platinum, pure polished | 440–1160 | 0.05–0.10 |
| | 1700–2960 | 0.12–0.17 |
| Silver, pure polished | 440–1160 | 0.02–0.03 |
| Stainless steels | | |
| Type 316, cleaned | 75 | 0.28 |
| Type 316, cleaned† | 450–1600 | 0.57–0.66 |
| Type 304, 42 hrs at 980°F | 420–980 | 0.62–0.73 |
| Type 310, oxidized from furnace service | 420–980 | 0.90–0.97 |
| Tungsten, aged filament | 80–6000 | 0.03–0.35 |
| Zinc | | |
| Polished | 440–620 | 0.05 |
| Oxidized by heating at 750°F | 750 | 0.11 |
| Galvanized iron, gray oxidized | 75 | 0.28 |
| Refractories, building materials, paints, and miscellaneous | | |
| Alumina, 50μ grain size | 1850–2850 | 0.39–0.28 |
| Asbestos | 100–700 | 0.93–0.94 |
| Brick, fireclay | 1832 | 0.75 |
| Carbon, heated | 260–1160 | 0.81–0.79 |
| Lampblack | 122–1832 | 0.96 |
| Carborundum | 1850–2550 | 0.92–0.82 |
| Glass (Pyrex, lead, soda) | 500–1000 | 0.95–0.85 |
| Magnesite brick | 1832 | 0.38 |
| Planed oak | 70 | 0.90 |
| Oil layers on polished Ni | | |
| Polished surface alone | | 0.04 |
| 0.001″; 0.002″ oil | | 0.27; 0.46 |
| 0.005″; thick layer | | 0.72; 0.82 |
| Paints, lacquers, varnishes | | |
| White enamel | 73 | 0.91 |
| Black lacquer | 76 | 0.88 |
| Oil paints, 16 colors | 212 | 0.92–0.96 |
| Al paints, varying Al content | 212 | 0.27–0.67 |
| Rubber, soft gray | 76 | 0.86 |
| Water | 32–212 | 0.95–0.96 |

* When *T*'s and ε's appear in pairs separated by dashes, they correspond; and linear interpolation is permissible.
† Results after repeated heating and cooling.

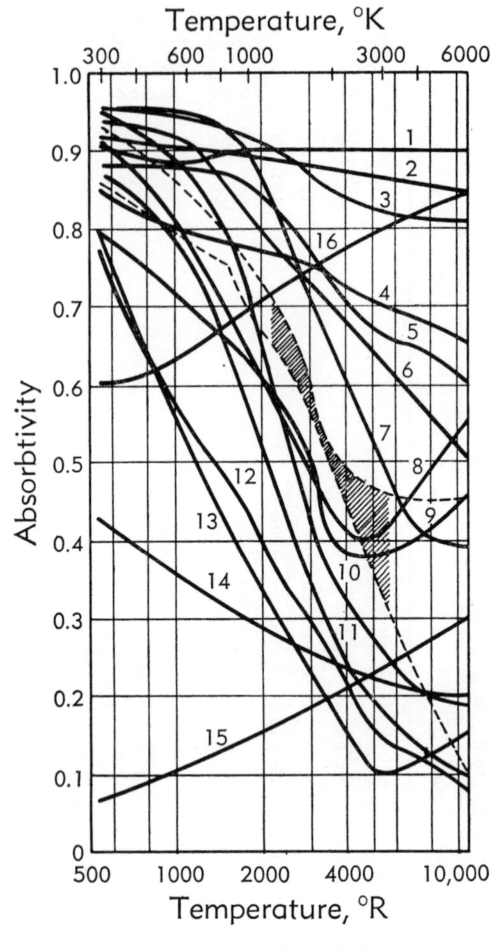


Key
1. Slate composition roofing
2. Linoleum, red brown
3. Asbestos slate
4. Soft rubber, gray
5. Concrete
6. Porcelain
7. Vitreous enamel, white
8. Red brick
9. Cork
10. White Dutch tile
11. White chamotte
12. MgO, evaporated
13. Anodized aluminum
14. Aluminum paint
15. Polished aluminum
16. Graphite

The two dotted lines bound the limits of data on gray paving brick, asbestos paper, wood, various cloths, plaster of Paris, lithopone, and paper

Fig. I,1b. Effect of source temperature on the absorptivity of surfaces for black radiation.

represented by $\alpha_0 T_1^m T_2^n$, with $n$ considerably greater than $m$ for non-metals, and both negative; and $n$ about the same as $m$ for bright metallic surfaces, and both positive. Then, since $\epsilon_1 = \alpha_{1,1} = \alpha_0 T_1^{m+n}$, the net flux at $S_1$ is

$$q_{1\rightleftharpoons 2} = \sigma S_1 \alpha_0 (T_1^{4+m+n} - T_1^m T_2^{4+n}) \tag{1-3}$$

It may readily be shown that, over a moderate temperature range, this reduces to

$$q_{1\rightleftharpoons 2} = \sigma S_1 \left[ \epsilon_{av} \left( 1 + \frac{n}{4} \right) \right] (T_1^4 - T_2^4) \tag{1-4}$$

with $\epsilon_{av}$ evaluated at the arithmetic mean temperature. Thus, although $\epsilon$ approaches $\alpha$ as $T_2$ and $T_1$ approach each other, the emissivity factor by which $\sigma(T_1^4 - T_2^4)$ should be multiplied is not $\epsilon$, but $\epsilon[1 + (n/4)]$. Eq. 1-4 can be used with small error over an absolute temperature ratio up to 2.

**I,2. The View Factor. Direct Interchange between Surfaces.** The relations just given were restricted to radiant interchange when a surface $S_1$ could "see" nothing but surroundings at $T_2$. The more complicated but important case of interchange in a system of several surfaces at different temperatures and emissivities involves the concept of a geometrical view factor $F$. $F_{12}$ is defined as the fraction of the radiation leaving a surface $S_1$ in all directions which is intercepted by a surface $S_2$. Evaluation of this factor is as follows: Visualize, on black surface $S_1$ of total emissive power $W_{b1}$, a small surface element $dS_1$ radiating in all directions from one side, and on a black surface $S_2$ a small surface element $dS_2$ intercepting some of the radiation from $dS_1$. Let the straight line connecting $dS_1$ and $dS_2$ have length $r$, and let $r$ make angles $\theta_1$ and $\theta_2$ with the normals to $dS_1$ and $dS_2$ respectively. The rate of radiation from $dS_1$ to $dS_2$, called $dq_{1\to 2}$, will be proportional to $dS_1 \cos \theta_1$, the apparent area of $dS_1$ viewed from $dS_2$; to $dS_2 \cos \theta_2$, the apparent area of $dS_2$ viewed from $dS_1$; and inversely proportional to the square of the distance separating the elements. Calling the proportionality constant $J_{b1}$, one may write

$$dq_{1\to 2} = J_{b1} \frac{dA_1 \cos \theta_1 \, dA_2 \cos \theta_2}{r^2} \tag{2-1}$$

This equation defines $J_{b1}$, the intensity of radiation from a black surface.

By integration of Eq. 2-1 over a receiving surface filling the field of view of $dS_1$, one obtains $W_{b1}dS_1$, the total rate of emission from $dS_1$ throughout the hemisphere. The integration gives $\pi J_{b1}dS_1$, from which one concludes that the emissive power $W_b$ of a black surface is $\pi$ times its intensity of radiation $J_b$. By integration of Eq. 2-1 over finite areas $S_1$ and $S_2$ to obtain the rate of radiation from one to the other and dividing the result by $S_1W_{b1}$, one obtains $F_{12}$, the desired fraction of the radiation leaving surface $S_1$ in all directions which is intercepted by surface $S_2$. Although the discussion has been restricted to black surfaces, it is apparent that for a nonblack surface $S_1$ the emissivity of which is independent of angle of emission, $F_{12}$ calculated by the method above will continue to represent the fractional radiation from $S_1$ intercepted by $S_2$ (though not necessarily absorbed unless $S_2$ is black).

Important and useful concepts in evaluating $F$'s are that

$$S_1F_{12} = S_2F_{21} \tag{2-2}$$

(since otherwise there would be a net heat flux between $S_1$ and $S_2$ when at the same temperature), that

$$F_{11} + F_{12} + F_{13} + \cdots = 1 \tag{2-3}$$

and that, of course, $F_{11} = 0$ when $S_1$ can "see" no part of itself.

Values of $F$ have been calculated for various surface arrangements on the assumption that emissivity $\epsilon_\theta$ is constant and independent of $\theta$ (exact for black surfaces, quite good for most nonmetallic, tarnished, or rough metal surfaces). These values of $F$ for a surface element $dS$ and a rectangle in a parallel plane appear in Fig. I,2a; for opposed parallel rectangles and disks of equal size as lines 1 to 4 of Fig. I,2b; for adjacent rectangles in perpendicular planes in Fig. I,2c; and for concentric cylinders in Fig. I,2d [*8*]. An important class of surfaces exists for which the

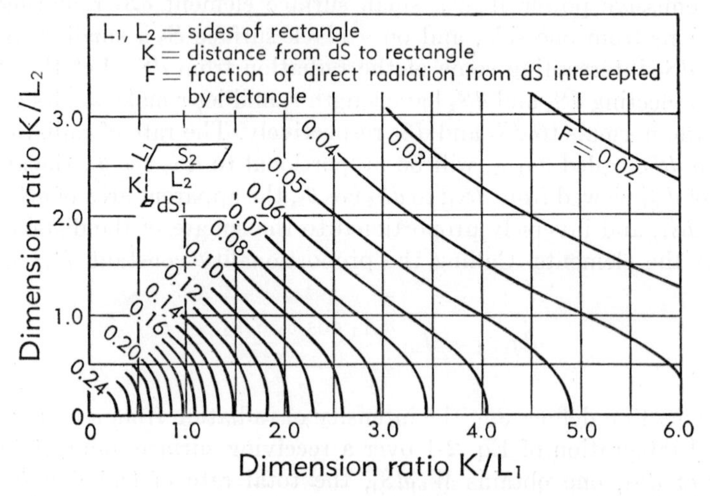


Fig. I,2a. View factor $F$ for direct radiation between an element $dS$ and a parallel rectangle with corner opposite $dS$.

view factor $F$ is capable of easy evaluation without a multiple integration of Eq. 2-1. These are surfaces, infinite in extent in one direction, which are generated by a straight line moving always parallel to itself. The surface is then represented by a curve on a plane normal to the generating line. If a surface $S_1$ is represented by the heavy-line curve $\overline{AB}$ (Fig. I,2e) and a surface $S_2$ by the heavy-line curve $\overline{CD}$, it may readily be shown [*5*, Chap. 4] that, per unit dimension normal to the drawing, $S_1F_{12}(\equiv S_2F_{21})$ is equal to the sum of the lengths of dotted lines in the figure representing crossed strings stretched from the ends of $S_1$ to the ends of $S_2$, less the sum of the lengths of uncrossed strings stretched between the ends of $S_1$ and the ends of $S_2$, all divided by 2; or, in terms of the sketch, by $(\overline{AD} + \overline{BEFGHC} - \overline{AJGHC} - \overline{BEKLD})/2$. Values of $F$ for other arrangements are treated in the literature [*9,10,11,12,13,14*].

The rate of radiation from a black surface $S_1$ to a black surface $S_2$

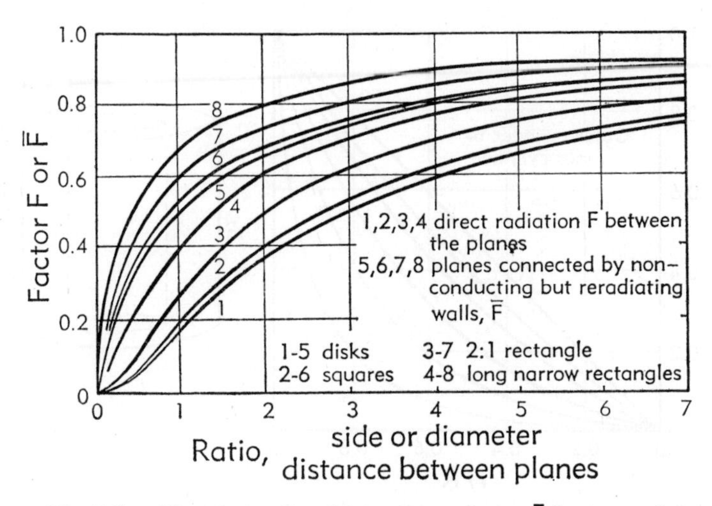


Fig. I,2b. View factor $F$ and interchange factor $\bar{F}$ for opposed parallel disks, squares, and rectangles.

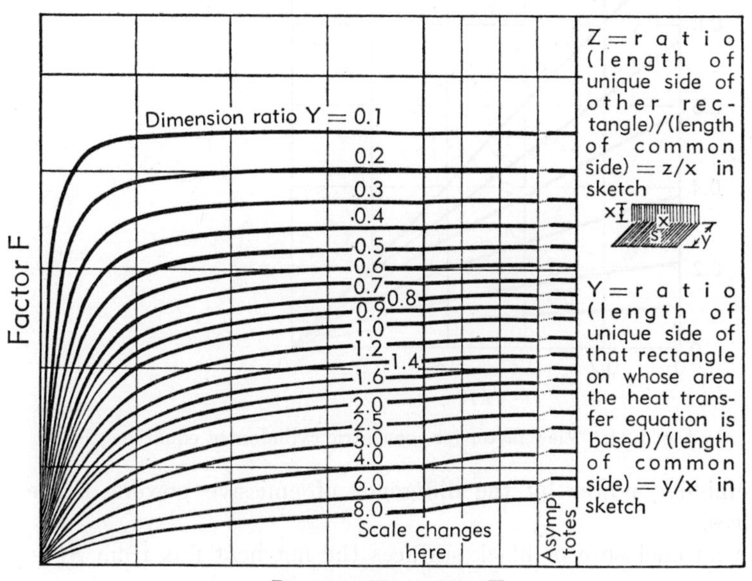


Fig. I,2c. View factor $F$ for direct radiation between adjacent rectangles in perpendicular planes.

is now $S_1F_{12}\sigma T_1^4$; from $S_2$ to $S_1$, it is $S_2F_{21}\sigma T_2^4$; the net interchange is their difference, which may be written as either $S_1F_{12}\sigma(T_1^4 - T_2^4)$ or $S_2F_{21}\sigma(T_1^4 - T_2^4)$. One thus reaches the important conclusion that interchange may be obtained by evaluating the one-way radiation from either surface to the other, whichever is more convenient, and then replacing

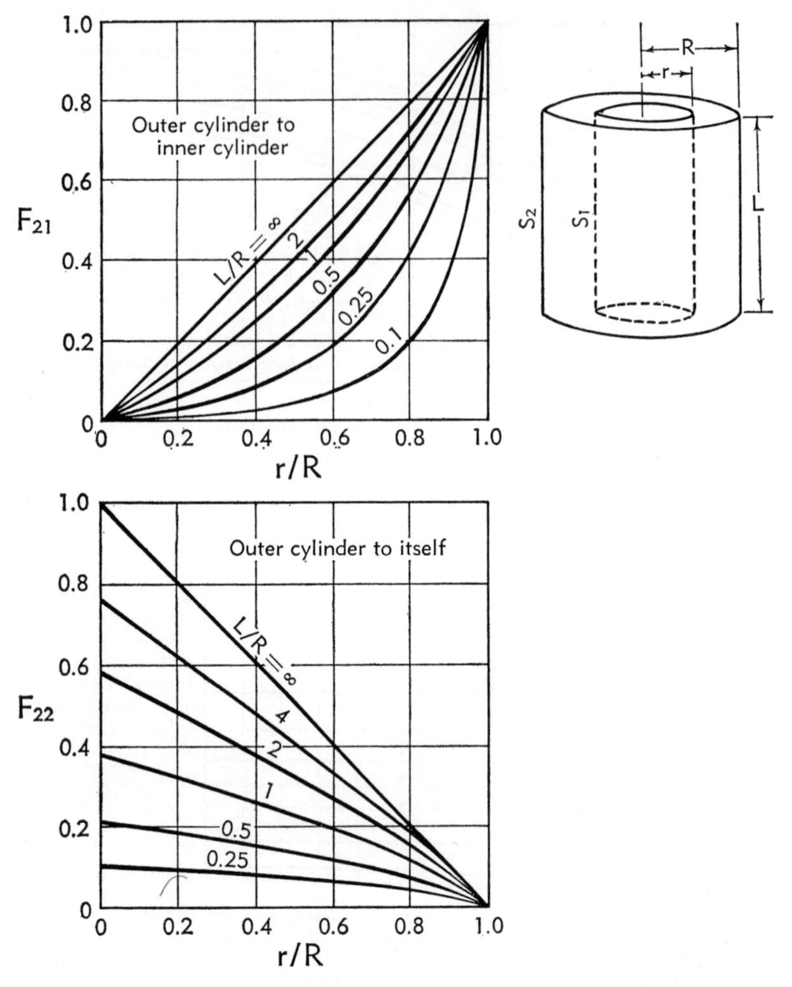


Fig. I,2d. View factor for concentric cylinders of equal length.

the emissive power by the difference of emissive powers of the two surfaces.

In an enclosure of black surfaces the net heat flux from $S_1$ is then given by

$$\begin{aligned} q_{1,\mathrm{net}} &= (S_1F_{12}\sigma T_1^4 - S_2F_{21}\sigma T_2^4) + (S_1F_{13}\sigma T_1^4 - S_3F_{31}\sigma T_3^4) + \cdots \\ &= S_1F_{12}\sigma(T_1^4 - T_2^4) + S_1F_{13}\sigma(T_1^4 - T_3^4) + \cdots \\ &= S_1\sigma T_1^4 - (S_1F_{11}\sigma T_1^4 + S_2F_{21}\sigma T_2^4 + S_3F_{31}\sigma T_3^4 + \cdots) \end{aligned} \tag{2-4}$$

The above relation permits evaluation of radiation exchange in black systems when the temperatures of all the zones are specified. The more complete analysis, allowing for the equilibrium temperature attained by surfaces which are not heat sinks or sources and for multiple reflection in a system of nonblack surfaces, will be withheld until the radiating characteristics of gases have been described, in order that allowance for the presence of such gases may at the same time be included.

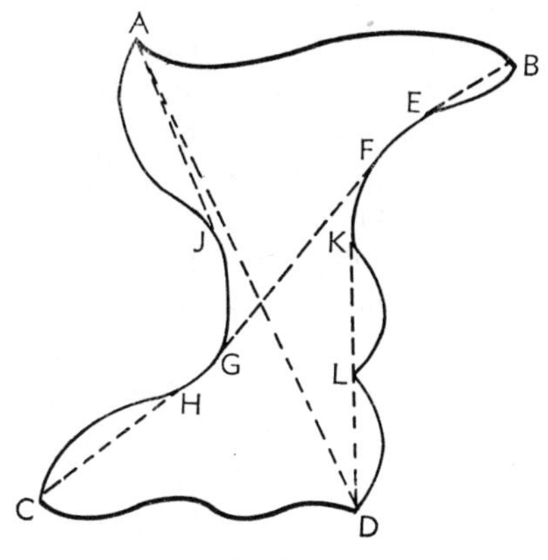


Fig. I,2e.

**I,3. Radiation from Flames and Gases.** The radiation from a luminous flame is due primarily to submicroscopic soot particles, of diameters 0.006 to 0.06$\mu$ before agglomeration, in the case of pulverized coal to suspended coke or ash particles of diameter 25$\mu$ and less, in the case of heavy residual fuel oils to coked bitumens of initial size 200 to 50$\mu$ or even less, and quite negligibly in all cases to so-called chemiluminescence, the radiation characterizing the chemical reactions involved. Superimposed on this luminous radiation is the important infrared radiation from combustion products, principally carbon dioxide and water vapor.

*Soot luminosity.* The first of these, soot luminosity, is important where combustion occurs under such conditions that hydrocarbon gases in the flame are subjected to heat in the absence of prior *intimate* mixing with sufficient air, producing thermal decomposition. This occurs, for example, near the surface of a volatilizing oil droplet or in the fuel-rich portion of a laminar diffusion flame. Turbulence, consequently, is of primary importance in minimizing luminosity due to soot; but chemical differences in hydrocarbons are also important, aromatic compounds being most prone to produce luminosity, and paraffins least. It is not possible, in the present state of knowledge, to predict the luminosity of a flame analytically; reliance must be put on experimental measurement of flames similar to that of interest. The work of the International Committee on Flame Radiation in this field is outstanding [*15,16,17*].

The planning and use of measurements on luminous flames depends on knowledge of the radiating and absorbing characteristics of a soot cloud. The monochromatic emissivity $\epsilon_\lambda$ of such a cloud equals its monochromatic absorptivity $\alpha_\lambda$, and is given in terms of the monochromatic absorption coefficient $k_\lambda$ by

$$\epsilon_\lambda = 1 - e^{-k_\lambda cL} \tag{3-1}$$

in which $c$ is the soot concentration and $L$ is the path length through the flame. The absorption coefficient $k_\lambda$ varies approximately as an inverse power function of $\lambda$ [*18,19,20,21*]. Suppose $k_\lambda$ to be representable by $k/\lambda^\alpha$ so that $\epsilon_\lambda$ is $(1 - e^{-kcL/\lambda^\alpha})$, and let $kcL$ be represented by $KL$, called the *absorption strength* of the flame. A little consideration will show that if $KL$ and the true flame temperature $T_f$ are known, the complete description of the thermal radiating characteristics of an isotropic flame can be inferred, including the monochromatic emissivity at any wavelength, the total emissivity $\epsilon_f$, the total emissive power of the flame $W_f(\equiv\epsilon_f\sigma T_f^4)$, and the effect of flame size and shape on the emission from its envelope. It may be shown [*5*, Chap. 4; *18*] that 2 properly chosen optical measurements on the flame suffice to determine these properties. Among the most useful pairs of measurements are: (1) red brightness temperature $T_r$ (determined with an optical pyrometer) and total emissive power $W_f$ (determined with a total radiation pyrometer; (2) $T_r$ for a single and for a doubled flame thickness, the latter by use of a mirror behind the flame; (3) red brightness temperature of the flame alone and of the flame backed by a target of known red emissive power, near that of the flame; (4) total emissive power of the flame alone and of the flame backed by a target of known total emissive power. The method of interpreting these data is presented elsewhere [*5*, Chap. 4].

The emissivity of luminous flames varies greatly, and the eye is no judge; a flame so bright that nothing on the other side of it can be seen may nevertheless be far from a black body. The total emissivity may vary from a maximum value near unity in a two-foot depth of a natural-gas diffusion flame down to the value due only to infrared radiation from combustion products, in a premixed gas-air flame. (For the latter value, due to $CO_2$ and $H_2O$, see below, this article.)

*Luminosity due to larger particles.* Reference here is to the particles from a pulverized coal or well-atomized residual fuel oil flame—particles large compared to the wavelength of radiation of interest and therefore acting simply to block out a beam passing through the flame. It may readily be shown that for such particles the emissivity of the flame surface, from the direction in which $L$ is the path length through the flame, is given by

$$\epsilon_f = 1 - e^{-cAL} \tag{3-2}$$

where $c$ is the number of particles per unit volume, and $A$ is the projected area of a particle. This may be applied to a heavy fuel oil flame to estimate the degree of atomization necessary to make luminosity of this kind significant. Assume a flame temperature of 3000°R, a fuel oil density of 1, a stoichiometric air requirement of 15 lb/lb fuel, 20 per cent excess air, and opaque particles which are uniform and of a diameter $D$ equal to the initial drop size. The concentration of drops can be shown to be $0.0000707/\pi D^3$ per ft$^3$; the projected area of a drop is $\pi D^2/4$. Then

$$\epsilon_f = (1 - e^{-1.77\times 10^{-5}L/D})$$

For a flame of 2 ft thickness and particles of 50$\mu$ (0.000164 ft) initial diameter, $\epsilon_f$ is 0.194 initially and decreases continuously as the particles burn away. This is slightly more than the emissivity due to nonluminous gases present, and markedly less than the emissivity due to soot in many flames. Whether the residual particles themselves contribute significantly to the flame radiation compared to soot luminosity or gas radiation thus depends on how finely the fuel is atomized.

*Gas radiation.* *$CO_2$ and $H_2O$.* Of importance in substantially all evaluations of heat transmission in combustion processes, whether from flames or from their cooler products, is the infrared radiation from the combustion products, water vapor and carbon dioxide, which overshadows convection at combustion temperatures. This radiation has its origin in simultaneous quantum changes in the energy levels of rotation and of interatomic vibration of molecules and, at the temperature levels reached in combustion processes, is of importance only in the case of the heteropolar gases. Of the gases encountered in heat transfer equipment, carbon monoxide, the hydrocarbons, water vapor, carbon dioxide, sulfur dioxide, ammonia, hydrogen chloride, and the alcohols are among those with emission bands of sufficient magnitude to merit consideration. Gases with symmetrical molecules, like hydrogen, oxygen, and nitrogen, have been found not to show absorption bands in those wavelength regions of importance in radiant heat transmission at temperatures met in combustion processes. Sec. H of this volume presents the molecular physical background for thermal radiation from gases.

If black body radiation passes through a gas mass containing $CO_2$ or $H_2O$, absorption occurs at certain wavelengths. Conversely, if the gas mass is heated it radiates at those same wavelengths. Consider a hemispherical gas mass of radius $L$ containing carbon dioxide of partial pressure $p_c$, and let the problem be the evaluation of radiant heat interchange between the gas at temperature $T_g$ and a small black element of surface at temperature $T_1$, located on the base of the hemisphere at its center. Per unit of surface the emission of the gas to the surface is $\sigma T_g^4 \epsilon_g$, where $\epsilon_g$ denotes gas emissivity. For carbon dioxide $\epsilon_g$ depends on $T_g$, the product term $p_cL$, and the total pressure $P_t$. The emissivity of carbon dioxide for $P_t = 1$ atm is given in Fig. I,3a, based on experimental data [*22,23*]. The line broadening due to pressure may be estimated from Fig. I,3b, which gives a correction factor $C_c$ by which the values from Fig. I,3a are to be multiplied (based on the data of Howard, et al. [24] and on unpublished data of HoLeong and Wu [25,26]). The absorption, by the gas, of radiation from the surface is $\sigma T_1^4 \alpha_{g1}$, where $\alpha_{g1}$ is the absorptivity of the gas at $T_g$ for black or gray radiation from the surface at $T_1$. Absorptivity is evaluated approximately by reading the gas emissivity at $T_1$ and at $p_c L T_1/T_g$ (the value giving the same molal concentration as at the gas temperature), then multiplying the result by $(T_g/T_1)^{0.65}$. The same correction factor $C_c$ applies to $\alpha_{g1}$ as to $\epsilon_g$ if the total pressure is not 1 atm.

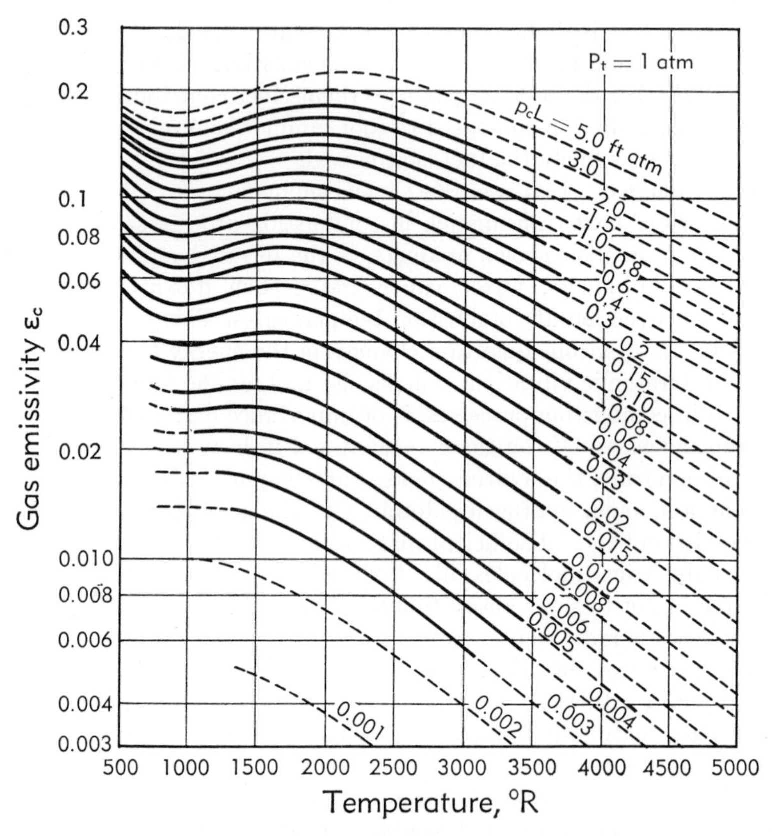


Fig. I,3a. Emissivity of carbon dioxide.

For water vapor, the gas emissivity depends on $T_g$ and $p_w L$ and on total pressure $P_t$ as before, and in addition on the partial pressure of water vapor $p_w$. Emissivity due to water vapor is given in Fig. I,3c (based on experimental data [22,23,27,28,29]) as a function of $T_g$ and $p_w L$, for $P_t = 1$ atm and for the "ideal" system with $p_w = 0$. Approximate allowance for departure from these special conditions is made by multiplying $\epsilon_g$ from Fig. I,3c by a factor $C_w$ read from Fig. I,3d as a function of $(p_w + P_t)$ and $p_w L$. The absorptivity of water vapor for black body radi-

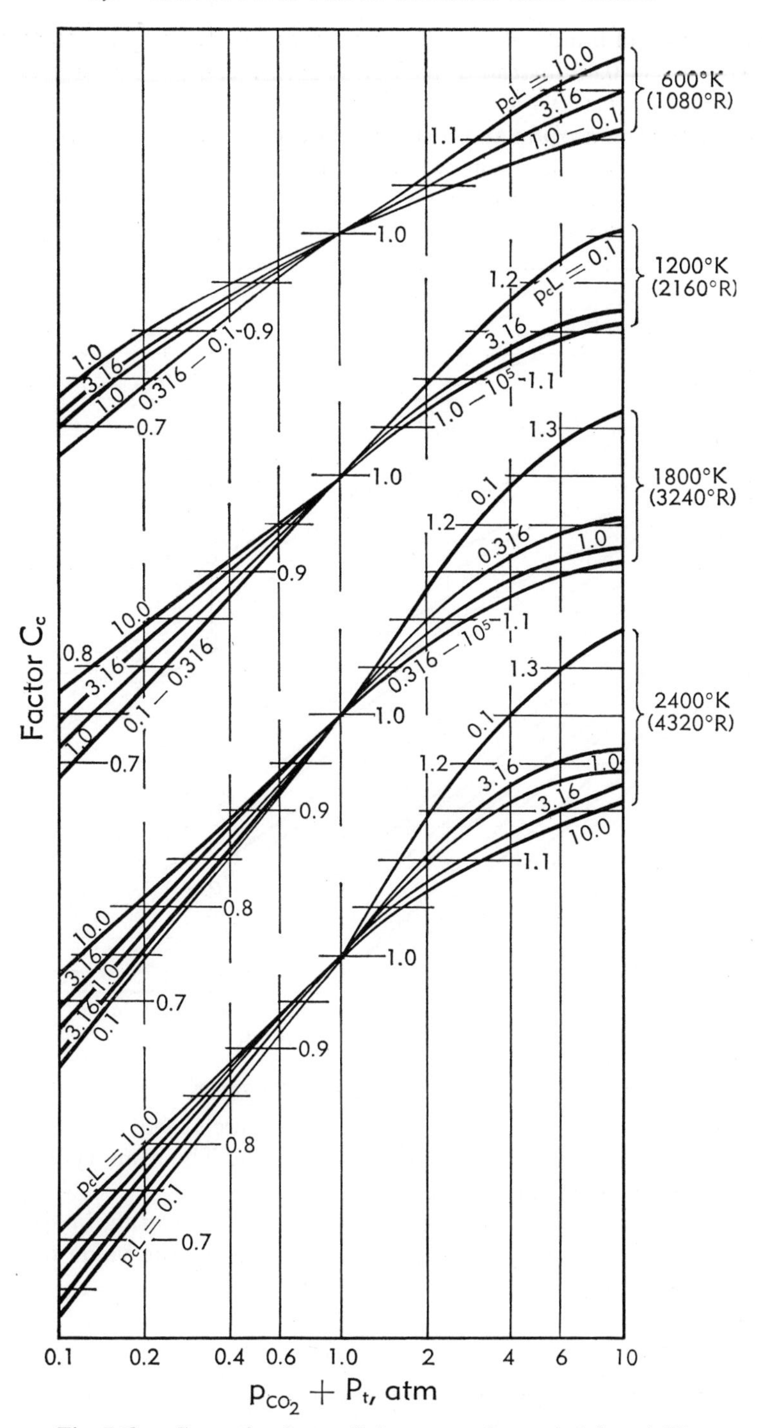


Fig. I,3b. Correction factor $C_c$ for converting emissivity of $CO_2$ at about 1 atm total pressure to emissivity at $P_t$ atm.

ation may be obtained like that of carbon dioxide, except for the use of an exponent of 0.45 instead of 0.65 on $(T_g/T_1)$. The correction factor $C_w$ still applies.

When carbon dioxide and water vapor are present together, the total radiation due to both is somewhat less than the sum of the separately calculated effects because each gas is somewhat opaque to radiation from the other. The amount $\Delta\epsilon$ by which to reduce the sum of $\epsilon_g$ for $CO_2$ and

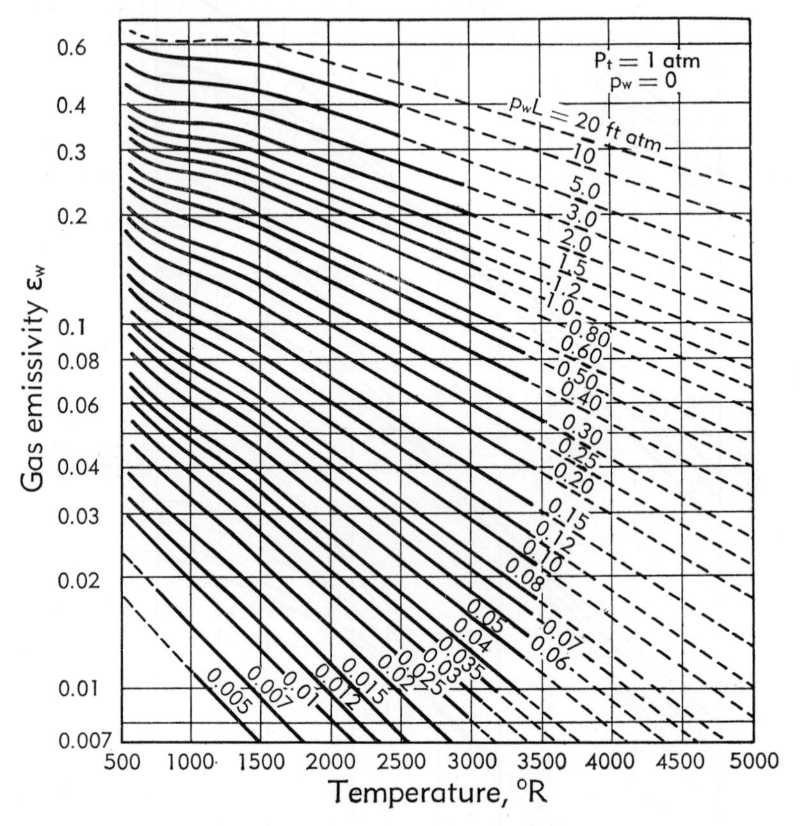


Fig. I,3c. Emissivity of water vapor.

$\epsilon_g$ for $H_2O$ (each evaluated as if the other gas were absent) to obtain the $\epsilon_g$ due to the two together is read from Fig. I,3e. The same type of correction applies in calculating $\alpha_g$.

Recapitulating by the use of subscripts on $\epsilon_g$ indicating in sequence the gas (c or w), the temperature on the plot, and the value of $pL$ at which $\epsilon$ is read, one has

$$\epsilon_g = \epsilon_{c,T_g,p_cL}C_c + \epsilon_{w,T_g,p_wL}C_w - \Delta\epsilon_{T_g} \tag{3-3}$$

$$\alpha_g{}^1 = \epsilon_{c,T_1,p_cLT_1/T_g}\left(\frac{T_g}{T_1}\right)^{0.65} C_c + \epsilon_{w,T_1,p_wLT_1/T_g}\left(\frac{T_g}{T_1}\right)^{0.45} C_w - \Delta\alpha_{T_1}$$

The formulation of radiant interchange between a gas and a black surface completely enclosing it, when the gas contains $CO_2$ and $H_2O$, is then

$$\frac{q_{g\rightleftharpoons 1}}{S_1} = \sigma(\epsilon_g T_g^4 - \alpha_{g1} T_1^4) \tag{3-4}$$

If the surface is gray, multiplication of the right side of the above by $\epsilon_1(\equiv \alpha_1)$ would make proper allowance for reduction in the primary beams from gas to surface and surface to gas, respectively; but some of the gas radiation initially reflected from the surface has further opportunity for absorption at the surface because the gas is but incompletely opaque to the reflected beam. Consequently, the factor to allow for surface emissivity lies between $\epsilon_1$ and 1, nearer the latter the more transparent the gas

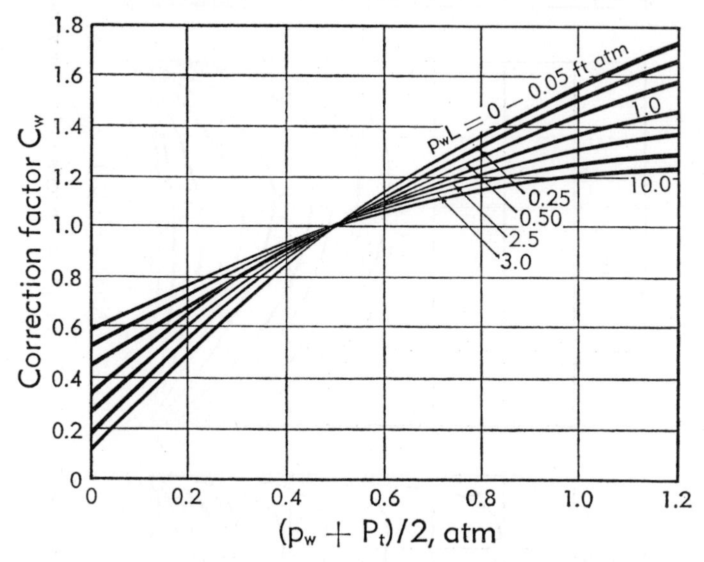


Fig. I,3d. Correction factor $C_w$ for converting emissivity of $H_2O$ to values of $p_w$ and $P_t$ other than 0 and 1 atm, respectively.

(low $p_xL$) and the more convoluted the surface. If the surface emissivity is above 0.8, use of the factor $(\epsilon_1 + 1)/2$ cannot be greatly in error. If $\epsilon_1$ is smaller, the more nearly rigorous method of Art. 5 may be used.

Although $\alpha_{g1}$ approaches $\epsilon_g$ as $T_1$ approaches $T_g$, $q/S$ of Eq. 3-4 does not in consequence reduce to $\sigma\epsilon_g(T_g^4 - T_1^4)$ for values of $T_1$ and $T_g$ close together. If over a restricted range of variables $\epsilon_g$ is assumed proportional to $(p_gL)^a(T_g)^b$, then $\alpha_{g1}$ is proportional to $(p_gL)^a(T_1)^{a+b-c}T_g^{c-a}$ where $c$ is the previously encountered exponent used in evaluating absorptivity—0.65 for $CO_2$ and 0.45 for $H_2O$. It may be shown that, when $T_g$ and $T_1$ are not too far apart,

$$\frac{q_{g\rightleftharpoons 1}}{S_1} = \sigma\left[\epsilon_{g,\text{av}} \frac{4 + a + b - c}{4}\right](T_g^4 - T_1^4) \tag{3-5}$$

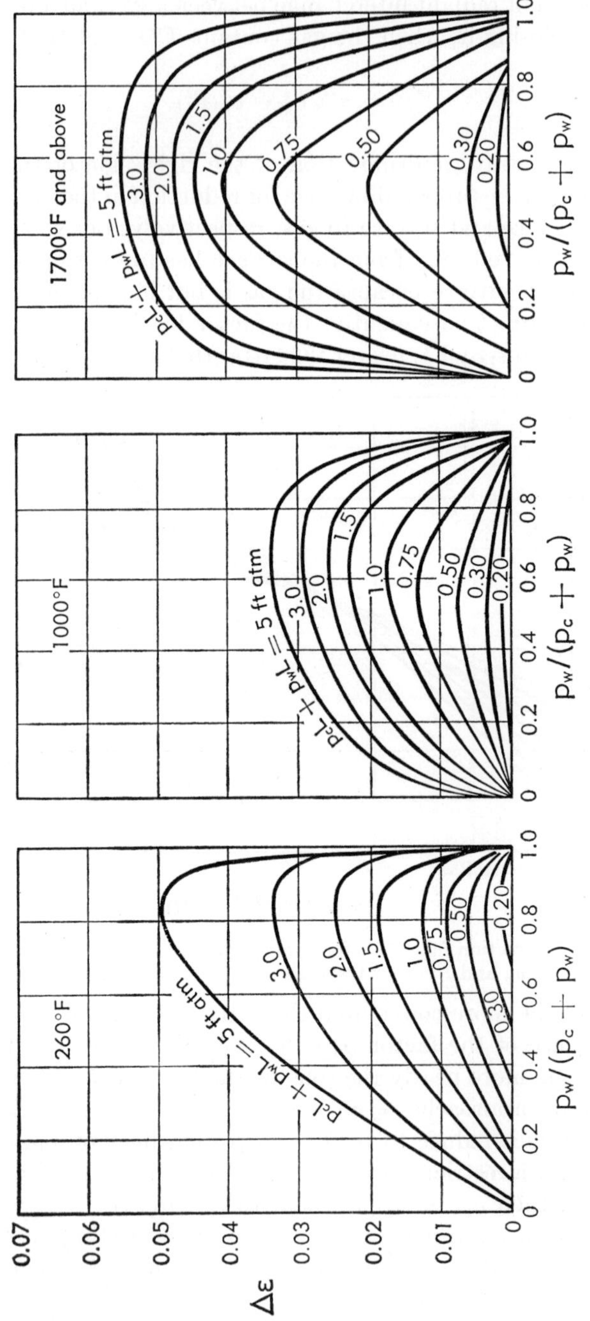


**Fig. I,3e.** Correction to gas emissivity due to spectral overlap of water vapor and carbon dioxide.

in which $\epsilon_{g,av}$ is the gas emissivity evaluated at the arithmetic mean of $T_g$ and $T_1$. Values of $a$ and $b$, which represent $\partial \ln \epsilon_g/\partial \ln p_gL$ and $\partial \ln \epsilon_g/\partial \ln T_g$, respectively, are given in Fig. I,3f for $CO_2$ and $H_2O$. When a mixture of the two gases is present, it is recommended that mean values of $a$, $b$, and $c$ be used in Eq. 3-5, the factors for the different gases being weighted in proportion to their emissivities. (A roughly approximate value of $(a + b - c)$ suffices, however, since an error of 0.1 in it produces an error of only 2.5 per cent in $q/S$.) The use of Eq. 3-5 when $T_g$ and $T_1$ do not differ by a factor greater than 2 leads to results of accuracy comparable to Eq. 3-4, and will usually save time as well by eliminating the necessity for the fairly tedious evaluation of $\alpha_{g1}$.

*Mean beam length.* The preceding expressions were formulated for the case of interchange between a gas hemisphere and a spot on its base,

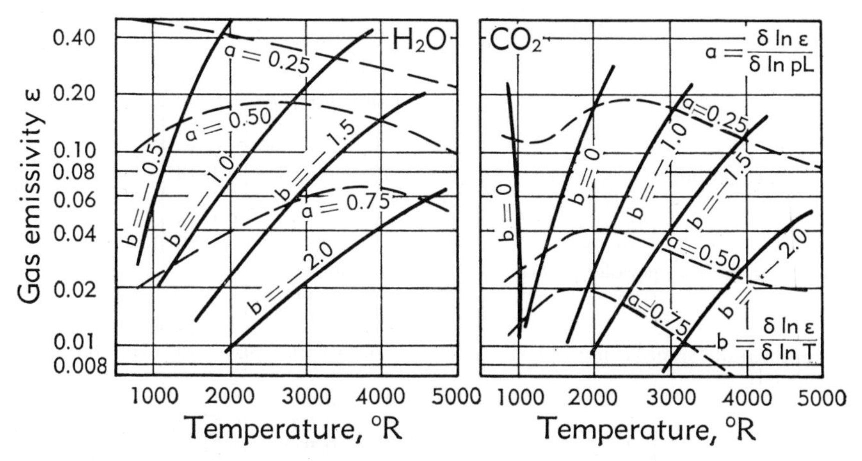


Fig. I,3f. Rate of change of emissivity with $T$ and $p_gL$, for $CO_2$ and $H_2O$.

i.e. for the case in which the path length $L$ of the radiant beam is the same in all directions. For gas shapes of practical interest, it is found that any shape is approximately representable by an equivalent hemisphere of proper radius, or that there is a *mean* beam length $L$ which can be used in calculating gas emissivities and absorptivities from Fig. I,3a and I,3c [*30,31*]. As $pL$ approaches zero, the mean beam length approaches as a limit the value $4x$ (ratio of gas volume to bounding area). For the range of $pL$ encountered in practice, $L$ is always less; 85 per cent of the limiting value is generally a satisfactory approximation [*32*]. Table I,3 summarizes the results of tedious graphical or analytical treatment of various shapes.

*Temperature variation along flow path.* If gas radiation occurs in a system in which there is a continuous change in temperature of the gas or surface, or both, along the gas flow path from one end to the other of the interchanger, and if the dimensions transverse to flow are small enough to make radiant exchange in the flow direction relatively un-

*Table I,3.* Beam lengths for gas radiation.

| Shape | Characterizing dimension $x$ | Factor by which $x$ is multiplied to obtain mean beam length $L$: When $pL = 0$ | Factor by which $x$ is multiplied to obtain mean beam length $L$: For average values of $pL$ |
|---|---|---|---|
| Sphere | Diameter | 0.67 | 0.60 |
| Infinite cylinder | Diameter | 1 | 0.90 |
| Semi-infinite cylinder, radiating to center of base | Diameter | | 0.90 |
| Right circular cylinder, height = diameter, radiating to base at center | Diameter | | 0.77 |
| Same, radiating to whole surface | Diameter | 0.67 | 0.60 |
| Infinite cylinder of half-circular cross section. Radiating to spot on middle of flat side | Radius | | 1.26 |
| Rectangular parallelopipeds | | | |
| 1:1:1, cube | Edge | 0.67 | *See footnote in table |
| 1:1:4, radiating to 1 × 4 face | Shortest edge | 0.90 | *See footnote in table |
| " " 1 × 1 " | | 0.86 | *See footnote in table |
| " " all faces | | 0.89 | *See footnote in table |
| 1:2:6, radiating to 2 × 6 face | Shortest edge | 1.18 | *See footnote in table |
| " " 1 × 6 " | | 1.24 | *See footnote in table |
| " " 1 × 2 " | | 1.18 | *See footnote in table |
| " " all faces | | 1.20 | *See footnote in table |
| 1: ∞ : ∞, Infinite parallel planes | Distance between planes | 2 | *See footnote in table |

* For parallelopipeds, multiply beam length suitable for $pL = 0$ by the following ratios [*32*]:

| When $p_cL$ or $p_wL$ = | 0.01 | 0.1 | 1 |
|---|---|---|---|
| Ratio for $CO_2$ | 0.85 | 0.80 | 0.77 |
| Ratio for $H_2O$ | 0.97 | 0.93 | 0.85 |

important, exact allowance for stream temperature variation can be made by conventional graphical integration. Let the heat transfer surface per unit length be designated by $P$, the local gas and surface temperatures at length $x$ by $T_g$ and $T_1$, the mass flow rate and heat capacity of the gas by $m$ and $c_p$, and the local heat transfer rate—by whatever mechanisms,

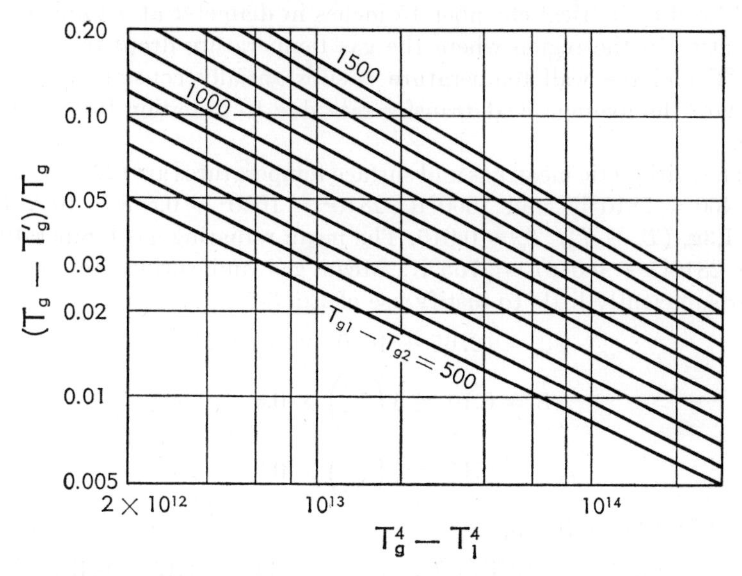


Fig. I,3g. Plot for calculation of mean gas temperature $T_g'$ in countercurrent gas radiant heat exchangers, in terms of arithmetic mean gas and surface temperatures $T_g$ and $T_1$ and gas-temperature change $T_{g1} - T_{g2}$. (Cohen [*33*].)

and expressible as a function of $T_g$ and $T_1$—by $(q/S)_{\text{local}}$. Then one may write

$$mc_p dT_g = (q/S)_{\text{local}} P dx \tag{3-6}$$

If the gas temperature at length $B$ is $T_{g,B}$, the above yields on integration

$$\frac{P}{mc_p} B = \int_{T_{g,0}}^{T_{g,B}} \frac{dT_g}{(q/S)_{\text{local}}} \tag{3-7}$$

Then a plot of the reciprocal of the local transfer rate vs. gas temperature yields a curve, the area under which is proportional to the length of the exchanger. This graphical procedure can be avoided, however, by evaluation of suitable mean gas and surface temperatures for use in Eq. 3-4 or 3-5 to obtain $(q/S)_{\text{av}}$. Fig. I,3g, from Cohen [*33*], gives the mean gas temperature for radiation $T_g'$ as a function of the four terminal temperatures. The mean surface temperature $T_1'$ is that corresponding to the point in the exchanger where the gas temperature is $T_g'$, and may be obtained by an enthalpy balance.

Rigorous allowance for temperature variations in a gas within the field of view of an element of radiation-receiving surface enormously complicates the problem; see end of Art. 4.

Application of the principles discussed is illustrated in the following example: Nonluminous combustion products of a hydrocarbon fuel, containing 10 per cent $CO_2$ and 15 per cent $H_2O$ by volume, flow through a black wall cylindrical chamber 15 inches in diameter at a total pressure of 5 atm. In the region where the gas temperature drops from 2700 to 2000°F and the wall temperature is substantially constant at 1200°F, estimate the average heat transfer rate due to radiation from $CO_2$ and $H_2O$.

The arithmetic mean gas and surface temperatures are $(2700 + 2000)/2 + 460 = 2810°R$, and 1660°R; $2810^4 - 1660^4 = 0.548 \times 10^{14}$. From Fig. I,3g, $(T_g - T_g')/T_g = 0.016$. The mean radiating gas temperature is then $2810(1 - 0.016) = 2765°R$. Mean gas and surface temperatures differ sufficiently little to justify use of Eq. 3-5.

$$T_{av} = (2765 + 1660)/2 = 2212°R \tag{3-8}$$

$$p_cL = 0.10 \times 5 \left(\frac{15}{12}\right) \times 0.8 = 0.50 \qquad (3\text{-}9)^2$$

$$p_wL = 0.15 \times 5 \left(\frac{15}{12}\right) \times 0.8 = 0.75 \qquad (3\text{-}10)^2$$

From Fig. I,3a and I,3b,

$$\epsilon_c \text{ (at } T = 2212°R, p_cL = 0.5) = 0.119 \times 1.15 = 0.137 \tag{3-11}$$

From Fig. I,3c and I,3d,

$$\epsilon_w \text{ (at } T = 2212°R, p_wL = 0.75) = 0.167 \times 1.6(?) = 0.267 \qquad (3\text{-}12)^3$$

$$0.404$$

From Fig. I,3e, the superimposed radiation correction[4] = 0.057

Total gas emissivity, $\epsilon_g = 0.347$

From Fig. I,3f, $a$ and $b$ for $CO_2 = +0.35$ and $-0.40$; for $H_2O$, $+0.52$ and $-0.85$. For the mixture, $a = 0.46$, $b = -0.7$, $c = 0.52$. Then, from Eq. 3-5,

$$\left(\frac{q}{S}\right)_{av} = 0.171 \left[0.347 \frac{4 + 0.46 - 0.7 - 0.52}{4}\right] (27.65^4 - 16.6^4)$$

$$= 24{,}500 \text{ BTU/ft}^2 \text{ hr}$$

[2] A smaller factor is used than for an infinite cylinder; the length of the system has not been specified.

[3] The pressure correction for $H_2O$ is far beyond the end of the plot; the extrapolation is based on the assumption that the pressure effect levels off above a few atmospheres pressure.

[4] In the absence of a recommendation, in the literature, as to the effect of total pressure on the correction $\Delta\epsilon$, it may be assumed to be increased by the average of $C_c$ and $C_w$. The effect is negligible in the present example.

A convection coefficient of about 22 BTU/ft$^2$ hr °F would produce the same transfer rate.

*Radiation from other gases.* Gas radiation plots similar to those for $CO_2$ and $H_2O$ have been prepared for $SO_2$, CO, and $NH_3$ [*5*, Chap. 4]. Infrared spectroscopic data available on many gases can serve as a basis for estimating radiant heat transfer although the data, particularly on the effects of temperature and total pressure, are often found to be inadequate. For a discussion of the methods of calculation the reader is referred to Sec. H.

**I,4. Radiant Exchange in an Enclosure of Source-Sink and No-Flux Surfaces Surrounding a Gray Gas.** One of the most complex problems of heat transmission is the evaluation of heat transfer in a combustion chamber, where all of the mechanisms of radiation so far discussed are operating simultaneously. Allowance is to be made for the following: (1) the combined actions of direct radiation of all kinds from the flame to the heat sink, (2) radiation from flame to refractory surfaces, thence back by reradiation or reflection through the flame (with partial absorption therein) to the sink, (3) multiple reflection of all nonblack surfaces, (4) convection, (5) external losses, and (6) for the fact that the refractory surfaces take up equilibrium temperatures which vary continuously over their faces. Allowance for space variation in temperature and emissivity of the gas introduces major complications, and the problem is here limited to consideration of a gas mass of uniform concentration and temperature equal to some set of mean values (see, however, the last part of Art. 4). The problem is otherwise capable of a solution free from seriously limiting assumptions. It will be convenient to group surface zones into two classes. *Source-sink* zones, such as a fuel bed, a carborundum muffle, a row of electric resistors, a liquid- or air-cooled surface and stock on a furnace hearth are designated by subscripts 1, 2, 3, . . . ; surface 1 has area $S_1$, temperature $T_1$, emissivity $\epsilon_1$. Completing the enclosure are the insulating refractory connecting walls, which are heat sinks only to the extent that they lose heat by conduction through the walls. If the difference between gas convection to the inside of such a wall and conduction through the wall to the outside is small compared to the radiation incident on the wall inside, then the assumption that the net radiant heat transfer at the wall surface be zero is an excellent one. It enormously simplifies the problem of source-to-sink heat transfer and the effect thereon of the refractory surfaces. All such zones will be referred to hereafter as *no-flux* surfaces, with the understanding that reference thereby is to radiant heat transfer alone, and the letter subscripts $R$, $S$, $T$, . . . will be appended to their properties.

Several restrictions are imposed at this point, some of them to be removed later. (1) All of the sources and sinks, including the gas as well as the surfaces, are assumed gray. A gray gas is one which exhibits, for radiation from whatever source, an absorptivity $\alpha$ equal to its emissivity $\epsilon$. Its emissivity and absorptivity vary, however, with path length. If the gas transmissivity $\tau$, equal to $1 - \alpha$, is established for radiation from one zone to another, the transmissivity for twice the mean beam length between zones is $\tau^2$, a conclusion which can be true only for a gray gas which does not produce a change in quality of the radiation transmitted by it. (2) Such reflection as occurs, whether at a source-sink or at a no-flux surface, must be diffuse reflection, a term describing reflection which, like black radiation, obeys the cosine principle that appeared in Eq. 2-1; and emission from any surface must likewise obey the cosine principle. Nonmetallic and oxidized metallic surfaces do not depart greatly from this characteristic. (3) A zone of the no-flux surfaces, or those of the source-sink surfaces which are not black, must be chosen small enough so that the intensity of radiation leaving the zone in consequence of irradiation by some other zone is uniform over the zone. This completes the assumptions. The additional nomenclature needed is the representation of transmittance from one zone through the gas to another zone by $\tau$ with appropriate subscripts to indicate the two zones involved.

*Flux between gray source-sink surfaces; the factor* $\mathfrak{F}_{12}$. The net flux between $S_1$ and $S_2$ occurs by a complex process involving multiple reflection from all source-sink surfaces as well as both reflection and reradiation from the no-flux surfaces; and one might at first consider the contribution of $S_R$, $S_S$, . . . to the net flux between $S_1$ and $S_2$ impossible to disentangle, since the equilibrium temperature of $S_R$, for example, depends on contributions from $S_3$, $S_4$, . . . as well as from $S_1$ and $S_2$. The new concept necessary here is that the refractory zone $S_R$ can be thought of as having a partial emissive power due to the presence of each of the source-sink zones and the gas, and a total emissive power equal to their sum. Thus the term $q_{1\rightleftharpoons 2}$ represents net flux between $S_1$ and $S_2$ consequent solely on their respective emission rates and includes, in addition to direct interchange $S_1F_{12}\epsilon_1\epsilon_2\sigma(T_1^4 - T_2^4)\tau_{12}$, the contributions due to multiple reflection at all surfaces, as well as such contributions by reradiation from the no-flux surfaces as are consequent on their partial emissive powers due to the existence of $S_1$ and $S_2$ alone as net radiators in the system. This is the necessary meaning of $q_{1\rightleftharpoons 2}$ if it is to become zero when $T_1 = T_2$. It is apparent that $q_{1\rightleftharpoons 2}$ must take a form equal to $\sigma(T_1^4 - T_2^4)$ multiplied by some factor which depends on the geometry of the whole enclosure, the emissivity of its source-sink surfaces and the transmittance of the gas, and that it can be expressed in the form

$$q_{1\rightleftharpoons 2} = S_1\mathfrak{F}_{12}\sigma(T_1^4 - T_2^4) \equiv S_2\mathfrak{F}_{21}\sigma(T_1^4 - T_2^4) \tag{4-1}$$

The problem is to evaluate the new factor $\mathfrak{F}$, called the over-all exchange factor. Plainly, it cannot depend on any system temperatures. Consequently, if the gas and all source-sink surfaces except $S_1$ are kept at absolute zero, and $q_{1\rightleftharpoons 2}$ (which now becomes simply $q_{1\to 2}$) is evaluated and used to determine $\mathfrak{F}$ in Eq. 4-1, that value of $\mathfrak{F}$ will be generally applicable regardless of the particular combination of temperatures of the source-sink surfaces. Space does not permit presentation of the detailed derivation here [*5*, Chap. 4; *34*]. Briefly, there are as many unknown emissive powers (due to reflection alone at all source-sink zones except one, and to reflection and/or emission at the no-flux zones) as there are zones; an energy balance may be written for each zone, thereby permitting a solution. The evaluation of $\mathfrak{F}$ necessitates the use of a determinant D, symmetrical about its major diagonal, and of order equal to the total number of zones into which the enclosing surface has been divided. To simplify the expression of D and the solution for $\mathfrak{F}$, a shorthand nomenclature is desirable. Let $S_1F_{1R}\tau_{1R}$ (which also equals $S_RF_{R1}\tau_{R1}$) be represented by $\overline{1R}$ (or its equivalent $\overline{R1}$, although the convention is adopted of mentioning small numbers first, and numbers before letters); because reflectivity $(1-\epsilon)$ appears so often, replace it (except in any final simplification) by $\rho$. Then

$$\mathrm{D} = \begin{vmatrix} \overline{11} - \dfrac{S_1}{\rho_1} & \overline{12} & \overline{13} & \cdots & \overline{1R} & \overline{1S} & \cdots \\ \overline{12} & \overline{22} - \dfrac{S_2}{\rho_2} & \overline{23} & \cdots & \overline{2R} & \overline{2S} & \cdots \\ \overline{13} & \overline{23} & \overline{33} - \dfrac{S_3}{\rho_3} & \cdots & \overline{3R} & \overline{3S} & \cdots \\ \vdots & \vdots & \vdots & & \vdots & \vdots & \\ \overline{1R} & \overline{2R} & \overline{3R} & \cdots & \overline{RR} - S_R & \overline{RS} & \cdots \\ \overline{1S} & \overline{2S} & \overline{3S} & \cdots & \overline{RS} & \overline{SS} - S_S & \cdots \\ \vdots & \vdots & \vdots & & \vdots & \vdots & \end{vmatrix} \tag{4-2}$$

With D defined, $S_m\mathfrak{F}_{mn}$ $(= S_n\mathfrak{F}_{nm})$ may be evaluated.

$$S_m\mathfrak{F}_{mn}\big]_{m\neq n} = -\frac{\epsilon_m S_m}{\rho_m}\frac{\epsilon_n S_n}{\rho_n}\frac{\mathrm{D}'_{mn}}{\mathrm{D}} \tag{4-3a}$$

$$S_n\mathfrak{F}_{nn} = -\frac{\epsilon_n S_n}{\rho_n}\left(\epsilon_n + \frac{\epsilon_n S_n}{\rho_n}\frac{\mathrm{D}'_{nn}}{\mathrm{D}}\right) \tag{4-3b}$$

where $\mathrm{D}'_{mn}$ is the cofactor of row $m$ and column $n$ of D, defined as $(-1)^{m+n}$ times the minor of D formed by crossing out the $m$th row and $n$th column.

Then

$$S_1\mathfrak{F}_{12} = \frac{\epsilon_1}{\rho_1}\frac{\epsilon_2}{\rho_2} S_1 S_2$$

$$\begin{vmatrix}
\overline{12} & \overline{23} & \overline{24} & \cdots & \overline{2R} & \overline{2S} & \cdots \\
\overline{13} & \overline{33} - \dfrac{S_3}{\rho_2} & \overline{34} & \cdots & \overline{3R} & \overline{3S} & \cdots \\
\overline{14} & \overline{34} & \overline{44} - \dfrac{S_4}{\rho_4} & \cdots & \overline{4R} & \overline{4S} & \cdots \\
\cdot & \cdot & \cdot & & \cdot & \cdot & \\
\cdot & \cdot & \cdot & & \cdot & \cdot & \\
\cdot & \cdot & \cdot & & \cdot & \cdot & \\
\overline{1R} & \overline{3R} & \overline{4R} & \cdots & \overline{RR} - S_R & \overline{RS} & \cdots \\
\overline{1S} & \overline{3S} & \overline{4S} & \cdots & \overline{RS} & \overline{SS} - S_S & \cdots \\
\cdot & \cdot & \cdot & & \cdot & \cdot & \\
\cdot & \cdot & \cdot & & \cdot & \cdot & \\
\cdot & \cdot & \cdot & & \cdot & \cdot &
\end{vmatrix} \qquad (4\text{-}4)$$

$$\overline{\qquad\qquad\qquad\qquad\qquad\qquad}$$
$$\mathrm{D}$$

The number of unique view factors $F$ necessary for evaluation of $\mathfrak{F}$ by Eq. 4-4 may be determined. By noting that in a $p$ zone system there are $p^2$ $F$'s in the determinant D but that (a) D is symmetrical and (b) any row or column of $F$'s adds to 1, it is seen that the number of unique $F$'s necessary is $p(p-1)/2$. If, in addition, each $n$ of the zones cannot see itself, the number is further reduced by $n$.

Eq. 4-4 can be used to make allowance for any degree of complexity of an enclosure, and to approach the true solution to any degree of approximation dependent on the number of zones into which a surface is divided. The guiding principle in deciding upon the number of zones necessary is that any reradiation or reflection must come from a zone small enough so that different parts of its surface do not have a significantly different view of the various other surfaces. Black source-sink surfaces need be zoned only according to temperature, but light gray ones may require further subdivision.

As one of the simpler examples of application of the determinant method, consider a system containing no emitting or absorbing gas. One case may be presented which covers a wide range of practical situations, i.e. the case of an enclosure divided into any number of no-flux zones but only two source-sink zones $S_1$ and $S_2$ (an especially justifiable assumption if the emissivities of $S_1$ and $S_2$ are so high as to make reflections from their surfaces relatively unimportant in the over-all heat transfer). From Eq. 4-4 it may readily be shown that for this case

$$\left.\frac{1}{S_1\mathfrak{F}_{12}}\right]_{\text{gas free}} = \frac{1}{S_1}\left(\frac{1}{\epsilon_1} - 1\right) + \frac{1}{S_2}\left(\frac{1}{\epsilon_2} - 1\right) + \left.\frac{1}{S_1\mathfrak{F}_{12}}\right]_{\substack{\text{gas free,}\\ \text{black surfaces}}} \qquad (4\text{-}5)$$

*Black source-sink surfaces; the factor* $\bar{F}_{12}$. Further to indicate the technique of application of the determinant method, let Eq. 4-4 be used to determine the interchange factor when all source-sink surfaces are black. The interchange factor for this case has been designated by $\bar{F}$, to indicate that it covers a more complex situation than $F$ but a less general one than $\mathfrak{F}$. Let the problem be to evaluate $\bar{F}_{12}$. Setting into Eq. 4-4 the condition that $\epsilon_1 = \epsilon_2 = \epsilon_3 \ldots = 1$ or that $\rho_1 = \rho_2 = \rho_3 \ldots = 0$, one can eliminate all rows and columns containing reference to any source-sink surface except 1 and 2 as follows.

Cancel $S_1/\rho_1$ out of the numerator and multiply the denominator first column by $\rho_1/S_1$ which, being zero, makes the first column $-1, 0, 0, 0, \ldots$ and reduces the order of D by one. Similarly, multiply the second column of the numerator and the second column of the new denominator by $\rho_3/S_3$, making them become $0, -1, 0, 0, \ldots$ each. Similarly, eliminate all terms containing numbers other than 1 and 2. One thus obtains

$$S_1\bar{F}_{12} = \frac{\begin{vmatrix} \overline{12} & \overline{2R} & \overline{2S} & \cdots \\ \overline{1R} & \overline{RR} - S_R & \overline{RS} & \cdots \\ \overline{1S} & \overline{RS} & \overline{SS} - S_S & \cdots \\ \vdots & \vdots & \vdots & \end{vmatrix}}{\begin{vmatrix} \overline{RR} - S_R & \overline{RS} & \cdots \\ \overline{RS} & \overline{SS} - S_S & \cdots \\ \vdots & \vdots & \end{vmatrix}} \tag{4-6}$$

If there is but one refractory zone, all rows and columns mentioning others may be crossed out, and Eq. 4-6 yields

$$S_1\bar{F}_{12} = \overline{12} + \frac{(\overline{1R})(\overline{2R})}{A_R - \overline{RR}} \tag{4-7}$$

This simple result, an approximation because all no-flux surfaces are assumed to be in equilibrium at a common temperature, is often adequate for estimating the transfer between $S_1$ and $S_2$.

If no emitting or absorbing gas is present in the system, Eq. 4-7 yields

$$\bar{F}_{12}\Big]_{\text{gas free}} = F_{12} + \frac{F_{1R}F_{R2}}{1 - F_{RR}} \tag{4-8}$$

The factor $\bar{F}_{12}$ for systems containing no interfering gas has been determined exactly for a few geometrically simple cases [*35*]. If $S_1$ and $S_2$ are equal parallel disks, squares, or rectangles connected by nonconducting but reradiating walls, $\bar{F}_{12}$ is given by Fig. I,2b, lines 5 to 8.

*Flux between gas and surfaces; the factor* $\mathfrak{F}_{1g}$. The treatment of the general problem of radiation in a gas-containing enclosure was not completed by presentation of Eq. 4-3 giving $S_m\mathfrak{F}_{mn}$. In addition to the various values of $q_{net}$ for different pairs of source-sink zones, one is interested in the net transfer between any one of such zones and the gas, which may well be the primary heat source of the system. The net radiant flux from the gas is given by

$$q_{g,net} = q_{g\rightleftharpoons 1} + q_{g\rightleftharpoons 2} + \cdots \tag{4-9}$$

and $q_{g\rightleftharpoons 1}$ is given by

$$q_{g\rightleftharpoons 1} = S_1\mathfrak{F}_{1g}\sigma(T_g^4 - T_1^4) \tag{4-10}$$

The problem is to evaluate $\mathfrak{F}_{1g}$. Let $S_1$ be the only original emitter in the system; all other source-sink zones and the gas are kept at absolute zero. $S_1$ radiates at the rate $S_1\epsilon_1$ per unit value of black emissive power at temperature $T_1$. Radiation streaming away from $S_2, S_3, \ldots, S_R, S_S, \ldots$ is due solely to reflection at $S_2, S_3, \ldots$, and to reflection and/or reradiation at $S_R, S_S, \ldots$. Of the total emission $S_1\epsilon_1$, the amount $S_1\mathfrak{F}_{11}$ returns to and is absorbed by $S_1$, $S_1\mathfrak{F}_{12}$ goes to and is absorbed by $S_2, \ldots,$ $S_1\mathfrak{F}_{1n}$ is absorbed by $S_n$. The residue must have been absorbed by the gas since all other surfaces are nonretaining. Then

$$S_1\mathfrak{F}_{1g} = S_1(\epsilon_1 - \mathfrak{F}_{11} - \mathfrak{F}_{12} - \cdots - \mathfrak{F}_{1n}) \tag{4-11}$$

Since it will have been necessary to evaluate all of these $\mathfrak{F}$'s except $\mathfrak{F}_{11}$ in fixing the radiant interchange in the system, $\mathfrak{F}_{11}$ is the only new factor requiring evaluation to determine $S_1\mathfrak{F}_{1g}$. Another approach to the problem [*5*, Chap. 4; *36*] yields the following direct formulation:

$$S_n\mathfrak{F}_{ng} = \frac{S_n\epsilon_n}{\rho_n}\frac{{}_g\mathrm{D}_n}{\mathrm{D}} \tag{4-12}$$

in which ${}_g\mathrm{D}_n$ is obtained by inserting, into the $n$th column of D (Eq. 4-2), the terms $-S_1 + (\overline{11} + \overline{12} + \cdots + \overline{1R} + \cdots)$, $-S_2 + (\overline{21} + \overline{22} + \overline{23} + \cdots + \overline{2R} + \cdots)$, $\cdots$, $-S_R + (\overline{R1} + \overline{R2} + \cdots + \overline{RR} + \cdots)$. Any one of these expressions may be written

$$-S_n[1 - (F_{n1}\tau_{n1} + F_{n2}\tau_{n2} + \cdots + F_{nR}\tau_{nR} + \cdots)]$$

the parenthetical term of which equals the weighted-mean transmissivity or transmissivity for the total radiation arriving at or leaving $S_n$ (and therefore identifiable with a single subscript, $\tau_n$). The complement of $\tau_n$ is the gas absorptivity and, because it is gray, the gas emissivity $\epsilon_{gn}$. Note that $\epsilon_{g1}$ and $\epsilon_{g2}$ differ only because the mean path lengths through the gas to $S_1$ and $S_2$ differ. Eq. 4-12 may of course be shown to be the equivalent of Eq. 4-11.

*Temperature of no-flux zones.* Before the use of Eq. 4-11 is discussed, the problem of interchange in a gray-gas-containing system requires one more item for completion. Near the beginning of Art. 4, the concept of partial emissive powers of a no-flux surface due to the separate effects of the various sources and sinks was presented. This leads to an evaluation of the equilibrium temperature of a no-flux surface. It may be shown [*5*, Chap. 4; *36*] that

$$T_R^4 = \frac{{}_1\mathrm{D}_R T_1^4 + {}_2\mathrm{D}_R T_2^4 + \cdots + {}_n\mathrm{D}_R T_n^4 + \cdots + {}_g\mathrm{D}_R T_g^4}{\mathrm{D}} \tag{4-13}$$

Since the sum of the $\mathrm{D}_R$'s in the numerator can be shown to equal D, Eq. 4-13 states that $T_R^4$ is a weighted mean of the fourth powers of the various original emitters present, including all source-sink surfaces and the gas—as it must of course be. Application of this relation to determine the equilibrium refractory temperature in a simple system consisting of a gray gas enclosed by a single heat-sink zone $S_1$ and a single no-flux zone $S_R$, with all values of $\epsilon_g$ taken to be the same, yields

$$T_R^4 = T_g^4 - (T_g^4 - T_1^4)\frac{1}{1 + \dfrac{1}{F_{R1}}\dfrac{\epsilon_g}{1-\epsilon_g} + \epsilon_g\left(\dfrac{1-\epsilon_1}{\epsilon_1}\right)\left(\dfrac{1}{F_{R1}}\dfrac{\epsilon_g}{1-\epsilon_g} + \dfrac{S_R}{S_1} + 1\right)} \tag{4-14}$$

When $S_1$ is black, the last term in the denominator drops out.

*Application of the factor* $\mathfrak{F}_{1g}$. Returning now to the use of $\mathfrak{F}_{1g}$, consider the same simple system just used in illustrating the calculation of $T_R$. From Eq. 4-11

$$\begin{aligned} S_1\mathfrak{F}_{1g} &= S_1\epsilon_1 - S_1\mathfrak{F}_{11} \\ &= S_1\epsilon_1\left(1 + \frac{\epsilon_1}{\rho_1}\frac{\begin{vmatrix}\overline{11} & \overline{1R}\\ \overline{1R} & \overline{RR}-S_R\end{vmatrix}}{\begin{vmatrix}\overline{11}-\dfrac{S_1}{\rho_1} & \overline{1R}\\ \overline{1R} & \overline{RR}-S_R\end{vmatrix}}\right) \end{aligned} \tag{4-15}$$

or

$$\frac{1}{S_1\mathfrak{F}_{1g}} = \frac{1}{S_1}\left(\frac{1}{\epsilon_1} - 1\right) + \frac{1}{S_1 - \overline{11} + \overline{1R}^2/(\overline{RR} - S_R)} \tag{4-16}$$

When $\epsilon_1$ becomes 1, $\mathfrak{F}_{1g}$ by definition becomes $\overline{F}_{1g}$ and, from Eq. 4-16,

$$S_1\overline{F}_{1g} = S_1 - \overline{11} + \frac{\overline{1R}^2}{(\overline{RR} - S_R)} \tag{4-17}$$

and

$$\frac{1}{S_1\mathfrak{F}_{1g}} = \frac{1}{S_1}\left(\frac{1}{\epsilon_1} - 1\right) + \frac{1}{S_1\overline{F}_{1g}} \tag{4-18}$$

For this system all direct view factors can be expressed in terms of the single one $F_{R1}$ as follows:

$$\overline{1R} = S_1 F_{1R}\tau_{1R} = S_R F_{R1}\tau_{1R}$$

$$\overline{11} = S_1 F_{11}\tau_{11} = S_1(1 - F_{1R})\tau_{11} = (S_1 - S_R F_{R1})\tau_{11}$$

$$\overline{RR} = S_R F_{RR}\tau_{RR} = S_R(1 - F_{R1})\tau_{RR}$$

Substitution of these values in Eq. 4-17 and replacement of $\tau$ by $1 - \epsilon_g$ gives

$$\overline{F}_{1g} = \epsilon_{11}\left(1 + \frac{\dfrac{S_R}{S_1}}{\dfrac{\epsilon_{11}/\epsilon_{RR} - \epsilon_{11}}{1 - \epsilon_{11}} + \dfrac{\epsilon_{11}}{1 - \epsilon_{11}} \cdot \dfrac{1}{F_{R1}}}\right) - \frac{(S_R/S_1)F_{R1}^2}{F_{R1} + \epsilon_{RR}(1 - F_{R1})}(\epsilon_{11} + \epsilon_{RR} - 2\epsilon_{R1} + \epsilon_{R1}^2 - \epsilon_{11}\epsilon_{RR}) \quad (4\text{-}19)$$

in which double-subscript $\epsilon$'s refer to an evaluation of gas emissivity based on a path length specific to the two surface elements mentioned. The problem, simple as it appeared to be, has a solution rather formidable for engineering use. If the various gas emissivities are assumed to be alike or if each one is replaced by their average value, called $\epsilon_g$, it will be noted that the second term on the right of Eq. 4-19 will vanish, giving

$$\overline{F}_{1g} = \epsilon_g\left(1 + \frac{\dfrac{S_R}{S_1}}{1 + \dfrac{\epsilon_g}{1 - \epsilon_g}\dfrac{1}{F_{R1}}}\right) \quad (4\text{-}20)$$

Some practical consequences of Eq. 4-18 and 4-20 are these: increasing the flame emissivity increases the heat transmission, but not proportionately; decreasing surface emissivity $\epsilon_1$ (and absorptivity) from one, when the flame is very transparent, produces but little effect on the heat transmission; but decreasing $\epsilon_1$ from one, when the flame is substantially opaque ($\epsilon_g = 1$), produces a proportional decrease in heat transmission.

The limitations on the validity of Eq. 4-18 and 4-20 must be borne in mind. They are restricted to a one-zone sink, a one-zone refractory or no-flux surface, and a gray gas. The first two assumptions are rigorously justifiable only when each element of $S_1$ (or $S_R$) shares its "view" of its own zone and of $S_R$ (or $S_1$) in the same ratio as every other element; and this in turn is true only when the two kinds of surfaces are intimately mixed in the same ratio on all parts of the enclosure, forming what one might call a "speckled" enclosure. Under those circumstances, the assumption made in going from Eq. 4-19 to 4-20, that the various $\epsilon_g$'s are representable by an average value, becomes valid; and $F_{R1}$ becomes $S_1/$

$(S_1 + S_R)$. If Eq. 4-20 is used as an approximation for a system which does not have a speckled enclosure, however, use of the true value of $F_{R1}$ is preferable.

Eq. 4-18 and 4-20 are well-known solutions, available and in use for many years [*5*, Chap. 3; *37*] before the determinant method of derivation was available; and their derivation from first principles was perhaps as simple as the one here presented, but only because of restriction to a two-zone system. With the new method available, summarized in Eq. 4-3, the decision as to the number of zones of heat-sink or refractory area into which the enclosure should be divided can be made to depend, as it should, on the importance of the particular problem and the time available for handling it, rather than on whether the engineer can see his way through a multizone solution.

*Allowance for space variation in gas temperature.* Many problems of heat exchange between combustion gases and their enclosing walls may be satisfactorily approximated by using mean values of gas temperature and composition. Where an accurate solution to the problem is of sufficient importance, however, allowance can be made for gradients in temperature and gas composition provided that knowledge is available of the flow pattern and progress of combustion; but the method is time-consuming [*38*]. For orientation as to the need for allowing for radiation due to gas temperature gradients, a simple solution is available [*39,40,41,42, 43*] for the following special case: When a unidirectional temperature gradient exists in the interior of a strongly absorbing gas far from its bounding walls, the radiant flux density $q/S$ is given by

$$\frac{q}{S} = -\frac{4}{3}\frac{\mu^2}{k}\sigma\frac{dT^4}{dx} = -\frac{16}{3}\frac{\mu^2}{k}\sigma T^3\frac{dT}{dx} \qquad (4\text{-}21)$$

where $k$ is the absorption coefficient of the gas (see Art. 5), and $\mu$ is the refractive index of the medium (1 for gases). To minimize the effect of a wall at distance $L$ from the plane of flux, the value of $kL$ must be greater than about 3; and to satisfy the condition of strong absorption

$$\left|\frac{d \ln T}{kdx}\right| \ll 1$$

Radiation exchange between a plane wall and an overlying gas, the isothermal surfaces in which are parallel to the wall, has also been treated [*5*, Chap. 4].

**I,5. Enclosure of Gray Source-Sink Surfaces Containing a Real (Nongray) Gas.** In the derivation of interchange factors for gray gas systems the single value of transmittance $\tau_{12}$ applied to *all* radiation leaving $S_1$ for $S_2$, whether originally emitted by $S_1$ or reflected from it after any number of passages through the gas. Only for gray gas is this true. For a *real* gas, with its characteristic absorption in certain spectral regions, the absorbable wavelengths are filtered out after a number of passages through the gas, and the transmittance of the gas for the remainder of the radiation approaches 1. The gray gas assumption thus leads to prediction of too large an interchange between gas and sinks, and too small an interchange between the source-sink surfaces. In obtaining a value of $S_1\mathfrak{F}_{1g}$ applicable to a real gas, it is desirable to retain the mechanics of gray gas formulation. Fortunately, this is possible.

For a gray gas the transmittance for the absorption path length represented by $p_gL$ is $e^{-kp_gL}$, where $k$ is the absorption coefficient of the gas, a constant independent of wavelength and therefore applicable to the integrated spectrum; and the absorptivity and emissivity equal $1 - e^{-kp_gL}$. The relation of transmittance to $p_gL$ for a real gas can be represented to any desired degree of accuracy by

$$\tau = xe^{-k_xpL} + ye^{-k_ypL} + ze^{-k_zpL} + \cdots \tag{5-1}$$

and the emissivity relation by

$$\epsilon = x(1 - e^{-k_xpL}) + y(1 - e^{-k_ypL}) + z(1 - e^{-k_zpL}) + \cdots \tag{5-2}$$

with $k_x$ representing the absorption coefficient applicable to fraction $x$ of the total energy spectrum of the gas, and with the condition

$$x + y + z + \cdots = 1 \tag{5-3}$$

Representing $e^{-k_xpL}$ by $\tau_x$, Eq. 5-1 yields for the transmittance $\tau_{ng}$ of $n$ layers of gas each of absorption path length $p_gL$:

$$\tau_{ng} = x\tau_x^n + y\tau_y^n + z\tau_z^n + \cdots \tag{5-4}$$

The components of which the total real-gas transmittance is composed are thus a series of gray body transmittances, each used with a weighting factor, $x$, $y$, . . . .

Consider now an enclosure of surfaces which aid in the transmission of radiation from the gas to $S_1$ only by the process of reflection at the other surfaces, i.e. a system of gray source-sink surfaces and completely reflecting, or white, no-flux surfaces. A little consideration will show that the real-gas solution for $S_1\mathfrak{F}_{1g}$ is obtainable as the weighted sum of a number of gray gas solutions, using successively $\tau_x$, $\tau_y$, and $\tau_z$ for the gas transmissivity and weighting each solution by the factors $x$, $y$, $z$, etc.; or

$$\mathfrak{F}_{1g} = x\mathfrak{F}_{1g}\Big]_{\substack{\text{based on}\\ \text{use of } \tau_x}} + y\mathfrak{F}_{1g}\Big]_{\substack{\text{based on}\\ \text{use of } \tau_y}} + \cdots \tag{5-5}$$

and similarly

$$\mathfrak{F}_{12} = x\mathfrak{F}_{12}\Big]_{\substack{\text{based on}\\ \text{use of } \tau_x}} + y\mathfrak{F}_{12}\Big]_{\substack{\text{based on}\\ \text{use of } \tau_y}} + \cdots \tag{5-6}$$

The reason for the restriction on the validity of Eq. 5-5 or 5-6, that any no-flux surfaces, if present, must be white rather than gray, needs consideration. A white refractory surface reflects all incident radiation without changing its quality, i.e. without changing the fractions of it for which the gas will exhibit absorptivity $1 - \tau_x$, $1 - \tau_y$, etc. But a gray refractory surface, to the extent that it absorbs and re-emits, changes the quality of the radiation. If, for example, a beam of radiation incident on $S_R$ from the gas has an emissivity of $\frac{1}{2}$ in one half of the energy spectrum, or a total emissivity and absorptivity of $\frac{1}{4}$, the resulting radiation leaving $S_R$ would be half absorbed by the gas on next passage through it if it left $S_R$ by reflection without change in character, and only $\frac{1}{4}$ absorbed if it left $S_R$ by emission as black radiation. Since the derivation of $S_1\mathfrak{F}_{1g}$ when $S_R$, $S_S$, . . . are present is based on attenuation by the gas in an amount independent of the history of a beam of radiation, the nongray gas solution represented by Eq. 5-5 applies rigorously only to systems in which any no-flux surfaces present are *perfect diffuse reflectors*. If allowance must be made for the grayness of any no-flux surface, it must be reclassified as a source-sink surface, say $S_3$, of unknown temperature, the value of which is obtained by introducing the condition that the sum of the interchanges of $S_3$ with the other surfaces and with the gas must be zero.

The point has been emphasized that for gray systems the two terms each representing one-way flux in the expression

$$q_{1\rightleftharpoons 2} = S_1\mathfrak{F}_{12}\sigma T_1^4 - S_2\mathfrak{F}_{21}\sigma T_2^4$$

differ only in temperature, that the $S\mathfrak{F}$ product may be factored out. The imposing of the nongray gas condition makes this no longer true. Gas absorptivity for radiation from a source at $T_1$ is no longer necessarily equal to gas absorptivity for radiation from a source at $T_2$, except in the limit as $T_1$ approaches $T_2$. Rather than use sequence of subscripts to indicate direction of the radiation, it is preferable to use an arrow and retain the equality of $S_1\mathfrak{F}_{12}$ and $S_2\mathfrak{F}_{21}$ as a matter of definition; but $S_1\mathfrak{F}_{1\rightarrow 2}$ does not now equal $S_1\mathfrak{F}_{1\leftarrow 2}$ except in the limit. $\mathfrak{F}_{1\rightarrow 2}$ is evaluated by use of the absorptivity of gas at $T_g$ for radiation from a black or gray source at $T_1$; $\mathfrak{F}_{1\leftarrow 2}$ uses gas absorptivity based on emission from $T_2$. Similarly the net interchange between gas and surface $S_1$ must now be written

$$q_{g\rightleftharpoons 1} = \sigma(S_1\mathfrak{F}_{1\leftarrow g}T_g^4 - S_1\mathfrak{F}_{1\rightarrow g}T_1^4) \tag{5-7}$$

with $S_1\mathfrak{F}_{1\leftarrow g}$ based on the gas emissivity and $S_1\mathfrak{F}_{1\rightarrow g}$ based on gas absorptivity for black or gray radiation from $T_1$. Plainly, however, if $T_g \gg T_1$, $\mathfrak{F}_{1\leftarrow g}$ is the term to evaluate rigorously, and it may be used with small error to represent both-way radiation. If $T_g$ and $T_1$ are not too far apart, $\mathfrak{F}_{1g}$ evaluated by the use of an effective emissivity given by the bracketed term in Eq. 3-5 will probably suffice for both $\mathfrak{F}_{1\leftarrow g}$ and $\mathfrak{F}_{1\rightarrow g}$.

Although Eq. 5-5 or 5-6 can in principle be used to handle an enclosure of any degree of complexity as to zoning, and filled with gas of radiating characteristics producing any shape of curve of $\epsilon_g$ vs. $p_gL$, a little consideration shows what an enormous amount of effort is involved if these expressions for $\mathfrak{F}$ contain many terms. A simplification is mandatory and, fortunately, feasible. If wall reflectivities are not very large, a beam of radiation from the gas is rapidly attenuated in its succession of reflections and transmissions, and the fitting of the $\epsilon_g - p_gL$ curve is important only for a few units of $p_gL$. The transmittance $\tau$ given by Eq. 5-4 can be made to equal true transmittance at 0 and at two integral multiples of $p_gL$ by assuming the gas gray throughout the energy fraction $x$ and clear throughout the fraction $y + z + \cdots = 1 - x$, i.e. by assuming that all the $\tau$'s but $\tau_x$ are zero and that an asymptotic transmissivity of $1 - x$ is approached as $p_gL = \infty$. An examination of Eq. 5-5 now indicates that, since all values of $\mathfrak{F}_{1g}$ on the right-hand side except the first are for non-absorbing gas and therefore are zero,

$$\mathfrak{F}_{1g} = x\mathfrak{F}_{1g}\Big]_{\substack{\text{based on}\\ \text{use of } \tau_x}} \tag{5-8}$$

For source-sink surface interchange, Eq. 5-6 yields

$$\mathfrak{F}_{12} = x\mathfrak{F}_{12}\Big]_{\substack{\text{based on}\\ \text{use of } \tau_x}} + (1 - x)\mathfrak{F}_{12}\Big]_{\substack{\text{based on}\\ \text{clear gas,}\\ \tau = 1}} \tag{5-9}$$

There remains only the evaluation of $x$ and $\tau_x$ from a gas radiation plot such as Fig. I,3a. Let the objective be to fit the $\epsilon_g$, $p_gL$ curve at 1 and 2 units of $p_gL$, and call the corresponding $\epsilon$'s read from the plot, $\epsilon_g$ and $\epsilon_{2\cdot g}$. From Eq. 5-4

$$1 - \epsilon_g = \tau_g = x\tau_x + (1 - x)$$

and

$$1 - \epsilon_{2\cdot g} = \tau_{2\cdot g} = x\tau_x^2 + (1 - x)$$

Solution of these gives

$$x = \frac{\epsilon_g^2}{2\epsilon_g - \epsilon_{2\cdot g}} \tag{5-10}$$

and

$$\tau_x = 1 - \frac{\epsilon_g}{x} = 1 - \frac{2\epsilon_g - \epsilon_{2\cdot g}}{\epsilon_g} \tag{5-11}$$

Recapitulating, $\mathfrak{F}_{1g}$ equals $x$ times a value of $\mathfrak{F}_{1g}$ from Eq. 4-12 (or Eq. 4-18 and 4-20) using a transmissivity of $1 - (\epsilon_g/x)$ or an emissivity of $\epsilon_g/x$, with $x$ defined by Eq. 5-10.

The determination of $x$ and $\tau_x$ from values of $\epsilon_g$ at $1p_gL$ and $2p_gL$ is recommended when $S_1$ has a low reflectivity and/or when $p_gL$ is large; but a small enclosure with heat-sink zones of high reflectivity may make the many-times-reflected radiation relatively more important. In that case some other pair of $\epsilon_g$ values may be used, such as $\epsilon_g$ and $\epsilon_{3\cdot g}$, or $\epsilon_{2\cdot g}$ and $\epsilon_{4\cdot g}$. Seldom is it necessary to add an extra term to Eq. 5-5.

**I,6. Application of Principles.** The procedures discussed above permit allowance for the effects of factors often casually handled in the past. The relations presented are not as easy to use as the relations of convective heat transmission; but this is because the mathematics of radiation in an enclosure, where every part of the system affects every other part, is intrinsically more complicated than the mathematics of heat transfer processes capable of expression in the form of a differential equation. With a little practice in manipulation of determinants[5] the reader should be able to evaluate $\mathfrak{F}$ factors for systems of a considerable degree of complexity in a reasonable time. If the higher order determinants encountered are evaluated numerically for the specific example of interest rather than algebraically to obtain results like Eq. 4-19, the time required for a solution is not prohibitive. Some of the special cases encountered are used so frequently, however, that algebraic formulation of their general solution is desirable. A few such cases are presented here.

*Real gas, gray sink $S_1$, and reflecting no-flux surface $S_R$.* The gray gas solution for this case, simplified by the use of a single path length and therefore a single $\tau_g$ for all zone pairs, was given in Eq. 4-18 and 4-20. Modification to allow for nongray gas gives

$$S_1\mathfrak{F}_{1\leftarrow g} = \frac{x}{\dfrac{1}{S_1}\left(\dfrac{1}{\epsilon_1} - 1\right) + \dfrac{1}{\dfrac{\epsilon_g}{x}\left(S_1 + \dfrac{S_R}{1 + \dfrac{\epsilon_g/x}{1 - \epsilon_g/x}\cdot\dfrac{1}{F_{R1}}}\right)}} \tag{6-1}$$

with $x$ equal to $\epsilon_g^2/(2\epsilon_g - \epsilon_{2\cdot g})$, and with $\epsilon_g$ evaluated for a path length given by Table I,3. If $S_1\mathfrak{F}_{1\rightarrow g}$ is wanted, $\alpha_{g1}$ replaces $\epsilon_g$.

*Real gas, enclosed by 2 gray sinks $S_1$ and $S_2$, and no $S_R$.* This variation on the previous case has interest for at least two reasons. Consider a gas, a primary heat sink $S_1$ and a refractory surface, the external loss from which is so large that it cannot be treated as a no-flux surface (the term no-flux still refers to radiant heat transmission only), because the internal gain by convection is so much less than the loss through the wall. Then the refractory surface becomes a secondary heat sink and is $S_2$ rather than $S_R$. Or consider a gas, a heat sink $S_1$ and a no-flux surface which is not justifiably classed as completely reflecting. As the discussion

[5] Evaluation of higher order determinants by mechanical computers is of course feasible. The labor of evaluation with pencil and slide rule has been so greatly reduced by the method of Crout [44], however, that fifth or sixth order determinants need no longer be considered formidable by the engineer not equipped with the newer devices.

in Art. 5 indicated, the no-flux surface must be treated as a source-sink type surface $S_2$. Three $\mathfrak{F}$'s are necessary for a complete solution. Based on the simplifying assumption that the $\tau$'s between zone pairs are all alike, Eq. 4-12 and 5-8 yield

$$\mathfrak{F}_{1g} = x(1 - \tau_x)\frac{\epsilon_1}{\rho_1}\frac{\dfrac{1}{S_1} + \dfrac{1}{S_2} + \left(\dfrac{1}{\rho_2\tau_x} - 1\right)\dfrac{1}{S_1F_{12}}}{\dfrac{\dfrac{1}{\rho_1} - \tau_x}{S_2} + \dfrac{\dfrac{1}{\rho_2} - \tau_x}{S_1} + \dfrac{\left(\dfrac{1}{\rho_1} - \tau_x\right)\left(\dfrac{1}{\rho_2} - \tau_x\right)}{S_1F_{12}\tau_x}} \tag{6-2}$$

$\mathfrak{F}_{2g}$ is obtained from the above by the interchange of subscripts 1 and 2. $S_1\mathfrak{F}_{12}$ is obtained from Eq. 4-4 and 5-6, which yield

$$S_1\mathfrak{F}_{12} = \frac{x\dfrac{\epsilon_1}{\rho_1}\dfrac{\epsilon_2}{\rho_2}}{\dfrac{\left(\dfrac{1}{\rho_1} - \tau_x\right)}{S_2} + \dfrac{\left(\dfrac{1}{\rho_2} - \tau_x\right)}{S_1} + \dfrac{\left(\dfrac{1}{\rho_1} - \tau_x\right)\left(\dfrac{1}{\rho_2} - \tau_x\right)}{S_1F_{12}\tau_x}}$$
$$+ \frac{(1 - x)\dfrac{\epsilon_1}{\rho_1}\dfrac{\epsilon_2}{\rho_2}}{\dfrac{\left(\dfrac{1}{\rho_1} - 1\right)}{S_2} + \dfrac{\left(\dfrac{1}{\rho_2} - 1\right)}{S_1} + \dfrac{\left(\dfrac{1}{\rho_1} - 1\right)\left(\dfrac{1}{\rho_2} - 1\right)}{S_1F_{12}}} \tag{6-3}$$

These three $\mathfrak{F}$'s are for use in the heat transfer equations

$$q_{g\rightleftharpoons 1} = S_1\mathfrak{F}_{1g}\sigma(T_g^4 - T_1^4) + h_1S_1(T_g - T_1) \tag{6-4a}$$
$$q_{g\rightleftharpoons 2} = S_2\mathfrak{F}_{2g}\sigma(T_g^4 - T_2^4) + h_2S_2(T_g - T_2) \tag{6-4b}$$
$$q_{2\rightleftharpoons 1} = S_1\mathfrak{F}_{12}\sigma(T_2^4 - T_1^4) \tag{6-4c}$$

(The difference between $\mathfrak{F}_{x\rightarrow y}$ and $\mathfrak{F}_{x\leftarrow y}$ is here ignored for simplicity of treatment.) If surface $S_2$ is losing heat to the outside at a rate $S_2U(T_2 - T_0)$, a heat balance on $S_2$ yields

$$q_{g\rightleftharpoons 2} = q_{2\rightleftharpoons 1} + S_2U(T_2 - T_0)$$

or

$$S_2\mathfrak{F}_{2g}\sigma(T_g^4 - T_2^4) = S_1\mathfrak{F}_{12}\sigma(T_2^4 - T_1^4) + S_2U(T_2 - T_0) - h_2S_2(T_g - T_2) \tag{6-5}$$

Assuming the source temperature $T_g$ and the primary sink temperature $T_1$ to be known, Eq. 6-5 permits a solution for the unknown refractory temperature $T_2$ (but trial-and-error because mixed in first and fourth powers).

The other application mentioned for this system of equations was to make allowance for grayness of a refractory surface. In this case $S_2$ is truly a no-flux surface, with $S_2U(T_2 - T_0) = h_2S_2(T_g - T_2)$. Then Eq. 6-5 can be readily solved for $T_2^4$. If this is put into Eq. 6-4a and 6-4b and the radiation terms of those two equations are added, one obtains

$$q_{\substack{\text{g, net loss} \\ \text{by radiation}}} = q_{\substack{\text{1, net gain} \\ \text{by radiation}}} = \left[ S_1\mathfrak{F}_{1g} + \frac{1}{\dfrac{1}{S_1\mathfrak{F}_{12}} + \dfrac{1}{S_2\mathfrak{F}_{2g}}} \right] \sigma(T_g^4 - T_1^4) \quad (6\text{-}6)$$

The bracket, allowing as it does for the radiation from gas to $S_1$ with the aid of $S_2$, is like the term $S_1\mathfrak{F}_{1g}$ for the system, gas–$S_1$–$S_R$ (with $S_2$ representing $S_R$) except that it now allows for the grayness of $S_2$. If, in Eq. 6-6, $S_2$ is assumed to be a white surface ($\rho_2 = 1$), it may be shown that the bracketed term reduces to the $S_1\mathfrak{F}_{1g}$ of Eq. 6-1.

*Estimation of heat transfer in a combustion chamber.* Although relations have been presented for evaluating radiant heat transmission in chambers filled with the combustion products of fuels, those relations have been restricted to idealized cases in which the gas temperature was uniform or was changing in one dimension along a flow path long compared to the transverse dimensions. Plainly, the average combustion chamber, in which combustion and mixing are occurring simultaneously and in a complicated flow path which involves recirculation as well, is far from typical of the idealized systems discussed. Those systems can nevertheless provide an indication of the performance to be expected and can in many cases be used for quantitative prediction. The simplest case to discuss is the limiting one in which all dimensions of the chamber are of the same order of magnitude, and in which the mixing energy provided in the incoming fuel and air produces a turbulent gas mixture uniform in temperature throughout and equal to the temperature of the gas leaving the chamber. Assume the problem to be the determination of heat transfer in the chamber, given the mean radiating temperature $T_1$ of the stock or heat sink, the chamber dimensions, and the fuel and air rates. Let the unknown mean gas temperature (and exit temperature) be $T_g$. Then the net heat transfer rate from the gas is given by

$$q_{g,\,\text{net}} = S_1\mathfrak{F}_{1g}\sigma(T_g^4 - T_1^4) + h_1S_1'(T_g - T_1) + U_RS_R(T_g - T_0) \quad (6\text{-}7)$$

The sink area $S_1'$ at which convection heat transfer occurs is indicated as possibly different from the area $S_1$ at which gas radiation occurs, because heat sink surfaces such as a row of tubes covering the gas outlet from the chamber, and therefore receiving by convection no heat which affects the mean gas temperature in the chamber, should be included in $S_1$ but not in $S_1'$. Convection from gas to $S_R$ has been assumed equal to the loss through $S_R$, which replaces it in the equation. With the outside air temperature $T_0$ known, Eq. 6-7 expresses a relation between two unknowns,

$q_{g,\,net}$ and $T_g$. The other relation is an energy balance, such as

$$q_{g,\,net} = i - mc_p(T_g - T_0) \tag{6-8}$$

where $i$ represents the hourly enthalpy of the entering fuel, air, and recirculated flue gas, if any, above a base temperature $T_0$ (water as vapor); and $c_p$ represents the heat capacity (mean value between $T_g$ and $T_0$) of the gas leaving the chamber, at hourly mass rate $m$. Eq. 6-7 and 6-8 may be solved, usually by trial and error, to give $q_{g,\,net}$ and $T_g$. The limitation on $q_g$, that it does not include gas convection at area $S - S'$, must be borne in mind.

The pair of equations just discussed applies strictly to one of two limiting combustion chamber types—that one in which the assignment of a mean flame temperature equal to the temperature of the gases leaving is justifiable. The method consequently predicts the minimum heat transfer of which the system is capable. Better agreement between predicted and experimental results is obtained on some furnaces when the assumption is made that flame temperature and exit gas temperature are not the same but differ by a constant amount. In a number of furnace tests used to determine what value of this difference produces agreement between experiment and the equations recommended, the difference was found to be about 300°F.

The other extreme in chamber types is that one in which combustion occurs substantially instantaneously at the burners (through complete premixing of fuel and air); the temperature attained is that generally known as theoretical flame temperature or adiabatic combustion temperature; and the temperature falls continuously as the gases flow from burner to outlet. When such a chamber is long compared to its cross section normal to the direction of gas flow, Eq. 6-7 may be considered as applying to a differential length, and the remarks in connection with Eq. 3-6 are applicable. One must, however, be prepared to examine the validity of the assumption that radiant flux in the gas flow direction is of secondary significance. Allowance for the improbability of attainment of adiabatic flame temperature at the hot end of the chamber may be made, though somewhat arbitrarily, by use of what Heiligenstädt [*45*] calls a pyrometric efficiency, the factor by which to reduce the adiabatic flame temperature to obtain the true value. If the gases are assumed constant at this temperature from burner inlet until, by the calculation method just outlined, they have lost enough heat to equal the difference between their entering enthalpy and that at their assumed temperature, and they are allowed thereafter to cool in step with their heat transfer rate, better agreement with experimental data can of course be obtained—provided there is knowledge of what to use for the pyrometric efficiency. It varies primarily with burner and chamber design and fuel type. A value of about 0.75 has been used in application to steel reheating furnaces. The chief function of the pyrometric efficiency concept is its use in fitting heat transfer theory to heat transfer data on combustion chambers. In other systems not too different in design, the same pyrometric efficiency can profitably be used.

The derivation of many of the relations presented in this section has been prevented by the space limitation. These derivations, together with an application of some of the principles to the solution of numerical problems, will be found in [*5*, Chap. 4].

## I,7. Cited References.


1. Foote, P. D. *J. Wash. Acad. Sci. 5,* 1 (1915).
2. Schmidt, H., and Furthmann, L. *Mitt. Kaiser-Wilhelm-Inst. Eisenforsch. Düsseldorf, Abhandl. 109,* 225 (1928).
3. Michaud, M. *Sc.D. Thesis,* Univ. Paris, 1951.
4. de Corso, S. M., and Coit, R. L. *Mech. Eng. 76,* 682 (1954).
5. McAdams, W. H. *Heat Transmission,* 3rd ed. McGraw-Hill, 1953.
6. Binkley, E. R. Heat transfer. *Am. Soc. Mech. Engrs. 40-46,* 1933–1934.
7. Sieber, W. *Z. tech. Phys. 22,* 130–135 (1941).
8. Person, R. A., and Leuenberger, H. *Union Carbide Co. private communication,* 1955.
9. Hottel, H. C. *Trans. Second World Power Conf. 18, Sec. 32-243,* 1930.
10. Hottel, H. C. *Mech. Eng. 52,* 699–704 (1930).
11. Hottel, H. C. *Trans. Am. Soc. Mech. Engrs. FSP 53,* 265–273 (1931).
12. Seibert, O. *Wärme 54,* 737–739 (1931).
13. Hooper, F. C., and Juhasz, I. S. *Fall Meeting Am. Soc. Mech. Engrs. Paper 52F19,* Sept. 1952.
14. Hamilton, D. C., and Morgan, W. R. Radiant-interchange configuration factors. *NACA Tech. Note 2836,* 1952.
15. Intern. Comm. on Flame Radiation. *J. Inst. Fuel London 24,* S (1951); *25,* S (1952).
16. Intern. Comm. on Flame Radiation. *Journée d'Etudes sur les Flammes,* Mar./June, 1953.
17. Sherman, R. A. *Trans. Am. Soc. Mech. Engrs. 79,* 1727–41 (1957).
18. Hottel, H. C., and Broughton, F. P. *Ind. Eng. Chem., Anal. ed. 4,* 166–175 (1932).
19. Senftleben, H., and Benedict, E. *Ann. physique 60,* 297 (1919).
20. Yagi, S. *J. Soc. Chem. Ind. Japan 40,* 50B (1937); *40,* 144 (1937).
21. Wolfhard, H. G., and Parker, W. G. *Proc. Phys. Soc. London B62,* 523 (1949).
22. Hottel, H. C., and Mangelsdorf, H. G. *Trans. Am. Inst. Chem. Engrs. 31,* 517–549 (1935).
23. Hottel, H. C., and Smith, V. C. *Trans. Am. Soc. Mech. Engrs. 57,* 463–470 (1935).
24. Howard, J. N., et al. Near-infrared transmission through synthetic atmospheres. *Air Force Cambridge Research Center Geophys. Research Paper 40,* 1955.
25. HoLeong, E. *Mass. Inst. Technol. Chem. Eng. Dept. Internal Rept.,* Feb. 1957.
26. Wu, W. *Mass. Inst. Technol. Chem. Eng. Dept. Internal Rept.,* June 1957.
27. Schmidt, E. *Forsch. Gebiete Ingenieurw. 3,* 57 (1932).
28. Schmidt, E., and Eckert, E. *Forsch. Gebiete Ingenieurw. 8,* 87 (1937).
29. Hottel, H. C., and Egbert, R. B. *Trans. Am. Inst. Chem. Engrs. 38,* 531–565 (1942).
30. Hottel, H. C. *Trans. Am. Inst. Chem. Engrs. 19,* 173 (1927).
31. Hottel, H. C. *Ind. Eng. Chem. 19,* 888 (1927).
32. Port, F. J. *Sc.D. Thesis in Chem. Eng.,* Mass. Inst. Technol., 1940.
33. Cohen, E. S. *M.S. Thesis in Chem. Eng.,* Mass. Inst. Technol., 1951.
34. Hottel, H. C. Notes on radiant heat transmission. *Mass. Inst. Technol. Chem. Eng. Dept.,* 1951.

35. Hottel, H. C., and Keller, J. D. *Trans. Am. Soc. Mech. Engrs., Iron and Steel 55-6*, 39–49 (1933).
36. Hottel, H. C. Notes on radiant heat transmission. *Mass. Inst. Technol. Chem. Eng. Dept.*, 1953.
37. Hottel, H. C. Notes on radiant heat transmission. *Mass. Inst. Technol. Chem. Eng. Dept.*, 1938.
38. Hottel, H. C., and Cohen, E. S. *A. I. Chem. Eng. J. 4*, 3–14 (1958).
39. Shorin, S. N. *Izvest. Akad. Nauk S.S.S.R., Otdel. Tekh. Nauk 3*, 1951.
40. Kellett, B. S. *J. Opt. Soc. Amer. 42*, 339 (1952).
41. Genzel, L. *Z. Physik 135*, 177–195 (1953).
42. Konakov, P. K. *Izvest. Akad. Nauk S.S.S.R., Otdel. Tekh. Nauk 3*, 1951.
43. Filippov, L. P. *Izvest. Akad. Nauk S.S.S.R., Otdel. Tekh. Nauk 1*, 155–156 (1955).
44. Crout, P. D. *Trans. Am. Inst. Elec. Engrs. 60*, 1235 (1941).
45. Heiligenstädt, W. *Arch. Eisenhüttenw. 1*, 25, 103 (1933).

# INDEX

absorption coefficient,
average, 499
specific, 493
absorptivity,
spectral, 492, 494
surface, 504
aerodynamic heating, 54
calculation of skin temperature, 406
correlation of theory and experiment, 412
high speed vehicles, 405
slip flow, 415
Allen, C. Q., 49
amplification of small disturbances, 68
Ashkenas, H., 157
Atsumi, S., 25

Bailey, G. W., 6
Barnes, H. T., 39
Batchelor, G. K., 219, 221, 227, 230–232, 237, 244, 250
Beer's law, 493
Bertram, M. H., 57, 67
Betz, A., 69
Biot number, 262, 264, 271
Birkhoff, G., 221
black body, energy distribution in radiation from, 502
black body radiation, 489
Blasius, H., 4, 344, 479
Blasius flow, 4
Blasius shear distribution, 344
Blasius solution, 440
Boden, R. H., 416
boiling heat transfer,
dimensional groups in, 334
mechanism, 328
nucleation in, 320
typical results, 314
with forced convection, 313
with free convection, 313
Boison, J. C., 67, 398, 402, 403
Boltz, F. W., 48
Boltzmann equation, 98
Bouguer-Lambert law, 493
boundary layer enthalpy, 349
boundary layer on flat plate, equations for turbulent compressible flow, 89
boundary layer parameters, equilibrium profiles, 137
boundary layer thickness,
displacement, 131, 450
boundary layer thickness, hydrodynamic, 440
thermal, 440
breakdown of laminar flow, 27
Bringer, R. P., 310
Brinich, P. F., 57, 61, 62
bubble growth, 323, 327
bubble population, in nucleate boiling, 321
bulk convection and gradient diffusion, 169
Burgers, J. M., 196, 247
burnout point, 315, 321
effect,
of pressure on, 316
of temperature on, 316
of velocity on, 316
in aerated water, 331
in carbon tetrachloride, 329
in Freon, 318, 331
in jet fuel, 318, 331
in nitric acid, 331
in water, 329
in water-aerosol solution, 329
Bursnall, W. J., 24, 25

carbon tetrachloride,
bubble growth in, 327
burnout point in, 329
centrifugal field, stabilizing action of, 51
Chandrasekhar, S., 219, 238, 239
Chapman, D. R., 107, 368, 392
Chou, P. Y., 246
Clauser, F. H., 130, 132, 134, 135, 144, 149, 391
Coker, E. G., 39
Colburn, A. F., 381
Coles, D., 57, 131, 132, 142, 391
Coles' wake function, 140
combustion chamber, estimation of heat transfer in, 537
composite hollow cylinder, heat flow in, 280
composite wall,
heat conduction in, 272
minimum weight criterion, 278
convective heat transfer, mechanism of, 339
convergence in the mean, 259
coolant, regenerative, 428
coolant Reynolds number, 468
Cope, W. F., 384

corners, flow and heat transfer near, 303
correlation, statistical, 199
correlation function, 199, 202, 203, 205, 206, 208, 209
  relation to spectral function, 211
correlation tensor,
  double, 203, 208
  triple, 205
correlations,
  in boiling heat transfer, 320, 335
  involving pressure, 206, 209, 236
Corrsin, S., 52, 164, 166, 168, 171, 176, 206, 241, 245
Craya, A., 247
critical pressure, in boiling heat transfer, 318
Crocco, L., 342, 443
Crocco transformation, 342
Czarnecki, K. R., 59, 62, 66, 398

Darcy's law, 432
decay of homogeneous turbulence,
  early period of, 232
  final period of, 231
  laws of, 230
Deissler, R. G., 291
density gradients, stabilizing and destabilizing effects, 53
Diaconis, N. S., 67
diffusion of energy, viscous, 84
dimensionless groups, in boiling heat transfer, 334
displacement thickness, 131, 450
dissociated air, properties of, 422
dissociation effects, 419
  of heat transfer near the stagnation point,
    laminar flow, 422
    turbulent flow, 424
double velocity correlations,
  longitudinal, 202
  transverse, 202
Drougge, G., 32
Drude's law, 491
Dryden, H. L., 10, 12, 29, 226, 250, 404
Dumas, R., 211
Dunn, D. W., 63, 65, 67
Duwez, P., 430

Eber, G. R., 66, 369, 398
Eckert, E. R. G., 310, 484
eddy diffusivity, 289, 291, 292, 305
  ratio, 294
eddy Reynolds number, 146
eddy viscosity, in boundary layers, 143
eigenfunctions, 257
eigenvalue problem, 257
eigenvalues, 257, 466
Einstein, H. A., 294
Ekman, V. W., 39
Elrod, H. G., 298
emissive power, 490, 492
  of metals, 492
emissivity, 502
  spectral, 492, 493
  total, 491, 493, 499, 505
Emmons, H. W., 6, 69
energy dissipation in isotropic turbulence, 212
energy spectrum, stability of, 239
energy transfer hypotheses in homogeneous turbulence, 238
enthalpy recovery factor, 349
entrance heat transfer, effect of various factors on, 301
entrance length,
  comparison of laminar and turbulent, 300
  effect of Prandtl number on, 300
entrance region, heat transfer in, 298
equation of energy and enthalpy, 85
equilibrium boundary layer according to Clauser, 135
equilibrium profiles, 136
error function, complementary, 262
Euler number, 447
exchange factor in radiant heat transfer,
  application to simple enclosure, 529
  from gas in enclosure, 528
  modification for real gas, 532, 534
  over-all, 524, 525
extinction coefficient, 493

Fage, A., 9, 11, 23, 47, 48, 49
Favre, A. J., 211
Feindt, E. G., 8, 11, 12, 18
Fila, G. H., 53
film boiling, 316, 333
film cooling, 429, 481
  critical injection velocity, 483
film heat transfer coefficient, 442
Fischer, W. W., 412
Flachsbart, O., 23
flatness factor, 200
flow separation, 130, 446
fluctuations, role of,
  in generating bubbles, 322
form of turbulent motions, general, 78
Forstall, W., 171, 181
Fourier equation, 435
Fourier series, 259
Fourier transform relation, 211, 218
  derived, 215
free stream boundaries of turbulent flow, 127, 163
free stream boundary, mechanism of spreading, 166

free turbulent flow,
behavior in terms of an eddy viscosity, 163
definition of, 158
general characteristics of, 158
laws of spreading and decay, 159
similarity conditions, 161
simplified equations,
of heat transfer, 162
of motion and continuity, 160
transport processes, 168
Frenkiel, F. N., 228
Freon, burnout point in, 318, 331
frequency distribution of turbulent fluctuations, 198
frequency of radiation, 490
friction, in boiling heat transfer, 332
friction velocity, definition of, 120
function set, orthogonal, 258

gas radiation, 513
carbon dioxide, 513
effect of temperature variation along flow path, 519
gases other than carbon dioxide and water, 523
interference of $CO_2$ and $H_2O$, 516
water-vapor, 514
gas transmittance,
gray, 532
real, 532
gas turbine blade, cooling of, 445
Gault, D. E., 25, 26
Gaussian distribution, 199
Gaviglio, J. J., 211
Gieseler, L. P., 56
Goland, L., 368
Goldstein, S., 52, 223, 229, 236
Görtler, H., 8, 46, 174, 180
Görtler instability, 8, 46, 69
Göttingen equivalent sand-grain roughness, 18
gray body, definition of, 504
Green, A. E., 223
Greenfield, S., 418
Gregory, N., 52
Grimminger, G., 366

Hall, A. A., 31
Hama, F. R., 10, 236
Hämmerlin, G., 46
Hantzsche, W., 362
Haslam, J. A. G., 38
heat conduction,
differential equation of, 255
radial, 266
variable specific heat, 281
variable thermal conductivity, 281
heat conduction, in composite slab, 272
in nozzle walls, 285
heat flux, Newtonian, 254
heat transfer,
across a turbulent stream, 454, 466
film cooling, 416, 418, 482
liquid metal, 301
mechanism of, in boiling heat transfer, 328
heat transfer coefficient, 260, 270, 448, 467, 468, 478
effective, 276
heat transfer and skin friction, Reynolds analogy, 104
heat transfer in a laminar boundary layer, exact solution, 446
Heisenberg, W., 217, 227, 237, 238
Hermann, R., 53
Higgins, R. W., 65, 398
Hill, J. A. F., 369
Hinze, J. O., 170, 174
Hislop, G. S., 31
hollow cylinder, heat conduction in, 266
Holstein, H., 9, 16
Homann, F., 365
homogeneous anisotropic turbulence, 201, 218
dynamical equations for, 219
homogeneous isotropic turbulence,
dynamical equations for, 210
kinematics of, 202
homogeneous medium, heat conduction in, 260
homogeneous turbulence, 200
Hopf, E., 196
horseshoe vortex, 30
Howarth, L., 210, 227

image source, 262, 263
independence principle, turbulent flow, 157
instability, turbulent boundary layer, 139
integral methods, 299
application of, to turbulent boundary layers, 153
intermittency factor, 164
invariant theory of turbulence, 206
isotropic turbulence, 200
dynamics, 208
energy dissipation in, 212
kinematics, 202
spectral theory of, 210
Iuchi, M., 11, 12

Jack, J. R., 67
Jacobs, E. N., 25

Jedlicka, J. R., 66
jet,
  angle of spreading, 176
  effect,
    of density, 176, 179
    of free stream, 179
      on heated jet, 182
  experiments on free stream effect, 181
  theory of free stream effect, 180
jet fuel, burnout point in, 318, 331
Johansen, F. C., 23
Jones, B. M., 24

Kampé de Fériet, J., 196, 219
Kenyon, G. C., 49
Kester, R. H., 107, 392
Kistler, A. L., 164, 166, 206
Klebanoff, P. S., 6, 15, 30, 45, 250
Knuth, E. L., 483
Kolmogoroff, A. N., 212, 223, 225, 228
Kolmogoroff's scales, 224, 229
Kolmogoroff's theory, 221, 223
Korkegi, R. H., 391
Korobkin, I., 367
Kovásznay, L. S. G., 238
Kuethe, A. M., 159, 180

laminar flow,
  cone solution, 362
  effect of variable free stream pressure and variable wall temperature, 368
  experimental knowledge, 368
  flat plate solution, 341
  heat transfer in, 341, 348
  heat transfer coefficient, 349
    for heated wind tunnels, 355
    free flight, 354, 355
  numerical calculations, 350
  stagnation point solution, 365
laminar layer, 293
laminar mixing region, 52
laminar sublayer, 435, 452, 454
Lange, A. H., 56
large scale structure of turbulence, 219
Laufer, J., 56, 57
law of the wake,
  according to Coles, 139
  illustration of, 142
  physical interpretation of, 142
law of the wall, 122
  fully rough, 148
Lee, R. E., 56
Lees, L., 56, 63, 396, 452
Lessen, M., 23
Levy, S., 368
Lewis, J. W., 50
Li, H., 294
Liepmann, H. W., 7, 8, 53
Lighthill, M. J., 248, 368
Lin, C. C., 56, 63, 65, 67, 211, 220, 225, 228, 229, 231, 236, 247, 291, 452
Linke, W., 21, 25
liquid metal heat transfer, 301
Loftin, L. K., Jr., 24, 25, 45
logarithmic velocity law,
  derivation of, 125
  range of validity of, 125, 132
  rough wall, 151
Loitsiansky, L. G., 32, 220, 227
Loitsiansky parameter, 221, 226
luminosity,
  large particle, 512
  oil flame, 512
  soot, 511, 512
Luther, M., 62

MacPhail, D. C., 50, 205
Maekawa, T., 25
magneto-hydrodynamic turbulence, 248
Malkus, W. V. R., 247
Mangler, W., 48
Mangler transformation, 48
Marte, J. E., 56, 57
Martinelli, R. C., 302
mass transfer, 297
mean beam length, 519
mean values in turbulent motion, 81, 197
Mickley, H. S., 391
Millikan, C. B., 124
Millionshchikov, M., 227, 236
Mitchner, M., 6, 247
Mituisi, S., 10
mixing in jets and wakes, 168
mixing length, 101, 143, 146
mixing length theory, 168
mixing zone, effect of density, 178
mixing zone of supersonic jet, 178
Moeckel, W. E., 57
momentum thickness, 110, 121, 131, 450
momentum transfer, across a turbulent stream, 454, 471
Morris, D. N., 368
Munk, M., 68, 69

Navier-Stokes equations, 82, 197, 461
Newtonian flow, 366
Nikuradse, J., 147, 375, 477
nitric acid, burnout point in, 331
nonblack radiator, 491
noncircular passages, 303
Norris, R. H., 412
nozzle walls, heat conduction in, 285
nucleate boiling, 316
  bubble population in, 321
nucleation, in boiling heat transfer, 320, 323, 335

nuclei, source of, in nucleate boiling, 321
nucleus, equivalent spherical diameter of, 320, 321
nucleus size, effect on bubble growth, 325
Nusselt number, 296, 306, 446, 449, 468

O'Brien, V., 206
Obukhoff, A. M., 238
Obukhoff spectrum, 225
optical depth, 492
origin of turbulence, 67
oscillations, Tollmien-Schlichting, 5

Pappas, C. C., 65, 107, 398
partial film boiling, 316
permeability of porous metal, 431
Phillips, O. M., 248
Planck's radiation law, 489
Pohlhausen, H., 439, 449
Poiseuille flow, 461, 462, 465
Poroloy, 431, 477
Poroloy process, 429
porosity, 430
porous medium, 430
Potter, J. L., Jr., 60
power formula, limitations, 122
power law, in turbulent flow,
  basis of, 119
  boundary layer thickness, 121
  skin friction, 120
  velocity distribution, 120
Prandtl, L., 49, 53, 122, 168, 290, 294, 341, 455
Prandtl mixing length, 382, 456, 473
  formula, 108
Prandtl number, 341, 440, 441
  turbulent, 102
pressure changes across turbulent boundary layer, 90
pressure correlation, 206, 209, 236
pressure gradient effect,
  on boundary layer, 130
  on skin friction, 133
pressure gradient parameter for equilibrium profiles, 146
Preston, J. H., 48, 49
probability distribution, 198
  joint, 199
propellant, 428
Proudman, I., 221, 232, 237, 239, 248

quasi-Gaussian approximation, 200, 236
Quick, A. W., 11, 29

radiant beam length, mean, 519
radiant exchange,
  among wall elements of black enclosure, 510
  black source sinks, no gas, 527
radiant exchange, real gas, gray sink and no-flux surface, 535
  real gas, 2 gray sinks, no-flux surface, 535
  system containing gray gas, 523, 528
  two source sinks, no gas, 526
radiant flux, 490
radiant interchange, nongray body in enclosure, 504
Rannie, W. D., 309, 454, 483
Rayleigh-Jeans radiation law, 490
real gas, 531
reattachment of separated boundary layer, 41
recovery factor, 54, 92
  effect of,
    Mach number on, 94
    Reynolds number on, 92
recovery temperature, 54
reference temperature, 306, 308
reflector, diffuse, 533
Regier, A., 52
Reichardt, H., 53, 294
Reid, W. H., 237, 244
Reis, F. B., 247
Reissner, E., 231
Reynolds, O., 288, 290, 349, 378, 454
Reynolds analogy, 290
  inboiling heat transfer, 333
Reynolds analogy factor, 349
Reynolds equations, 197
Reynolds number, 296, 349, 441, 455
  local boundary layer, 20
Reynolds stresses, 197
Riabouchinsky, D., 52
Richardson, L. F., 244
Riddell, F. R., 157
Rivas, M. A., Jr., 369
Robertson, H. P., 203, 206
rocket motors,
  effect of film cooling on heat transfer in, 416, 418
  heat transfer in, 415, 419
    due to radiation, 417
Rosenhead, L., 23
Rotta, J., 246
roughness, 147
  aerodynamic effect, 147
  effect on shape parameter, 152
  effect on transition, 8, 38, 49, 62
  equivalent sand-grain, 147
  limit,
    for aerodynamically smooth condition, 149
    for fully rough condition, 149
  sand-grain, 18, 45
  spherical, 45

roughness, three-dimensional, 45
roughness Reynolds number, 147
Rubesin, M. W., 368, 391

scales of turbulence, 78
Scherbarth, K., 11
Scherrer, R., 65, 398
Schiller, L., 10, 21, 25, 39
Schlichting, H., 5, 32, 53, 447, 452
Schlichting's computation of transition, 37
Schröder, K., 29
Schubauer, G. B., 5, 6, 15, 25, 30, 41, 45, 241, 250
secondary motion, 40
Seiff, A., 66
semi-infinite solid, heat conduction in, 262
separation, 21, 29
separation "bubble," 24, 29
Shapiro, A. H., 171, 181
shear flow,
  definition of, 76
  relation to turbulence, 76
  statistical theory, 245
shear layer, reattachment of, 24, 41
shear layers, transition of, 21, 29
shearing stress, 454
Shen, S. F., 247, 291
Short, B. J., 392
Shoulberg, R. H., 369, 393
Sibulkin, M., 362
similarity in isotropic turbulence, 224, 225, 229
Sinclair, A. R., 59, 62, 66, 398
skewness factor, 200
skin friction,
  compressible flow,
    basis of theories, 107
    empirical laws, 113
    experiment and theory compared, 116
  for transpiration-cooled walls, 446
  fully rough wall, 148
skin friction coefficient, 449, 457, 464, 478
  definition of, 113, 120
  determination from velocity profile, 134
skin friction laws in compressible flow, von Kármán and Prandtl hypotheses compared, 112
skin-friction logarithmic law,
  Prandtl-Schlichting formula, 128
  Squire-Young formula, 128
  von Kármán formula, 127
  von Kármán-Schoenherr formula, 128
skin friction measurements, incompressible flow, 129
Skramstad, H. K., 5, 6
Slack, E. G., 58
small scale structure of turbulence, 221
Smith, A. M. O., 39
Smith, J. M., 310
Smith, J. W., 368
Snodgrass, R. B., 67
Sommer, S. C., 392
Spangenberg, W. G., 250
spectral analysis of turbulence,
  one-dimensional, 214
  three-dimensional, 216
spectral function, relation to correlation function, 211
spectral radiancy, 489
spectrum,
  equation for change of, 213
  of disturbances, 68
Squire, H. B., 180, 365
stability in accelerated and retarded flow, 32
stabilization,
  cooling required for, 396
  effect of centrifugal field, 51
  effect of density gradient, 53
stagnation enthalpy, 446
stagnation point, 447
  instability, 46
Stalder, J. R., 58
Stanton, T. E., 349
Stanton number, 104, 349
statistical averages, 198
statistical theory of turbulence, 196, 201
Stefan-Boltzmann constant, 490
Stefan-Boltzmann law, 502
Stephens, A. V., 38
Sternberg, J., 55
Stewart, R. W., 200, 232
Stine, H. A., 368
structure of turbulence,
  large scale, 219
  small scale, 221
Stuart, J. T., 52
Stüper, J., 11
subcooling, 313, 316
supercritical carbon dioxide, heat transfer in, 310
supercritical fluids, 309
surface erosion, 284
surface melting, 284
surface of discontinuity, 23
surface tension,
  boiling heat transfer, 321, 322
  effect on bubble growth, 325
sweat cooling, 429
Szablewski, W., 180, 182

Tani, I., 10–12
Tatsumi, T., 237

Taylor, G. I., 30, 39, 50, 205, 210, 212, 222, 223, 241, 250, 290
Taylor turbulence parameter, 31, 57
Taylor's cellular ring vortices, 50
temperature,
  defect, 272
  difference ratio, 468, 469
  distribution, 294, 295, 308
  effect,
    on bubble growth of, 327
    on radiation of space variation in, 531
  mean value in gas radiation, 521
  of no-flux walls in enclosure, 529
temperature-velocity relationship in turbulent boundary layer, 91, 95, 109
Tetervin, N., 130, 154
Theodorsen, T., 30, 52
thermal boundary layer, 437, 442
thermal capacity, 278
thermal diffusivity, effect on bubble growth, 327
thermal properties,
  variable, 280
  of various materials, 260
thermal shield,
  thick, 277
  thin, 276
thermal shock, 270
thermal stresses, 268
thermoelastic equations, 269
thickness number, hollow cylindrical shell, 268
three-dimensional effects,
  significance in boundary layers, 156
  yawed flow, 157
Tidstrom, K. D., 15, 45
Tollmien, W., 5, 452
Tomotika, S., 47
Townsend, A. A., 144, 159, 164, 166, 168, 171, 172, 206, 225, 227, 230, 232, 251
transition,
  at boundary of a jet, 52
  at hypersonic speed, 67
  at supersonic speed, 54
  determination by local parameters, 37
  dimensional analysis, 19
  effect of,
    cooling, 397
    curvature, 8
    cylindrical wires, 10, 49
    distributed roughness, 16
    flat ridges, 11
    heat transfer, 53, 54, 63
    Mach number, 55
    noise, 46
    nose shape, 54, 57
    pressure gradient, 6
    roughness, 8, 38, 49, 62
transition, effect of, sand-grain roughness, 18, 45
    scale of turbulence, 31, 47, 57
    shock waves, 55
    single roughness elements, 8, 61
    spherical roughness elements, 15, 45
    supply turbulence, 399
    surface roughness, 403
    surface temperature, 53
    three-dimensional roughness elements, 15, 45
    turbulence, 30, 41, 47, 55
    two-dimensional roughness elements, 10
    waviness, 8, 38, 45
  in flow between rotating cylinders, 49
  in pipe,
    of annular cross section, 40
    of circular cross section, 39
    of rectangular cross section, 40
    of square cross section, 40
    with curved axis, 40
    with sharp-edged entrance, 40
  in propeller wake, 46
  in rough pipes, 40
  near rotating disk, 52
  on airfoils, 32, 38, 41, 58
    effect of,
      angle of attack, 43
      roughness, 43
    flight data, 45
  on airplane configurations, 45
  on airplanes in flight, 45
  on bodies of revolution, 46, 47, 49
  on concave surfaces, 8
  on cone, 55
  on cone cylinder, 59
  on convex surfaces, 8
  on elliptic cylinder, 41
  on flat plate, 31, 57
  on hollow cylinder, 8, 11, 55, 61
  on ogive cylinder, 59
  on paraboloid cylinder, 65
  on prolate spheroid, 48
  on Rm-10 model, 59, 65
  on sphere, 46
  physical mechanism of, 28
  relation to stability of laminar boundary layer, 396
transmittance,
  evaluation from gas radiation chart, 534
  gas, 532
transpiration-cooled boundary layer,
  heat transfer in, 437
  laminar,
    approximate solution, 438
    compressible, 442
    pressure gradient, 445

transpiration-cooled pipe flow,
  heat transfer in, 460
  perturbation parameter, 462
transpiration cooling, 429, 438
transport coefficients, turbulent, 102
transport processes, fundamental considerations, 97
transport theory,
  comparison with experiment, 170
  critical examination of, 169
triple velocity correlations, 205
Trouncer, J., 180
Tsien, H. S., 415, 483
Tsuji, H., 236
turbulence,
  origin in shear flow, 76
  sustaining mechanism, 77
turbulence, statistical theory of,
  correlation function, 199, 202, 203, 205, 206, 208, 209
    relation to spectral function, 211
  correlation tensor,
    double, 203, 208
    triple, 205
  correlations involving pressure, 206, 209, 236
  decay of homogeneous turbulence,
    early period of, 232
    final period of, 231
    laws of, 230
  diffusion (see turbulent diffusion)
  double velocity correlations,
    longitudinal, 202
    transverse, 202
  energy dissipation in isotropic turbulence, 212
  energy spectrum, stability of, 239
  energy transfer hypotheses, 238
  flatness factor, 200
  Fourier transform relation, 211, 218
    derived, 215
  frequency distribution of turbulent fluctuations, 198
  homogeneous anisotropic turbulence, 201, 218
    dynamical equations for, 219
  homogeneous isotropic turbulence,
    dynamical equations for, 210
    kinematics of, 202
  homogeneous turbulence, 200
    invariant theory of, 206
  isotropic turbulence, 200
    dynamics, 208
    energy dissipation in, 212
    kinematics, 202
    spectral theory of, 210
    von Kármán-Howarth equation, 210
  Kolmogoroff's scales, 224, 229
turbulence, Kolmogoroff's theory, 221, 223
  Loitsiansky parameter, 221, 226
  mean values, 81, 197
  Obkhoff spectrum, 225
  pressure correlation, 206, 209, 236
  probability distribution, 198
    joint, 199
  quasi-Gaussian approximation, 200, 236
  Reynolds equations, 197
  shear flow, 245
  similarity, 224, 225, 229
  skewness factor, 454
  spectrum of turbulence,
    equation for change of, 68
    relation to correlation function, 211
  statistical averages, 198
  structure of turbulence,
    large scale, 219
    small scale, 221
  vortex-stretching, 223
  vorticity scale, 210
turbulent "bursts," 6
turbulent diffusion, 240
  coefficient of, 242
  Gaussian distribution associated with, 243
  general behavior and effect, 79
  involving more than one particle, 243
  time scale of, 242
turbulent energy transfer among various frequencies, 214
turbulent exchange coefficient, 102, 170
  boundary layer, 145
  compared to kinematic viscosity, wake and jet, 175
turbulent flow, 27, 370
  cone solution, 388
  cones, von Kármán momentum integral, 388
  effect of variable free stream pressure and variable wall temperature, etc., 391
  equation of continuity,
    mean motion, 82
    total motion, 82
  flat plate solution, 370
  friction coefficient, 381
  heat transfer, 288, 372
  kinetic energy equation,
    mean motion, 83
    total motion, 84
  momentum equation, mean motion, 82
  nature of, 76, 196
  Navier-Stokes equation, total motion, 82
  properties by analogy to laminar flow, 79

turbulent flow, recovery factor, 372
  Reynolds analogy factor, 378
  rough walls, 391
  stagnation point solution, 388
  status of experimental knowledge,
    heat transfer, 393
    skin friction, 391
turbulent heat transfer, 288
turbulent motion,
  dynamical effects, 249
  effect of damping screens on, 249
  in compressible fluid, 247
  in wind tunnels, 249
  mean value defined, 81, 197
turbulent Prandtl number, 371, 373
turbulent shear flow, statistical theory of, 245
turbulent spots, 6, 69
turbulent structure of shear flows, bibliography for,
  diffusion and heat transfer, 188
  free flows, 188
  instrumentation, 189
  statistical theories, 186
  vorticity and structure of turbulence, 185
  wall-bounded flows, 186

Uberoi, M. S., 171, 176, 241
universal skin friction law, 151

van der Hegg Zijnen, B. G., 170, 174
van Driest, E. R., 67, 293, 342, 349, 350, 370, 373, 374, 379, 382, 383, 388, 389, 391, 396, 398, 402, 403
vapor flow, in boiling heat transfer, 328
vapor pressure, effect on boiling heat transfer of, 325
variable fluid properties,
  analysis of heat transfer for, 303
  effect of, on heat transfer in air, 304
variable properties, effect in liquid heat transfer of, 307
velocity, effect on bubble growth, 328
velocity correlations of higher orders, 206
velocity-defect law, 123
velocity distribution, turbulent, 292, 305
velocity-distribution formula,
  plane jet, 174
  plane wake, 172
  round jet, 174
velocity profile,
  effects of free stream, 125
  H-parameter family, 130
view factor, 507
viscous sublayer, 374
von Doenhoff, A. E., 25, 45, 130, 154
von Doenhoff-Tetervin integral method, 154
von Kármán, Th., 122, 203, 205, 210, 225, 227, 229, 231, 238, 246, 290, 291, 374, 458
von Kármán logarithmic skin friction law derivation, 127
von Kármán logarithmic velocity, 457
von Kármán momentum equation, 134, 154, 438
von Kármán momentum integral, 383
von Kármán similarity hypothesis, 291
von Kármán similarity law, 382
von Kármán vortices, 27
von Kármán-Howarth equation, 210, 220, 222
von Kármán-Prandtl logarithmic equation, 292
vortex layer, 21
vortex pattern, regular, 27
vortex-stretching in turbulent motion, 223
vorticity scale of turbulence, 210

Walker, W. S., 52
Wanlass, K., 368
water,
  aerated, burnout point in, 331
  boiling heat transfer to, 329
water-aerosol solution,
  bubble growth in, 327
  burnout point in, 329
wave length of radiation, 489
wave number of radiation, 491
wedge-type flow, 449
Weinbaum, S., 435
Wendt, F., 50
Wendt, H., 362
Wheeler, H. L., 431, 435, 479
Wieghardt, K., 484
Wien's displacement law, 490
Wien's radiation law, 490
Wilkins, M. E., 66
Williams, E. P., 366
Wilson, R. E., 384
Wright, E. A., 6

Yamamoto, K., 11, 12
Young, G. B. W., 366
Yuan, S. W., 476